CLASSIFICATION OF CARBONATE ROCKS— A SYMPOSIUM

Since 1926, the Association has published, in addition to the monthly *Bulletin*, occasional books and symposia, variously referred to as special volumes or special publications, and identified only by title and year of publication.

Realizing that the numbering of such publications is of considerable convenience to librarians and authors, the Executive Committee on June 1, 1962, took action to designate future books as Memoirs, beginning with *Classification of Carbonate Rocks* as Memoir No. 1. No attempt will be made to assign numbers to special volumes already published.

Published with the aid of a fund established by the New York Committee
for the mid-year meeting of the Association, November 1926

Memoir 1

CLASSIFICATION OF CARBONATE ROCKS

a symposium

A Symposium arranged by the Research Committee of The American Association of Petroleum Geologists

Including papers presented orally under joint auspices of the Association and the Society of Economic Paleontologists and Mineralogists, at Denver, Colorado, April 27, 1961.

Edited by WILLIAM E. HAM

Published by The American Association of Petroleum Geologists, Tulsa, Oklahoma, U.S.A. 1962

Published, November 1962
Reprinted by offset, July 1963

LIBRARY OF CONGRESS CARD CATALOGUE NO. 62-20504

Composed, Printed and Bound by The Collegiate Press
GEORGE BANTA COMPANY, INC.
Menasha, Wisconsin

CONTENTS

FOREWORD

The symposium on the classification of carbonate rocks presented in this volume was built on a concept that had its beginning at Los Angeles in March 1958. R. Dana Russell, at that time chairman of the Research Committee of The American Association of Petroleum Geologists, called an informal meeting on March 9 for an expression of opinion as to the desirability of establishing a generally acceptable system of classification and nomenclature of carbonate rocks. There was general agreement that such an effort was desirable, that it should be done as a function of the Association, and that a clear distinction should be made between classification of major rock types on the one hand, and nomenclature of texture, fabric, and mineral composition on the other.

Further action was taken at the Dallas meeting in March 1959. The Carbonate Rock Subcommittee was established as a division of the AAPG Research Committee, and L. L. Sloss was named temporary chairman. It was concluded that neither a single classification nor a single set of nomenclatural terms could be recommended by the subcommittee. It was further agreed that the first work of the subcommittee would be concerned with the assembly and publication of classifications in current use.

The present chairman was appointed in May 1959, and an active solicitation of manuscripts was begun. Major oil companies specializing in research on carbonate rocks gave full cooperation by releasing unpublished classifications, some of which had been in intracompany use since the early 1950's. Papers submitted by their geologists make up more than half the papers included in this volume.

Two of the symposium papers deserve special mention. That of Powers is a revision and enlargement of an earlier classification published by Bramkamp and Powers in 1958; and that of Folk is a revised form of his classification published in 1959.

With the exception of the review article by Ham and Pray, all papers in this volume were presented orally at a symposium on the classification of carbonate rocks at Denver on April 27, 1961, under the joint auspices of The American Association of Petroleum Geologists and the Society of Economic Paleontologists and Mineralogists.

In this collection of papers an attempt has been made to cover the full range of concepts, including those emphasizing descriptive classification, genetic classification, the importance of depositional fabric, the classification of ancient as well as modern carbonates, the application of classification to interpretation within major carbonate provinces, and finally, a review setting forth the complex background and problems against which the classifications have been devised.

For the subcommittee,

Frank W. Beales
Robert J. Dunham
Dan E. Feray
Alfred G. Fischer
Robert L. Folk
Leslie V. Illing
Morris W. Leighton
James G. Mitchell
Henry F. Nelson
William J. Plumley
Lloyd C. Pray
John Rodgers
Morris Rones
L. L. Sloss
Curt Teichert
Grant Steele
James Lee Wilson
William E. Ham, *Chairman*

Norman, Oklahoma
June 23, 1961

MODERN CONCEPTS AND CLASSIFICATIONS OF CARBONATE ROCKS[1]

WILLIAM E. HAM[2] AND LLOYD C. PRAY[3]
Norman, Oklahoma, and Littleton, Colorado

ABSTRACT

Limestones and dolomites form the economically important and exceedingly complex family of carbonate rocks. They are set distinctly apart from related rock families by their intrabasinal and highly local origin, their genetic dependence upon organic activity, and their extreme susceptibility to post-depositional modification.

The successful classification of carbonate rocks requires detailed knowledge of their multiple components and genetic processes. Such knowledge has been greatly increased during a period of accelerated investigations since 1940, with the result that the modern classifications are marked improvements over their predecessors.

Most of the newer classifications utilize a practical blending of descriptive and genetic parameters. The parameters most commonly used are depositional fabric, particularly the relative abundance of coarser carbonate particles (grains) as compared with the finer grained particles (matrix or micrite); the size and genetic types of the grains or of in-place biotic constituents; the mineralogy; and the nature and degree of post-depositional modification. Secondary parameters include porosity, cementation, the degree of abrasion or rounding of the grains, admixtures of noncarbonate material, and a host of others.

The symposium classifications of carbonate rocks and two allied articles of this volume are briefly reviewed and compared. Despite the differences in approach, purpose, and experience among the various authors, the resulting classifications show strong similarities and therefore indicate that a basis of mutual understanding is being realized.

INTRODUCTION

Approximately 75 per cent of the total land area of the earth is directly underlain by sedimentary rocks, and these strata have thicknesses that locally range up to 8–10 miles. Roughly one-fifth of this sedimentary mass is made of the carbonate rocks—limestone and dolomite. These carbonates are widely distributed; they range in age from Precambrian to Recent; and they are divisible into several hundred different types. Together with sandstones, they contain practically all the world's supply of petroleum, and calculations show that petroleum reserves are about equally divided between the family of sandstones and the family of carbonates. Also contained in the carbonate rocks are impressive and economically valuable deposits of metals. With such widespread distribution in time and space, with such economic importance, and with more than their share of geologic complexities, the carbonates are manifestly worthy of study and classification.

From the beginning of geological study in Europe and America, up to the middle of the twentieth century, little attention was given to detailed petrologic study and classification of the carbonate rocks. Progress toward understanding the complexity of carbonates and their facies relationships lagged far behind the progress being made in many other aspects of geology. It is a sad commentary that until recently the standard treatment of carbonate rocks was only to note by use of modifiers the color, the "crystallinity," and the presence of megascopically obvious fossils, and to record the dominant composition by the terms limestone or dolomite. Such simple characterizations are rarely adequate because they ignore meaningful characteristics that can provide a basis for facies differentiation or can be useful in genetic interpretation. The prevailing inadequacy of the methods of description of carbonate rocks, and the general lack of detailed petrologic information, can be readily ascertained by reading any randomly chosen textbook used in training geologists.

Geological literature, however, contains some notable examples of critical treatment of the carbonate rocks. An outstanding early work dealing with classification is that of Grabau (1904, 1913) in America, who introduced the terms calcilutite, calcarenite, and calcirudite, all of which are still in common usage. The relatively recent publication by Johnson (1951) deserves citation for its contribution toward identification of biotic constituents in limestones. Cayeux (1935) of France published an outstanding monograph describing many types of carbonate rocks; the monograph is profusely illustrated with thin-section photomicrographs. Black (1938) of England provides an excellent introduction to carbonate rocks and

[1] Manuscript received, December 29, 1961.

[2] Oklahoma Geological Survey.

[3] The Ohio Oil Company.

reveals a detailed understanding of them by his use of such terms as shell-fragment limestones, organic limestones with a mudstone matrix, reef limestones, sediment-binding algal limestones, pellet limestones, and calcite mudstones. Sander (1936) of Austria stands out for his contributions to a study of depositional fabric, for his conclusion that fruitful interpretative results may be obtained by a study of it, and for the recognition that internal sedimentation is common. The foregoing geologists, and others not cited, have furnished knowledge which is highly useful in the formulation of modern classifications, even though only a few of these earlier workers were directly concerned with classification.

In recent years there has been a revolution in the field of carbonate geology. It is no exaggeration to say that more research has been done on carbonate rocks in the period 1940–1960 than was accomplished in all the preceding years. Although this kindling of interest came from various sources, there can be little doubt that a major factor was the increased awareness of the economic significance of carbonate rocks as oil reservoirs. The enormous reservoirs of oil discovered during the 1930's in carbonate facies in the Middle East, and the discovery in the late 1940's of petroleum in carbonate buildups or "reefs," such as in the Devonian of Canada or the Pennsylvanian of West Texas, contributed much to the new interest in carbonate rocks. Carbonate research thus became a natural part of increased emphasis on exploration research sponsored by many major petroleum companies. Coincident with, and partly encouraged by, the new economic interest, came a stimulation of carbonate research in many colleges, universities, and in state and federal geological organizations.

Out of these investigations came the realization that the carbonates form a truly complex group of rocks, difficult to study and difficult to interpret without much more information than was generally available. The fund of established information generally was insufficient even for a comprehension of the problems, and it was certainly inadequate for the establishment of efficient petroleum exploration programs. Without exception the pre-existing systems for describing, naming, and classifying the carbonate rocks proved to be unsatisfactory, and new approaches were sought by which the rocks could be better characterized. In the opinion of the writers, these older systems proved to be inadequate because they were based more on philosophical concepts of the rocks than on an intimate knowledge of the rocks themselves.

The most active groups working on carbonates during this period were in the research laboratories of major oil companies. Although their largest expenditure of effort went into detailed studies of specific carbonate rocks and facies, nomenclatural terms as well as systems of rock classification were established in many laboratories. A substantial part of the results of this research effort is presented here, as five of the company classifications thus evolved have been released for inclusion in this symposium volume.

The two detailed classifications published in recent years are by Folk (1959) and by Bramkamp and Powers (1958). They represent a marked departure from the older classifications and set the trend for the more modern systems, as they are comprehensive and are based on the examination of extremely large suites of carbonate rocks. These two classification systems, slightly modified from the original versions, also are included here.

The present state of knowledge of carbonate rocks is well sampled in the symposium papers. Although much remains to be learned, it happily represents a significant advancement over the earlier days when petrographic study of carbonate rocks was rare, when calcite cement was not distinguished from lime mud matrix, when grain packing was not considered, when the turbulence or other aspects of depositional environment were largely ignored, and when the term "recrystallized" either was reserved for calcitic or dolomitic metamorphic rocks or was applied indiscriminately to any carbonate rock in which crystals could be observed.

DISTINCTIVENESS AND COMPLEXITY OF THE CARBONATE ROCKS

Granted that the carbonate rocks are widely distributed, widely ranging in age, and have a characteristic chemical composition, we can now ask ourselves the question as to whether they form a group sufficiently distinct to stand apart from other sedimentary rocks, and if so, what the distinguishing characters are. For if these characters are notably different, then does it not also follow that the problems associated with them will likewise be different? Any student of carbonate rocks already knows that these questions must be answered in the affirmative.

The outstanding distinctive aspects of carbonate rocks are their intrabasinal origin, their dependence on organic activity, and their susceptibility to post-depositional modification. In comparison with other sedimentary rock families, moreover, the carbonate family is significantly polygenetic. And, finally, in addition to involving nearly every genetic process known to be important in sedimentation, the carbonate rocks participate extensively in the metamorphic processes of metasomatic replacement and recrystallization.

In past years carbonate rocks have been strongly compared with other sediments—particularly calcarenites with sandstones, and calcilutites with shales. Interpretation by analogy can undoubtedly continue to be a fruitful approach, provided, however, that it does not lead to unjustified complacency. In the following section it will be shown that carbonates have important differences from sandstone and shale in at least three essential respects, that recognition of these differences is essential, and that these differences create special problems in the nomenclature and classification of the carbonate rocks.

Local intrabasinal origin.—Most carbonate sediment is of intrabasinal origin, and much has been formed at or very close to the point of final deposition. This aspect, shared with such sedimentary rocks as evaporites and coals, places the group in marked contrast to sandstones and shales formed of sedimentary particles derived from sources lying outside the depositional basin. The nature and thickness of carbonate deposits are sensitive to the interplay of basin configuration and the dynamics of physical processes operating on the water of the basin, but the factors that determine the original character and that localize the deposits of most carbonates are manifestly different from those of terrigenous clastics.

Perhaps the best examples of in-place deposition of carbonate rocks are those of the true reefs, where organisms build wave-resistant structures far above the level of the adjacent contemporaneous sediments, controlling their own depositional environment and strongly modifying the bordering environments. This has no counterpart in other types of sedimentary rocks. Less dramatic, yet amenable to proof of intrabasinal and of highly local origin, are many carbonate deposits of stable shelves or platforms of Recent and past seas. Recognition of the local, intrabasinal origin of carbonate sediments is essential and too often has been overlooked in the interpretation of these rocks.

Dependence on organic activity.—Most carbonate rocks are highly dependent upon some type of organic activity, and they generally reflect their organic heritage by showing recognizable biotic elements, either as grains of intact or fragmented fossil remains, or as plant and animal material in position of growth. Although the organic origin of the coarser skeletal material normally is easy to determine, as discussed in the paper by Feray, Heuer, and Hewatt (this volume), the origin of the finer grained sediment is generally difficult or impossible to interpret by methods currently available. The formation of conventionally "inorganic" carbonate sediments, such as oölites and grapestone, may also be dependent upon some little understood organic activity.

Organisms exert a stronger influence on the early post-depositional history of carbonate sediments than on most other sediments. The carbonates commonly have been deposited in environments where extensive reworking by organisms is possible. Sediment-burrowing or sediment-ingesting organisms may obliterate primary textures or structures and create new ones; organisms may fragment or aggregate primary sediment in addition to moving it; and if the organisms have calcareous shells or skeletons, these are added to the sediment. Pellet limestones and carbonate pellets, widely distributed in time and space, and generally attributed to fecal activity of organisms, also testify to the significance of organic reworking of carbonate sediments.

Interpretation of texture in the organically formed carbonate rocks is a far more difficult problem than in common sandstones and shales. This is true even for those clastic carbonate rocks that are composed entirely of transported material. The interpretation of size, shape, and sorting in the calcarenites, especially those containing clasts of skeletal origin, poses problems not generally encountered in the sandstones. In sandstones, the shape and specific gravity of the clasts are more nearly constant, and a diameter measure of size is the major key to interpreting the hydraulic properties of the sedimentary particles. The concept of size expressed as a diameter has little meaning for irregular skeletal remains. Carbonate clasts of organic origin commonly reflect growth characteristics and may be either highly irregular or of constant shapes, depending on the organisms which furnished them rather than on the abrasional history of the particle. Commonly overlooked also is the wide range in specific gravity of the organic carbonate materials. Although the calcite or aragonite shell material has a specific gravity near that of terrigenous minerals such as quartz or feldspar, voids commonly reduce the specific gravity of the clast enough to be of critical significance for interpretation. This is normally recognized in clasts with large voids (articulated brachiopods or ostracodes, chambered foraminifers, or cellular fragments such as of bryozoans and corals). Where pores are very small this is commonly overlooked. Errors of this type are especially prevalent for skeletal material of crinoids or of other echinoderms which may have had initial porosities of 50 per cent or more.

Because the size of hydraulically equivalent particles increases significantly as their specific gravity diminishes, interpretations of sorting based on analogy to sandstones can be misleading. Not only can a well-sorted carbonate rock have clasts of widely differing visual sizes, but even more common are carbonate rocks with clasts of equal size, in which the uniformity of size reflects only the growth size of the organisms and is unrelated to sorting by transportation. These features are an integral part of the distinctiveness and complexity of the carbonate rocks.

Susceptibility to postdepositional modifications.—In their susceptibility to postdepositional modification, carbonate rocks are in a class by themselves. The closest analogies between carbonates and sandstone or shale end at the time of deposition, for processes of solution, cementation, recrystallization, replacement, and the introduction of internal sediment create distinctive and complex changes in the highly soluble carbonate rocks. Major factors in the formation of these numerous diagenetic changes are the following.

1. The higher solubility of the carbonate minerals as compared to other common sedimentary minerals in sandstones and shales.
2. The different solubilities and stability relationships of aragonite, high- and low-magnesium calcite, and dolomite.
3. The wide range in crystal size of the carbonate minerals which can occur in the initial sediment, leading to different rates of solution and recrystallization.
4. The high initial porosities and permeabilities of many carbonate sediments. These provide access for solutions of compositions that differ from those in which the sediments were deposited.

Slight variations of physical and chemical conditions trigger the change from equilibrium to inequilibrium for one or more of the carbonate minerals, and similar slight changes can create reversals of diagenetic process.

The final effects of diagenesis have a profound bearing on interpretation, description, and classification of the carbonate rocks. They also lead to many problems, some examples of which are cited here. Does the sparry calcite of many carbonate rocks represent cementation in original void space, or does it represent recrystallization of original lime mud? If cement, was it introduced early or late in the diagenetic history of the rock? How many cycles of carbonate cementation or solution occur in a body of carbonate rock? Does the internal sediment that precedes the sparry calcite cement in some rocks represent entrapped sea-floor sediment or is it the less soluble residue of rocks leached subsequent to deposition? To what extent are the compositional changes that occur in carbonate rocks, such as dolomitization or silicification, related to changes on or just below the sea floor, and to what extent are they related to much later introduction of magnesium- or silica-bearing solutions? Is the porosity a residuum of the primary porosity, or has it resulted from secondary solution, and if the latter, is the localization of the solution fortuitous or is it related to primary features of the rock? Has compaction appreciably changed the rock volume from that of the initial sediment? Are all pellets initial clasts, or are some of them diagenetic aggregates? Is the anhydrite plugging of a dolomite reservoir the result of diagenesis or is it related to primary evaporite precipitation?

These and a multitude of other significant questions are everyday problems in the study of carbonate rocks, and analogies with other classes of sedimentary strata are of relatively little value in their solution. Currently, there are far more critical problems than there are answers in the field of diagenesis, and each unsolved problem shows why it is so difficult to erect a consistent descriptive or genetic classification of the carbonate rocks.

KINDS OF CLASSIFICATION AND THEIR PARAMETERS

Classification of natural objects is the subdivision of the infinite array of individual objects into meaningful groups. It represents a basic step in the scientific method. A prime purpose of classification is to facilitate communication of ideas or descriptive data, and a major test of any classification is the ease and accuracy with which it communicates these concepts to interested scientists. A second major purpose is to provide the investigator with the benefit derived from the organization of data and interpretations that is required in using a rigorous classification system.

Can there be a single or best classification for the complex group of carbonate rocks? To us the answer appears to be "no." There are at least as many specific classifications as there are specific purposes to be served by classification. Even if special-purpose classifications, such as those based on chemical content of the rocks, are eliminated from consideration, a single system for general-purpose use does not appear to be attainable at this time.

The classifier of carbonate rocks is faced at once with the problem of choosing whether his classification should be purely descriptive or purely genetic, or a blending of them to bring out the better qualities of each. Secondly, he must choose the set of parameters to be used in subdividing the broad spectrum of rock types into meaningful classes. The types of classifications and some of their parameters are discussed briefly in this section.

DESCRIPTIVE AND GENETIC CLASSIFICATIONS

According to the basic purpose desired, the two major types of classification are characterized as *descriptive* and *genetic*. For a sampling of some recent viewpoints on this general subject the reader is referred to Pettijohn (1948, 1949, 1957), Lombard (1949), and Rodgers (1950). The main purpose of the *descriptive* classification is to permit grouping of carbonate rocks on the basis of those observable features of the rock (chemical, mineralogical, biologic, physical, textural, or other) that can be objectively determined. In a purely descriptive classification, interpretations regarding origin of the rock are not required as a part of the classification process. The selection of the parameters for a descriptive classification is made according to the purpose that the classification will serve. In general, the broader the purpose the more difficult it becomes to keep a classification purely descriptive.

According to Rodgers (1950, p. 298) a descriptive classification

> . . . by grouping the like and separating the unlike . . . calls attention to the genetically significant correlations between likenesses and unlikenesses . . . what distinguishes a good [descriptive] classification . . . from a poor one is that the properties chosen are those that best bring out such correlations and thus lead toward genetic understanding. . . .

For descriptive classifications meeting the general needs of the geologic profession, we agree with Rodgers. Despite the conceptual appeal of a classification which is *purely* descriptive, careful consideration will indicate that such classifications generally result in very broad classes—so broad, in fact, that they will not satisfy the needs of most geologists concerned with classification of carbonate rocks.

The opposite type of classification is *genetic*. Here the objective is to communicate directly the origin of the rocks, rather than the descriptive features by which the origin can be interpreted. The categories are illustrated by such examples as "chemically precipitated limestones," "fore-reef talus limestones," "fecal pellet limestones," "low-energy limestones," "beach rock," or "hydrothermal dolomite." The selected groupings can range widely according to the purpose of the classification. For the orderly presentation of types of limestones, to permit an understanding of the geologic process, or to review the potential origins of carbonate rocks, genetic classifications have much merit. Most textbook classifications are essentially genetic. Examples in recent texts are those by Pettijohn (1949, 1957), Krumbein and Sloss (1951), and Williams, Turner, and Gilbert (1954). An earlier example is the text by Black (1938), in which is contained an excellent treatment of carbonate rocks. The classic treatment by Grabau (1904, 1913) likewise is purely genetic. For many purposes, to quote again from Rodgers (1950, p. 299)

> . . . those genetic traits that have the highest correlation with descriptive data will provide the most useful operational criteria.

Despite the usefulness of genetic classifications, they do not meet the geologists' most general requirement, which is to be able to classify a given specimen or suite of specimens prior to the time when the origin of the rock can best be inferred or determined. Indeed, the use of strictly genetic classifications puts "the cart before the horse" for most geologic investigations.

In conclusion, it appears that practical classifications of carbonate rocks that will best satisfy the requirements of geologists can be neither purely descriptive nor purely genetic. We favor classifications based as fully as possible on purely descriptive parameters, but into which genetic interpretations are carefully blended where they can be reasonably inferred, and where the use of an interpretive decision results in a more meaningful category than would otherwise be possible. It will be noted that this approach is used by authors of most detailed classifications presented in this symposium.

PARAMETERS NORMALLY USED IN CARBONATE CLASSIFICATIONS

Much of the value of any system of classification relates directly to the choice of properties or parameters used in establishing the classes. In the classification of sedimentary rocks the two most fundamental parameters are composition and texture, and these are used in most classifications of carbonate rocks. Some of the more commonly used compositional elements are mineralogy, chemical composition, or the composition expressed according to the types of grains (such as oölites, fossils, pellets). A wide range of textural features also is used. These commonly relate to depositional textures, such as size or sorting of the grains or clasts, to interpretations of "textural maturity," or to diagenetic textural features. Genetic aspects, such as depositional environment, clastic *vs.* nonclastic origin, and organic *vs.* nonorganic origin, are only indirectly related to texture or composition. These also provide a basis for subdividing the complex of carbonate rocks.

Some of the major parameters used in classifying carbonate rocks are briefly discussed in this section. It should be noted that almost all detailed systems of carbonate rock classification use more than one parameter, some purely descriptive, some largely descriptive with genetic overtones, and some largely or purely genetic. Moreover, it is pertinent to observe that in most detailed classifications the parameters used differ within several of the broader categories. For example, those features that are useful in subdividing the pervasively recrystallized carbonate rocks are different from those used in subdividing the limestones that retain all or most of their depositional characteristics.

Mineralogy.—The mineral composition of carbonate rocks provides a relatively simple and important basis for subdivision, as only three minerals—calcite, aragonite, and dolomite—are quantitatively important. The distinction between dolomite and the calcium carbonate minerals, calcite and aragonite, is highly significant and forms a basic compositional element in nearly all systems of classification.

Distinctions within the varieties of calcium carbonate are rarely used in classification but are of much importance in the interpretation of both carbonate sediments and rocks. In particular, the distinction between high- and low-magnesium calcite (Chave, 1954), and between these forms and aragonite, is of great value in deciphering diagenetic history.

The mineral identity of noncarbonate constituents, such as chert, glauconite, or quartz, is commonly given as a modifying term in naming or describing carbonate rocks, but these accessory constituents do not provide a practical basis for primary subdivision.

Chemical composition.—This is a simple, objective approach. It is useful in industry where rock products are marketed according to specified content of such components as CaO, MgO, SiO_2, and P_2O_5. Although chemical composition is used in a general way by all geologists, it is not sufficiently useful to be considered a major parameter for carbonate rock classifications. Probably the compositional aspect of most significance is the Ca/Mg ratio, and this commonly is better expressed by reference to the mineral composition.

"Insoluble" residues.—This parameter formed a major element in the classification of limestones proposed by Krynine (1948), and it has the advantage of being easy to use. It provides a poor basis for meaningful differentiation within the carbonate rock group, however, and is not used as a significant factor in any of the current classifications.

Identity of the carbonate grains.—Many carbonate rocks are clastic in nature. For this broad group the identity of the clasts forms a compositional parameter of paramount importance, as the clastic material can dominate thick sequences and extensive realms of carbonate rocks. The concept is recognized in all detailed classifications of this volume. These primary constituents of the rock, variously called grains, particles, or clasts, range widely in size. Those of coarse silt, sand, or larger sizes can normally be identified as to origin, resulting in categories such as oölites, pellets, "intraclasts," lumps, or biotic constituents, the latter consisting largely of the secreted hard parts of animals or plants. The biotic constituents are commonly amenable to further subdivision on the basis of whether they are skeletal or nonskeletal, intact or fragmented, or can be identified with the secreting organism. The types of biotic constituents are also useful in classifying the nonclastic carbonate rocks, such as a reef "framework," or rocks in which entire shells or organisms cannot be interpreted as either clastic or nonclastic components.

It should be recognized that use of this parameter generally requires an interpretive decision as to origin of the clast, and at the very least, for many carbonate rocks, it introduces genetic overtones into the classification process.

Depositional textures.—This category represents a wide variety of separate parameters and provides a basis of subdivision of the carbonate rocks that is of major interpretive significance. Depositional fabric is the primary parameter in the classifications of Folk, Powers, Dunham, Leighton and Pendexter, and Thomas. It is the most important element in the classification of Plumley, Risley, Graves, and Kaley, although in this genetic classification the depositional fabric is indirectly used.

The textural features that are most used in classification of the clastic carbonate rocks are the size and sorting of the component particles. Size has long been used and is the major consideration in the well-established terms of Grabau—calcirudite, calcarenite, and calcilutite. Most classifications presented in this volume represent a significant departure from the earlier approaches that emphasized the *average* size of the clasts. The newer approach shifts the focus more to the sorting, and specifically to measures of the *relative abundance* of clay or silt-size particles as compared to those of coarser sizes. Specific terminology varies, but the finer particles are variously referred to as "micrite," "microcrystalline ooze," "lime mud," or "matrix," and the coarser particles commonly as "grains" or "clasts." The precise boundary used to distinguish "grains" from "micrite" differs in the various classifications throughout the range of silt sizes (0.004 mm to 0.06 mm). The new classifications place much emphasis on the presence of even small amounts of micrite, and on its significance in interpreting the turbulence of the depositional environment. It is implicit, although not directly stated in most classification papers, that a source of micrite exists in all carbonate depositional environments, and that the absence of micrite in rocks retaining their depositional textures can be safely interpreted to mean its removal or nondeposition owing to water turbulence. Verification of this fundamental assumption is needed for some depositional environments.

The de-emphasis on the average size of the clasts in carbonate rocks reflects the increased understanding of the complexity of the size concept in many carbonate rocks that are composed of particles which had widely differing initial specific gravities and shapes, as well as the difficulty of recognizing whether many of the particles have originated in place or have been transported. Thus, to borrow Dunham's useful expressions, "currents of removal" are of more utility than "currents of delivery" in the interpretation of carbonate rocks.

Major emphasis on depositional texture implies the ability to distinguish diagenetic textures from primary textures. This is an interpretative or genetic decision of great importance, and more and better criteria are needed to permit this decision to be made with greater assurance than at present. Particularly critical is the problem of interpretation of the origin of sparry calcite, which can be either an open-space filling (cementation) or can represent recrystallization of earlier material, such as micrite. Even though the penetrative studies of Bathurst (1958, 1959) represent major advances in this area, further work is needed.

Textural maturity.—This parameter, which implies recognition of progressive degrees of abrasion and sorting of the clasts of a sedimentary rock, is an important consideration in the present article by Folk, and is recognized in many of the other classifications. However, as with considerations of size and sorting, the concept is far more difficult to apply to carbonate rocks than to sandstones, owing largely to the widely differing original sizes, shapes, and specific gravity of the clasts, and to the difficulty of interpreting the point of origin of the clasts.

Diagenetic factors.—A highly practical basis for distinguishing major categories of carbonate rocks is the degree of post-depositional modification. All detailed systems use some form of this concept. It is most commonly used to refer to the degree of modification of both composition and texture. For interpretative work, the tendency is to make maximum use of the depositional parameters for the basic classification, and to indicate degree of obliteration of the original properties by use of modifying terms such as "dolomitic" and "partly recrystallized." The comprehensive systems of classification also establish major categories for carbonate rocks in which the alteration process is so pervasive that interpretation and classification, based on the original sediment, are impossible. Thus, the degree of diagenetic alteration is fully recognized, but it cannot be given the prominence reserved for the primary constituents and fabrics.

Most of the extensive reduction of primary porosity of carbonate sediments is a post-depositional or diagenetic process. Both porosity and cementation are important descriptive and interpretive aspects, yet they are given little significance in most carbonate classifications except those by Leighton and Pendexter, and by Thomas.

Clastic versus nonclastic origin.—Many of the carbonate rocks are composed of sedimentary particles that have been transported, at least slightly, from the site of origin of the particles, even though nearly all particles are of intrabasinal origin. Except for organic remains in position of growth, all the sedimentary particles have undergone at least slight transportation. Sedimentary structures in many carbonate rocks, such as cross-lamination, clearly indicate the clastic (transported) nature of the particles. However, the genetic interpretation as to clastic or transported *versus* nonclastic or nontransported is difficult or impossible to make for many sedimentary particles, and thus the utility of this aspect as a major parameter is diminished. Nevertheless, most detailed classifications in this volume treat the broad group of "clastic carbonate rocks" separately from a group interpreted to have been formed by in-place organic growth.

The problem becomes especially difficult with the finer grained carbonate materials that form the micrite. Criteria are currently lacking to determine the origin of this material. Is it largely an "inorganic" precipitate, or a product of abrasion or comminution of coarser carbonate particles of intrabasinal or perhaps even extrabasinal origin? The difficulties of this interpretation are well illustrated by the current controversy regarding the origin of the lime muds in the Recent sediments of the Bahama Islands. A study of isotopic composition (Lowenstam and Epstein, 1957) represents a new approach to these problems, and is a welcome beginning in an attempt to solve them.

Organic versus inorganic origin.—This time-honored division of carbonate rocks has frequently been used as a major parameter in genetic classifications, but this basis of distinction is of little utility in a detailed approach to classification. One of the difficulties is the current lack of knowledge as to the importance of organic processes in formation of the groups of carbonate rocks classically considered to be "inorganic," such as oölites, or chemical precipitates. If microscopic forms of algae, bacteria, or other organisms and organic complexes can be proven to have influenced or controlled extensive precipitation of calcium carbonate, the distinction between organic and inorganic will lose much of its former significance.

In rocks that are clearly organic in origin, the recognition of the major types of biotic or organic constituents is of much importance. This is discussed earlier under compositional parameters.

"Energy" levels.—The concept of the "energy" or water turbulence of the depositional environment provides a significant interpretive parameter for classification of carbonate rocks. "High-energy" and "low-energy" carbonate sediments are those which have been deposited respectively in turbulent or quiet waters. The energy concept is well recognized in most modern classifications, although indirectly, by the focus on the relative abundance of "grains" and "matrix." An "Energy Index" is the principal parameter in the classification of Plumley and others, and it is inferred from both the composition and texture of the rock.

Depositional environment.—This genetic parameter groups carbonate rocks on the basis of the specific geomorphic depositional environment, such as lagoon, barrier or patch reef, offshore bar, or beach. Broader kinds of groupings are shelf, platform, shelf edge, basin slope, or basin; or the depth groupings of littoral, neritic, bathyal, or abyssal. For ancient rocks these are all genetic parameters, and though of much importance in understanding the interrelationships of various facies, they are of little value in a working classification of carbonate rocks when the need is a system for treating individual specimens.

THE SYMPOSIUM CLASSIFICATIONS

In the following section the contributions to this symposium volume are briefly reviewed and compared (Table I). The classifications presented in two of the nine papers (Plumley and others, and Feray and others) are primarily genetic in approach. One paper (Nelson and others), although it gives no general classification, considers the nomenclature of skeletal limestones and of various

TABLE I. COMPARISON OF THE SYMPOSIUM CLASSIFICATIONS

	Feray, Heuer, and Hewatt	*Leighton and Pendexter*	*Folk*	*Plumley, Risley, Graves, and Kaley*	*Dunham*	*Powers*	*Thomas*	*Nelson, Brown, and Brineman*	*Imbrie and Purdy*
Comprehensive classification of all carbonates	x	xx	xx	xx	x	xx	xx		
Classification primarily descriptive		x	x		x	x	x		x
Classification primarily genetic	x			x				x	
Classification emphasizing texture	x	xx	xx	xx	xx	xx	xx	x	x
Classification emphasizing particle composition	x	xx	xx	xx	x	xx	x	x	xx
Sorting emphasized		xx	xx	xx	xx	xx	xx		xx
Pore space emphasized		xx	x	x	xx	xx	xx		
Depositional fabric emphasized		x	x	x	xx	x	x		
Major role played by organisms	xx	x	x	xx	x	x	x	xx	x
Skeletal *vs.* nonskeletal elements divided	xx	xx	x	xx	x	x	x	xx	x
Terminology of carbonate rock bodies (reefs, etc.)								xx	
Treatment of reefs	x	x	x	x	x	x	x	xx	
Criteria for transported *vs.* in-place particles		x	x	xx	x			xx	
Intrabasinal source of carbonates emphasized	x	x	x	x		x		xx	x
Energy indicators emphasized		x	x	xx	x	x	x		
Discussion of "natural" rock divisions			x	x		x	x		xx
Discussion of land-derived clastics	x	x	x	x		x	x		
Internal sedimentation considered		x	x	x	x				
Cementation emphasized		x	x	x	x		xx		
Dolomitic rocks emphasized		x	x	x	x	x	x		
Recrystallization emphasized	x	x	x	x	x	xx	x		
Regional aspects discussed		x	x	x		x	x		xx
Case histories cited				xx		xx	xx		x
Rock types well illustrated		xx	xx	xx	xx	xx	xx		
Mathematical analyses used in classification									xx
System amenable to logging and map making	x	xx	xx	xx	xx	xx	xx	x	xx
Evaporites discussed		x	x	x		xx	xx		

x = Considered.
xx = Major emphasis.

types of carbonate rock bodies and utilizes genetic interpretations as the major basis of classification. Five of the papers utilize a descriptive approach to classification, yet each of these applies genetic interpretation where it serves a practical purpose. Six of the papers treat the general case of all carbonate rocks. Two of them (Powers and Thomas) deal specifically with the carbonate rocks in the petroliferous regions of Arabia and Western Canada, and in each of them the practicality of their respective classifications is illustrated by extensive application to case histories. One paper (Imbrie and Purdy) does not present a classification, but specifically tests the application of the Folk classification to modern carbonate sediments on a part of the Great Bahama Bank. More than half of the papers are profusely illustrated. Finally, all of the classifications are amenable in some degree to logging and map-making techniques, examples of which are given in the papers by Plumley and others, by Thomas, and by Powers.

Each of the papers represents extensive experience with carbonate sediments or rocks, and the classifications presented have all been tested in practice. The enormous amount of work involved is appreciated when it is realized that the total effort contributed by the 18 authors probably represents at least 200 man-years of experience in studying carbonate rocks. The points of agreement far outweigh the points of disagreement; and most of the deviation occurs where there are differences in personal experience or in the ultimate goals sought by the classifiers.

Feray, Heuer, and Hewatt

The writers emphasize both the value of a genetic classification and the difficulties inherent in the erecting of one. Instead of naming the rock types, beyond those terms already in common use, they set up families of limestone by process of origin. Those limestones of detrital origin derived by mechanical weathering of terrestrial outcrops are set apart, and primary consideration is given to those derived by physicochemical and biochemical processes within a carbonate depositional basin. Biochemical limestones, produced directly by the influence of organisms, are divided first into *skeletal accretions* (formed by in-place organic secretion) and *skeletal aggregates* (as in reef framework), and second into *nonskeletal* grains which yield by aggregation formed by grain-by-grain accumulation of skeletal materials, as on organism-rich banks, the normal micrgranular limestones, calcilutites, and pelletal calcarenites. The contrasting physicochemical group is characterized by nonskeletal grains, chiefly of the oölitic, microgranular, and pelletal calcarenite types. One point emphasized is that microgranular limestones so common in the geologic record are derivable either by mechanical, physicochemical, or biochemical processes.

An integral part of this paper is devoted to the results of experimental crushing of shell material and the determination of the minimum size of particle that can still be identified as to origin after crushing. The authors conclude that most shell material can not be so recognized in sizes less than $\frac{1}{16}$ mm. They infer that an important element in carbonate rock classification is thus not readily available to classifiers, and moreover that the organic contribution to sediments is more—perhaps considerably more—than can be shown. Diagenetic changes by solution, cementation, recrystallization, and replacement locally work great changes on carbonates and thereby increase the problems of interpretation.

They recommend a novel approach to developing a generally accepted limestone classification. This would be by study of an extensive collection of carbonate rocks which would form a reference set, in a manner somewhat analogous to type specimens of fossils. The specimens would be accompanied by descriptions of pertinent field, biologic, mineralogic, and geochemical data prepared by a team of experts in these specialties. The final assembly of data into categories would comprise the essential framework of a classification.

Leighton and Pendexter

These authors present a comprehensive system of classification which utilizes both descriptive and genetic approaches. They recognize that most limestones are clastic textured, and differentiate these mechanically deposited, clastic limestones from the group formed by in-place organic growth, such as creates reef framework. The basic types of limestones are modified by the element of recrystallization. The system utilizes pre-existing carbonate terminology as much as possible, although some definitions are sharpened. A rather complete glossary is a useful feature of their article.

The clastic limestones are composed of variable amounts of four basic textural elements. These are the coarser clasts or *grains*, the finer grained lime mud or *micrite*, the chemically precipitated *cement*, and the *voids*. Of these four textural elements, the basic rock is primarily determined by the ratio of grains to micrite, whereas the amounts of cement and voids are indicated by modifiers. The boundary between grains and micrite is arbitrarily set at 0.03 mm, distinctly coarser than the boundary (0.004 mm) set by Folk, who originated the term micrite. The all-important grains are divided into five categories—detrital, skeletal, pellets, lumps, and coated or encrusted grains. These five grain types together with the ratio of grains to micrite form the basic parameters used in subdividing the clastic limestones into 16 classes.

The nonclastic textured limestones, characterized by a textural element formed by in-place organic growth, are subdivided into three groups based on genetic features.

The dolomitic or pervasively recrystallized rocks are treated separately. The dolomitic rocks are subdivided on the basis of the percentage of dolomite in the rock, and on the basis of a genetic interpretation of the dolomite as primary or secondary. The proposed classification system permits the use of rock names and modifiers to include both primary and diagenetic features, as in the example of a "dolomitic skeletal-micritic limestone."

The classification chart is so arranged that its vertical axis (grain/micrite ratio) reflects physical action; specifically, the degree of wave or current agitation, whereas the horizontal axis indicates relative influence of mechanical, biological, and chemical factors. The classification has been devised largely for studies of thin sections, but is adaptable for binocular-microscope examination of suitably prepared specimens. The article provides detailed discussion of the use and background of the classification system, and is accompanied by numerous illustrations and quantitative data on specific rocks.

Folk

The attempt is made here, as it is in the work of Leighton and Pendexter, to erect a classification that is applicable to all carbonate rocks. The article is a review and slight amplification of the author's earlier paper (Folk, 1959). In addition it contains a discussion of the concept of textural maturity of carbonate rocks. The Folk classification has been applied extensively in the past few years, a tribute to its soundness and comprehension, and to the ease with which its newly coined terms can be utilized and understood.

We are indebted to Folk for including his article in this symposium volume, even though the essence of his classification has been published elsewhere, so that the symposium may be more nearly complete in terms of modern works.

The Folk classification deals largely with limestones of clastic origin, and in common with the classification of Leighton and Pendexter and others, these limestones are separated from those believed to have been formed by in-place organic growth, and from those carbonate rocks in which recrystallization or other diagenetic effects have extensively modified the primary rock features. The Folk classification for the clastic group is built around six major elements—intraclasts, pellets, fossils or fossil fragments, oölites, microcrystalline calcite ooze or micrite, and sparry calcite cement. *Intraclasts* are defined as carbonate particles formed by erosion of penecontemporaneous, generally weakly consolidated carbonate sediment from the adjacent sea floor. These also include particles, such as the grapestone and lumps of Illing (1954), even though the latter may be aggregated rather than erosional particles. Intraclast specifically excludes fragments of consolidated limestone derived from an emergent land area. *Pellets* are generally subspherical aggregates of microcrystalline carbonate ooze containing no distinctive internal structure, and in any given rock generally show a remarkable uniformity in shape and size. Folk places an upper size limit on pellets at about 0.15 mm. Larger grains of similar structure are classed as intraclasts, although many geologists, including the reviewers, use the term pellet for any sand-sized or silt-sized grain of "pellet" characteristics. *Fossils* and fossil fragments together with oölites are not discussed because of their "self-evident" nature and because descriptions of them have been published elsewhere. *Microcrystalline calcite ooze* or *micrite* consists of grains 1–4 microns in diameter, in most rocks now calcite, although possibly they were originally aragonite. Folk believes that these grains originate chiefly by chemical or biochemical precipitation and are locally transported. Calcareous dust produced by abrasion cannot be genetically distinguished from the above type by suitable existing criteria, but in Folk's opinion such dust normally is quantitatively unimportant. Micrite is to be distinguished from silt-sized carbonate particles, although this is difficult to do in practice without thin sections. Common usage of the term micrite by some authors includes finer silt sizes as well as clay sizes (*see* Leighton and Pendexter). *Sparry calcite cement* is clear calcite, having a grain size no smaller than 4 microns, that generally forms as a chemically precipitated pore filling. Folk urges caution in distinguishing between sparry calcite which originates as a cement from that formed by recrystallization, but gives few criteria for distinguishing these contrasting types.

Folk places primary emphasis in classification of the bulk of carbonate rocks ("clastic textured limestones" of Leighton and Pendexter) on the relative proportions of *allochems* (intraclasts, pellets, fossils, and oölites), *micrite*, and *sparry calcite cement* and utilizes these three groupings as end members at the apices of a triangular diagram. The field of the triangle is divided into three areas—Type I rocks with a dominance of allochems and sparry calcite cement, Type II rocks with a dominance of allochems and micrite, and Type III rocks with a dominance of micrite. Type I limestones are interpreted to represent deposition in a turbulent environment; Type II limestones indicate weak, short-lived currents or a rapid rate of formation of microcrystalline ooze; and those of Type III are interpreted to imply both a rapid rate of precipitation and a lack of persistent current activity. Two other major types of limestones are differentiated on the basis of genesis. They consist of Type IV for those formed of in-place organic structures, such as algal stromatolites or reefs, and Type V carbonate rocks for those extensively modified by recrystallization or dolomitization.

Rock names are formed in the Folk system by combinations of the roots of names given to the six basic components, yielding names such as *intrasparite* (intraclasts cemented by sparry calcite), or *biomicrite* (fossils in lime mud matrix). Fuller descriptions are made by adding modifying terms, such as brachiopod-bryozoan biomicrite which designates the types of fossils, or by use of other suitable modifiers to denote such aspects as the grain size, admixtures of terrigenous material, or replacement minerals, such as chert. Distinctive field properties, as well as factual or inferred data pertaining to genesis and environment, are also used as modifiers to complete the first phase of the classification scheme.

The present article by Folk expands appreciably upon the classification published in 1959 by subdividing the limestones of the three major families (Types I, II, and III) into eight groups based on the concept of textural maturity, analogous to the concept of textural maturity of sandstones. This provides a spectrum of textural types representing deposition in environments of different physical energy (water turbulence), and establishes quantitative limits for these groups based upon the relative proportions of allochems and micrite, and upon the sorting and rounding of the allochems.

The two articles by Folk supplement each other and jointly provide a practical and comprehensive system for classification of the carbonate rocks. A weakness in the system concerns rocks composed of clasts of silt-sized material. Except for those in the coarse silt sizes (which Folk groups with those of similar composition whose grains are of sand size), the calcisiltites are relatively neglected, yet others (for example, Thomas, this volume) place great emphasis on them because they locally form highly productive petroleum reservoirs. The relative lack of emphasis on porosity in the Folk system is also a disadvantage, particularly to those concerned with the exploration for petroleum in carbonate reservoirs.

Plumley, Risley, Graves, and Kaley

This genetic classification treats carbonate rocks according to the turbulent energy of the physical environment in which the sediment was deposited, dividing them into five major limestone types which constitute a grading spectrum from quiet water (I) to strongly agitated water

(V). The classification is named the Energy Index system (EI). The observational parameters upon which the classification is based, as well as the interpretive principles, are rather similar to those presented by Leighton and Pendexter, Folk, and others, and hence the differences between this "genetic" classification and the other more "descriptive" classifications are more apparent than real. Primary considerations are of textural nature, including size, sorting, and roundness of granular particles, together with the amount and size of the fine-grained (clay and silt size) carbonate matrix. Considerations of secondary importance are the compositional attributes—chiefly mineralogy and the types of grains or fossils. The focus of the classification is on depositional features, rather than on diagenetic aspects, thus reflecting a fundamental concern with environmental interpretation. In contrast to many of the other classifications presented in this symposium, this classification does not propose names for any of the various types of limestones, and diverse kinds of rocks are included under each of the energy classes.

Type I rocks (quiet water sediments) and Type II rocks (intermittently agitated water sediments) are both characterized by the presence of more than 50 per cent of microcrystalline calcite matrix and are distinguished by the amount of fragmentation or abrasion of fossil material. Within each type, three subtypes are recognized. The subtypes of Type I are differentiated on the amount of argillaceous material and the amount of fossil material, whereas two of the subtypes of Type II are differentiated chiefly on the basis of the size of the non-matrix clastic particles, and a third is characterized by alternating laminae of lime mud and coarser clastic carbonate—an important type of carbonate rock that is not specifically recognized in the other symposium classifications.

Type III carbonates (slightly agitated water sediments) contain less than 50 per cent microcrystalline matrix in which either the matrix or the included clastic particles, or both, have good sorting. Three subtypes are differentiated on the basis of the size of the coarser clastic particles, which can range from silt size (micrograined) through very fine-grained to fine-grained (0.125 mm) sand sizes. Type IV rocks (moderately agitated environments) contain clastic carbonate particles of medium to very coarse size (Wentworth scale), and the matrix material, if present, is poorly sorted. Normally, matrix materials are washed away from this environment and are quantitatively minor. Finally, the most strongly agitated water sediments (Type V) contain carbonate clasts coarser than 2 mm, and in which the fossils are generally broken and abraded. Type V also contains those rough-water, in-place, framework-builders that are typical of reef-type limestone accumulations. One of the difficulties of the classification is that it does not permit the simultaneous placement of a single rock into more than one category, even though it can be shown that the rock could originate in environments with widely contrasting water turbulence. For example, Type V limestones of the variety characterized by in-place growth of organisms that have a wave-resisting potential may or may not have actually grown in a wave turbulent zone. However, the difficulties of placing a single sample in a specific environment are minimized when the classification is applied to a vertical succession of carbonate rock types.

One of the tests of the classification is its applicability to stratigraphic interpretation, and the authors discuss and illustrate the use of their classification for two specific examples in the geologic record. Systematic changes in depositional turbulence for three wells located across the top of a Pennsylvanian carbonate buildup in Texas are shown through the use of a logging technique involving moving averages of the energy index, and the utility of the resulting logs for both correlation and facies interpretation is demonstrated. The construction of areal maps contoured on the basis of the Energy Index (EI) is illustrated for the Smackover formation (Jurassic) for Arkansas and Louisiana, and it is shown that the linear band of highest energy coincides approximately with the region of known production of petroleum from the Smackover.

Dunham

As is indicated by the title, the prime concern of the Dunham article is the depositional fabric of carbonate rocks. The paper is a highly significant and original contribution and contains much valuable insight for students of carbonate rocks. The clastic carbonate rocks are subdivided into four major groups based upon the relative proportions of the coarser clastic particles (grains) and the finer matrix or lime mud. In this classification, the boundary between grains and mud is arbitrarily set at 20 microns. Instead of using fixed proportions of grains to mud for establishing major types of carbonate rocks, Dunham bases his subdivision on whether the mud forms the essential framework of the rock, with the coarser grains not in mutual contact; or whether the essential framework is provided by the coarser grains with the mud occurring as an interstitial, nonsupporting matrix. This concept is of far-reaching importance in dealing with the wide variety of shapes represented by the coarser clasts, especially by the fossils, in carbonate rocks. The mud-supported class is divided into *mudstone*, containing less than 10 per cent grains, and into *wackestone*, which contains more than 10 per cent grains. These rocks are equivalent to most calcilutites and to many calcisiltites and calcarenitic mudstones. Grains arranged in a self-supporting framework, yet containing some matrix of lime mud, yield a rock called *packstone*. If no mud is present the rock is called *grainstone*. These four divisions of mudstone, wackestone, packstone, and grainstone together form a group which characterizes the full range of clastic-textured carbonate rocks.

Two other major groups are included in the classification—*boundstone* and *crystalline carbonate*. *Boundstone* applies to most reef rock, stromatolites, and some biohermal and biostromal rocks in which the original components were bound together during deposition, and remain substantially in position of growth. *Crystalline carbonate* is used for those rocks in which depositional textures are not recognizable, owing to recrystallization or replacement. Dolomites and dolomitic limestones are included in the classification system. Commonly there is preserved sufficient relict information to permit their classification according to the origin of grains, but not to allow an interpretation of their depositional fabric.

The names used by Dunham are essentially for rock families. His primary effort deals with the question of whether or not the grains were originally in mutual contact, and therefore self supporting, or whether the rock is characterized by the presence of framebuilders and algal mats. Here there is strongly implied a determined effort to understand more critically the distribution and genesis of original porosity in carbonate rocks, and to establish principles for use in the interpretation of diagenetic modifications. The author has ingeniously used a series of photographs to illustrate how certain grains, invertebrate fossils, and plants or plant fragments can be arranged in a self-supporting framework of exceptionally high original porosity. By this feature alone the medium-textured carbonate rocks can be set apart from their nearest cousins, the sandstones, whose subangular grains cannot be packed in such an arrangement, and therefore cannot produce a comparably high original porosity.

Powers

The work of Powers is a remarkably detailed investigation of the highly prolific Upper Jurassic Arab-D carbonates. From wells drilled and cored over a 20-year period, some 4,000 thin sections were cut and 1,200 were analyzed by point counting. The classification resulting from this work, and the regional inferences derived from it, were checked against areas of modern carbonate sedimentation in the nearby Persian Gulf. The classification is both objective and simple, and at the same time it is directly amenable to many of the needs of petroleum geology. It is a moderate revision of the classification proposed earlier by Bramkamp and Powers (1958). The classification is primarily directed toward the clastic-textured carbonates, and the products of diagenetic modification of these rocks.

Classification is made into four simplified classes of carbonate rocks—aphanitic, calcarenitic, calcarenite, and coarse clastic. They are divided mainly by texture, and the classes are closely related to the Wentworth grade scale. Great prominence is given to the cleanly washed calcarenites, which have little or no matrix or cement and which preserve up to the present time the original (Jurassic) porosity of the rock. The constituents of the clastic-textured carbonates are mainly calcareous algae, algal nodules, stromatoporoids, Foraminifera, skeletal fragments, and grains, pellets, and pellet aggregates or lumps.

Recrystallization and replacement also are considered. In the strongest alteration the original texture is obliterated, generally by crystalline dolomite; but in the preceding two stages of moderate to strong alteration, there is either an introduction of dolomite or a simple recrystallization of calcitic components.

The coded system of Powers' rock types, applicable to logging, correlation, and areal mapping, is an added feature of the classification. By logging the lithologic units, along with percentages of the various constituents, Powers shows that the Arab-D zone is divisible into a lower unit of mixed lime mud and nonskeletal sand, a middle unit dominantly of mudstone, and an upper unit of clean-washed calcarenite. Above is bedded anhydrite. These stratigraphic units are easily correlatable, and they indicate that the upper unit represents a time of shoaling environment, directly preceding the formation of evaporites.

The porosity and permeability of carbonate rocks, of major interest to petroleum geologists, is shown to be related directly to two factors—the degree of original sorting, reaching a maximum in well-sorted, clean-washed calcarenites, and the extent to which dolomite replaces original constituents of the rock. When porosity and permeability are plotted on strip logs against lithology, it is shown (1) that dolomite has an exceptionally high affinity for lime mud, and (2) that within the range of 5–75 per cent dolomitization, permeability decreases to about 2–3 millidarcies and then, with 80 per cent dolomitization, increases abruptly to 300 md. At higher percentages of dolomite it decreases slowly and, above 95 per cent, the rock is virtually impermeable.

THOMAS

The approach of Thomas is somewhat different because, unlike most other authors, he has not used thin sections or other specialized techniques of sample preparation, but has depended largely upon binocular microscope examination of relatively untreated cuttings, cores, and rock fragments.

The classification is directly related to porosity and permeability, and it will doubtless find favor among those primarily concerned with reservoir characteristics. Thomas applies his classification to four specific examples of carbonate facies in Western Canada.

The classification is based on four size grades—clay-sized or *cryptograined* limestone (less than 10 microns), very fine silt *chalky* limestones (10 microns), *silt* limestones (10–60 microns), and *sand-textured* limestones (greater than 60 microns). The silt-sized rocks are given great importance, and two terms—microgranular and micrograined—ordinarily used interchangeably by most geologists, are given precise meanings. *Microgranular* is referred to as that texture in rocks wherein the particles are mostly 10–60 microns in diameter, are of a common size (well sorted), and the finer clay-sized matrix is absent. Thomas indicates that this class is significant because it is likely, whether dolomitized or not, to have high porosity. *Micrograined* limestones, on the other hand, have particles of the same size range but they are poorly sorted and are admixed with clay-sized lime mud. Effective porosity is low, even in dolomitized equivalents.

The sand-sized carbonates are divided into two types, *cemented* and *uncemented*. If uncemented, or uncemented and dolomitized, effective porosity is high; but if cemented, or if cemented and dolomitized, porosity is low. The principal types of such limestones are *skeletal*, *nonskeletal*, *organic lattice*, and *conglomerate-breccias*. An "uncemented skeletal limestone" is an example of one of the rock types.

The role of early cementation by clear calcite is judged to be of prime importance, as it inhibits porosity at an early stage in carbonate rock sedimentation and also inhibits the dolomitization process, by which a later porosity might be developed. The author relates the well-sorted and uncemented carbonate rocks to a shoal environment, and believes the patterns of depositional facies can be predicted to assist in petroleum exploration. Locally, they grade into dolomitic equivalents, partly with effective porosity, before grading further into cryptocrystalline carbonates and into evaporites that generally are tight or have ineffective porosity.

The process of leaching of calcitic skeletal grains in an early porous dolomitic matrix is shown by Thomas to be of importance in developing porosity in the Elkton (Mississippian) carbonate rocks of Alberta.

The classification is designed to treat reefs as well as the carbonates associated with them. Reef-like buildups in the Devonian Swan Hills complex of central Alberta are characterized by reef-fringed reservoirs of high porosity, which enclose nonproductive lime muds. An organic lattice framework containing well-sorted granular infillings accounts for the porosity, and the conclusion is reached that granularity ratios furnish a superior tool in the search for petroleum. A series of symbols has been devised, using the parameters of the classification, to make easily reproducible log strips.

The sorting of grains in the finer textured rocks, the presence or absence of cement in the coarser textured ones, and the presence of a framebuilding organic lattice, form the main elements of the Thomas classification.

Nelson, Brown, and Brineman

This work is not to be considered a classification of most rocks in the carbonate realm, but is restricted almost wholly to a consideration of the nomenclature of reefs and other carbonate rock bodies. It thus reflects an absorbing interest in the origin and history of these structures, and a desire to correct the chaotic situation caused by conflicting usages of terms such as reef, bank, or bioherm. *Skeletal limestone* is defined by the authors as a limestone made of *in-place organisms*, other types being set aside as *fragmental*, *aphanitic* (less than 60 microns), and *macrocrystalline* (more than 60 microns). All other authors in this volume use the term skeletal in a different sense, applying it to discrete grains of skeletal or of organic origin, and describing the in-place organisms as framebuilders or as organic lattice.

Most of the report is a review of the literature on reefs, bioherms, biostromes, and banks, in each of which there is dynamic in-place growth of organisms. Some well-defined criteria for the recognition of in-place *versus* transported skeletal remains are given. The authors conclude that (1) reefs are characterized by a biologic potential to erect a rigid, wave-resistant framework, (2) banks are skeletal limestone deposits formed by organisms which do not have the bioecologic potential to erect such framework, (3) bioherms are moundlike or lenslike accumulations, and (4) biostromes are bedded structures without conspicuous buildup with reference to the surrounding beds. Excellent examples of limestone banks are cited and illustrated.

Imbrie and Purdy

This article differs from all others in the symposium volume, for instead of presenting a classification covering a wide range of carbonate rocks, it deals only with Recent sediments from 40 stations in a part of the Great Bahama Bank. Statistical techniques are applied to evaluate essential parameters and to group the sediments into major types.

The writers found that 12 components are sufficient for normal characterization of these modern carbonate sediments. The components are distinguished according to composition and consist of fragments of corals, algae, and other organisms as well as pellets, grapestone, and oöliths. All other constituents in a textural class less than $\frac{1}{8}$ mm are grouped under the term lime mud. A mathematical scheme was devised in an attempt to interrelate as many as possible of these parameters, using a data processing machine (IBM 650) that would accommodate 40 samples rapidly and accurately. The primary objective was to obtain the simplest set of interrelations and to determine whether certain natural boundaries were shown by the samples, as indicated by gross mapping of the bottom sediments.

It was found that 89 per cent of the processed information on 40 samples can be explained by only four factors. By additional transformations it could be shown that the data are arranged into five discrete clusters, corresponding to the following facies—oölite, oölitic, grapestone, lime mud, and coralgal (mixture of coral and algal fragments). The boundaries are considered to reflect significant discontinuities in the dynamic system responsible for the occurrence and distribution of the sediments, and it is further considered that the distribution and abundance of grain types are highly interdependent units within a tightly organized marine ecosystem.

Imbrie and Purdy believe that this distribution probably is the result of modern processes and has not been significantly inherited from a mature environment of an earlier (Pleistocene?) time, for C^{14} dates of the sediments give values that are younger than 2,500 years.

Imbrie and Purdy compare their classification of the Bahamian sediments with that obtained using the Folk classification. This results in a close fit for the cleanly washed carbonate sands of the shelf lagoon and outer platform, but reveals rather wide discrepancies for the muddy sands of the shelf lagoon. To use Folk's classification for the comparison of cleanly washed sands, it is necessary to assume that the presently existing voids will be filled with sparry calcite (oösparite, biosparite). But it must be remembered that the classification of Folk is intended for all carbonate rocks, of all ages and all environments, and therefore should include the Bahamian sediments, although perhaps not making a best fit with the data and classification of Imbrie and Purdy. One example of disparity is that the distinction between biosparite and pelsparite does not correspond with a natural dividing line among Bahamian sediment samples.

SUMMARY AND CONCLUSIONS

Perhaps the greatest measure of success achieved by the publications in this symposium volume is the recognition that classification of the carbonate rocks is based first of all upon detailed knowledge and a penetrating insight into the problems of these rocks. The various classifications merely reveal the extent of knowledge through the framework of their rock classes. The kinds of classes submitted invariably reflect the primary interests of the investigators, and thus we see many kinds of classifications. Happily we also see that among them many strong threads of common interest and approach are interwoven.

To help in accomplishing the goals of better classification and understanding of the carbonate rocks, the use of thin sections, polished surfaces, etched surfaces, and transparent peels is now standard practice for those seriously concerned with this complex family of sedimentary rocks. Simpler techniques may suffice for much routine work, particularly if the more specialized techniques are used to supplement them. The simpler approaches include acid etching, sawing or grinding a smooth surface, and the direct examination of carbonate rock surfaces with a hand lens or low-power binocular microscope. Wetting freshly broken, cut, or ground surfaces with water, clove oil, or mineral oil, helps greatly.

Most of the classifications presented here reveal the marked shift in emphasis from the average size of the carbonate particles comprising a rock, to the relative proportions of the coarser particles or grains and of the finer grained constituents—the matrix or micrite. Nearly all classifiers distinguish three major groupings of carbonate rocks, the clastic-textured group, the group characterized by in-place organic growth, and the group in which diagenesis has pervasively modified the primary features of the rock. Despite the emphasis on a descriptive approach to classification by many of the authors, the above major groupings are distinctly genetic. However, more descriptive approaches are utilized by most classifiers in subdividing the rocks in each of these three major groupings. The parameters of primary concern for most classifications are the depositional fabric, particularly the relative abundance of grains and matrix; the size and nature of the grains (for example, oölites, pellets, fossils); and the nature and degree of post-depositional modification. Aspects of lesser significance in most classifications include cementation, porosity, the degree of abrasion or rounding of the clasts, admixtures of terrigenous material, and authigenic components.

Many of the classification systems provide for codification by letter, number, or symbol, or combinations of them, thus making it possible to construct quantitative logs and maps which show changes in carbonate rock succession or in areal distribution that are helpful in reconstructing the sedimentary environment, in correlation, or for other interpretations.

The strictly genetic approach used by some classifiers seeks a laudable goal. It is to be pursued even more vigorously when knowledge of carbonate rocks is considerably increased and when interpretive criteria are much more numerous. At the present time we need much additional definitive information on nearly all aspects of carbonate sedimentation and diagenesis. Some of the specific needs relate to dolomitization; to the interrelationships of carbonates and evaporites; to a better understanding of the processes of internal sedimentation, of cementation, and of recrystallization; to better methods for determining the origin of the finer grained carbonate particles; to a more basic understanding of the geochemical processes involved in deposition and diagenesis; and to an enormous number of ecological criteria that pertain both to modern seas and to ancient rocks.

It remains clear that the carbonate rocks are an exceedingly complex family of sedimentary rocks, and that only the beginning of an adequate understanding has been achieved to date. In the final analysis, there is no substitute for a detailed knowledge of the processes involved in creating the carbonate rocks, and there is no substitute for a *critical look at the rocks themselves*.

REFERENCES

Bathurst, R. G. C., 1958, Diagenetic fabrics in some British Dinantian limestones: Liverpool and Manchester Geol. Jour., v. 2, pt. 1, p. 11–36.

——— 1959, Diagenesis in Mississippian calcilutites and pseudo-breccias: Jour. Sed. Petrology, v. 29, p. 365–376.

Black, Maurice, reviser, *in* Hatch, F. H., and Rastall, R. H., 1938, The petrology of sedimentary rocks, 3d ed.: London, George Allen and Unwin Ltd., 383 p.

Bramkamp, R. A., and Powers, R. W., 1958, Classification of Arabian carbonate rocks: Geol. Soc. America Bull, v. 69, no. 10, p. 1305–1318.

Cayeux, Lucien, 1935, Les roches sédimentaires de France, roches carbonatées: Paris, Masson et Cie.

Chave, K. E., 1954, Aspects of biogeochemistry of magnesium: Jour. Geology, v. 62, pt. 1, no. 3, p. 266–283; pt. 2, no. 6, p. 587–599.

Folk, R. L., 1959, Practical petrographic classification of limestones: Am. Assoc. Petroleum Geologists Bull., v. 43, no. 1, p. 1–38.

Grabau, A. W., 1904, On the classification of sedimentary rocks: Am. Geologist, v. 33, p. 228–247.

——— 1913, Principles of stratigraphy: New York, A. G. Seiler and Co.

Illing, Leslie V., 1954, Bahaman calcareous sands: Am. Assoc. Petroleum Geologists Bull., v. 38, no. 1, p. 1–95.

Johnson, J. Harlan, 1951, An introduction to the study of organic limestones: Colorado School Mines Quart., v. 46, no. 2.

Krumbein, W. C., and Sloss, L. L., 1951, Stratigraphy and sedimentation: San Francisco, W. H. Freeman and Co., 497 p.

Krynine, P. D., 1948, The megascopic study and field classification of sedimentary rocks: Jour. Geology, v. 56, no. 2, p. 130–165.

Lombard, A., 1949, Critères descriptifs et critères génétiques dans l'étude des roches sédimentaires: Soc. Belge Géol. Bull., v. 58, no. 2, p. 214–271.

Lowenstam, H. A., 1950, Niagaran reefs of the Great Lakes area: Jour. Geology, v. 58, p. 430–487.

——— and Epstein, S., 1957, On the origin of sedimentary argonite needles of the Great Bahama Bank: Jour. Geology, v. 65, no. 4, p. 364–375.

Pettijohn, F. J., 1948, A preface to the classification of the sedimentary rocks: Jour. Geology, v. 56, no. 2, p. 112–117.

——— 1949, Sedimentary rocks: New York, Harper and Bros.; 2d ed., 1957.

Rodgers, John, 1950, The nomenclature and classification of sedimentary rocks: Am. Jour. Sci., v. 248, no. 5, p. 297–311.

Sander, Bruno K., 1936, Contributions to the study of depositional fabrics—rhythmically deposited Triassic limestones and dolomites; translated by E. B. Knopf: Am. Assoc. Petroleum Geologists, pub. 1951.

Williams, H., Turner, F. J., and Gilbert, C. M., 1954, Petrography, an introduction to the study of rocks in thin sections: San Francisco, W. H. Freeman and Co.

BIOLOGICAL, GENETIC, AND UTILITARIAN ASPECTS OF LIMESTONE CLASSIFICATION[1]

DAN E. FERAY,[2] EDWARD HEUER,[3] AND WILLIS G. HEWATT[3]
Dallas and Fort Worth, Texas

ABSTRACT

Classification of limestones should consider (1) mode of origin of $CaCO_3$ (chemical [biochemical or physicochemical] and mechanical), (2) form of $CaCO_3$ (skeletal [secretionary] or nonskeletal [accretionary or particulate]), and (3) the processes of deposition and accumulation of units of limestone. The biological and other genetic aspects of limestones are interrelated but commonly difficult to evaluate. Studies of modern carbonate sediments demonstrate that organisms play a dominant role in the formation of skeletal and nonskeletal material. Disintegration of skeletal material to fine sand and smaller size generally renders such material unrecognizable regarding its skeletal nature and biological origin. Nonskeletal carbonate sediments of biological origin resemble, and are difficult to distinguish from, carbonates of physico-chemical origin.

Progressive lithification and diagenetic changes with increasing age of the carbonate rocks compound the problems of identifying the nature and origin of carbonate particles. The result is a decrease in the uniformity and accuracy of description and classification of carbonate sediments.

The varied concepts of classification of carbonate sediments have resulted from variation in background, interest, methods employed, and purpose of an investigation. The geographic extent and geologic range of the investigation likewise impart a control to the problem of each limestone classification. Ultimately, the classification of carbonate rocks will have to provide for the needs of the field geologist, subsurface geologist, paleontologist, petrographer, and geochemist. Each of these fields of investigation is concerned with only a part of the total evidence available to be used in classification of carbonate rocks. A three-stage procedure of description of carbonate rocks, each with its applicable terminology, is necessary before all descriptions and purposes concerned with carbonate rocks can be satisfied. These stages consist of (1) field description of limestone units, (2) low-power binocular description of samples, and (3) thin-section and geochemical description of samples. Most descriptive data in the procedure are ultimately based on field observations. Generally, it is only after all three stages have been fulfilled that origin can be assigned to ancient carbonate rocks.

INTRODUCTION

Limestones consist of carbonate in the form of calcite, aragonite, magnesium-calcium carbonate, or dolomite. This paper is primarily concerned with the calcium carbonate constituents of limestone.

Calcite and aragonite occur in limestone as either skeletal or nonskeletal constituents resulting from a biochemical (organic) or physicochemical (inorganic) origin. Organisms are responsible for all skeletal constituents, and they indirectly form nonskeletal constituents as a result of their vital activities. Biochemical nonskeletal constituents closely resemble physicochemical constituents, and they cannot always be differentiated. The ultimate purpose of limestone classification is to impart genetic concepts. Therefore, recognition of the biochemical (skeletal and nonskeletal) constituents in limestone, and the understanding of the role of organisms in the formation of limestone, are vital to any classifica-

[1] Part of a symposium arranged by the Research Committee, and presented at Denver, Colorado, April 27, 1961, under joint auspices of the Association and the Society of Economic Paleontologists and Mineralogists. Manuscript received, May 16, 1961.

[2] Mobil Professor of Geology, Southern Methodist University, Dallas, Texas.

[3] Department of Geology, Texas Christian University, Forth Worth, Texas.

We started working together as part of a team investigating limestones for the Field Research Laboratory, Mobil Oil Company, in 1952. Other members of this group included Harry H. Emmerich, V. Eugene Hanes, Henry F. Nelson, W. A. Jenkins, C. D. McClure, W. B. Huckaby, E. Glover, and W. H. Twenhofel (consultant). This group provided biological, paleontological, mineralogical, chemical, and sedimentation experience and data. In addition, numerous individuals concerned with limestone research made valuable contributions to our knowledge through informal discussions. These individuals include Robert R. Shrock, H. A. Lowenstam, Norman D. Newell, Curt Teichert, L. V. Illing, R. W. Fairbridge, Frank E. Lozo, Robert N. Ginsburg, James M. Parks, Lloyd Pray, J. Harlan Johnson, and John H. Halsey.

In addition to this paper, we also participated with Henry F. Nelson and W. A. Jenkins in the preparation of the movie, "Recent Carbonate Deposits in the Florida Keys." This film and the paper "Skeletal Limestone Classification" by Nelson, Brown, and Brineman (this volume) represent various aspects of carbonate research undertaken by the Geological Research Group of Socony Mobil Oil Company, Field Research Laboratory.

tion of limestones that is based on origin, or contains genetic implications.

In addition to the biological and genetic aspects of limestone classification, the utilitarian aspects are of equal importance. Any workable classification scheme, regardless of genetic implications, will have to be useful to field and laboratory geologists. Both field and laboratory descriptive procedures are necessary to describe a limestone adequately, before it can be ultimately classified in the broad sense.

The purpose of the present contribution is to make available some of our views and conclusions concerning the interrelationships of the *biological-genetic-utilitarian* aspects of limestone classification. These views are the result of more than 10 years of study of limestones and associated sediments ranging in age from Cambrian to Recent. The studies have been based upon field observations which were regional in nature, and have included detailed petrographic, mineralogical (X-ray), and geochemical studies. The biological and paleontological background of our efforts is responsible for our concern with the significance of the biochemical constituents of limestones.

HISTORICAL SYNOPSIS OF LIMESTONE CLASSIFICATION

This paper is concerned with various aspects of limestone classification, and a brief review of such classifications is in order as a background for further considerations. *Limestone* as a rock term is ambiguous at the outset. Rocks composed entirely of calcite or dolomite are high in "lime" content. Pettijohn (1957, p. 383) has called attention to this, but states that established usage has and will continue retention of the term as a principal rock type.

Four of the more generally used or accepted classifications are those presented by Twenhofel (1950), Pettijohn (1957), Johnson (1951), and Folk (1959). In addition, Grabau (1913) presented a well-conceived and well-organized scheme of classification. Grabau's classification did not meet with general usage, although its influence may be seen in later classifications.

The classification presented by Twenhofel (1950, p. 356) recognized the following genetic categories

I. Chemical origin
  A. Organic
    1. Accumulation of skeletal and protective structures of organisms
    2. Vital activities of organisms
      a. Photosynthesis of organisms
      b. Bacterial processes
  B. Inorganic
    1. Mingling of solutions
    2. Escape of carbon dioxide from water
    3. Evaporation
II. Mechanical origin.

Johnson (1951, p. 1) presented a classification of limestone involving three genetic categories

I. Organic
II. Inorganic or chemical
III. Mechanical or clastic.

Pettijohn's (1957, p. 382) classification grouped limestones into three main categories which are genetic, and several subcategories which are petrographic

I. Autochthonous (accretionary and biochemical) limestone
  A. Biohermal limestones
  B. Biostromal limestones
  C. Pelagic limestones
II. Allochthonous (detrital) limestone
  A. Calcirudites
  B. Calcarenites
  C. Calcilutites
III. Metasomatic limestone
  A. Dolomitic limestones and dolomites.

Folk (1959) classified limestones into the following categories which are essentially petrographic, although the four main categories were formulated principally on the basis of their genetic significance

I. Sparry allochemical rocks
  A. Intrasparrudite-intrasparite
  B. Oösparrudite-oösparite
  C. Biosparrudite-biosparite
  D. Biopelsparite
  E. Pelsparite
II. Microcrystalline allochemical rocks
  A. Intramicrudite-intramicrite
  B. Oömicrudite-oömicrite
  C. Biomicrudite-biomicrite
  D. Biopelmicrite
  E. Pelmicrite
III. Microcrystalline rocks
  A. Micrite-dismicrite
IV. Undisturbed biohermal rocks
  A. Biolithite.

It is obvious that although all four schemes attempt to classify limestones, the emphasis is quite different. Twenhofel's and Johnson's schemes are similar, but differ drastically from

Pettijohn's and Folk's schemes. The same terms are used in more than one of the classifications, but with different meanings. The classifications of Twenhofel, Johnson, and Pettijohn each has a different genetic basis, whereas Folk's classification has a very different, implied genetic basis. It appears to us that within each scheme the genetic basis is not consistent. Each contains categories of origin and nature or form of calcium carbonate. The process of deposition of calcium carbonate is also considered. It is our opinion that origin of calcium carbonate is the principal basis for genetic classification inasmuch as calcium carbonate can be deposited or can accumulate in a variety of ways after it is formed.

Twenhofel's classification will be used in this paper as a basis for discussion of the various problems involved in any classification of limestones.

FACTORS INFLUENCING LIMESTONE CLASSIFICATION

Limestone classifications vary greatly; therefore, it is important to evaluate the reasons for such variations. Various factors influence the presentation of any classification scheme. Some of the most significant factors are (1) scientific background, (2) interest, (3) purpose of investigation, and (4) method of investigation. The impact of each of the factors varies with each investigator. Each factor merits discussion in order to understand better the problem of classification.

Scientific background.—This factor includes academic training as well as professional experience. In general, geologists concerned with limestone classification have a primary training that is either *biological* (*paleontological*), *mineralogical*, *petrographical*, or *geochemical*. Seldom is a geologist equally trained in all four disciplines. Generally speaking, the classification of limestones, as well as other rocks, is a problem of petrology. As such, the mineralogical, petrographical, and geochemical background would seem to be a natural requisite. Such backgrounds are essential, but limestones are unlike other rocks in that they may consist largely or wholly of biochemical or biological constituents. Because of this, a biological background is essential to any serious study of limestones. It is important to recognize that whereas one background of training may be critical for the understanding of certain types of limestone, the spectrum of types is so broad that all four disciplines are necessary for complete understanding of limestones.

Fields of interest.—In general, one's training generally controls one's field of interest in geology. Regardless of training, however, many geologists have become interested in limestone because of its economic significance as petroleum reservoir rock, and its value as a raw material in industry. Field geology, subsurface geology, stratigraphy, paleontology, mineralogy, petrology, and geochemistry deal with limestones as a principal rock type and subject of investigation. In addition, geologists are interested in limestones in regard to such specific attributes as skeletal constituents, chemical and mineralogical constituents, texture, structure, and reservoir characteristics. Such varied interests range from strictly field evaluation of limestones to primarily laboratory analysis of limestones. Any fundamental classification scheme must consider all fields of interest and their needs and limitations in regard to classification. The geologist's field of interest, in large part, determines his approach to the problem of limestone classification.

Purpose of investigation.—Classifications of limestone have been developed to serve particular purposes. The quarry and petroleum industries are concerned with limestone for entirely different reasons, and a scheme of classification useful to one would not be suitable to the other. Although limestones are variously classified in order to satisfy almost every purpose of limestone investigation, a limestone classification should be both (1) descriptive, and (2) interpretive.

The descriptive aspect of limestone classification is necessary for the field definition and mapping of rock units. The subsurface geologist requires a descriptive basis to delineate and map various reservoir properties of limestone. The descriptive aspect of limestone classification should be primarily objective in character.

After limestones are classified from objective description, and the immediate purpose of the investigation is served, the geologist is normally confronted with the need for interpretation of the objective data. This need generally arises from the desire to predict from visible attributes unobserved features such as facies changes, changes in thickness, variations in constituents, and other properties. Such predictions are related to the origin of the limestone and require chemical, physical, and biological environmental analyses. The interpretive aspect of classification is basically subjective in nature, and therefore varies with each investigator.

Methods of investigation.—Studies of limestone fall into two broad categories in regard to methods of investigation; one is field methods, and the other is laboratory methods. If a classification scheme is based on only one of these sources of data, it will be unsuitable for the other area of interest. For example, a classification based on characteristics determinable only in the laboratory is of little or no value to the field geologist.

The field investigation of limestone deals with readily visible paleontologic and lithologic features including bedding and other sedimentary structures, thickness, and stratigraphic and geographic relations. These gross features are as significant in regard to origin of the limestone as are its fine constituents and texture. The fine details of limestone, only determinable in the laboratory, cannot be accurately interpreted without knowledge of the gross characteristics.

The laboratory methods of investigation, including petrographic, paleontologic, and geochemical analyses, yield important descriptive data that may be critical for interpretation of the origin of the limestone. Data regarding the diagenesis of the limestone comes primarily from laboratory analysis. Laboratory analysis, however, commonly will only refine the data and the interpretations resulting from field observations. Because laboratory analysis is costly, both from the standpoint of time and equipment, critical attention to sampling technique and methods of field study yields the most rewarding results for the time and expense involved.

KNOWLEDGE DERIVED FROM STUDY OF MODERN CARBONATES

Study of modern carbonate sediments offers much precise information concerning the origin of calcium carbonate—both calcite and aragonite, its nature or form, and processes of deposition and accumulation. The study of modern carbonates is especially critical in regard to the problem of origin of limestones and the genetic basis of classification. The work of numerous geologists on Recent carbonates has provided much of the fundamental knowledge that is now the basis for classification and interpretation of limestones. We have been particularly impressed with the studies of Illing (1954), Lowenstam and Epstein (1957), Newell and collaborators (1951, 1955, 1957, 1959, 1960), Ginsburg (1956), and Emery, Tracey, and Ladd (1954).

Figure 1, which presents a modified and expanded version of Twenhofel's (1950, p. 356) classification, will be used as a basis for examining some of the knowledge derived from the study of modern carbonates that bears on limestone classification. The modifications we have made are

1. *Biochemical* is substituted for *organic*
2. *Skeletal* and *nonskeletal* carbonates comprise the *biochemical* limestones
3. *Physicochemical* is substituted for *inorganic*
4. *Mechanical* relates only to the process of formation of carbonate particles by erosion, and does not relate to the process of *mechanical deposition* of carbonate particles.

The figure shows the relationship between the mode of origin of calcium carbonate (basis of Twenhofel's classification), the nature or form of calcium carbonate, and the process of deposition and accumulation of calcium carbonate.

Chemical origin of calcium carbonate.—Chemical limestones include all limestones composed of aragonite or calcite formed by either biochemical or physicochemical processes. The biochemical processes involve both the secretion of calcium carbonate as skeletal structures, and the precipitation of calcium carbonate as nonskeletal material indirectly resulting from the vital activities of organisms. Physicochemical processes precipitate calcium carbonate as the result of changes in physical and chemical conditions in the water not attributable to the life activities of organisms. All physicochemically precipitated calcium carbonate is nonskeletal in form.

Biochemical origin of calcium carbonate.—The biochemically produced calcium carbonate results either directly or indirectly from the life processes of organisms. Organisms produce calcium carbonate in either a *skeletal* or *nonskeletal* form.

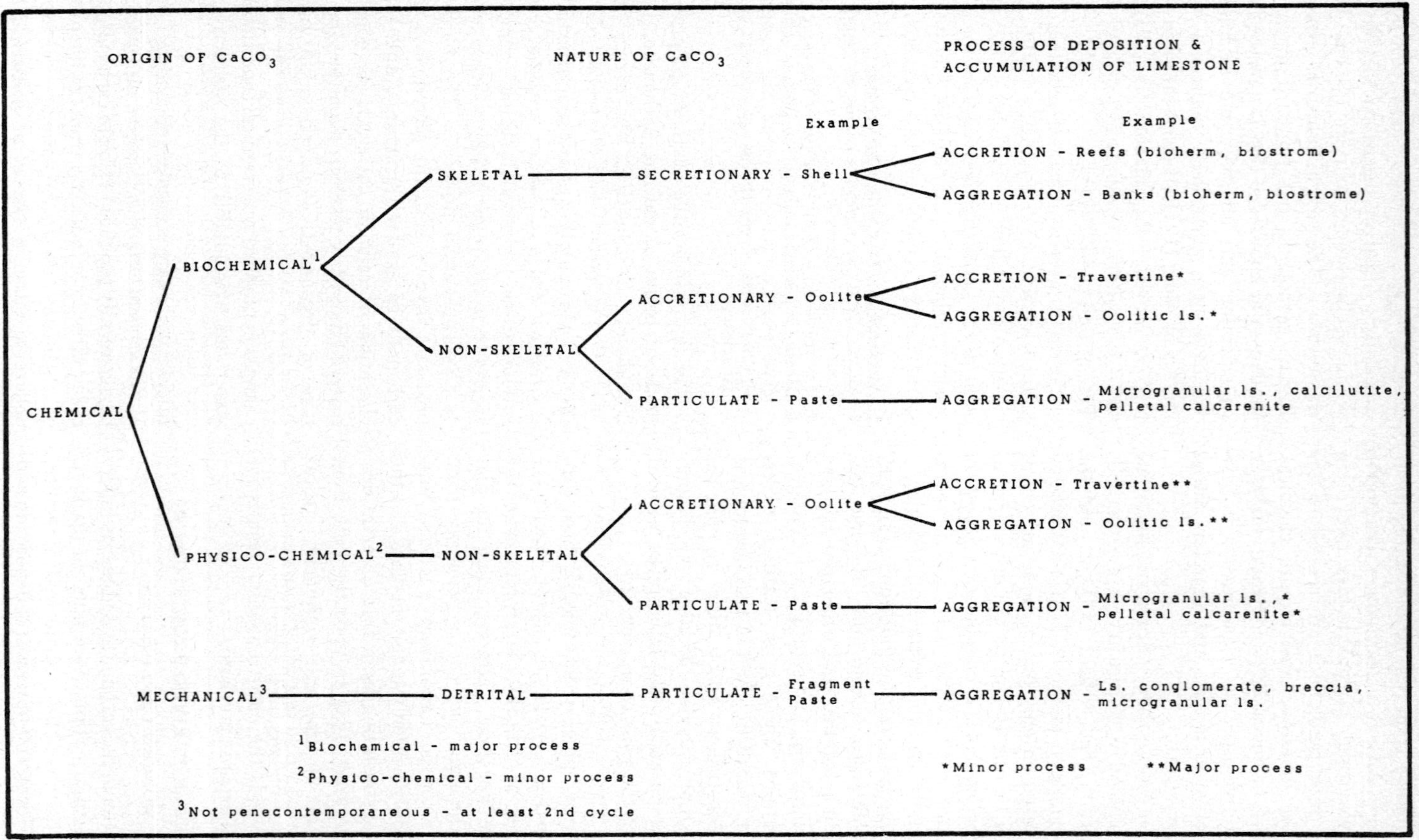

FIG. 1.—Origin, nature, and process of accumulation of limestone.

Skeletal calcium carbonate is produced by organisms that utilize $CaCO_3$ to build supporting or protective structures for their soft tissue. This process may be regarded as a direct formation of organic calcium carbonate. *Nonskeletal* calcium carbonate may be produced both by organisms that do and do not utilize calcium carbonate for skeletal-building purposes. This calcium carbonate, which is not a part of the skeletal structure of organisms, is a metabolic by-product. This may be regarded as an indirect formation of organic calcium carbonate. Twenhofel (1950, p. 357–373) and Revelle and Fairbridge (1957, p. 259–269) discuss in detail various aspects of the formation of biochemical calcium carbonate.

Physicochemical origin of calcium carbonate.—The fact that calcium carbonate may be formed in an aqueous solution by chemical reactions that are in no way related to organic activity is well known. These physicochemical processes include (1) mingling of solutions that produce reactions leading to precipitation, (2) precipitation resulting from escape of carbon dioxide from water due to rise of temperature, decline of pressure, or agitation of water, and (3) precipitation through evaporation and rise in salinity and saturation. Of the three processes, it is thought that loss of carbon dioxide from water is of greatest importance, although in certain cases, evaporation can be of great significance in calcium carbonate precipitation. Regardless of the process, physicochemical precipitation produces *nonskeletal* calcium carbonate.

Calcium carbonate of skeletal nature.—Regardless of the manner of chemical origin, calcium carbonate can be divided into two types, *skeletal* and *nonskeletal.* The *skeletal* material is biochemical in origin and is secretionary in nature. Skeletal material is produced by organisms progressively secreting calcium carbonate in order to provide progressive enlargement of the skeletal structure in keeping with the growth of the organisms. Skeletal material is produced as either external protective and supporting structures, or as internal supporting structures, and may constitute a unified skeletal framework or individual skeletal elements.

The limestone petrologist is faced with the problem of distinguishing between skeletal and nonskeletal constituents. On the surface this does not appear significant, but as one delves into the problem it becomes evident that the distinction is often difficult to make, particularly in fine-grained limestones. For example, Lowenstam and Epstein (1957) have found that certain algae secrete needles of aragonite internally. When the algae die these needles are set free to become incorporated in the bottom sediment, and cannot then be distinguished from physicochemically formed needles. Also, Illing (1954) has discussed the manner in which skeletal material can lose its identity by progressive reduction in size, secondary infilling, and recrystallization.

The fact that calcareous skeletons of organisms can be recognized as such arises from their exhibiting characteristics of form and structure distinct from those shown by masses of calcium carbonate resulting from nonskeletal processes. Although it is true that the skeletons secreted by any particular group of organisms tend to show a greater constancy of form, and a more complex and systematic arrangement of parts, than do sedimentary objects of nonskeletal origin, knowledge and observation of these general attributes alone hardly suffice to differentiate skeletal and nonskeletal material. The identity of skeletal carbonate can be consistently and accurately established only (1) if one has knowledge of specific features of form and structure known to be characteristic of the skeletons of lime-secreting organisms and known not to occur as nonskeletal carbonate, and (2) if the skeletal carbonate observed does in fact show characters of form and structure known only to be of skeletal origin.

Even if one were to agree that knowledge of the form and structure of skeletons of lime-secreting organisms is sufficient to allow differentiation of skeletal and nonskeletal carbonate (although this certainly is not the case insofar as knowledge of skeletal microstructure is concerned), it is probably fair to say that most students of carbonate rocks, including ourselves, are insufficiently grounded in this knowledge, and much of the skeletal material in carbonate sediments escapes notice because of this. The point that we would like to emphasize, however, is that much of the skeletal carbonate in carbonate sediments escapes notice because it does not show recognizable char-

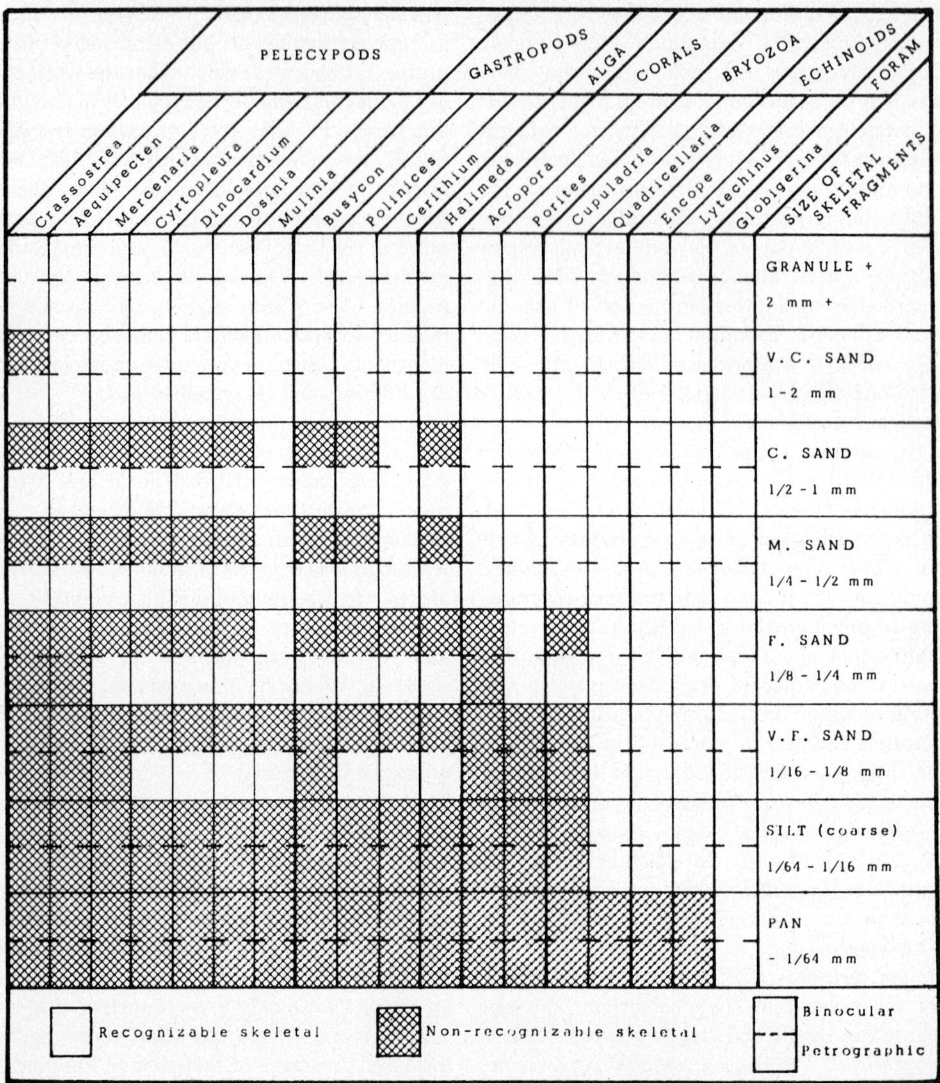

FIG. 2.—Recognizability of fragmental material—Recent organisms.

acters of form or structure known to be only of skeletal origin.

We are not concerned here with the loss of skeletal identity that results from recrystallization. We are concerned rather with the loss of skeletal identity resulting from fragmentation of skeletal material. This problem seems particularly worthy of emphasis because (1) it does not seem to have attracted the attention of students of carbonate rocks as much as the problem of recrystallization, (2) much of the skeletal material in carbonate sediments is fragmentary, and (3) it bears on the problem of the origin of fine-grained carbonate variously called microgranular carbonate, micrite, calcilutite, calcisiltite, and carbonate paste.

Figure 2 shows the relationship between loss of skeletal identity and size of skeletal material based upon a study of fragmented skeletons representing 18 genera of Recent lime-secreting organisms belonging to seven major taxa. The purpose of this diagram is to bring out the fact that much, if not most, of the skeletal material in carbonate sediments is likely to be unrecognizable as such when fragmented to a size smaller than $\frac{1}{16}$ millimeter. Whole skeletons of each of the genera listed were crushed with a mortar and pestle and sieved into the indicated size fractions. Part of the material from each size fraction was mounted on glass slides for examination under a petrographic microscope at 50 to 160 magnifications. The remainder was retained for examination under a binocular microscope at 10 to 100 magnifications. The material of fine-sand size and coarser, that was mounted for petrographic examination, was thin sectioned to reveal the microstructure of the skeletal material, and grain mounts were made of the finer material.

For each genus studied the fragmental material comprising a particular size fraction was considered to be recognizably skeletal if the bulk of the material showed features of form or structure known to be characteristic of the genus or higher taxon and not known to occur in nonskeletal carbonate. If the fragmental material comprising the bulk of a particular size fraction did not show such features, the skeletal nature of the material was considered to be unrecognizable. Knowledge of the identity of the skeletal material prior to microscopic examination has undoubtedly biased the results of this study. It seems likely that the boundary between recognizable and unrecognizable skeletal material would have been drawn at a coarser fragment size if the identity of the fragmental material had been unknown before examination.

It is evident from Figure 2 that the skeletal identity of the gastropod, pelecypod, and *Halimeda* fragments, based on observation of form and structure in three dimensions under the binocular microscope, was lost in considerably coarser fractions than the skeletal identity of fragments of the same genera based on observation of skeletal microstructure in unoriented thin sections under the petrographic microscope. In each of the other groups the skeletal identity of the material was lost under the binocular microscope at essentially the same fragment size as under the petrographic microscope. In view of the importance of microstructure as a criterion of skeletal identity in the finer fragment sizes, several examples of specific characters of skeletal microstructure used in this study are cited below.

In the pelecypod and gastropod genera studied, for example, the fragmented material was recognizably skeletal under the petrographic microscope so long as the characteristic patterns produced by the branching and wedging of the primary lamellae of the crossed-lamellar structure could be observed. When the size of the shell fragments had been reduced to the point that the crossed-lamellar structure was no longer evident, the microstructure that could be observed was strikingly similar to that shown by prepared thin sections and grain mounts of fragmented nonskeletal calcite and aragonite. In *Crassostrea* and *Aequipecten*, and to a lesser extent in *Mercenaria* and *Busycon*, the crossed-lamellar structural pattern was more coarsely developed than in the other mollusk genera studied, and consequently loss of skeletal identity occurred in the coarser size fractions.

The identity of *Halimeda* fragments as skeletal material was lost when the openings in the skeleton originally occupied by branching algal threads could not be observed. Under the petrographic microscope these openings generally were not evident in fragments smaller than $\frac{1}{16}$ millimeter.

The identity of coral fragments as skeletal material was best established under the petrographic microscope by observation of the trabeculae that characterize the microstructure of the septa. When the coral fragments were so small that the trabecular structure was no longer evident, the fibrous microstructure that could still be observed could not be differentiated from that of nonskeletal carbonate.

The echinoid fragments were recognized as skeletal material to a minimum size of $\frac{1}{64}$ millimeter under the petrographic microscope from observation of the characteristic latticework of microscopic rods.

The chamber form and the perforate character of the test wall of *Globigerina* were retained by fragments smaller than $\frac{1}{64}$ millimeter, and allowed a ready means of recognizing the skeletal nature of the material throughout the size range studied.

Figure 3 shows the results of a study of two sieved samples of Recent carbonate sediments, employing the criteria of skeletal recognizability and the petrographic techniques discussed above. Only the more abundant constituents of the

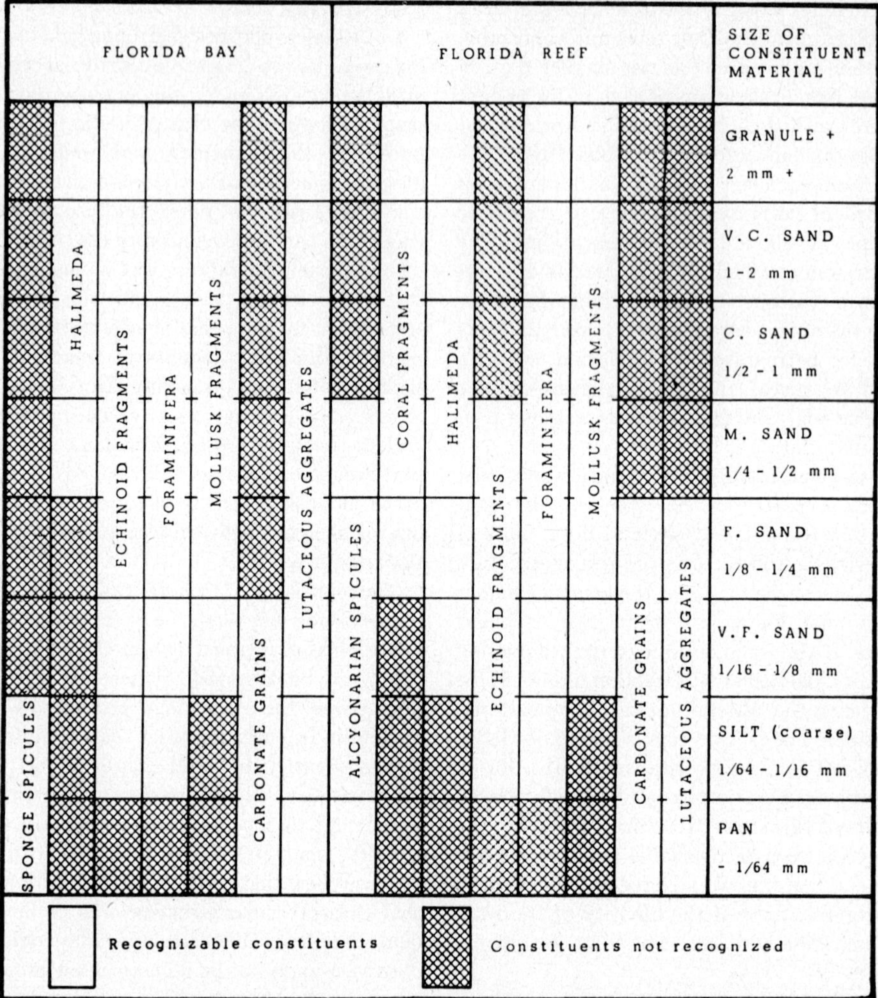

FIG. 3.—Recognizability of constituents—Recent carbonates.

samples were considered. Among the skeletal constituents only the sponge spicules of the Florida Bay sample and the alcyonarian spicules of the Florida reef sample could be recognized at a particle size of less than $\frac{1}{64}$ millimeter. Attention is also directed to the fact that the peneroplid and miliolid Foraminifera in these samples did not retain their skeletal identity in the finest fraction, in contrast to *Globigerina* shown on Figure 2. It seems certain that much of the material in these samples comprising lutaceous (=calcilutaceous) aggregates and carbonate grains smaller than $\frac{1}{16}$ millimeter, is unrecognizable skeletal material resulting from natural attrition of the skeletons of corals, *Halimeda*, echinoids, Foraminifera, and mollusks.

Calcium carbonate of nonskeletal nature.—Figure 1 shows that nonskeletal material is either biochemical or physicochemical in origin and is either accretionary or particulate in nature.

Evaporation of water or loss of carbon dioxide produces several types of accretionary calcium carbonate, such as tufa, travertine, caliche, oölites, and pisolites. Physicochemical processes are believed to be of major importance in the production of nonskeletal, accretionary calcium carbonate, and biochemical processes are believed to be of minor importance.

In marine limestones, oölites are the most significant accretionary form of nonskeletal calcium carbonate. Newell, Purdy, and Imbrie (1960, p. 489–496) have shown that Bahamian oölites consist of two types of concentric laminations, one of oriented aragonite and the other of unoriented cryptocrystalline aragonite. The former is a physicochemical precipitate, whereas the latter is possibly a biochemical precipitate.

Nonskeletal accretionary material that is biochemical in origin may also result from algae and other plants extracting carbon dioxide from water. The resulting calcium carbonate precipitate covers leaves, stems, and the bases to which plants are attached. The precipitated material is of fine silt and clay size and may accumulate in an accretionary manner, having no skeletal structure.

Nonskeletal calcium carbonate also precipitates physicochemically and biochemically as separate, individual particles. The particles range from clay to silt in size, and accumulate to form a loose sediment commonly called lime "paste." Upon deposition the paste may undergo radical change in form. The most striking change is aggregation of the particles into larger grains. Illing (1954, p. 16, 24–35) and Newell, Imbrie, Purdy, and Thurber (1959, p. 216–225) discuss the role of organic, physical, and chemical agencies in the aggregation of these clay size particles to form pellets, friable aggregates, irregular grains of aragonite matrix, lumps, and grapestone. The role of organisms in aggregation is a significant aspect of the environment of accumulation of these aggregate grains.

The foregoing discussion and Figure 1 set forth the fact that nonskeletal calcium carbonate in the form of paste may originate from either biochemical or physicochemical processes. It has also been shown by foregoing discussion and Figures 2 and 3 that attrition of skeletal material produces paste. The constituents of paste are, therefore, derived from biochemical (skeletal and nonskeletal) and physicochemical origins, but in natural samples of paste the constituents derived from different origins cannot be distinguished from one another. Although paste cannot be assigned a unique origin for purposes of genetic classification, it is our opinion that biochemical processes are the major source of paste constituents, and that physicochemical processes are a minor source.

Mechanical origin.—Figure 1 reveals that calcium carbonate particles may be of chemical origin or mechanical origin. The former is the only primary source of calcium carbonate; the latter represents a second cycle source of calcium carbonate particles. It is our belief that the mechanical category should not include penecontemporaneously fragmented calcium carbonate such as reef detritus, reef breccia, broken shell fragments, or intraformational conglomerates. Fragmentation of calcium carbonate in place is as common a phenomenon as aggregation of fine particles into large grain aggregates, both being a product of the environment that produces the original calcium carbonate. Penecontemporaneous fragmentation may or may not be related to physical energy sources in the environment. Organisms can fragment the material by their normal activities. Mechanically derived particles, therefore, are those produced by erosion of preexisting limestones. Such particles are at least second cycle. They are deposited out of place of origin and at a time unrelated to their origin. Rarely is a limestone composed entirely of second cycle limestone constituents. Erosion and transporting agents are generally moving other terrigeneous clastics to sites of deposition. In areas of limestone terrane, limestones of mechanical origin may be significant. Such limestones are detrital in nature, as are other terrigeneous clastics, and consist of particles ranging in size from clay and silt (paste) to large fragments.

Deposition and accumulation of limestone.—Various schemes of classification are concerned with the genetic significance of processes of transportation and accumulation of calcium carbonate. These processes are significant in regard to the final deposition of calcium carbonate to form limestone, but are to be distinguished from those processes discussed earlier, that are responsible for the origin of the calcium carbonate.

Calcium carbonate is deposited to form limestone either by (1) continuous or discontinuous outward solid growth from solution, that is, by *accretion*, or (2) by accumulation of separate individual particles, that is, by *aggregation*, to form a mass that is later lithified. In order that one may clearly visualize the difference between these two processes of accumulation, it might be well to refer to sampling procedures. If one were to sample an accretionary deposit in the process of accumulation, he would have to break a sample from the deposit, much as he would sample any indurated rock. In contrast, sampling a deposit accumulating by aggregation requires only scooping up the loose or unconsolidated material without any breakage. Figure 1 shows the relationship between the origin and nature of $CaCO_3$ and its accumulation by accretion and aggregation to form limestone.

The most prominent example of accumulation of calcium carbonate by accretion is that of skeletal reefs. This is the only type of marine accretionary limestone deposit known to us. In the case of skeletal reefs, the framebuilding organisms of the reef construct a rigid framework by secreting calcium carbonate as skeletal material, and use the skeletons of their predecessors as a base for outward growth of the reef; thus resulting in accretion. The shape of the reef is a reflection of both the organisms and environment. Nelson, Brown, and Brineman (this volume) discuss this type of deposit in detail.

Travertine, tufa, and caliche are the only other accretionary limestones, and these are generally not common in the geologic column, although they may be locally important. In these limestones both the origin and the deposition of the calcium carbonate result from accretionary processes.

Accumulation of calcium carbonate by aggregation is the dominant process of limestone deposition. Calcium carbonate particles coming from chemical or mechanical origins accumulate by aggregation. The particles may be either skeletal or nonskeletal in nature. Depending on the environment and causes of aggregation, these limestone accumulations may resemble accretionary limestones in gross character. Specifically, shell fragments may be heaped up or accumulate locally so that the deposit is biohermal in shape. Such deposits grossly resemble a biohermal reef, whereas they are in reality a biohermal shell bank (see Nelson, Brown, and Brineman, this volume), Individual oölites, which are accretionary units, accumulate by aggregation to form an oölitic limestone. Aggregation does not necessarily imply any definite energy relationships. Individual shells may accumulate, in place, to form a coquina. Organisms may fragment the shells, in place, to form a skeletal carbonate sand. Carbonate mud and aggregates of the carbonate mud may accumulate, in place, to form a microgranular and pelletal calcarenite. Each of these sediment types may also accumulate by aggregation after transportation from point of origin.

LIMITATIONS TO THE CLASSIFICATION OF ANCIENT CARBONATES

The character of ancient limestones may have resulted from (1) original constituents, textures, and structures, (2) predominance of diagenetic features, or (3) mixture of original features and diagenetic features. Because it is desirable to classify limestones on a genetic basis, it is important to understand the extent to which ancient limestones are subject to genetic classification.

Preservation of original constituents.—In Recent sediments the carbonate constituents are generally well preserved. We have seen from the preceding discussions, however, that there are definite limitations to the accuracy with which the identity of skeletal and nonskeletal constituents can be established and their origins determined. In spite of these limitations, the work of Illing (1954) and Newell, Imbrie, Purdy, and Thurber (1959) has demonstrated the accuracy with which knowledge of organism communities and physical aspects of the environment can be related to the nature and distribution of modern carbonate sediments on Great Bahama Bank.

The precision of environmental analysis of ancient limestones is also dependent upon the preservation of original constituents, textures, and structures. Even where these features are well preserved, however, it is rarely possible to observe the three-dimensional aspects of either the individual constituents or the limestone bodies. This limitation affects the accuracy with which the constituents can be identified, and the accuracy with which the distribution and interrelations of the various attributes of the rock body can be determined.

Effect of diagenesis.—Limestones are very susceptible to such diagenetic changes as solution, cementation, recrystallization, and replacement. These diagenetic changes may begin soon after deposition and continue throughout the history of the limestone. Diagenesis affects limestones in different ways and to different degrees. Consequently, there is an inherent nonuniformity in the accuracy of environmental analysis of ancient limestones.

In some cases the diagenetic change is merely cementation, accompanied by good preservation of the original constituents. In other cases the diagenetic effect can be intense, resulting in the obliteration of all primary constituents and associated features. As the original character of the constituents is lost through diagenetic change, secondary characteristics, and even new constituents, become dominant in the limestone. Several cycles of reorganization and replacement may occur, rendering the limestone unrelated to its original character. Diagenesis of limestone, therefore, results in a decrease of primary characteristics and an increase in secondary characteristics with increasing age of the limestone. In general, there is an increase in the dolomite content of limestones with increasing age. We have noted that pre-Mississippian carbonate rocks are generally more dolomitic than post-Mississippian carbonate rocks.

Ancient limestones that have lost their original characteristics are not susceptible to environmental analysis, and no classification of limestones related to primary origin can be based on secondary constituents, textures, or structures.

UTILITARIAN ASPECTS OF LIMESTONE CLASSIFICATION

Purposes of limestone classification.—Any consideration of limestone classification must recognize that all purposes cannot be served by one classification. Each classification must be erected on a basis that will best serve the purpose for which it is established. Any limestone classification, however, should serve the useful functions of (1) organizing knowledge of limestone in a systematic fashion so that generalizations pertaining to the purpose of the classification can be made, and (2) facilitating the formulation of a systematic nomenclature that will provide a means of communication regarding the limestones.

Regardless of the various purposes and bases of limestone classification, which arise from different fields of interest and purposes of investigation (see above), it is our opinion that there should be one fundamental form of limestone classification erected on a genetic basis and applied to all limestones. Such a classification would be similar in principle to biological classification based on phylogeny in the sense that (1) limestones would be grouped on the basis of common origin, and (2) the classification would take into account the evolutionary change in skeletal constituents of limestones. A basic nomenclature would be derived from this classification. As in biological classifications, subsidiary classifications may be constructed in keeping with the data and the purpose of the classifications.

Limestone classification and nomenclature.—Our recommendations for the development of a genetic classification of limestones are

1. *Establishment of a carbonate rock collection.* Many of the differences of opinion regarding limestone result from the fact that geologists do not see or work with the same rocks. A rock collection for geologists can serve the same function of reference and comparison as a collection of fossils serves the paleontologist. Such a collection should be geographically world wide, range stratigraphically from Precambrian to Recent, and include the known spectrum of limestone types and constituents. The collection should consist of samples based on field studies.

2. *Systematic compilation of descriptive data.* Data from the rock collection should be compiled by a team consisting of a field geologist, paleontologist, mineralogist, petrologist, and geochemist. The data necessary as an objective basis for limestone classification must come from both field and laboratory observations. The following three-step procedure for data gathering is recommended (1) field description including stratigraphic relationships, (2) binocular analysis of specimens comprising rock collection, and (3) petrographic, mineralogical, and geochemical analysis of speci-

mens comprising the rock collection. This procedure starts with the gross aspects of the limestone and proceeds to finer detail. Each step provides data unobtainable by the other steps. All steps are necessary before an adequate description of the limestone can be made.

3. *Designation and grouping of limestone types.* As the descriptive data are compiled, the specimens can be sorted into limestone types. Each type should be represented in the collection by a group of specimens showing its range in variation and essential characteristics. Interpretation of the genetic significance of the descriptive data will allow inferences to be drawn regarding origin and depositional environment, and the limestone types may then be grouped into categories that comprise the framework of the classification.

4. *Application of nomenclature.* As the classification takes shape, previously published names applicable to the limestone types and categories should be utilized. If published names are not applicable to particular limestone types or categories, new names must be coined.

A classification based on the foregoing program would solve many of the problems of limestone classification that result from a narrow or specific background and a limited spectrum of samples. The objective basis of the classification—the rocks—would be available for reference and comparison, which should lead to better understanding of limestones in general.

REFERENCES

Emery, K. O., Tracey, J. I., Jr., and Ladd, H. S., 1954, Geology of Bikini and nearby atolls: U. S. Geol. Survey Prof. Paper 260-A, p. 1–265.

Folk, R. L., 1959, Practical petrographic classification of limestones: Am. Assoc. Petroleum Geologists Bull., v. 43, no. 1, p. 1–38.

Ginsburg, R. N., 1956, Environmental relationships of grain size and constituent particles in some south Florida carbonate sediments: Am. Assoc. Petroleum Geologists Bull., v. 40, no. 10, p. 2384–2427.

Grabau, A. W., 1913, Principles of stratigraphy: New York, A. G. Seiler and Co.

Illing, L. V., 1954, Bahaman calcareous sands: Am. Assoc. Petroleum Geologists Bull., v. 38, no. 1, p. 1–95.

Johnson, J. Harlan, 1951, An introduction to the study of organic limestones: Colorado Sch. Mines Quart., v. 146, no. 2.

Lowenstam, H. A., and Epstein, S., 1957, On the origin of sedimentary aragonite needles of the Great Bahama bank: Jour. Geology, v. 65, no. 4, p. 364–375.

Newell, N. D., 1955, Bahaman platforms, *in* Poldervaart, H., ed., Crust of the earth, a symposium: Geol. Soc. America Spec. Paper 62, p. 303–315.

——— Imbrie, John, Purdy, E. G., and Thurber, D. L., 1959, Organism communities and bottom facies, Great Bahama bank: Am. Mus. Nat. History Bull., v. 117, art. 4, p. 181–228.

——— Purdy, E. G., and Imbrie, John, 1960, Bahamian oölitic sand: Jour. Geology, v. 68, no. 5, p. 481–497.

——— and Rigby, J. K., 1957, Geological studies on the Great Bahama bank, *in* Regional aspects of carbonate deposition: Soc. Econ. Paleont. and Mineral. Spec. Pub. No. 5, p. 15–72.

——— Rigby, J. K., Whiteman, A. J., and Bradley, J. S., 1951, Shoal-water geology and environments, eastern Andros Island, Bahamas: Am. Mus. Nat. History Bull., v. 97, art. 1, p. 1–29.

Pettijohn, F. J., 1957, Sedimentary rocks, 2d ed.: New York, Harper and Bros.

Revelle, Roger, and Fairbridge, Rhodes, 1957, Carbonates and carbon dioxide, *in* Treatise on marine ecology and paleoecology; v. 1, Ecology: Geol. Soc. America Mem. 67, p. 239–296.

Twenhofel, W. H., 1950, Principles of sedimentation, 2d ed.: New York, McGraw-Hill Book Co., Inc.

CARBONATE ROCK TYPES[1]

M. W. LEIGHTON[2] AND C. PENDEXTER[2]
Tulsa, Oklahoma

ABSTRACT

Several groups of limestones are recognized on the basis of their textural differences. Most of them give evidence of mechanical deposition and they are described as clastic textured. The various types within this clastic-textured group owe their characteristic appearances to the kinds and amounts of four textural components—grains, lime mud (micrite), cement, and void (pores). A nonclastic-textured group of limestones is built up of a fifth textural component, the organic framebuilders. A sixth textural component, recrystallization calcite, modifies the basic limestone types.

Carbonate grains, which are analogous to sand or silt grains, form the rock framework for the mechanically deposited limestones. If grouped together, they are capable of yielding an effectively porous rock. Recognizable carbonate grain types are grouped into five divisions (1) detrital grains—fragments derived from pre-existing rocks, (2) skeletal grains—broken or whole, (3) pellets—grains composed of micritic material, (4) lumps—grain aggregates or composite grains, and (5) coated grains—grains with concentric coating or with rims of calcium carbonate enclosing or encrusting a central nucleus. Important subvarieties of grains are recognized within these gross divisions.

The lime mud or micritic material in a limestone is roughly equivalent to the argillaceous material in a "dirty" sandstone or mudstone. Micritic material refers to unconsolidated or lithified ooze or mud of either chemical or mechanical origin, and is given an arbitrary upper size limit of 0.03 mm. Cement is the clear crystalline component that occupies the interstices between grains and is similar in appearance and distribution to silica cement in sandstones. Void spaces have various shapes and distribution, depending in part on other textural features and in part on genesis. Recrystallization calcite refers to those calcite mosaics resulting from grain enlargement or conversion processes, and excludes calcite cement.

Basic limestone rock types are recognized by (1) noting the types and amounts of grains or framework builders where present, and (2) estimating the relative proportions of grains, framebuilders, and micritic material. A classification based on these objective and measurable features has been developed. These features are used in the rock name. Other features, such as porosity, cementation, grain size, and color, are restricted to the rock description or are used as modifiers before the rock name.

Dolomites must be treated somewhat differently. The system for describing and naming dolomites is based primarily on a compositional grouping into calcareous dolomites and pure dolomites. These groups are modified by appropriate textural terms.

INTRODUCTION

It is the purpose of this paper to review some of the important characteristics that distinguish carbonate rock types and to show how these may be used to group the different appearing types into a meaningful classification.[3] In so doing, we will present a system for naming carbonate rocks and a clearly defined terminology for describing them. The emphasis is mainly on the textural features. A glossary of terms used in this paper is given in Appendix A.

Carbonate rocks, by definition, are those containing more than 50 per cent carbonate minerals. In the past it has been customary to recognize two

[1] Part of a symposium arranged by the Research Committee, and presented at Denver, Colorado, April 27, 1961, under joint auspices of the Association and the Society of Economic Paleontologists and Mineralogists. Manuscript received, April 21, 1961. Published by permission of the Jersey Production Research Company, affiliate of Standard Oil (N. J.), and the parent company.

[2] Jersey Production Research Company.

This paper is a condensation of a "Carbonate Rock Manual" (Revised edition) circulated by the Jersey Production Research Company to Standard Oil of New Jersey and affiliates. It is the product not only of the immediate authors but also of their associates and affiliate geologists who tested and applied the classification and offered many helpful suggestions, comments, and constructive criticisms throughout the course of the work on carbonate rock types. Only a few of these geologists are mentioned here, namely, C. V. Campbell, H. H. Hall, R. M. Mitchum, J. B. Sangree, and D. A. White, of the Jersey Production Research Company; C. C. Daetwyler, Scripps Institution of Oceanography and on leave from Jersey Production Research Company; and P. A. Williams, Standard Oil (N. J.).

[3] Readers will note that the 1960 classification recently published by Karl H. Wolf, formerly a trainee with a Standard Oil of New Jersey affiliate, is identical in most respects to the classification presented herein. The classification in this paper reached its final form in the course of a carbonate rock conference held for all Jersey affiliates April 9–11, 1958. The basic framework was established earlier, having been distributed as a progress report to Jersey affiliates in May 1955. Subsequent field testing led to modifications and acceptance by Jersey affiliates of the present scheme of describing and classifying carbonate rocks.

A. TEXTURAL COMPONENTS OF LIMESTONES

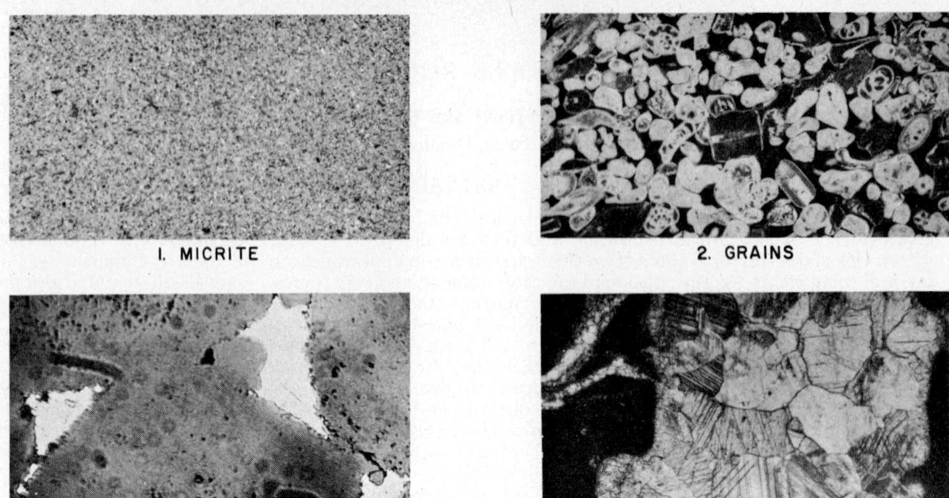

1. MICRITE 2. GRAINS 3. PORES 4. CEMENT

B. GRAIN TYPES IN LIMESTONES

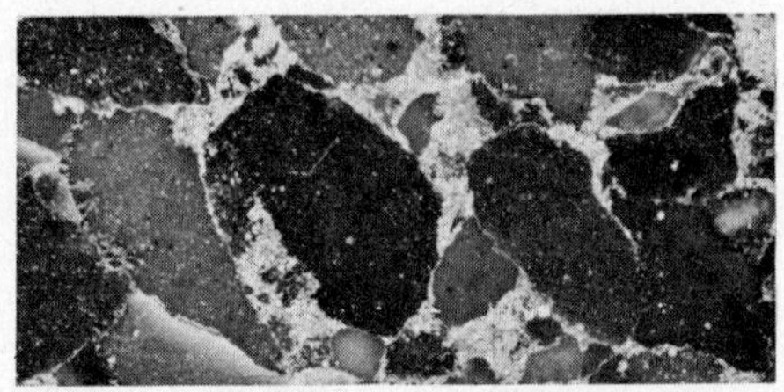

1. ROCK FRAGMENTS

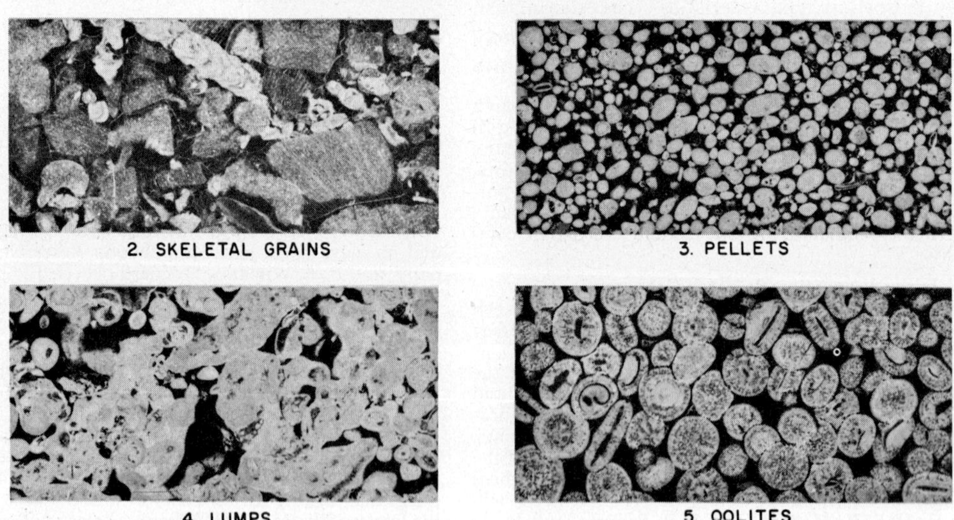

2. SKELETAL GRAINS 3. PELLETS 4. LUMPS 5. OOLITES

PLATE I

broad compositional divisions—limestones and dolomites. These divisions are treated separately here, inasmuch as we have found that a dual nomenclature system, one for limestones and one for dolomites, is the most practical and is required for objectivity.

TEXTURAL FEATURES OF LIMESTONES

Textural components.—Most limestones may be characterized by the types and relative amounts of four textural components—grains, lime mud (micrite),[4] cement, and pores (Plate I-*A*). These four components form the basis for describing and classifying a large proportion of limestones.

Grains are discrete particles capable of forming a rock framework. They are similar to sand and silt grains in a sandstone or siltstone. If grouped together, grains are capable of yielding an effectively porous rock. For work under the binocular microscope, we are using an arbitrary lower size limit of 0.03 mm, the division between medium and coarse silt. This artificial boundary is intended only as a guide in what is actually a gradational size sequence from *grains* to *lime mud.* The boundary may be changed when working with magnifications that allow recognition of grains within the micrite category defined in this paper.

Lime mud, ranging from unconsolidated ooze to its lithified equivalent, is a common textural component of limestones. The term *micrite* is used for those particles that were once mudlike. Micritic material in limestones is roughly equivalent to argillaceous material in a dirty sandstone or mudstone. It refers to ooze or mud of either chemical or mechanical origin and is given an arbitrary upper size limit of 0.03 mm.

[4] The use of the term micrite is modified slightly after R. L. Folk (1959). Micrite replaces the term "matrix" that we formerly used for the mud-like component.

Cement is the clear crystalline component that fills the spaces between grains. The sparry calcite or dolomite cement in limestones is similar in appearance and distribution to the silica cement in sandstones.

Pores, from the standpoint of oil occurrence, are the most important textural component of carbonate rocks. Pore space, however, changes with the type, roundness, size, shape, sorting, and packing of grains, the amount of micritic material, and the amount of cement. Porosity is also affected by leaching and post-depositional mineral changes.

Whereas most limestones may be described in terms of these four textural components, one group must be characterized by a fifth textural component, *in-place organic structures.* The rigid in-place framework of these limestones consists of such framebuilders as corals, bryozoa, and algae. In some cases, rock specimens are composed solely of framebuilders. More commonly, however, the limestones in this group are a mixture of in-place builders and mechanically deposited grains and lime mud.

A sixth textural component, *recrystallization calcite,* serves to modify the basic limestone types. The term *recrystallization calcite* is used for those patchy mosaics of calcite that have resulted from alteration of finer grained calcite particles. Cement is excluded from the definition. Bathhurst (1958) believes that such diagenetic modification of an initial fabric results from grain growth, a process that occurs in low porosity materials in the solid state.

Grain types.—Five grain categories are recognized in limestones (Table I). These are (1) detrital grains, (2) skeletal grains, (3) pellets, (4) lumps, and (5) coated grains. Examples from each of these divisions are illustrated in Plate I-*B* and subsequent plates. Clear identification of

---

←

EXPLANATION OF PLATE I

A. Textural components of limestones.
1.—Micrite, ×8.
2.—Grains, ×8.
3.—Pores (white), ×8.
4.—Clear calcite cement, ×8.

B. Grain types in limestones, ×8.
1.—Rock fragments (etched surface).
2.—Skeletal grains.
3.—Pellets.
4.—Lumps.
5.—Oölites.

TABLE I. CATEGORIES OF GRAIN TYPES RECOGNIZED IN LIMESTONES.

Major Categories	*Examples*	
1. Detrital Grains	Rock fragments Intraclasts	
2. Skeletal Grains	Crinoidal Molluscan Algal Foraminiferal	Fragmental and Nonfragmental
3. Pellets	Fecal pellets Grains of micrite	
4. Lumps	Composite grains Algal lumps	
5. Coated Grains	Oölites and superficial oölites Pisolites	
	Algal- or foraminiferal-encrusted grains	

grain types is essential to a good petrographic description. A good description is essential to worthwhile interpretation of the history of the rock.

Detrital grains are made of debris derived from pre-existing rocks. They may originate as pieces broken from weakly consolidated penecontemporaneous sediments or as pieces broken from rigid rocks. To the former type of detrital grains, R. L. Folk (1959) attaches the name *intraclasts*. Within a single specimen the detrital grains may be essentially of one rock type (oligomictic) or of varied rock types (polymictic) (Pettijohn, 1949).

Skeletal grains are remains of the hard parts secreted by organisms. Skeletal grains include crinoidal debris, molluscan grains, algal remains, and coralline fragments. The term "skeletal grains" is not restricted to broken or fragmental shell remains but is used, as well, for whole forms—such as foraminiferal tests—which have been deposited as sediment.

Pellets are grains of micritic material lacking significant internal structure. They commonly are of ovoid shape, and range in size from very coarse silt to fine sand. We recognize pellets of various origins. Some are *fecal pellets*. Others may represent a process of accretion whereby fine particles adhere to each other during alternate periods of transportation and deposition; Illing (1954) calls these "grains of matrix." Still others may represent bits of lime mud torn from the sea floor and rolled around before coming to rest. If recognized as the latter, the grains are best classified as detrital (Folk's *intraclasts*).

Lumps are composite grains typically possessing surficial irregularities and believed to have formed by a process of aggregation. Illing (1954) states, "Grains lying in contact with each other on the sea bed tend to become cemented together and form a composite sand grain or 'lump'." In ancient sediments, the composite grain character may not be easily distinguishable. These grains are generally recognized by their lobate outline, reflecting surficial irregularities. Additional aids in recognition of lumps are their textural similarity to the material in which they occur, and their association with a limited number of particular limestone types such as oölitic and pellet limestones. Algal lumps range in size up to algal "biscuits," and possess irregularly concentric algal material.

Coated grains are those having concentric or enclosing layers of calcium carbonate around a central nucleus. These include oölites, pisolites, and algae-encrusted or Foraminifera-encrusted skeletal grains.

Genetic grouping of grain types.—The types of grains can be grouped into two genetic groups, fragmental and nonfragmental. Detrital grains and certain subvarieties of skeletal grains are fragmental. Lumps, coated grains, most pellets, and some skeletal grains (for example, whole Foraminifera tests) are nonfragmental. The coated grains and lumps are formed by accretionary processes. These processes are diametrically opposed to the destructive processes that yield fragmental grains.

Relative amounts of textural components.—The different-appearing limestones owe their "looks" not only to the kind of textural component but also to the relative amounts of each. A rock composed predominantly of grains will naturally have a different appearance than one composed predominantly of the micritic component. A gradation in the relative abundance of grains to micritic material is illustrated in Plate II-*A*. A grain-micrite ratio is useful in describing this variation. A high ratio (greater than 1) represents a rock composed of more than 50 per cent grains; a ratio of 1 signifies 50 per cent grains and 50 per cent micrite; and a low ratio (less than 1) indicates a rock containing less than 50 per cent grains. Although not yet thoroughly tested, a similar ratio of framebuilders (plus grains) to micritic material might be used to express similar gradations in limestones which contain in-place organic structures.

Variations in the relative proportions of specific grain types also affect the appearance of the rock. The grains may be of one type, for example, pellets, or they may consist of a mixture of types, for example, oölites, pellets, and skeletal grains. Rocks composed of only grains or of only micrite represent "end members" in our concept of carbonate rock types.

For the large group of clastic-textured limestones, the relative proportions of grains and micrite, modified by their sizes, shapes, and packing arrangement, govern the character of initial porosity development. The maximum amount of cement that can exist is also controlled by these factors and by the effects of leaching. Thus, cement and pore space are textural components that are largely dependent on the two primary textural components—grains and micrite. For this reason we stress the recognition of grains and micrite to determine the initial rock character, and use the other textural components as secondary features to modify a large proportion of the basic limestone rock types.

LIMESTONE ROCK TYPES

This section includes a brief review and photographs of a number of different-appearing limestone types. Included are examples of (1) micritic limestones, (2) detrital limestones, (3) skeletal limestones, (4) pellet limestones, (5) lump limestones, (6) limestones with coated grains, (7) limestones with organic structures, and (8) gradational limestone types. Groups 2–7 demonstrate how limestones may be subdivided into rock types according to the kind of grain and the ratio of grains to micrite. The manner of defining limestone rock types is shown graphically in Plate II-*B*.

The following brief generalized summary for each group should not obscure the fact that the types are gradational. Point-count data and mineral composition are provided for selected samples and are tabulated in Appendix B. The photographs of thin sections or peels are negative prints. Although thin section photographs are used predominantly in this paper to demonstrate textural features, there is little need for more than a binocular microscope and a properly prepared surface to see the same features in hand samples or in cuttings.

Micritic limestones.—Photographs *A* and *B* in Plate III illustrate limestones composed of 90 per cent, or more, micrite. Two subtypes of these micritic limestones are recognized—*microclastic* and *microcrystalline.* The microclastic type is characterized by dull luster, muddy appearance, and the occasional presence of fossil fragments, silt-sized quartz grains, or discrete calcite grains. In thin section the very finely divided calcite lacks crystal outlines or well-developed cleavages, and has a dusty appearance. Some chalks may belong in this group. The microcrystalline micritic limestones are characterized by a high luster and a mosaic of tightly interlocking calcite crystals. In thin section the calcite is very clear and transparent. Sparry calcite veins are common and grade texturally into the main rock component.

The microclastic micritic limestones are commonly associated with skeletal limestones, and gradations between the two are commonly observed. The microcrystalline micritic limestones are most commonly associated with finely micrograined laminated dolomites and anhydrite.

Detrital limestones.—Grains in the detrital limestone group (Plate III-*D*, *E*, and *F*) are detrital fragments derived from older limestones. This group, which may contain up to 90 per cent micrite, includes *limestone conglomerates* and *limestone breccias.* Detrital limestones are commonly composed of fragments from several textural types in a variety of orientations. Some carbonate rocks have a breccia appearance due to mineral vein networks or slumping of the sediment before consolidation. The term *brecciated* is applied to such rocks. The pre-deformation texture of these rocks can be visually reconstructed, and only one or two rock types comprise the blocks.

Skeletal limestones.—Skeletal fragments are the dominant grain type. Complete gradations from skeletal limestone (>90 per cent grains) to skeletal-micritic limestone (90-50 per cent grains) to micritic-skeletal limestone (50-10 per cent grains) to micritic limestone (<10 per cent grains) are commonly observed. Some of the variations in content of micritic material and skeletal grain type are shown in Plates II-*A*, III-*G-N*, and IV-*A*, *B*.

Skeletal fragments may be mixed in various proportions with detrital grains or such nonfragmental grains as lumps, oölites, and pellets. Commonly, however, skeletal remains can be recognized as being derived from one type of organism. In such cases, the name of the organism is used to name the rock. Common examples are crinoidal limestone (Plate III-*K*), foraminiferal limestone (Plate III-*L*), molluscan limestone, and algal limestone (Plate III-*N*). Thus, if one fossil type predominates, it is used in naming the rock. Further details on rock names are given in the sections on Classification and Nomenclature.

Pellet limestones.—Pellets are the dominant grain type (Plate IV-*C-E*). Mixtures of skeletal grains and micrite are common. (See Plates IV-*C*, *D* and VII-*A-D*.) In limestone sequences where micrite is the chief binding agent, gradations from pellet limestone to micritic limestone have been seen. Such gradations are comparable to those often seen in the skeletal limestone—micritic limestone sequences. In such sequences it may be difficult to recognize the pellets because their composition is the same as that of the binding material.

This and subsequent limestone groups differ from the skeletal and detrital groups in that the majority of grains are believed to have formed dominantly by accretionary rather than fragmentation processes.

Lump limestones.—Lump limestones are those in which lumps are the predominant grain type (Plate IV-*F-I*, and VII-*E-H*). These grains, like pellets, are believed to form by accretionary processes. Consequently, they are classed as nonfragmental. In many cases the accretionary agent can be recognized as algae, and the resulting grain is called algal lump (Plate IV-*I*).

Limestones with coated grains.—Three grain types are recognized in this group. They all have layers that have been deposited either upon previously deposited layers or upon a central nucleus. The grain types are

Oölite—Small spherical or subspherical accretionary grain generally less than 2.0 mm in diameter. In thin section, oölites display concentric structure and may exhibit radial structure (Plate IV-*K*). Superficial oölite is a type of oölite possessing a recognizable nucleus, in which the thickness of the accretionary coating is less than the radius of the nucleus (Plate IV-*L*).

Pisolite—A grain similar to an oölite, but less regular in form (commonly crenulated), and generally 2.0 mm or more in diameter (Plate V-*A*).

Algal- or Foraminifera-encrusted grains—A carbonate grain having a nucleus (generally a skeletal or rock fragment) about which algae or Foraminifera have formed encrustations. A limestone with algal-encrusted grains is shown in Plate V-*B*.

Rocks of this group may have a matrix of grains of a much smaller size. The binding agent of the grains, particularly the oölites, is commonly clear calcite cement. However, there are rare examples of limestones with oölites in micritic matrix (Plate IV-*J*).

Limestones with organic structures.—The major framework of these limestones has been secreted by organisms such as algae and corals, and the fossil remains are still in their approximate growth position. Skeletal fragments, pellets, lumps, and micrite commonly surround the organic framework (Plate V-*C*, *D*, and *E*) and, on a point-count basis, may even be the major constituents. However, the name of the framework-building organism is used in naming the rock.

»»→

EXPLANATION OF PLATE II

A. Different-appearing limestones.—The photographs (×8) depict differences due to varying amounts of grain and micrite.

B. Defining limestone rock types.—The types of grains and the relative proportion of micrite and grains are used in defining limestone rock type. Only two grain types—superficial oölites and rock fragments—are illustrated here.

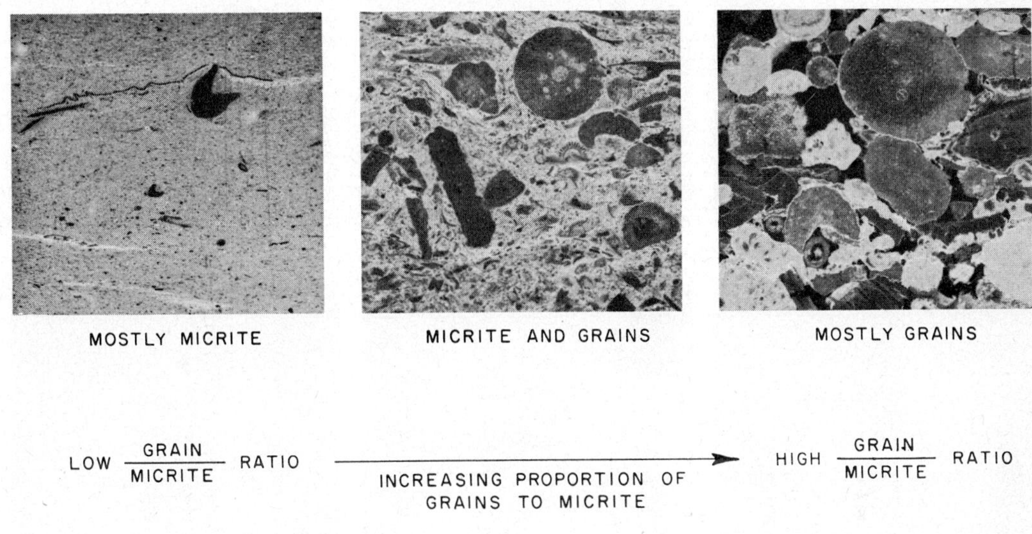
A. DIFFERENT APPEARING LIMESTONES
MOSTLY MICRITE
MICRITE AND GRAINS
MOSTLY GRAINS
LOW GRAIN/MICRITE RATIO
INCREASING PROPORTION OF GRAINS TO MICRITE
HIGH GRAIN/MICRITE RATIO

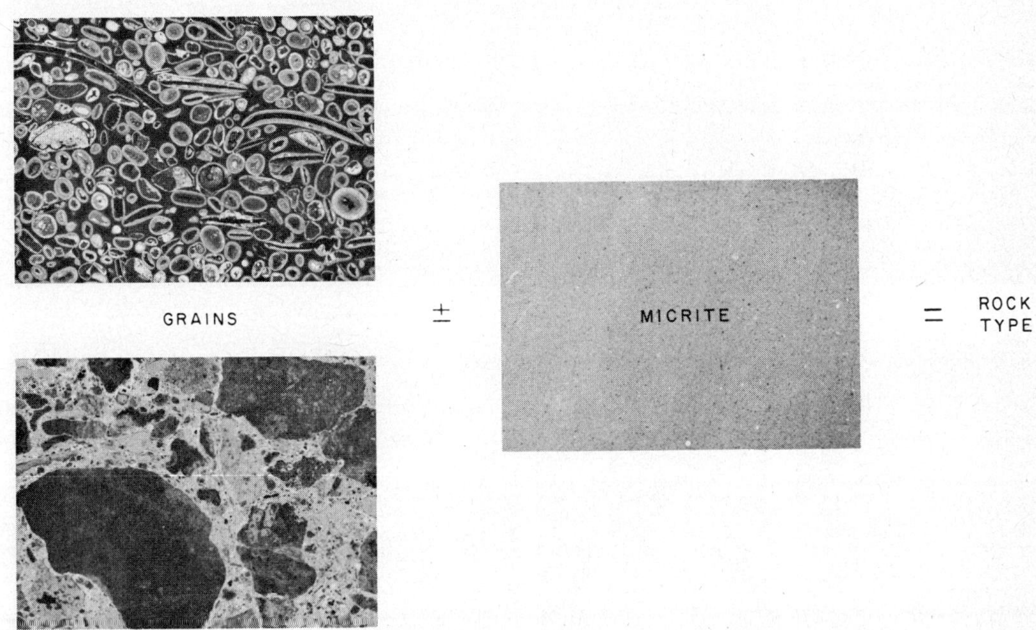
B. DEFINING LIMESTONE ROCK TYPES:
GRAINS
±
MICRITE
=
ROCK TYPE

Plate II

LIMESTONE ROCK TYPES

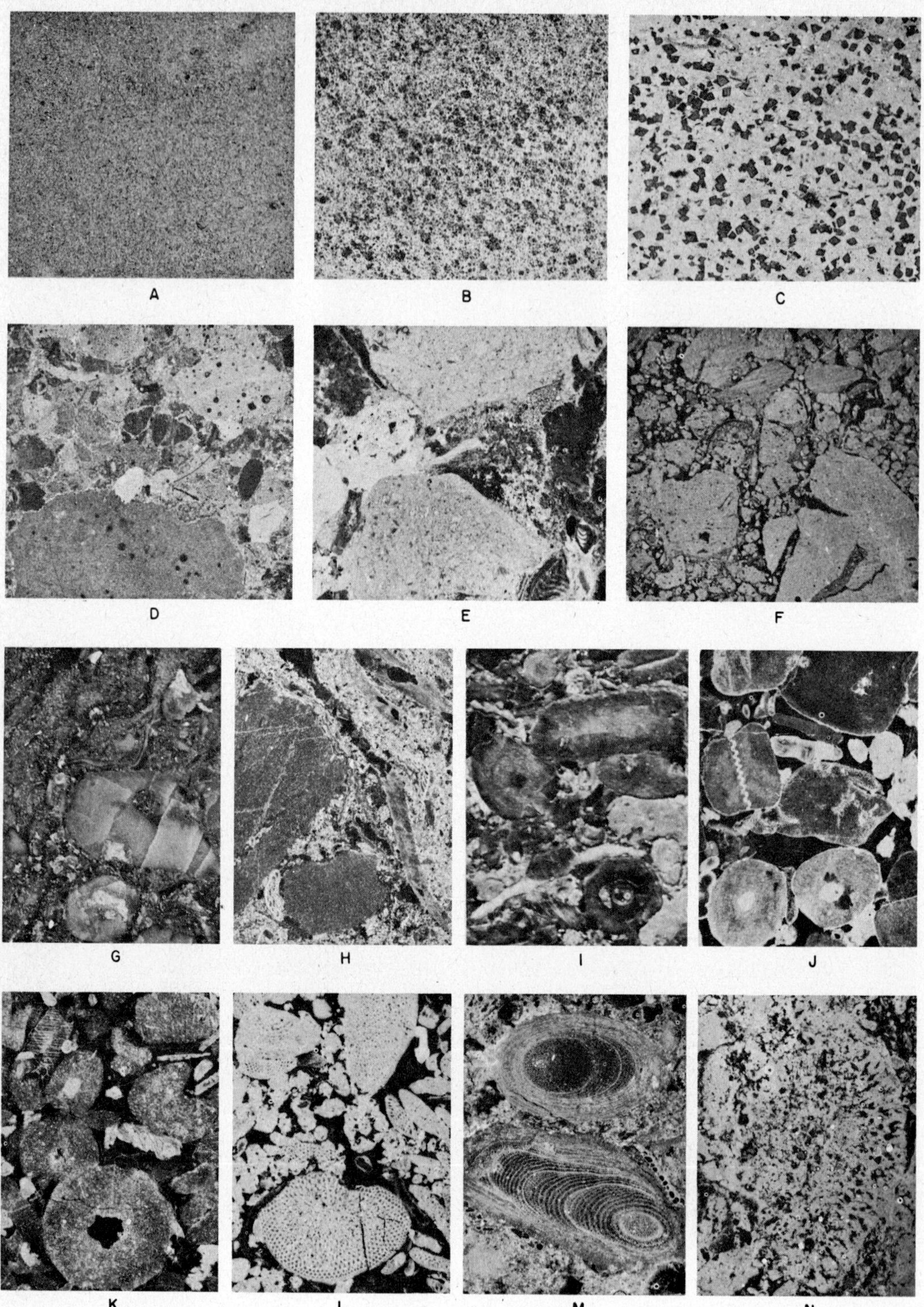

PLATE III

Coralline, algal, and bryozoan limestones are common types. Rocks of this group are referred to in some of the literature as biochemical limestones.

Gradational limestone types.—The limestone textural types illustrated so far have represented rocks in which one grain type was predominant, or in which there were certain proportions of grains and micrite. In many limestones, two or more grain types occur in approximately equal amounts and both are used in naming the rock. Examples are skeletal-pellet limestone (Plate V-*F*), skeletal-lump limestone (Plate V-*G*), and oölitic-skeletal limestone.

Grouping of limestone rock types.—Two genetic groups of limestone rock types are recognized—(1) those that are mechanically deposited, (2) those that are formed in place by chemical or biochemical processes. The mechanically deposited limestones include fragmental and nonfragmental rock types. Among the fragmental are the detrital limestones and a large number of skeletal limestone types.[5] Nonfragmental, mechanically deposited limestones include those limestones with coated grains, lump limestones, and fecal pellet limestones. Limestones with organic structures, caliche, and travertine, are nonfragmental, nonmechanically deposited types.

OCCURRENCE OF LIMESTONE TYPES

Many limestone rock types recur in different parts of the same section and the same sedimentary basin, in the same-age sediments of different basins, and in different-age limestone

[5] Many foraminiferal limestones (classed here as skeletal limestones) are composed of whole unbroken tests and are therefore nonfragmental.

←

Explanation of Plate III

LIMESTONE ROCK TYPES

A. Micritic limestone (microclastic type).—Dominantly micrite with few quartz silt grains. Mississippian Lodgepole fm., Gallatin Co., Montana, ×8.

B. Micritic limestone (microcrystalline type).—Composed of interlocking mosaic of calcite crystals 0.03 mm diameter. Mississippian Charles fm., Hot Springs Co., Wyoming, ×8.

C. Dolomitic micritic limestone.—Dolomite rhombs scattered in matrix of micrite. Jurassic Arab fm., Saudi Arabia, ×8.

D. Conglomeratic-micritic limestone.—Composed of subangular to subrounded micritic limestone fragments with a calcareous clay matrix. Triassic limestone, Sicily, ×8.

E. Limestone conglomerate.—Composed of subrounded to rounded limestone rock fragments and fossil debris. Miocene age, Philippines, ×8.

F. Detrital limestone (with intraclasts).—Contains fragments of pellet and micritic limestone derived from nearby, partially consolidated bed. Pennsylvanian Hermosa fm., San Juan Co., Utah, ×8.

G. Skeletal-micritic limestone.—Contains fragments of crinoids, mollusks, bryozoa, and corals in a micritic matrix. Pennsylvanian Hermosa fm., San Juan Co., Utah. Photograph of an etched sample, ×8.

H. Same as *G*, but a thin section photograph instead of an etched sample photo, ×8.

I. Skeletal limestone (mixed debris).—Large subangular fossil fragments (crinoid, bryozoa, algal?) closely packed and surrounded by calcite cement. Mississippian Mission Canyon fm., Williams Co., North Dakota. Photograph of an etched sample, ×4.

J. Same as *I*, but a thin section photograph instead of an etched sample photo, ×8.

K. Crinoidal limestone.—Composed of crinoid columnals surrounded by clear calcite cement. Mississippian Madison group, Uintah Co., Utah, ×8.

L. Foraminiferal (*Orbitolina*) limestone.—Composed dominantly of Orbitolinas, skeletal fragments, and detrital grains tightly cemented by clear calcite. Cretaceous Apon fm., Venezuela, ×8.

M. Coralline algae limestone.—Large coralline algae remains scattered in a matrix of fossil debris and micrite. Miocene age, Philippines, ×8.

N. Limestone with algal segments.—Contains algal segments up to 5.0 mm diameter, algal spheres, shell fragments, and lumps embedded in a matrix of cement and micrite. Mississippian Charles fm., Big Horn Co., Wyoming, ×8.

LIMESTONE ROCK TYPES

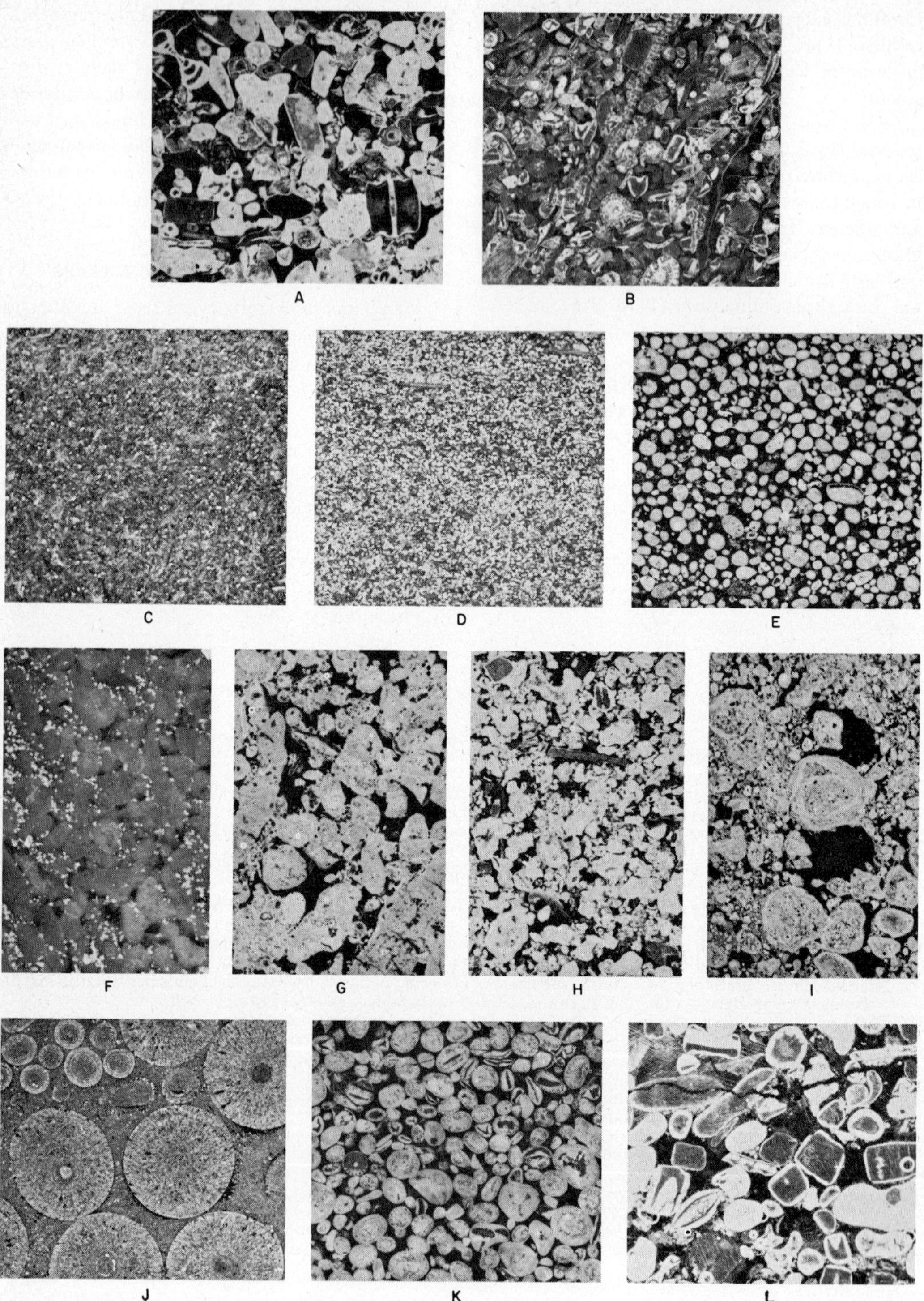

PLATE IV

sediments throughout the world. A few examples are given in Plates VI and VII.

It should not be inferred from the plates that the frequent repetition of limestone rock types regardless of age invalidates their usefulness in stratigraphic correlation. Similar textural rock types differ sufficiently in detail (for example, color, luster, degree of consolidation, weathering characteristics, and genera or species of fossil remains) and in their manner of vertical succession, that they are extremely useful in local stratigraphic correlations.

The basic textural components (grains, micrite, cement, and pores) and the way they are put together to constitute a limestone rock fabric are duplicated the world over. This repetition of similar appearing limestone types suggests that some standardization in limestone terminology and description is not only possible and desirable, but that such standardization would form a descriptive basis for meaningful interpretations.

TEXTURAL CLASSIFICATION OF LIMESTONES

Study of vertical and lateral rock associations for a number of carbonate sequences revealed fundamental limestone properties that are influenced by depositional conditions and that would account for the similar- and the different-appearing limestones. Attempts were made to organize these rock properties into a descriptive system of terminology, keeping in mind the needs and problems of the geologist in the field, on a well, or in the laboratory. Attempts to derive a useful system or classification were guided by these four requirements.

1. The classification should be based on those features in a rock that are both observable and measurable.

←«««

Explanation of Plate IV

LIMESTONE ROCK TYPES, CONTINUED

A. Skeletal limestone (mixed debris).—Well sorted, subrounded to rounded fossil fragments consisting of shell debris, crinoid remains, Foraminifera, small bivalves, algal accretions, and Bryozoa embedded in a calcite cement. Mississippian Mission Canyon fm., Williams Co., North Dakota, ×8.

B. Skeletal limestone (mixed debris).—Fossil fragments of various sizes, mostly crinoids and shell debris; scattered oölites; faintly banded; tightly cemented with clear calcite. Mississippian Lodgepole fm., Gallatin Co., Montana, ×8.

C. Pellet-micritic limestone.—Consists of pellets averaging .07 mm diameter and scattered skeletal debris. Grains surrounded by 10 per cent micritic matrix plus calcite cement. Photograph of an etched surface. Mississippian Lodgepole fm., Gallatin Co., Montana, ×5.

D. Same as *C*, but a thin section photograph instead of an etched surface photo, ×8.

E. Pellet limestone (ovoid-grain sand).—The ovoid grains have an almost constant 2:1 ratio of long axis to short axis, and are believed to be fecal pellets. This is a photograph of a plastic impregnated sample of Recent sediment, Gulf of Batabano, Cuba, ×8.

F. Lump limestone.—Has many elongate lumps (6.0×1.0 mm) composed of grain aggregates and micrite. Tightly cemented. Photograph of an etched surface. Mississippian Charles fm., Park Co., Wyoming, ×8.

G. Same as *F*, but a thin section photograph instead of an etched surface photo, ×8.

H. Lump limestone.—Consists of irregularly shaped lump grains, shell, and crinoid fragments with an average diameter of 0.35 mm. Tightly cemented. Mississippian Charles fm., Park Co., Wyoming, ×4.

I. Algal lump limestone.—Coarse accretionary grain aggregates showing faint, irregularly concentric structure (believed to be due to algal activity) in a matrix of pellets, algal spheres, micrite, and pores. Mississippian Mission Canyon fm., North Dakota, ×8.

J. Oölitic-micritic limestone.—Chalky oölites averaging 2.5 mm diameter in a matrix of small oölites (0.1 mm) and chalky micrite. Silurian Chimney Hill fm., Pontotoc Co., Oklahoma, ×8.

K. Oölitic limestone.—Medium- to coarse-grained oölites and scattered lumps partially cemented by clear calcite. Slightly porous. Mississippian Charles fm., Park Co., Wyoming, ×8.

L. Superficial oölitic limestone.—Medium- to coarse-grained crinoid and bryozoa fragments with thin, concentric oölitic coating. Slightly cemented. Mississippian Lodgepole fm., Gallatin Co., Montana, ×8.

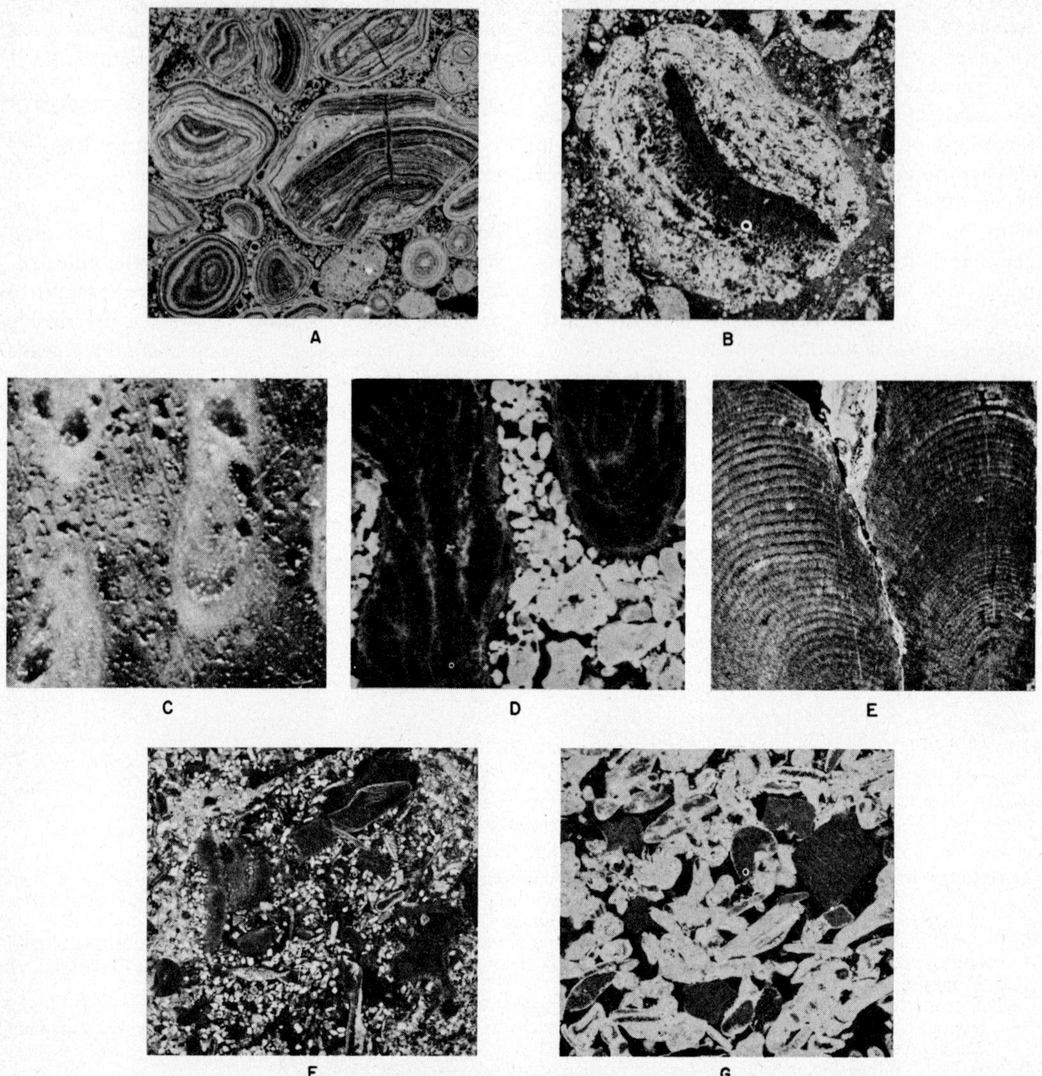

PLATE V

EXPLANATION OF PLATE V

LIMESTONE ROCK TYPES, CONTINUED

A. Pisolitic limestone.—Bimodal distribution of coarse-grained pisolites in a very fine-grained matrix of pellets and algal spheres. Mississippian Mission Canyon fm., Dunn Co., North Dakota, ×8.

B. Algae-encrusted skeletal limestone.—Large biscuit-like grains of algae-encrusted fossil debris in finer matrix of grains and micrite. Ordovician Bromide fm., Oklahoma, ×8.

C. Coralline limestone.—Coral branches surrounded by loosely cemented lumps and pellets (etched sample). Mississippian Charles fm., Big Horn Co., Wyoming, ×4.

D. Same as *C*, but a thin section photograph instead of an etched sample photo, ×8.

E. Algal limestone.—Large algal heads in a finely micrograined dolomite matrix. Mississippian Charles fm., Williams Co., North Dakota, ×8.

F. Skeletal-pellet limestone.—Sand-sized fossil debris (crinoids, bryozoa) and silt-sized pellets surrounded by calcite cement. Mississippian Lodgepole fm., Gallatin Co., Montana, ×8.

G. Skeletal-lump limestone.—Mixture of skeletal grains (largely crinoid debris) and composite grains. Mississippian Charles fm., Big Horn Co., Wyoming, ×8.

TEXTURAL CLASSIFICATION OF LIMESTONES

GRAIN /MICRITE RATIO (a)	% GRAINS (b)	GRAIN TYPE (c)					Organic Frame-Builders	No Organic Frame-Builders
		Detrital Grains	*Skeletal Grains*	*Pellets*	*Lumps*	*Coated Grains*		
		Detrital Ls.	Skeletal Ls.	Pellet Ls.	Lump Ls.	Oolitic Ls. Pisolitic Ls. Algal encr. Ls.	Coralline Ls. Algal Ls. Etc.	Caliche Travertine Tufa
9:1	~90%							
		Detrital-Micritic Ls.	Skeletal-Micritic Ls.	Pellet-Micritic Ls.	Lump-Micritic Ls.	Oolitic-(Pisolitic-Etc.) Micritic Ls.	Coralline-Micritic Ls. Algal-Micritic Ls. Etc.	
1:1	~50%							
		Micritic-Detrital Ls.	Micritic-Skeletal Ls.	Micritic-Pellet Ls.	Micritic-Lump Ls.	Micritic-Oolitic (Pisolitic Etc.) Ls.	Micritic-Coralline Ls. Micritic-Algal Ls. Etc.	
1:9	~10%							
		← Micritic Limestone →						

Fig. 1.—The textural classification of limestones is based on the presence or absence of grains and framebuilders and their type; and on the relative proportions of grains (or framebuilders) to micritic material. (a) "Micrite" in the grain-micrite ratio refers to lime mud or its consolidated equivalent. (b) Percentages of grains or framebuilders may be used in place of a grain-micrite ratio and should be computed on a cement- and pore-free basis. (c) See text for further subdivisions and modifications of this classification. Where a commonly used name is not likely to be misunderstood, such as "limestone conglomerate," its use is preferred to the name listed in the classification.

2. The rock names should be descriptive—using simple terms that readily convey a mental picture.

3. New terms should be avoided wherever possible.

4. The classification must be sufficiently flexible to meet the needs of both detailed and general studies.

The resulting classification is shown as Figure 1. Its purpose is to provide an aid for objectively and meaningfully describing limestones. The two bases of the classification chart are (1) the relative proportions of grains to micrite (expressed by a grain-micrite ratio), and (2) the type of limestone grain or framebuilder.

The grain-micrite ratio, along the vertical axis, is the sum of the percentages of grains divided by the percentage of micrite. It best expresses the observed gradations from a rock containing all grains to a rock containing all micrite. It excludes cement, vug, fracture, vein fillings, and recrystallized areas. These are produced by diagenetic or essentially post-depositional changes. The ratio is expressed as follows

$$\text{Grain-Micrite Ratio} = \frac{\%(\text{detrital grains} + \text{skeletal grains} + \text{pellets} + \text{lumps} + \text{coated grains} + \text{mineral grains})}{\%\ \text{micrite}}$$

The ratio can usually be estimated by a quick visual inspection of the rock. It expresses the proportion of larger particles to smaller particles, and, therefore, is a function of grain size and of sorting.

Horizontal subdivisions of the chart (Fig. 1) are used to group the rocks into categories depending on the principal grain type.

The last two columns are for (1) limestones that contain organic structures, with the framebuilding organism essentially in place, and (2) the relatively grainless and nonorganic limestones which include caliche, travertine, and tufa.

NOMENCLATURE SYSTEM

Pure limestones.—Before using the chart, most geologists will want to examine limestones for the recognizable and measurable textural components discussed earlier. With experience and a properly prepared rock surface, cement, micrite, pores, and most grain types can be recognized at a glance.

Once the geologist is familiar with the textural and compositional components of limestones, the chart will help him attach a name to the samples.

»»→

Explanation of Plate VI

REPETITION OF LIMESTONE TYPES

A, B. Micritic-skeletal limestones with molluscan debris, ×8.
A.—Pennsylvanian Cherryvale fm., Daviess Co., Missouri.
B.—Jurassic, Pakistan.

C, D. Skeletal-micritic limestones, ×8.
C.—Mississippian Mission Canyon fm., North Dakota.
D.—Lower Eocene, Pakistan.

E, F. Algal limestones (fragmental), ×8.
E.—Pennsylvanian Plattsburg fm., Clinton Co., Missouri.
F.—Pennsylvanian Hermosa fm., Apache Co., Arizona.

G, H. Algae- and foraminiferal-encrusted limestones, ×8.
G.—Pennsylvanian Hermosa fm., San Juan Co., Utah.
H.—Jurassic, Pakistan.

REPETITION OF LIMESTONE TYPES

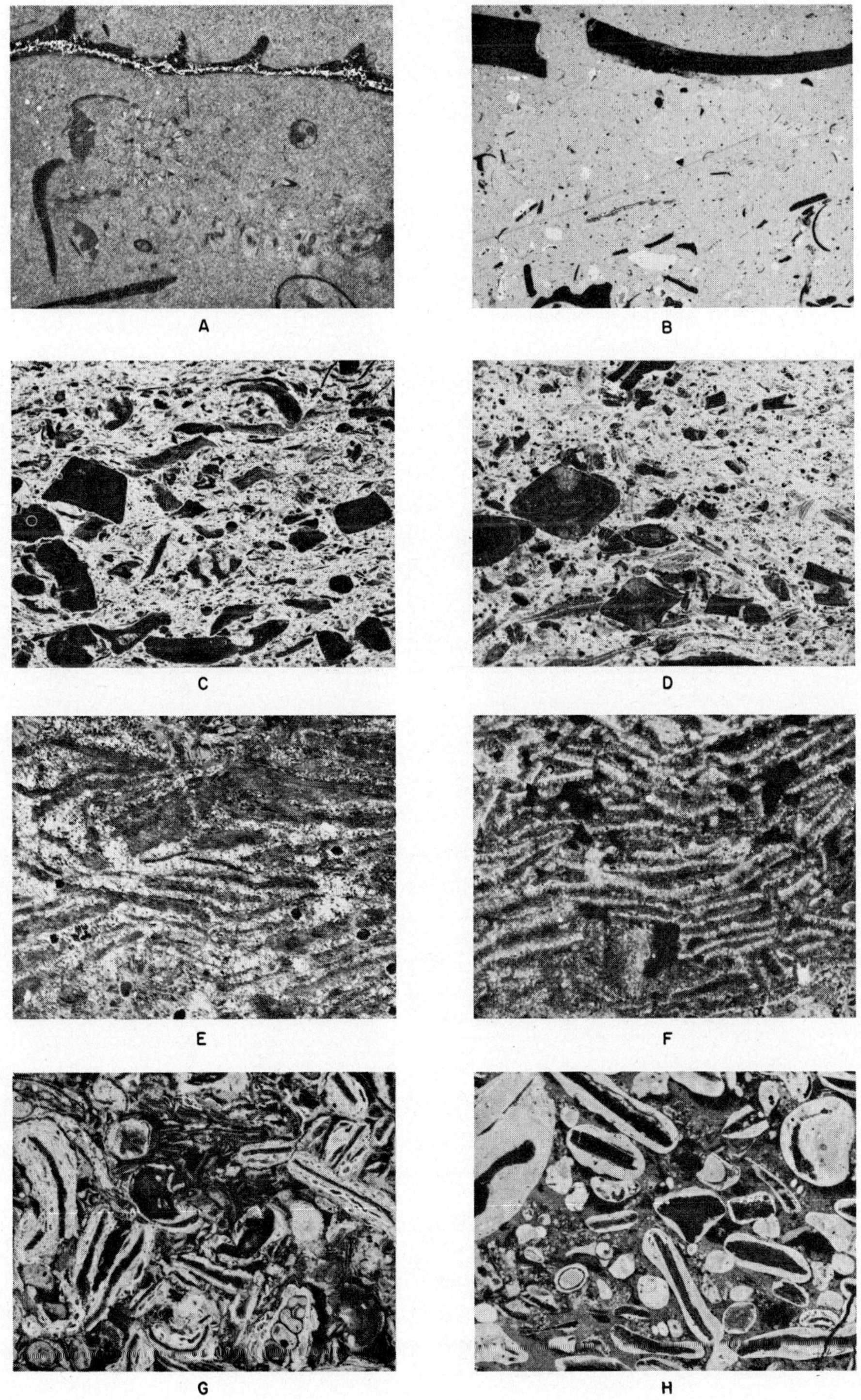

PLATE VI

REPETITION OF LIMESTONE TYPES

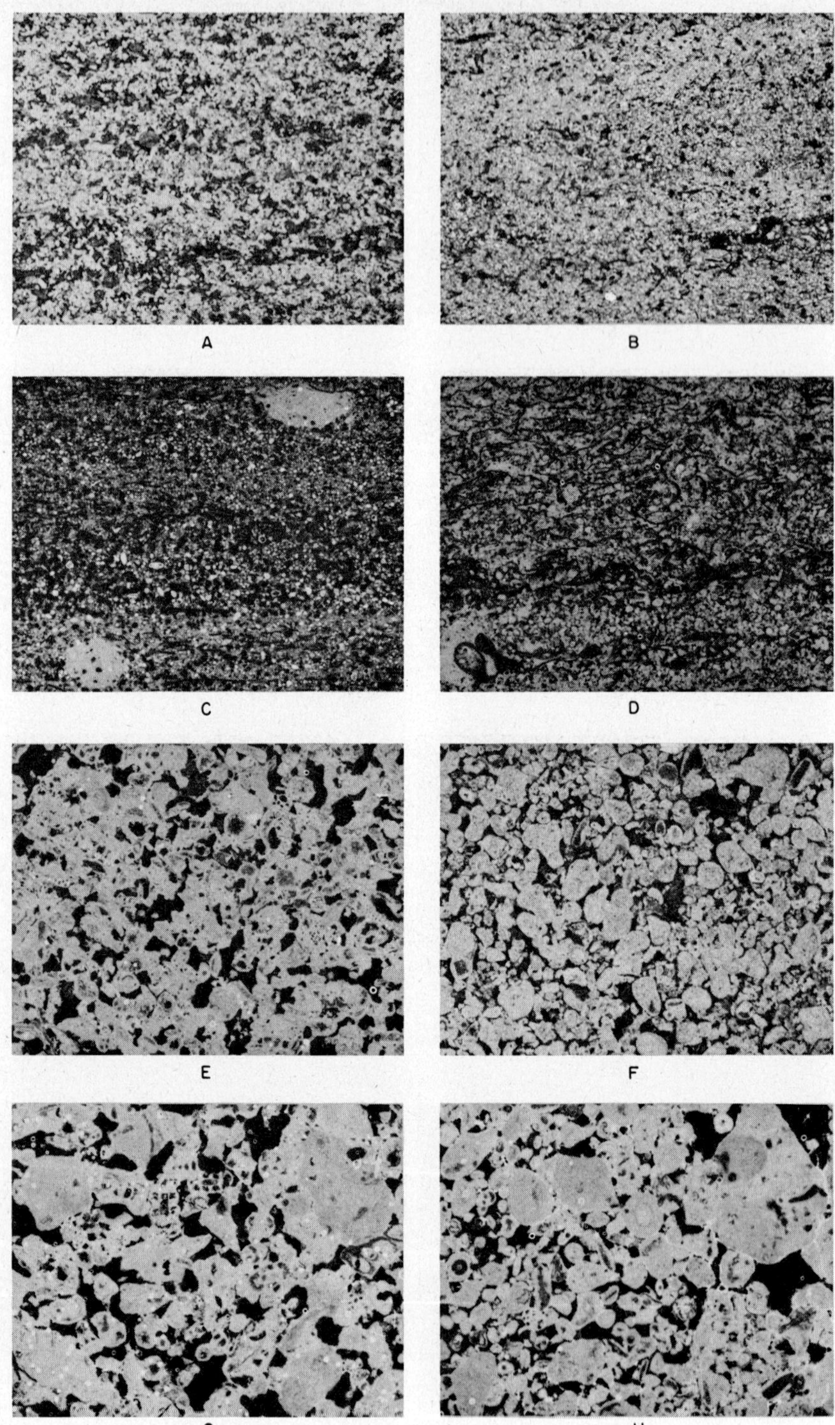

Plate VII

This is done by (1) determining the presence or absence of grains and of organic structures, (2) observing grain types and their relative amounts, and (3) estimating the relative amounts of grains and micrite. *Step 1* will tell whether the rock belongs to one of the first five groups of limestones on the chart, or to one of the last two. If grains are present, *Step 2* will tell which of the first five limestone groups matches the samples, and *Step 3* will position the samples along the vertical axis of the chart.

In forming a rock name, the major textural component is listed first, separated from the minor component by a hyphen. For example, *crinoidal-micritic limestone* is applied to a rock with 50–90 per cent crinoid fragments and 50-10 per cent micrite. Examples of rock names are provided with each of the rock type photographs in the plates accompanying this article.

Where commonly used rock names are not likely to be misunderstood, their use should be continued. Such terms as *limestone breccia* and *limestone conglomerate* should be used if it is understood that the grains constitute more than 90 per cent of the solid particles of the rock, and a large proportion of the grains are pebble size or larger. Similarly, *crinoidal limestone* or *foraminiferal limestone* should be used instead of skeletal limestone, and *chalk* instead of micritic limestone, if the terms are deemed applicable.

On the other hand, such terms as fossiliferous limestones and crystalline limestones cover such a broad range of carbonate rock types that they have little meaning. Referring to the classification chart (Fig. 1), fossiliferous limestones include all the subdivisions listed under "Skeletal Grains" and all those under "Organic Framebuilders." Similarly, we have found that "crystalline" (used in the sense meaning interlocking particles exhibiting crystal faces) has been used for most crinoidal limestones, many of the limestones containing skeletal grains some of the limestones containing detrital grains, and even micritic limestones.

This classification permits substitution of conventional terms where their use cannot be misunderstood. If some geologists prefer to use such terms as calcirudite, calcarenite, and calcisiltite, these may be substituted for the word "limestone." An example would be crinoidal-micritic calcarenite. We do not recommend this for general usage, however, because calcarenite, calcirudite, etc., are terms covering broad grain-size categories of limestones. We feel it is better to use the adjectives "fine-grained," "medium-grained," etc., where needed.

←

Explanation of Plate VII

REPETITION OF LIMESTONE TYPES, CONTINUED

A, B. Pellet-micritic limestones, ×8.
- *A.*—Mississippian Charles fm., Park Co., Wyoming.
- *B.*—Jurassic, Pakistan.

C, D. Skeletal-pellet limestones, ×8.
- *C.*—Jurassic, Pakistan.
- *D.*—Mississippian Lodgepole fm., Big Horn Co., Wyoming.

E, F. Lump limestones, ×8.
- *E.*—With Foraminifera. Jurassic Arab fm., Saudi Arabia.
- *F.*—With crinoid debris. Mississippian Charles fm., Wyoming.

G, H. Lump limestones, ×8.
- *G.*—Jurassic Arab fm., Saudi Arabia.
- *H.*—Mississippian Mission Canyon fm., Big Horn Co., Wyoming.

Further subdivision may be made to meet specific needs. For example, a bimodal distribution of grains, such as smaller oölites occurring between larger oölites, can be described by the phrase "coarse-grained oölitic limestone with intersitital fine-grained oölites." Or, for those rocks in which the type of the smaller interstitial grains cannot be recognized with certainty, the phrase "skeletal limestone with granular matrix" has been found useful.[6]

Where two or more grain types are present in approximately equal amounts, both are used in the rock name. The grain in greatest abundance is mentioned first. For example, a rock containing 60 per cent skeletal grains and 40 per cent pellets is called a *skeletal-pellet limestone* (see Plate V-*F*). The grain names are separated by a hyphen. If one type grades into another in the same sample, such terminology as *skeletal limestone grading to pellet limestone* may be used. Or, if limestone types occur in alternating beds in the same sample, it may be named thus—*banded skeletal and pellet limestones*. Limestones with organic structures are commonly gradational or mixed with "grain-type" limestones (see Plate V-*D*). Some reef rocks fall into this category. Even where an in-place framework-building organism is the minor constituent, the rock is still recognized as a limestone in the organic framebuilders group. A

$$\frac{\text{framebuilder} + \text{grain}}{\text{micrite}} \text{ ratio}$$

may be used instead of the grain-micrite ratio for limestones in this group.

Dolomitic limestones and impure carbonates.—By definition, a carbonate rock has a composition of greater than 50 per cent, by weight, of carbonate minerals, generally calcite or dolomite. Carbonate-to-noncarbonate gradations are common. Noncarbonate rocks containing 10 per cent to 50 per cent carbonates may be simply named calcareous (or dolomitic) sandstone, claystone, or shale. The manner of occurrence of the carbonate, whether as grains, cement, or micrite, should be indicated in the description of the rock.

A compositional scheme for classifying carbonate-to-noncarbonate gradations is shown in the triangular diagram in Figure 2. The two most important carbonate minerals—calcite and dolomite—occur as two of the end members, and mineral impurities as the third end member. Relative amounts of dolomite and calcite are shown both as a dolomite-calcite ratio and as per cent dolomite of the total carbonate. Instead of the word "impure," we recommend the use of the appropriate compositional term such as argillaceous or quartzose. Four subdivisions are recognized in the gradation between the two pure carbonate end members. These are limestone, dolomitic limestone, calcareous dolomite, and dolomite.

Although the textural classification of limestones applies to the pure $CaCO_3$ end member, compositional terms from the triangle can be added to extend its usefulness. If a rock is dolomitic and primary limestone textures are recognized, the rock is given the appropriate textural names preceded by the compositional term "dolomitic" (see Plate III-*C*). A rock containing 50 per cent skeletal grains and 20 per cent dolomite rhombs scattered in 30 per cent micritic matrix would be called a *dolomitic skeletal-micritic limestone.*

For the carbonate rocks containing 10 to 50 per cent of argillaceous or quartzose material, the suggested nomenclature system combines both composition and texture, for example, quartzose skeletal-micritic limestone. Quartzose limestone is the compositional element of the rock name; skeletal-micritic is the textural element. The system proposed applies to both limestone and dolomite, though the textural element in naming a dolomite may be simply a grain-size designation if a relict texture cannot be recognized.

LIMESTONE DESCRIPTION

A simple rock name does not replace a clear, concise description but only supplements it. Depending on the uses to which they will be put, sample descriptions should include information on cementation, porosity, permeability, oil staining, color, nature of the grains and matrix material, their percentages, their size, sorting, fossil content, impurities and accessory minerals, sedimentary structures, and type of rock association. Graphic logs are extremely helpful in systematically recording this rock information.

Details on methods of describing limestones are

[6] We suggest that the word "matrix" be used for the interstitial material between grains, whether this interstitial material be smaller grains, lime mud, or cement.

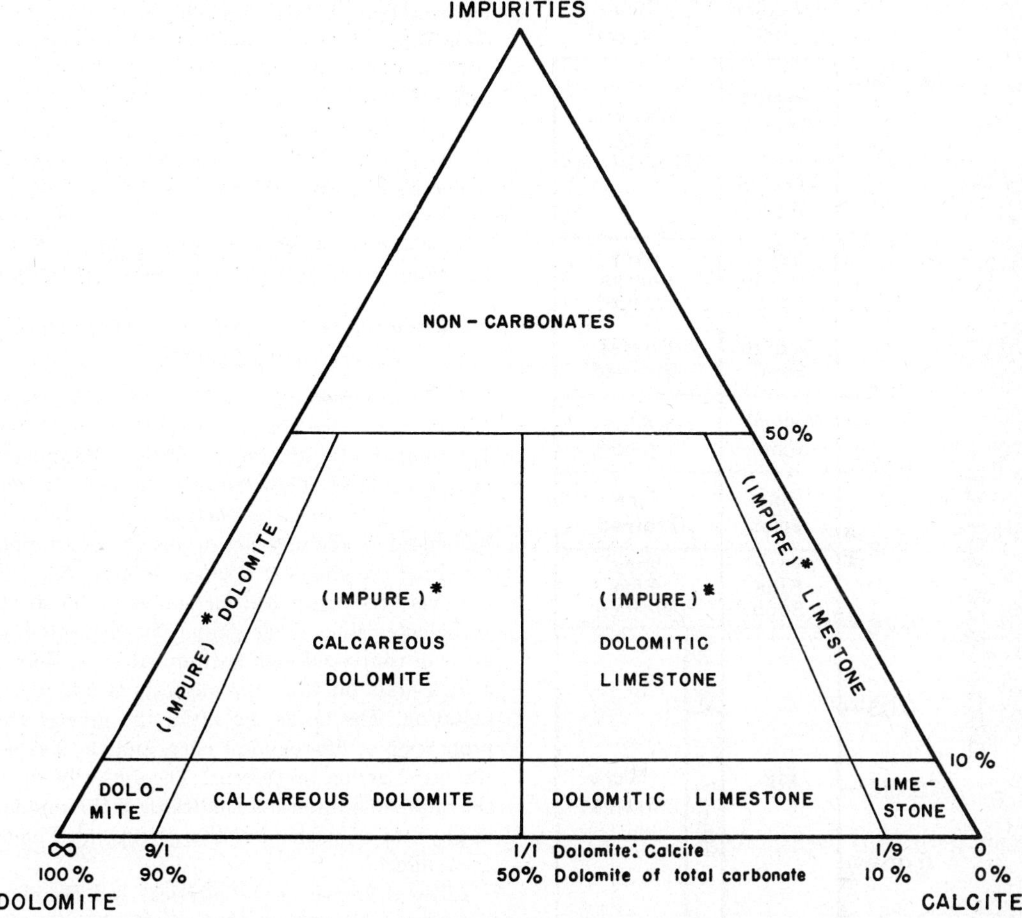

FIG. 2.—Compositional terminology for carbonate rocks. Percentages of impurities and the ratio of dolomite: calcite is used to define compositional groups for carbonate rocks, that is, those rocks containing more than 50 per cent carbonate minerals. Percentages of calcite and dolomite may be used in place of the dolomite: calcite ratio for the pure carbonate series along the base of the triangle.

* An appropriate compositional term should be substituted for the word "impure" where possible.

not included in this paper. Rather, only specific highlights of certain modifiers are presented here.

The three important textural components which are not considered in naming limestones (cement, pore space, and recrystallization calcite) are used as descriptive modifiers of the basic rock name—for example, well-cemented oölitic limestone, porous foraminiferal limestone, or partially recrystallized pellet limestone. Details concerning the nature and amount of these components may be given in the sample description.

A slightly modified Wentworth grade scale, as shown in Figure 3, is proposed for carbonate rocks. The same size terms used for sandstones are equally suited to the large majority of limestones. Indeed, many limestones bear a close textural similarity to sandstones. We have also found the size terms suited to dolomites, and believe that one grade scale for sedimentary rocks should simplify future descriptions.

It has been our experience that sedimentary textures are generally preserved if the rock is predominantly limestone. Nevertheless, postdepositional textural modifications are, locally, and in places regionally, important and should be considered as a possibility when examining any

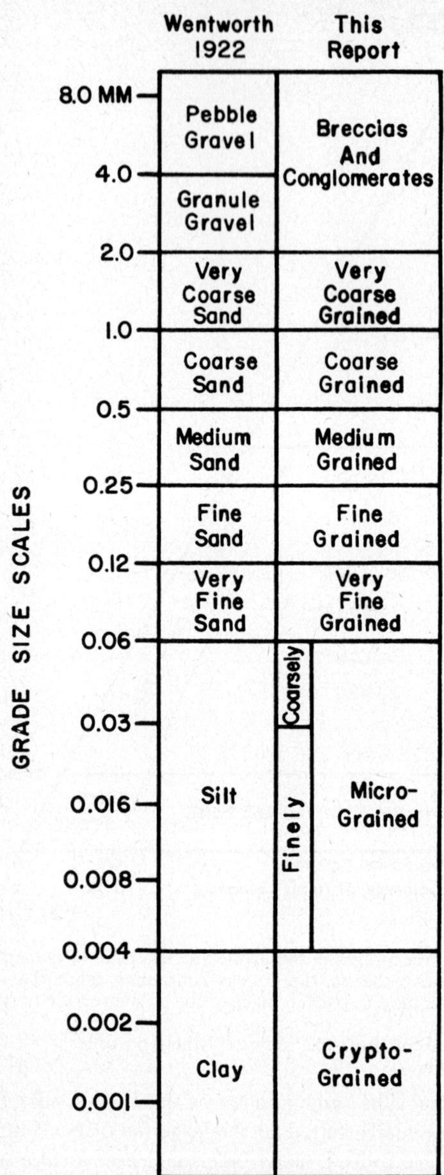

FIG. 3.—Grade scales for sedimentary rocks. The Wentworth grade scale was proposed for "clastic sediments." It has been modified for carbonate rocks as shown.

carbonate rocks. In addition to cementation, major post-depositional processes that alter the primary rock character are (1) compaction, (2) solution, (3) recrystallization and crystal inversion, (4) replacement, (5) mineralization, and (6) deformation. The modifications imposed by post-depositional processes on the initial sedimentary texture commonly make not only the naming difficult, but also the interpretation of the sedimentary environment. In many cases, careful study of a limestone section will show rock sequences from which the process of alteration can be determined. Careful description of the end products of these processes is required for an accurate interpretation of the history of the rocks.

DEPOSITIONAL CONDITIONS OF LIMESTONE FORMATION

Inferences from classification chart.—The grain-micrite ratio—the vertical axis of the chart (Fig. 1)—compares the amount of coarse to the amount of fine material. Theoretically, the ratio is controlled by wave or current action. It would also be influenced by the presence or absence of a source for either the grains or micrite. In large measure, however, the main control seems to be water turbulence. Fine muds cannot be deposited in areas of continued high bottom currents. Hence, a high grain-micrite ratio suggests strong water agitation. The lower the ratio, the greater the proportion of lime mud or ooze, and the weaker the wave action or current. Theoretically then, the ratio can be used as an indicator of the amount of physical or mechanical energy expended upon the sediment.

Little is known of the physical and chemical control of grain type, the basis for positioning the limestones horizontally in the classification chart. However, the textural features of grains, their rounded edges, tendency to occur in sorted groups, striking resemblance to ordinary sand and silt grains, and sporadically broken shape, indicate that mechanical agencies are primarily responsible for their distribution in the sediments. During the history of transportation and deposition of grains, varying degrees of chemical influence seem to affect their mode of origin and morphology. Detrital and skeletal grains are shaped largely by destructive processes.

On the other hand, characteristics of some grain types, such as lumps, oölites, and pisolites, suggest that they result from constructive or accretionary processes. They grow or are built up during the formative stages of the sediment that contains them. Periods of accretion may alternate with periods of fragmentation, as during alternate periods of deposition and transportation; but the dominant mode of formation of these grains is constructive rather than destructive. Constructive chemical forces (precipitation) are also largely responsible for the limestones containing framebuilding organic structures and for travertines, caliche, and calcareous tufa. The manner of formation of pellets commonly cannot be distinguished; some appear to be fragments, others secreted or accreted particles.

To summarize, the vertical axis of the classification reflects physical action or the degree of wave or current agitation (if we neglect source effects). The horizontal axis indicates the relative influence of chemical and mechanical factors, with the chemical influence increasing to the right.

Observed environments and conditions of deposition.—The occurrence of carbonate sediments in modern depositional areas has been examined by a number of geologists. These studies provide basic information on sediment type that will permit more reliable interpretation of the environments of ancient rocks. Among the most useful published articles on environments of Recent sediment types are those by Daetwyler and Kidwell (1959), Newell and Rigby (1957), Ginsburg (1957), Lowenstam (1955), Illing (1954), Fairbridge (1950), McKee (1949), Eardley (1938), and Black (1933). A synthesis of these papers shows that different types of lime sediments result from a complex interplay of physical and chemical forces. Chiefly responsible for the different-appearing sediment types are the direction, magnitude, and duration of wave and current action and the chemistry of the water in which the carbonates are formed and deposited. Sediment types are not directly related to water depth. Of the many processes that control sediment types, one may dominate in one area, another in a second area, and perhaps a combination, in a third.

Although similar physiographic environments do not necessarily contain similar sediment types, certain generalizations are possible. For example, lime muds occur in areas of quiet water. Such areas are found in the shallow, protected waters on the lee side of Andros Island in the Bahamas (Newell and Rigby, 1957), in the central portion of Pacific coral atolls (McKee, 1949), the leeward side of many reefs in the Australian Barrier Reef complex (Fairbridge, 1950), and as deep-sea oozes at oceanic depths. Skeletal sands may be found on the margins of carbonate banks and platforms (Daetwyler and Kidwell, 1959; and Illing, 1954), in wave- and current-agitated areas. Oölitic sands and those containing lumps are commonly found near the margins of banks or platforms, but occur on the interior side of the marginal shelf skeletal sands (Daetwyler and Kidwell, 1959, Illing, 1954). They are controlled by the movement of oceanic waters onto shallow platforms, and by warming effects which lead to supersaturation of calcium carbonate. Precipitation occurs, giving rise to layers around individual grains or to the binding agent for composite grains. Intermittent high wave or current energy further characterizes the areas where oölites and lumps are found. Gradational sediment types containing varying proportions of the mud and grain components have been identified and described in zones that are intermediate in character between highly agitated and quiet-bottom conditions.

Thus, apparent relationships exist in Recent sediments between depositional environments and those textural parameters expressed by grain type and grain-micrite ratio. The limestone classification, which is based on these objective and measurable features, then, must have environmental significance.

DOLOMITES

Dolomites are carbonate rocks composed of more than 50 per cent, by weight, of the mineral dolomite. They form important reservoirs for hydrocarbons along the Canadian reef chain, in the Ordovician Red River formation of the Williston basin, in the Mississippian Madison of the Big Horn basin, at Abqaiq and Ghawar of the Middle East, and at many other places.

We believe the different types can best be accommodated by a descriptive system of nomenclature. In some cases the origin of dolomite as a modified limestone rock type is clear. In other cases this is not so. The system for naming dolomites is based primarily on a compositional grouping, and modified by appropriate textural terms.

Compositional terminology.—Two compositional groups of dolomites are recognized—(1) calcareous dolomites containing 50–90 per cent dolomite, and (2) relatively pure dolomites containing 90 per cent, or more, dolomite. Each of these groups is subdivided according to textural modifications.

1. *50–90 per cent dolomite content*—These rocks are named *calcareous dolomites.* Limestone grains or textures that remain as calcite are listed as such in parentheses after the name; those that have been converted to dolomite are listed as dolomitized portions of the rock in parentheses following the name.

   Example—*calcareous dolomite* (calcareous skeletal fragments with calcareous and dolomitized matrix).

2. *90 per cent, or more, dolomite content*—The simple name *dolomite* is used to designate a relatively textureless rock composed of more than 90 per cent dolomite. Where a relict limestone texture can be recognized, the limestone textural name with the prefix *dolomitized* is given in parentheses following the rock name, *dolomite.*

   Example—*dolomite* (dolomitized oölitic limestone).

Textural variations.—Calcareous dolomites are illustrated in Plate VIII-*A*-*C*. In most cases, where these rocks represent a stage in the dolomitization of limestones, the limestone texture is much obscured. However, it is commonly possible to recognize unaltered calcareous grains, such as skeletal fragments, and these are listed as such in parentheses following the general name of calcareous dolomite.

Pure dolomite rock types are illustrated in Plate VIII-*D*-*L*. Dolomitized limestone refers to those rock types or portions of rocks, now completely dolomite, in which limestone textures are recognizable. Dolomitized oölites, pellets, and lumps are commonly recognizable (Plate VIII-*J*, *K*). Skeletal remains may be seen converted to dolomite (Plate VIII-*L*)—especially certain types of algae. Commonly, the former presence of skeletal grains is indicated by molds in the dolo-

→

Explanation of Plate VIII

DOLOMITIC ROCK TYPES

A. Calcareous dolomite (oölitic).—Composed of coarse-grained oölites and very fine-grained dolomite crystals with up to 3 per cent micritic limestone and calcite cement. Etched section. Mississippian Mission Canyon fm., Park Co., Wyoming, ×4.

B. Same as A, but a thin section photograph instead of an etched sample photo, ×8.

C. Calcareous dolomite (calcitic skeletal grains).—Contains skeletal fragments, irregular pellets, molds of fossil debris, and coarsely micrograined dolomite rhombs. Etched sample. Mississippian Charles fm., Big Horn Co., Wyoming, ×4.

D. Medium-grained dolomite with rhombic texture.—Porous network of medium grained euhedral to subhedral dolomite rhombs. Jurassic Arab fm., Saudi Arabia, ×8.

E. Very fine-grained dolomite with mosaic texture.—Tightly packed mosaic of dolomite crystals. Ordovician Ellenburger fm., Travis Co., Texas, ×8.

F. Finely micrograined dolomite.—Texturally uniform, relatively pure dolomite with average crystal size of 0.03 mm. Mississippian Charles fm., Park Co., Wyoming, ×8.

G. Dolomite breccia.—Angular to subangular dolomite fragments in a matrix of micrograined dolomite crystals. Mississippian Mission Canyon fm., Big Horn Co., Wyoming, ×8.

H. Laminated dolomite.—Laminae microfaulted in photograph. Laminae contain quartz silt grains. Anhedral interlocking finely micrograined dolomite rhombs. Mississippian Charles fm., Big Horn Co., Wyoming, ×8.

I. Dolomite with fossil molds—Vuggy, coarsely micrograined dolomite. Vugs are end product of leaching of fossils. Molds of crinoid and shell debris. Pennsylvanian Hermosa fm., San Juan Co., Utah, ×8.

J. Dolomitized oölitic limestone.—Very fine-grained dolomite with relict coarse-grained oölites, and very fine-grained pellets. Mississippian Lodgepole fm., Park Co., Wyoming, ×8.

K. Dolomitized algal-lump limestone.—Relict clastic texture showing composite grains roughly concentric (algal lumps) in a matrix of relict pellets. Vuggy porosity. Permian Capitan fm., Winkler Co., Texas, ×8.

L. Dolomitized skeletal-oölitic limestone.—Porous dolomite with relict coarse-grained oölites and relict medium-grained Foraminifera. Pennsylvanian Hermosa fm., San Juan Co., Utah, ×8.

DOLOMITIC ROCK TYPES

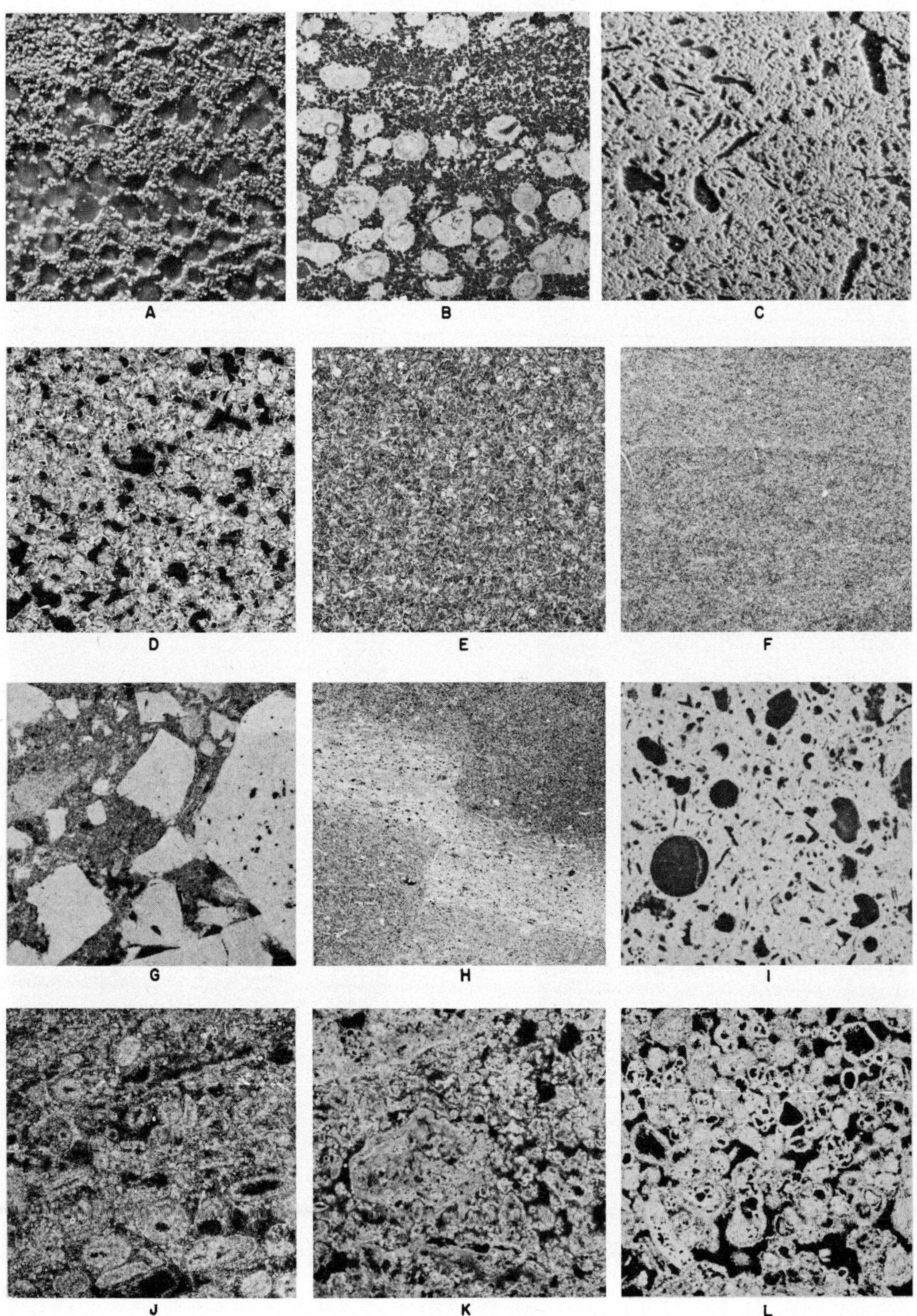

Plate VIII

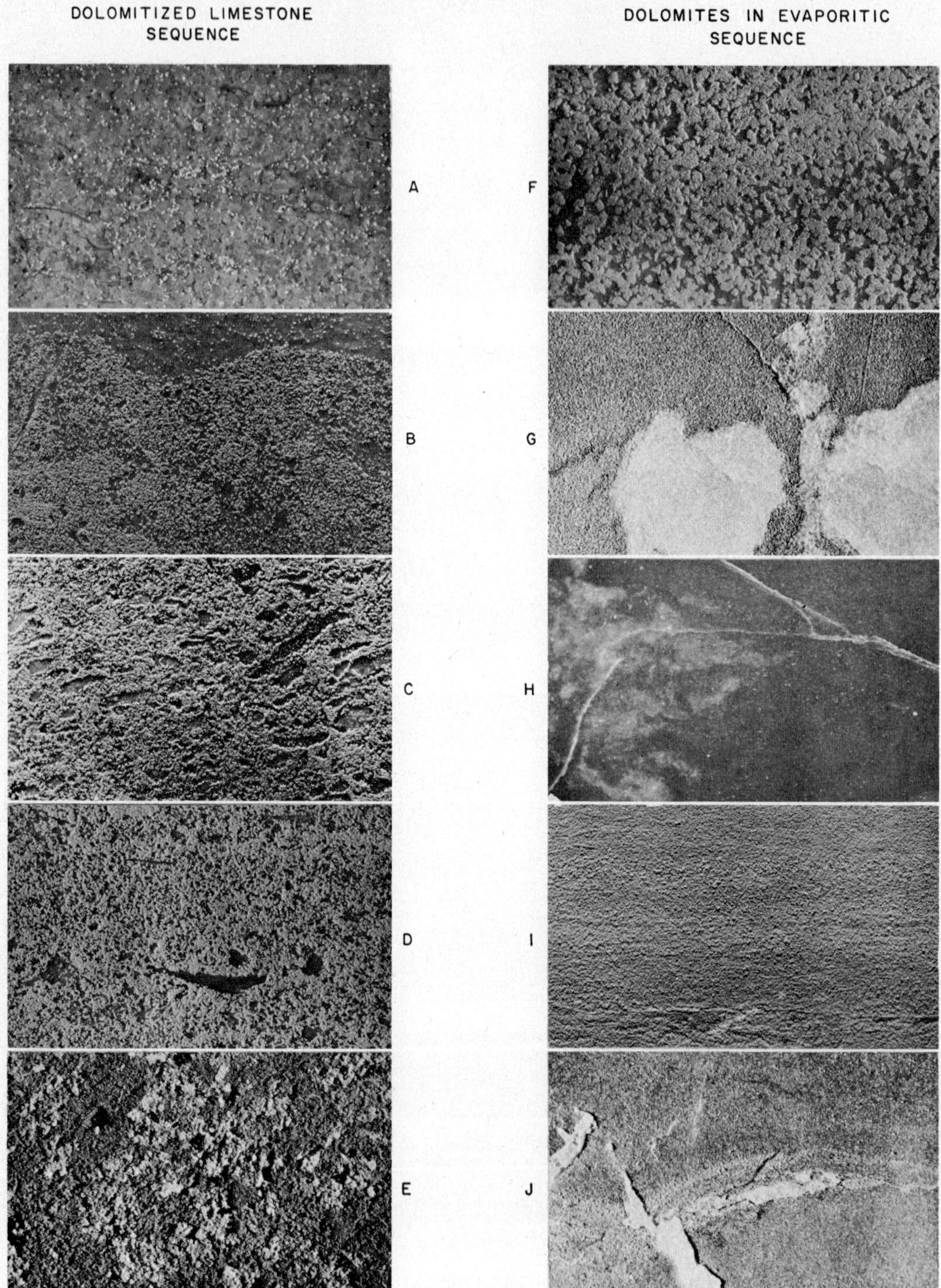
DOLOMITE SEQUENCES
DOLOMITIZED LIMESTONE SEQUENCE
DOLOMITES IN EVAPORITIC SEQUENCE
A
B
C
D
E
F
G
H
I
J

PLATE IX

mitized rocks (Plates VIII-*I*). Dolomitized limestones are commonly the end product of a sequence—limestone-dolomitic limestone-calcareous dolomite-dolomitized limestone. In cases where relict textures are not seen, the presence of a dolomite in such a sequence suggests that it is a dolomitized limestone.

In naming the dolomite types, a prefix indicating average size of dolomite crystals may be added to the word dolomite for otherwise relatively featureless dolomite types (Plate VIII-*D*, *E*, and *F*). Descriptive terms such as sucrosic (or rhombic) and mosaic can be added as modifiers, either before or after the name—for example, sucrosic, fine-grained dolomite or dolomite with mosaic texture. Other commonly observed dolomite types are dolomite breccias (Plate VIII-*G*), and laminated dolomites (Plate VIII-*H*). The finely micrograined dolomites (Plate VIII-*F*) and these last three types are commonly associated with evaporitic sequences; they may contain anhydrite and authigenic quartz crystals, and are generally nonporous.

Genetic implications.—In spite of attempts to avoid genetic implications in naming dolomites and dolomitic rocks, it is impossible to do so completely. An example is the use of the term "dolomitized limestone." In addition, the association of finely micrograined dolomites, laminated dolomites, and dolomitic breccias with anhydrite, chert, and microcrystalline micritic limestone, has led to the use of the term *dolomites in evaporitic sequences* for the grouping. These dolomites are similar to those described as "evaporitic dolomites" in the literature (Eadie, 1956). This avoids the controversial name "primary."

As implied in the above section, there appear to be at least two distinct groups of dolomitic rocks, based on textural character and rock associations—those referred to as dolomites in evaporitic sequences and those that are clearly the product of dolomitization of limestones. The characteristics of each group are listed in Table II and a typical sequence of each type is shown in Plate IX.

SUMMARY AND CONCLUSIONS

A classification of limestones, based on measurable rock features, is presented. Although the classification is descriptive and objective, it is believed to have environmental significance in that the textural bases of the classification are strongly influenced by depositional processes, both in theory and in observed natural situations. The rock types defined by this classification can be recognized by experienced geologists in the field and on the well with simple examination techniques. The groups or types of limestones should be modified or subdivided as required for more detailed studies. Application of the classification and the nomenclature system has led to a better understanding of the make-up of limestones, and to more precise and standardized terminology for limestone sequences in Standard Oil of New Jersey operating areas. In addition, the classification may be used as a guide to indicate some of the

---

←

Explanation of Plate IX

DOLOMITE SEQUENCES

Typical sequences are illustrated of the two groups—dolomitized limestones, and dolomites in evaporitic sequences. Photos are of etched samples, ×4.

A. Oölitic limestone with skeletal debris. Dolomite content = 2 per cent.
B. Dolomitic lump limestone. Band with dolomite content = 20 per cent, in wavy contact with limestone containing 2 per cent dolomite.
C. Dolomitic lump limestone. Dolomite content = 40 per cent.
D. Dolomitic lump-skeletal limestone. Dolomite content = 25 per cent.
E. Dolomite with fossil molds. More than 90 per cent dolomite, and very porous.
F. Dolomitic micritic limestone (microcrystalline type). Dolomite content = 30 per cent.
G. Dolomite with large patches of anhydrite. Rhombs tightly interlocked.
H. Micritic limestone (microcrystalline type). Patches of sparry calcite grade textually into main part of rock. Trace of anhydrite.
I. Finely micrograined dolomite. Weakly laminated.
J. Micritic limestone with thin laminae of finely micrograined dolomite. Anhydrite and chert veins.

TABLE II. CHARACTERISTICS OF DOLOMITE GROUPS

Dolomites in Evaporitic Sequences	*Dolomitized Rocks*
Generally finely micrograined	May be very coarse grained
Associated with anhydrite, chert, and microcrystalline micritic limestone	Associated with limestone sequences
May be laminated or brecciated	May contain fossil molds
Contain no relict limestone texture	Commonly contain relict limestone textures and belong to gradational sequences showing increased development of dolomite

major textural types of limestones that need to be considered in mapping sedimentary patterns which in turn may offer a key for contouring porosity trends.

As with the limestones, dolomite rock types commonly repeat themselves in rocks of different ages and in different geographic locations. The characterization of two major dolomite groups, for example, dolomites in evaporitic sequences and dolomites resulting from the replacement of limestones, offers the geologist additional comparative data for assessing the history of a dolomitic sequence.

The naming system for both dolomites and limestones must be kept flexible to allow for the detailed variations that occur with geologic time and with the location. The present system of grouping, naming, and describing carbonate rock types has evolved as new information on them was revealed by detailed studies in a number of areas. It is expected that such evolution will continue.

REFERENCES

American Geological Institute, 1957, Glossary of Geology and related sciences, J. V. Howell, ed.: Natl. Acad. Sci.-Natl. Resch. Council Pub. 501.

Bathurst, R. G. C., Diagenetic fabrics in some British Dinantian limestones: Liverpool and Manchester Geol. Jour., v. 2, pt. 1, p. 11–36.

Black, Maurice, 1933, The algal sediments of Andros Island, Bahamas: Royal Soc. London Philos. Trans., Ser. B, v. 222, p. 165–192.

Chayes, Felix, 1949, A simple point counter for thin-section analysis: Am. Mineralogist, v. 34, no. 1, p. 1–11.

Cumings, E. R., 1932, Reefs or bioherms?: Geol. Soc. America Bull., v. 43, no. 1, p. 331–352.

Daetwyler, C. C., and Kidwell, A. L., 1959, The Gulf of Batabona, a modern carbonate basin: 5th World Petrol. Cong., New York, Proc. Sec. I, p. 1–21.

DeFord, Ronald K., 1946, Grain size in carbonate rocks: Am. Assoc. Petroleum Geologists, v. 30, no. 11, p. 1921–1928.

Eardley, A. J., 1938, Sediments of Great Salt Lake, Utah: Am. Assoc. Petroleum Geologists Bull., v. 22, no. 10, p. 1305–1411.

Edie, R. W., 1956, Origin and characteristics of evaporitic dolomites: Alberta Soc. Petroleum Geologists Jour., v. 4, p. 16–23.

Fairbridge, R. W., 1950, Recent and Pleistocene coral reefs of Australia: Jour. Geology, v. 58, no. 4, p. 330–401.

Folk, R. L., 1959, Practical petrographic classification of limestones: Am. Assoc. Petroleum Geologists Bull., v. 43, no. 1, p. 1–38.

Ginsburg, R. N., 1956, Environmental relationships of grain size and constituent particles in some South Florida carbonate sediments: Am. Assoc. Petroleum Geologists Bull., v. 40, no. 10, p. 2384–2427.

——— 1957, Early diagenesis and lithification of shallow-water carbonate sediments in south Florida, *in* Regional aspects of carbonate deposition: Soc. Econ. Paleont. and Mineral. Spec. Pub. No. 5, p. 80–99.

Grabau, A. W., 1913, Principles of stratigraphy: New York, A. G. Seiler and Co.

Himus, G. W., 1954, A dictionary of geology: Baltimore, Md., Penguin Books.

Holmes, A., 1928, The nomenclature of petrology with references to selected literature, 2d ed.: London, Murby, 284 p.

Illing, L. V., 1954, Bahaman calcareous sands: Am. Assoc. Petroleum Geologists Bull., v. 38, no. 1, p. 1–95.

Krumbein, W. C., and Sloss, L. L., 1951, Stratigraphy and sedimentation: San Francisco, W. H. Freeman and Co.

Krynine, P. D., 1948, The megascopic study and field classification of sedimentary rocks: Jour. Geology, v. 56, no. 2, p. 130–165.

Lowenstam, H. A., 1955, Aragonite needles secreted by algae and some sedimentary implications: Jour. Sed. Petrology, v. 25, no. 4, p. 270–272.

Lyell, Charles, 1840, Principles of geology, 6th ed.: London, John Murray.

McKee, E. D., 1949, Geology of Kapingamarangi Atoll, Caroline Islands, *in* Scientific investigations in Micronesia: Pacific Sci. Board, Natl. Resch. Council.

Newell, N. D., and Rigby, J. K., 1957, Geological studies on the Great Bahama Bank, *in* Regional aspects of carbonate deposition: Soc. Econ. Paleont. and Mineral. Spec. Pub. No. 5, p. 15–72.

Payne, T. G., Stratigraphical analysis and environmental reconstruction: Am. Assoc. Petroleum Geologists Bull., v. 26, no. 11, p. 1697–1770.

Pettijohn, F. J., 1949, Sedimentary rocks: New York, Harper and Bros.; 2d ed., 1957.

Rodgers, John, 1954, Terminology of limestone and related rocks—an interim report: Jour. Sed. Petrology, v. 24, no. 4, p. 225–234.

Thornbury, W. D., 1954, Principles of geomorphology: New York, John Wiley and Sons, p. 480–481.
Wentworth, C. K., 1922, A scale of grade and class terms for clastic sediments: Jour. Geology, v. 30, no. 5, p. 377–392.
Winston, J. C., 1947, The Winston dictionary, encyclopedia ed.: Philadelphia, The John C. Winston Co.

APPENDIX A

GLOSSARY

The glossary defines the terms commonly used to describe carbonate rocks. It is not intended as a complete listing of all rock terms.

Allogenic. Term meaning generated elsewhere; applied to those constituents that came into existence outside of, and previous to, the rock of which they are now a part; for example, the pebbles of a limestone conglomerate. Compare **authigenic.** (Holmes, 1928.)

Anhedral. Refers to individual crystals devoid of crystal boundaries or faces. (Pettijohn, 1957.)

Articulate. Refers to fossils having two or more parts joined together in their natural relationship; for example, valves of mollusks or brachiopods or columnals of crinoids.

Authigenic. Generated on the spot; applied to those constituents that came into existence with or after the formation of the rock of which they are a part; for example, the cements of sedimentary rocks. Compare **allogenic.** (Holmes, 1928.)

Bioherm. An organic reef or mound built by corals, stromatoporoids, gastropods, echinoderms, foraminifera, pelecypods, and other organisms. (After Thornbury, 1954.)

Biostrome. Term for stratiform deposits, such as shell beds, crinoid beds, and coral beds, consisting of, and built mainly by, organisms or fragments of organisms, and not swelling into moundlike or lenslike forms. (After Cumings, 1932.)

Breccia. A rock made up of angular rock fragments, most of which are larger than 2.0 mm diameter.

Brecciated. Refers to a rock that has been converted into, or resembles, a breccia. (Webster's Collegiate Dictionary, 1943, 5th edition.)

Calcarenite. Mechanically deposited carbonate rocks consisting of sand size carbonate grains (1/16 to 2 mm diameter). (After Pettijohn, 1957.)

Calcilutite. Refers to a rock composed of more than 50% silt and clay size carbonate particles. (After Pettijohn, 1957.)

Caliche. A lime-rich deposit, generally gravel, sand, or desert debris, cemented by porous calcium carbonate, and formed in the soils of certain semi-arid regions.

Carbonate rocks. Rocks composed of more than 50%, by weight, of carbonate minerals. For practical microscopic work, area percentages, which approximate weight percentages, are used because they are easier to estimate and measure.

Cement. Clear, crystalline material occurring in the interstices between grains and matrix material. Crystal size is generally greater than 0.031 mm.

Chalk. A porous, fine textured, and somewhat friable variety of limestone, normally light colored. (Pettijohn, 1957.)

Clastic particles or grains. Particles of either fragmental or chemical origin that have been rolled around before coming to rest in a sediment. (After Krynine, 1948.)

Clastic textured. Having a texture that shows evidence, such as cross-stratification or size sorting of particles, that the sediment was deposited mechanically. (Rodgers, 1954.) Compare with **nonclastic textured.**

Coated grains. Grains possessing concentric or enclosing layers of calcium carbonate; for example, oölites, pisolites, superficial oölites, and algal-encrusted skeletal grains.

Conglomerate. A consolidated accumulation of pebbles, cobbles, or boulders.

Coquina. Carbonates consisting wholly, or nearly so, of mechanically sorted fossil debris. Most commonly applied to the more or less cemented coarse shell debris. For the finer shell detritus of sand size of less, the term *microcoquina* is more appropriate. (Pettijohn, 1957.)

Cryptograined. A size term referring to particles of clay size—those less than .004 mm diameter.

Crystalline texture. Refers to a texture characterized by interlocking particles, many of which have crystal faces or boundaries. (Krumbein and Sloss, 1951.)

Dense. Compact. (Webster, 1943); having its parts crowded together. (Winston, 1947.)

Detrital limestone. Limestone formed from the debris of older rocks. (Cole, 1912, cited in A.G.I., 1957, p. 79.) *Detrital* is used to refer to rocks, such as breccias and conglomerates, that are composed of fragments of pre-existing rocks. Lyell (1840) defined detrital as debris derived from pre-existing rocks. *Petroclastic limestone* is considered synonymous with detrital limestone.

Dolomite. A carbonate rock composed of more than 50%, by weight, of the mineral dolomite. For practical microscopic work, areal percentages are used instead of weight percentages.

Dolomitic. Where used in a rock name **"dolomitic"** refers to those rocks that contain 10%–50% of the mineral dolomite. *Dolomitic* can also be used as a general term applying to a group of rocks that are dolomite bearing.

Dolomitized. Refers to rocks or portions of rocks in which limestone textures are discernible, but which have been converted to dolomite.

Euhedral. Refers to individual crystals exhibiting crystal boundaries or faces. (Pettijohn, 1957.)

Fragmental. Refers to broken or detached debris. Detrital fragments and fragments derived from the skeletons of organisms, are included under this definition.

Grains. Discrete particles larger than 0.031 mm. They may form the rock framework, similar to sand grains in a sandstone, or they may be subordinate to smaller particles in the rock.

Grain size. A term relating to the size of grains. (*See* above.)

Granular. Applied to sedimentary rocks made up of grains. (A.G.I., 1957.)

Limestone. A carbonate rock composed of more than 50%, by weight, of the mineral calcite. (For practical microscopic work, areal percentages are used instead of weight percentages.)

Lithographic. Pertaining to a compact carbonate rock having about the same particle size and textural appearance as the stone used in lithography. (DeFord, 1946.) Characterized by conchoidal fracture.

Lumps. In recent sediments, "lumps" are composite grains typically possessing superficial re-entrants and believed to have formed by a process of aggregation. (After Illing, 1954.) In ancient sediments, the "composite grain character" may not be easily distinguishable; however, the following criteria are useful in recognizing these grains —(1) lobate outline, reflecting superficial re-entrants, (2) grains texturally similar to the material in which they occur, (3) rock association.

Matrix. The natural material in which any fossil, pebble, crystal, etc., is embedded. (Webster, 1943; A.G.I., 1957.) If the particles in the rock are of different orders of size magnitude, the term matrix is used for the smaller individual units that fill the interstices between the larger grains. (Krynine, 1948.)

Mechanical. Pertaining to particles of sediment brought to their place of final deposition by agents such as water currents, wind currents, or gravity; for example, shell sand, aragonite needle mud. (Rodgers, 1954.)

Micrite. Consolidated or unconsolidated ooze or mud of either chemical or mechanical origin. (For practical purposes, micritic material consists of particles less than approximately 0.031 mm diameter). (Modified from Folk, 1959.)

Micritic limestone. A limestone of 90% or more micrite. *Microclastic* and *microcrystalline* limestones are two varieties of micritic limestone, the former possessing a clastic texture and the latter a texture of microscopically interlocking crystals. *Aphanitic limestone*, *matrix limestone*, and *calcilutite* are practically synonymous with *micritic limestone*.

Micrograined. A grain-size term pertaining to carbonate particles smaller than 0.0625 mm and larger than .004 mm diameter. Comparable to silt sizes in quartzose sediments. *Coarsely micrograined* is a grain-size term referring to particles ranging from approximately 0.03 to 0.06 mm diameter. *Finely micrograined* refers to particles less than 0.03 mm diameter to clay size (cryptograined) particles.

Nonclastic textured. Having a texture showing no evidence that the sediment was deposited mechanically. (Rodgers, 1954.) Compare with **clastic textured.**

Nonmechanical. Pertaining to sediment formed at its place of final deposition, as by chemical precipitation or organic secretion—for example, travertine; organic reef deposits made of corals and calcareous algae in position of growth. (Rodgers, 1954.)

Oölite. Small spherical or subspherical accretionary grain generally less than 2.0 mm diameter. In section, oölites display concentric structure and may exhibit radial structure. (After Pettijohn, 1957.)

Superficial oölite—A type of oölite in which the thickness of the accretionary coating is less than the radius of the nucleus.

Organic structures. Whole or fragmentary remains of fossil organisms.

Pellet. A grain composed of micritic material, lacking significant internal structure and generally ovoid in shape. Most pellets in limestones are very fine sand to coarse silt size grains.

Pisolite. A grain type similar to an oölite, and generally 2 mm or more diameter. Pisolites are less regular in form than oölites and commonly crenulated. (After Himus, 1954.)

Recrystallization. A term signifying a process wherein original crystal units of a particular size and morphology become converted into crystal units with different grain size or morphology, but the mineral species remains identical before and after the process occurs. (After Folk, 1959.)

Recrystallization calcite. Those patchy mosaics of calcite crystals which interrupt or replace a finer grained calcite fabric.

Reef. A structure erected by framebuilding or sediment-binding organisms. At the time of deposition, the structure was a wave-resistant or potentially wave-resistant topographic feature.

Skeletal. Pertaining to debris derived from organisms that secrete hard material around or within organic tissue. The term *bioclastic* is considered to be synonymous with *skeletal*.

Sparry. Refers to clear, transparent or translucent, readily cleavable, crystalline particles generally having an interlocking mosaic texture.

Spherulite. Applied to minute bodies of oölitic nature in which only a radial structure is visible. The surfaces of such bodies, unlike those of oölites, are somewhat irregular. (Pettijohn, 1957.)

Subhedral. Refers to individual crystals exhibiting a few crystal boundaries. (Pettijohn, 1957.)

Sucrosic. Sugary. Generally applied to certain types of dolomites.

Travertine. A fairly dense, banded deposit of $CaCO_3$ especially common in caverns, and formed by evaporation of spring and river waters. (Pettijohn, 1957.)

Tufa. A spongy, porous rock which forms a thin surficial deposit about springs and rivers. It has a reticulate structure and is weak, semifriable, and limited in extent.

APPENDIX B

TEXTURAL AND MINERAL COMPOSITION OF SELECTED CARBONATE ROCK TYPES

Plate No.	Name	Serial No.	Textural Components (per cent)										Grain-Micrite Ratio	Mineral Composition (per cent)				
			Micrite	Detrital and Mineral Grains	Skeletal Grains	Pellets	Lumps	Oölites and Superficial Oölites	Encrusted Grains and Pisolites	Framebuilders	Cement	Other (Vein Filling, Chert, Dolo. Rhombs)		Calcite	Dolomite	Insoluble Residue		
																Quartz	Clay	Other
III-*A*	Micritic ls.	780-A	96	3	1	0	0	0	0	0	0	0	.04	96	0	3	2	1
III-*B*	Micritic ls.	1854	Visual estimate										<0.1	92	Tr		8.2	
III-*D*	Detrital-micritic ls.	2927	14	80	0	0	0	0	0	0	0	6[a]	5.7	Visual estimate				
II	Detrital-micritic ls.	2942	48	51	1	0	0	0	0	0	0	0	1.1	Visual estimate				
III-*G, H*	Skeletal-micritic ls.	2955	47	0	49	0	0	0	0	0	0	4[b]	1.0	Visual estimate				
III-*I, J*	Skeletal ls.	1349	0	2	74	0	0	7	0	0	17	0	∞	98	0		2.2	
IV-*A*	Skeletal ls.	1348	0	0	51	0	19	3	0	0	27	0	∞	99	0		0.7	
IV-*B*	Skeletal ls.	850	1	4	49	0	0	12	0	0	34	0	65	92	1	2	1	0.5
III-*K*	Crinoidal ls.	795	Visual estimate										>9.0	93+	1	—	—	—
III-*N*	Ls. with algal segments	1105	3.5	0	54.5	0	33	0	0	0	7.5	1.5[c,f]	27	Visual estimate				
III-*L*	Foraminiferal-detrital ls.	2815	0	30	35	0	0	0	0	0	35	0	∞	Visual estimate				
IV-*C, D*	Pellet-micritic ls.	852	10	2	6	46	0	0	0	0	36	0	5.2	94	0	1	1	0.5
VII-*A*	Pellet-micritic ls.	1736	13	0	17	40	0	0	0	0	29	0	4.4	99+	0		0.17	
IV-*F, G*	Lump ls.	1743	9	0	27	0	55	0	0	0	9	0	9.1	99.5	0		0.52	
IV-*H*	Lump ls.	1787	5	0	1	0	74	0	0	0	16	4[c]	15	89	10		0.79	
IV-*J*	Oölitic-micritic ls.	5947	37	0	tr.	0	0	63	0	0	tr.	0	1.7	Visual estimate				
IV-*K*	Oölitic ls.	1741	0	0	0.5	3.5	0	71	0	0	25	0	∞	99+	0		0.77	
IV-*L*	Superficial oölitic ls.	861	2	15	12	2	0	40	0	0	29	0	35	Visual estimate				
V-*F*	Micritic-skeletal-pellet ls.	856	45	1	17	13	0	0	0	0	20	4[c]	.69	Visual estimate				
V-*C, D*	Coralline ls.	1086	4	0	3.5	34.5		0	0	47.5	10.5	0	21.4[d]	99+	0		0.11	
V-*E*	Algal ls.	1337	Visual estimate										—	85	7		8.2	
VIII-*A, B*	Calcareous dolo.	1804	3?	0	0	0	0	36	0	0	3?	58[c]	—	47	53		0.06	
VIII-*C*	Calcareous dolo.	1087	0	0	30	0	0	0	0	0	0	70[c]	—	42	57		1.11	
VIII-*E*	Fine-grained dolo.	843	Visual estimate										—	2	90	—	—	5
VIII-*F*	Finely micrograined dolo.	1735	Visual estimate										—	0	98		2.3	
VIII-*H*	Laminated micrograined dolo.	1545	Visual estimate										—	0	95		5.4	
VIII-*J*	Dolomitized oölitic ls.	1993	0?	0	0	30[e]	4[e]	38	0	0	0	28[c]	—	0	95		5.3	

Note.—Point-count data and dolomite-calcite analyses are rounded off to nearest whole number. Textural components were established by point-count methods in thin sections. Calcite and dolomite mineral were determined by X-ray analysis on bulk samples. Insoluble residues were determined after HCl treatment except for 780-A and 850 which were determined by X-ray methods.

[a] Calcite veins
[b] Chert
[c] Dolomite
[d] Computed as % (Grain+Framebuilders)/%Micrite
[e] Dolomitized-relict grains
[f] Calcite mosaics

SPECTRAL SUBDIVISION OF LIMESTONE TYPES[1]

ROBERT L. FOLK[2]
Austin, Texas

ABSTRACT

In the writer's previous classification of limestones, rocks were divided into three major families. A more sensitive division can be made into eight groups forming a complete spectrum of textural types, representing deposition in environments of different physical energy. Basis for the classification is (1) relative proportion of allochems and carbonate mud, (2) sorting of allochems, and (3) rounding of allochems. A complete parallel exists between these limestone types and the sequence of textural maturity in sandstones, even to the existence of textural inversions. However, rounding appears to be accomplished best in environments where the energy level is too great for good sorting.

INTRODUCTION

The limestone classification discussed herein was developed by the writer in essentially its present form in 1948, and used throughout thesis work on the Beekmantown rocks of central Pennsylvania (Folk, 1952). It has been continually tested in teaching and in graduate research at The University of Texas since 1953, was presented orally at the A.A.P.G. meetings in St. Louis (April, 1957), and was published nearly three years ago (Folk, 1959). A decade of experience has shown that the classification is comprehensive, simple to learn, and can be very fruitfully used by a beginning, non-specialized graduate student as well as by an experienced sedimentary petrographer. The present paper is not going to propose any changed classification of carbonates or lay down a second barrage of hybrid words. It is included in this work simply as a matter of completeness, so that all current carbonate classifications may be united in one volume. The first part of this paper is largely a skeleton summary of parts of the 1959 classification, and the reader is referred to that publication for details, photomicrographs, presentation of evidence, environmental significance, and the like. The rest of this paper consists of amplification of several facets of the system, more in the nature of adjectival methods of rock description, rather than classification.

The basic philosophy of this classification is that carbonate rocks are essentially similar to sandstones and shales in their method of deposition. Their textures are controlled largely by the current or wave regimen at the site of deposition, because their mode of accumulation is the same as that of other mechanical sediments. An area of vigorous current action usually produces well-winnowed calcarenites, with large amounts of pore space that later is filled by crystallization of clear, sparry calcite cement. These correspond to the sandstones or conglomerates that occur along beaches or high-energy zones, which are winnowed rocks with pore spaces similarly filled with chemical cements (calcite, quartz, etc.). Areas of sluggish currents generally contain much lime mud, with or without admixed fossils or other carbonate aggregates; these ordinarily have no large open pores, hence no sparry calcite, and result in the dense-matrixed calcilutite or "lithographic" limestones. These correspond to the terrigenous shales or clayey sandstones, which similarly have very little chemically precipitated cement. This general philosophy appears to be followed by nearly all modern limestone classifications and the fact that it has been evolved independently in widely different areas (for example, Bramkamp and Powers, 1958, for Arabian carbonates) indicates that the philosophic concept is indeed a valid one. The only differences are matters of where to draw the boundary lines between classes, and what to call the several types. These arguments are really immaterial, for what matters is how well the rock is *described;* classification is simply a convenient handle, and if everyone would describe rocks in a systematic and uniform way, each worker with his own cherished scheme could give it whatever pet name he likes.

[1] Part of a symposium arranged by the Research Committee, and presented at Denver, Colorado, April 27, 1961, under joint auspices of the Association and the Society of Economic Paleontologists and Mineralogists. Manuscript received, April 12, 1961.

[2] The University of Texas.

THE MAJOR CONSTITUENTS OF LIMESTONES

Disregarding admixture of terrigenous sand or clay, and replacement by dolomite, chert, etc., limestones are made up of three end members—(1) discrete carbonate aggregates, or "allochems," analogous to the sand or gravel grains of terrigenous rocks, (2) microcrystalline calcite ooze, analogous to the clay in a shale or clay matrix in a sandstone, and (3) sparry calcite, normally a chemically precipitated, pore-filling cement, like the cement in a "clean" sandstone.

ALLOCHEMS

A collective word is needed to embrace all the organized carbonate aggregates that make up the bulk of many limestones. "Particles" or "grains" are not precise enough as these words can refer to isolated single crystal units; a specific word is needed for a specific purpose. The writer proposes "allochem"—"allo-" meaning "out of the ordinary," and "chem" being short for chemical precipitate—to indicate that these are not ordinary chemical precipitates as the chemist thinks of them, but are complexes that have achieved a higher order of organization, and, in nearly all cases, have also undergone transportation. Only four allochem types are volumetrically important in limestones, although there are a few others, such as pisolites and spherulites, that occur rarely. These four are (1) intraclasts, (2) oölites, (3) fossils, and (4) pellets. Fossils (skeletal material) and oölites need no further discussion here, but intraclasts and pellets are more controversial and require some clarification.

Intraclasts.—The term "intraclast" has been used by this writer to describe fragments of penecontemporaneous, generally weakly consolidated carbonate sediment that have been eroded from adjoining parts of the sea bottom and redeposited to form a new sediment (hence the term "intraclast," signifying that they have been reworked from *within* the area of deposition and *within* the same formation). It does *not* refer to single fossils, oölites, or pellets momentarily laid down and then picked up, but only to *clusters* of such grains bonded together by welding, by carbonate cement, or lime mud—proving that they had once been a part of a coherent sediment.

Intraclasts may be produced by erosion of sedimentary layers almost immediately after they have been laid down, or under more severe conditions, may be produced by erosion of layers that had become buried some feet below the sea floor. Consequently, the sediment layers from which they are derived can show a complete range of degrees of consolidation or lithification. Some intraclasts are reworked from surficial carbonate mud when that mud is still very plastic and barely cohesive; these on redeposition are generally plastically deformed, and commonly have vague or mashed boundaries. Other early formed intraclasts are the Bahama "grapestone" aggregates of Illing (1954), which are clusters of pellets that have become stuck together by incipient cementation shortly after deposition; these later may be picked up and transported, and thus may show various degrees of abrasion. In this writer's opinion, however, the most common mode of formation of intraclasts is by erosion of portions of a widespread layer of semi-consolidated carbonate sediment, with erosion reaching to depths of a few inches up to a few feet in the bottom sediment. These fragments (which commonly show bedding) are then abraded to rounded or somewhat irregular shapes, and the abraded margin of the intraclast cuts indiscriminately across fossils, earlier intraclasts, oölites, or pellets that were contained inside the intraclast. This indicates abrasion of intraclasts that had become consolidated enough so that these included objects would wear equally with the matrix. These intraclasts could be formed either by submarine erosion (such as might be caused by storm waves or underwater slides), by mild tectonic upwarps of the sea floor, or by low tides allowing wave attack on exposed, mud-cracked, carbonate flats. Specifically *excluded* are fragments of consolidated limestone eroded from ancient limestone outcrops on an emergent land area.

Intraclasts range from very fine sand size to pebble or boulder size, as in the familiar "edgewise" limestone conglomerates. Generally, they are well rounded, and the form varies from equant to highly discoidal. Less commonly, they may be subangular to subround, and some may possess irregular protuberances like the "grapestone" of Illing (1954). Intraclasts may be composed of any type of limestone or dolomite; thus many have complex internal structure and contain fossils, oölites, quartz silt, pellets, and previously formed intraclasts—in fact, the internal structure is their most important diagnostic feature. However, some are composed of homogeneous microcrystalline calcite ("lithographic" limestone), and these are difficult to differentiate from pellets if they are smaller than about 0.2 mm.

There is vast confusion in terminology embroiling the ideas of "intraclast," "pellet," "bahamite," "grapestone," "pelletoid," "lump," "lithoclast," "fragment," "pebble," and the like. The writer uses "intraclast" to cover the complete spectrum of reworked contemporaneous carbonate sediment—from material that was reworked from the immediate sea bottom perhaps a few days after original deposition (providing it was coherent enough to remain aggregated), to material torn by deeper erosion of sediment buried perhaps many feet below the surface, so long as it is *not* consolidated into hard rock. Erosion of much older, lithified, hard limestone from carbonate outcrops exposed on land is something else entirely, and produces the terrigenous rock known as a calclithite (Folk, 1959), which is tectonically related to arkose in that it is generally the result of faulting; this process does *not* produce intraclasts, which by definition have to be torn from nearly contemporaneous sediment. In some cases these are difficult to tell apart, but the reworked lithified material can generally be identified by the presence of reworked, much older fossils, associated *angular* chert fragments, evidence of weathering or oxidation, and just plain old geological common sense—particularly if aided by extensive use of field boots. To these, the terms "lithoclast," "pebble," etc., can legitimately apply, because these are *rock* (not sediment) fragments.

Another line of confusion is present between "intraclast" and "grapestone" or "bahamite." Fragments of reworked contemporaneous lime sediment have been recognized in limestones for years by many geologists—a striking example being the edgewise conglomerates so common in lower Paleozoic limestones. Then Illing (1954) discovered carbonate aggregates in the process of formation in the Bahamas, and coined the term "grapestone" for them because these weakly cemented aggregates of pellets had a bumpy outer surface resembling a cluster of grapes. So far, so good—we have one specific type of intraclast whose mode of genesis is well established in Recent environments. Next, Beales (1958) described Paleozoic carbonates in Canada with abundant intraclasts, but implied that they had largely formed by the grapestone method and proposed the term "bahamite" for them. Still later, Murray (1960), in a general discussion of limestone deposition, refers to bahamites and does not even mention intraclasts. In short, we are in danger of the tail wagging the dog—the inclusive term "intraclast," which covers a wide range of particles that originate in many different ways and in many stages of coherence, is being replaced by the distinctly genetic term "bahamite" which should refer to only one specific type of intraclast, important in some stratigraphic sections but generated by only *one* of the many ways in which intraclasts can form. Bahamites or grapestones seem to be the most important type of intraclasts forming in modern limestone environments; but this was by no means true throughout much of the Paleozoic or Mesozoic. "Intraclast" should be used as a broad class term without specifying the precise origin; if the particles have bumpy outer surfaces and look like little-abraded pellet aggregates, then "bahamite" or "grapestone" can be used legitimately for this specific type of intraclast; "plasticlast" (for lime mud torn up while still soft and very mushy) is another type; "pelecypod (or gastropod) cast" is still another; "coprolite," "shelf-edge clast," and "tidal-flat clast" might be other varieties. Many intraclasts cannot be tied down to a specific genesis, especially if they have undergone abrasion to smooth the edges; thus, for most rocks one would have to use the noncommittal word "intraclast," unmodified and untrammeled by any detailed genetic connotations.

Pellets.—These bodies are rounded, spherical to elliptical or ovoid aggregates of microcrystalline calcite ooze, devoid of any internal structure. In any one rock they show a remarkable uniformity of shape and size, ranging in different specimens between 0.03 mm and about 0.15 mm, although the most common size is 0.04 to 0.08 mm. This writer follows Hatch and Rastall (1938) and considers them as probably invertebrate fecal pellets because of their constant size, shape, and extra-high content of organic matter. They are distinguished from oölites by lack of radial or concentric structure, and from intraclasts by lack of complex internal structure, uniformity of shape, extremely good sorting, and small size. Generally, with a slight amount of practice, one has no difficulty in identifying them; however, the writer has seen some rocks in which he found it impossible to draw any sharp line between tiny intraclasts and large pellets.

It is possible that some pellet-appearing objects may form by recrystallization processes, a sort of auto-agglutination of once-homogeneous calcareous mud; of such nature may be the "grumeleuse" structure of Cayeux (1935, p. 271). However, nearly all the pellets studied by the writer have been obviously current-laid grains because they are interbedded with quartz silt and generally are delicately laminated and cross-bedded. Some pellets may show vague boundaries; the seeming vagueness of the borders is partly an optical effect due to the small size of the near-spherical pellets and the thickness of the thin section, but in other rocks it is caused by recrystallization of pellets, matrix, or both, to produce microspar, which blurs the boundaries. Pellets are generally richer in organic matter than the surrounding material in the slides, thus showing as brownish objects when convergent light is used; this feature is, in fact, very helpful in recognizing them if they are embedded in a microcrystalline calcite matrix. It is important to emphasize that "pellets," as here used, are very tiny and very well sorted, with a distinct upper size limit at about 0.15 mm. *They are invisible in the field*, and also are generally invisible under the binocular microscope, even on etched surfaces; pellet rocks are almost without exception described as "micrite" unless examined in thin section or by acetate peel. The so-called "pellets" or "pelletoid limestones," as seen in the field, are, in almost all cases, made up of small, well sorted, equant, rounded intraclasts—not true pellets.

A few lithified limestones and many Recent carbonate sediments contain well sorted, equant to rodlike, well rounded, homogeneous lumps of lime mud 0.2 mm to 1 mm long. These lack the complex internal structure of most intraclasts, and further, are too uniform in size and shape; yet they are too big for the pellets as defined above, and as defined by Hatch and Rastall (1938). Although probably coprolites, it is often difficult in ancient limestones to establish firmly the fecal origin, especially if these particles have become abraded. Thus, in composition counts, the writer would arbitrarily class them together with intraclasts in order to preserve a purely descriptive, reproducible line at 0.2 mm between pellets and intraclasts. Uncomfortably, sometimes one must sacrifice a little of the genetic significance in order to gain operator reproducibility.

Pellets as described here are a specific, distinct type of object with a distinct particle size, as will quickly become evident to anyone who studies representative suites of lower Paleozoic rocks. The larger coprolites? are much more rare in lithified, ancient limestones, and in few, if any, instances do they make up a large portion of the rock volume. If they *were* abundant in some specimen, one might coin a new rock name for them. (This author would be reluctant to suggest "coprosparite" and "copromicrite," but those who like a neat pigeonhole for everything can use these words, if they dare.) Fundamentally, the distinction between pellets and intraclasts is a *descriptive* one; pellets are particles of a given size, shape, sorting, and lack internal structure; anything *over* a given size, or with complex internal structure, is called an intraclast instead. However, the writer feels strongly that nearly all pellets do originate in one way, that is, as fecal matter of (probably) a particular group of invertebrates; and although bodies of many diverse origins are grouped as intraclasts (even including the rare large coprolites), one type—that reworked from lithified, much older carbonate beds—is specifically excluded. In this way the term "intraclast" does acquire a slight genetic taint—that is, one should be able to show that the material was essentially unlithified, and nearly contemporaneous, when it was reworked.

MICROCRYSTALLINE CALCITE OOZE (MICRITE)

This type of calcite forms grains 1–4 microns in diameter, generally subtranslucent with a faint brownish cast in thin section. In hand specimen, this is the dull and opaque ultra-fine-grained material that forms the bulk of "lithographic" limestones and the matrix of chalk, and may range in color from white through gray, bluish and brownish gray, to nearly black. Single grains under the polarizing microscope appear to be equant and irregularly round, although electron-microscope study by E. Hal Bogardus and J. Stuart Pittman at the University of Texas has shown that some microcrystalline calcite forms polyhedral blocks bounded by sub-planar (crystal?) faces much like the surfaces of novaculite-type chert (Folk and Weaver, 1952). These may have been produced by welding or incipient recrystallization, perhaps the inversion from an original aragonite ooze to calcite. Microcrystalline carbonate ooze is considered as forming very largely by rather rapid chemical or biochemical precipitation in sea water, settling to the bottom, and at times undergoing some later drifting by weak currents. This is analogous with the mode of deposition of snow, which also is precipitated in a fluid medium (the atmosphere), then settles down and either lies where it falls, or may be swept into drifts. It is here considered as a normal chemical precipitate, despite the fact that it may undergo slight drifting; furthermore, some of it may form in place as a diagenetic segregation or concretion.

Certainly some 1- to 4-micron calcite is "dust" produced by abrasion of skeletal debris, hence would not be a chemical precipitate; yet the writer thinks that this dust is normally quantitatively minor, and, in any case, it behaves hydraulically as ordinary ooze. As yet no criteria are known whereby it might be identified in thin section; therefore it is included with ordinary, chemically precipitated ooze in this classification. Microcrystalline ooze, in addition to being the chief constituent of lithographic limestone, also forms the matrix of poorly washed limestones and is aggregated to form pellets, intraclasts, and some unusual oölites.

The term "micrite" was introduced as a contraction of "microcrystalline calcite," to serve (1) in referring to the matrix of microcrystalline calcite as a rock constituent (for example, brachiopods in micrite matrix), (2) as a combining term in the classification of carbonates (for example, "biomicrite"), and (3) to serve alone as the designation for a rock made up almost entirely of microcrystalline calcite. It is both shorter and more specific than the terms "lime mudstone," "calcilutite," or "aphanitic limestone," all of which, if one goes by etymology as well as by field usage, can refer to silt-sized as well as to clay-sized carbonate. "Micrite" refers only to *clay-sized carbonate.* Thus many rocks made of 0.05 mm fecal pellets or finely broken fossil debris could be correctly described in the field as lime mudstone, calcilutite, etc., whereas they would definitely *not* be micrite. A peel or thin section is generally necessary to prove that a rock is a true micrite and not a calcisiltite, although an intelligent estimate, and commonly a correct one, can be made in the field or with binocular microscope.

Sparry calcite cement.—This type of calcite generally forms grains or crystals 10 microns or more in diameter, and is distinguished from microcrystalline calcite by its clarity as well as coarser crystal size. The name *spar* alludes to its relative clarity both in thin section and hand specimens, paralleling the term used by Sander (1951, p. 1, 3). It is difficult to draw a sharp boundary between these two types of calcite that are genetically different; the writer has vacillated at different times between grain-size boundaries of 10, 5, and finally, 4 microns—but drawing the boundary strictly on grain size is not very satisfactory. Clarity is certainly a distinguishing feature between the two types, but clarity in itself is partially a function of the coarser grain size and lack of impurities, and is almost impossible to define quantitatively for practical work. Morphology helps—for example, if the calcite grains encrust allochems in radial fringes, the writer terms them sparry calcite regardless of their precise crystal size—but the differentiation remains very subjective in borderline cases which, fortunately, are uncommon.

Sparry calcite generally forms as a simple pore-filling cement, precipitated in place within the sediment just as salt crystallizes on the walls of a beaker. Grain size of the crystals of spar depends upon size of the pore space and rate of crystallization; in most limestones, the spar averages from 0.02 to 0.10 mm, although crystals of 1 mm or more are not uncommon in limestones with large pore spaces. In some rocks, sparry calcite is not an original precipitate but has formed by recrystallization of finer carbonate grains or microcrystalline calcite.

CLASSIFICATION OF CARBONATE ROCKS

All the six constituents listed above may be mixed in a wide range of proportions to form limestone beds. The problem in classification is one of trying to systematize these variations and attempt to draw quantitative boundaries between types so that the rock names may be reproducible between workers. Many classifications are admirable in principle except that they shy away from trying to draw any quantitative and objective lines; imagine the chaos if a granite were defined as a rock containing "much K-feldspar with some quartz." Precise division lines are commonly arbitrary, but necessary if one is to try to reproduce the results of colleagues.

THREE MAIN LIMESTONE FAMILIES

A practical division into three major limestone families can be made by determining the relative proportions of three end members (1) allochems, (2) microcrystalline ooze, and (3) sparry calcite cement.

Allochems represent the framework of the rock and include the shells, oölites, carbonate pebbles, or pellets that make up the bulk of most limestones. Thus, they are analogous with the quartz sand of a sandstone or the pebbles of a conglomerate. Microcrystalline ooze represents a clay-size "matrix" whose presence signifies lack of vigorous currents, just as the presence of a clay-mineral matrix in a sandstone indicates poor washing. Sparry calcite cement simply fills up pore spaces in the rock where microcrystalline ooze has been washed out or was not available—just as porous, non-clayey sandstones become cemented with chemical precipitates, such as calcite or quartz cement. Thus, the relative proportions of microcrystalline ooze and sparry calcite cement are an important feature of the rock, inasmuch as they show the degree of "sorting" or current strength of the environment—analogous with textural maturity in sandstones. If we plot these two constituents and the allochemical "framework" as three poles of a triangular diagram, as in Figure 1, the field in which normal limestones occur is shown by the shaded area; divisions between the three major textural families of limestone are also shown. A similar field appears if one plots terrigenous rocks on a triangle with the three analogous poles of sand plus silt, clay, and orthochemical cement.

Type I limestones (designated as "Sparry Allochemical rocks") consist chiefly of allochemical constituents cemented by sparry calcite cement. These rocks are equivalent to the well sorted terrigenous conglomerates or sandstones, in that solid particles (here, intraclasts, oölites, fossils, or pellets) have been heaped together by currents powerful or persistent enough to winnow away any microcrystalline ooze that otherwise might have accumulated as a matrix, and the interstitial pores have later been filled by directly precipitated sparry calcite cement. These sparry limestones have textures and structures similar to winnowed terrigenous rocks, for example, cross-bedding and good grain orientation, and may show good sorting and abrasion of grains. The relative proportion of sparry calcite cement and allochems varies within rather restricted limits because of the limitations of packing, since sparry calcite normally does not make a rock in its own right. This limestone type generally forms on beaches, bars, or submarine shoals, but can also form in lower energy areas where for some reason no lime mud is produced or available.

Type II limestones (designated as "Microcrystalline Allochemical rocks") also contain allochems, but here currents were not strong enough or persistent enough to winnow away the microcrystalline ooze, which remains as a matrix; sparry calcite is very subordinate, or lacking, simply because no pore space was available in which it could form. These rocks are equivalent texturally to the clayey sandstones or conglomerates, which also tend to have little chemical cement. In these rocks the restrictions of packing impose a certain maximum on the amount of allochems; yet there is no minimum, and Microcrystalline Allochemical rocks are found with percentages of allochems (intraclasts, oölites, fossils, or pellets) varying continuously from about 80 per cent down to almost nothing (Fig. 1). The reason for this is that microcrystalline

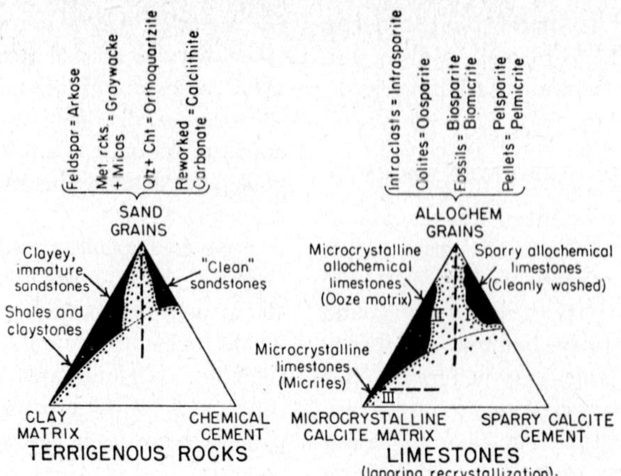

FIG. 1. Diagram comparing limestone classification in this paper with analogous classification of terrigenous rocks. Shaded areas are those parts of composition triangle which occur most commonly.

Terrigenous rocks could be classified by proportions of sand grains (structural framework fraction), clay matrix, and chemical cement, the proportions of the last two being an index to degree of sorting. Non-recrystallized limestone can be classified by the proportion of allochems (structural framework fraction), microcrystalline calcite matrix, and sparry calcite cement, the proportions of the last two also being an index of sorting.

Three basic limestone families are proposed: sparry allochemical limestone (type I), representing good sorting; microcrystalline allochemical limestone (type II), representing poorly winnowed sediments; and microcrystalline limestone (type III), analogous with claystone in terrigenous triangle. Just as one uses composition of sand grains for further classification of terrigenous rocks into arkose, graywacke, orthoquartzite, and calclithite, each ranging from clayey to non-clayey, so one uses composition of allochems for division of limestones into subvarieties such as intrasparite or biomicrite.

ooze can form a rock in its own right (comparable with claystone in the terrigenous series), and can accept any amount of allochem material that becomes mixed with it. Thus the boundary line between *Microcrystalline Allochemical rocks* and *Microcrystalline rocks* is entirely arbitrary, and has been set at 10 per cent allochems.

Type I limestones indicate strong or persistent currents and a high-energy environment, whereas type II limestones indicate weak, short-lived currents or a rapid rate of formation of microcrystalline ooze. Most limestones can be assigned readily to one or the other of these two classes because generally, either sparry calcite or microcrystalline calcite is clearly dominant. In some rocks there are transitions, inasmuch as washing may be incomplete and the ooze may be only partly removed. In normally calm environments with an abundance of ooze, momentary episodes of increased wave or current energy may sort laminae only a millimeter or so thick, whereas adjacent layers will be full of ooze; or a quick swash with rapid redeposition of allochems and small amounts of entrapped ooze may result in pores being partly and irregularly filled with carbonate mud.

In many of these rocks the lime mud has fallen to the bottom of the original pore, producing the "geopetal" structure of Sander (1951). It may be of environmental importance to recognize these poorly washed limestones, as they probably develop in transitional energy zones between the distinct -sparites and -micrites. However, this type is not important enough to warrant any new name as transitions are present between rock types in any classification. As sort of a rule of thumb, the writer uses such terms as "poorly washed biosparite," and "poorly washed intrasparite," where spar and micrite are subequal, for example, where one-third to two-thirds of the interallochem area is spar and the other one-third to two-thirds is micrite (Fig. 4).

Type III limestones (the Microcrystalline rocks) represent the opposite extreme from type I, inasmuch as they consist almost entirely of microcrystalline ooze with little or no allochem material; "lithographic" limestone belongs to this class. These rocks imply both a rapid rate of precipitation of microcrystalline ooze, together with lack of persistent strong currents. Texturally, they correspond with the claystones among the terrigenous rocks; most form in very shallow, sheltered lagoonal areas, or on broad, submerged shelves of little relief and moderate depth where wave action is cut off by the very width of the shelf. Some may also form in deeper offshore areas.

Some microcrystalline rocks have been disturbed either by burrowing organisms or by soft-sediment deformation, and the resulting openings are filled with irregular "eyes" or stringers of sparry calcite ("birds-eye"). Other beds of microcrystalline ooze have been partially torn up by bottom currents and rapidly redeposited, but without the production of distinct intraclasts. These are considered as Disturbed Microcrystalline rocks, and a special symbol and rock term ("dismicrite") is used for them (Table I; Fig. 3). They seem to be quite common in the shallow but protected lagoonal facies of limestones, where burrowers and sudden bottom disturbances are common. Wolf (1960) has pointed out that pelmicrite and biomicrite may also show these disturbed areas; he suggests using "dispellet limestone," but the present writer would prefer to describe these rocks as "disturbed pelmicrite," "disturbed biomicrite," etc. If the disturbance is definitely attributable to burrowing, terms like "burrowed pelmicrite" are preferable.

Parts of some limestones are made up of organic structures growing in place and forming a coherent, resistant mass during growth, as exemplified by parts of many bioherms (Cumings and Shrock, 1928). These rocks, because of their unique mode of genesis, are placed in a special class, type IV, and termed "biolithite" (Table I; Fig. 3). This rock class is very complex and needs much subdivision itself, but no attempt to do so is made in this paper other than to suggest "blue-green algal biolithite," "rudistid biolithite," or "coral biolithite," as examples. It is doubtful if a good, *generally usable* classification of these can be developed; probably it is best simply to give an in-

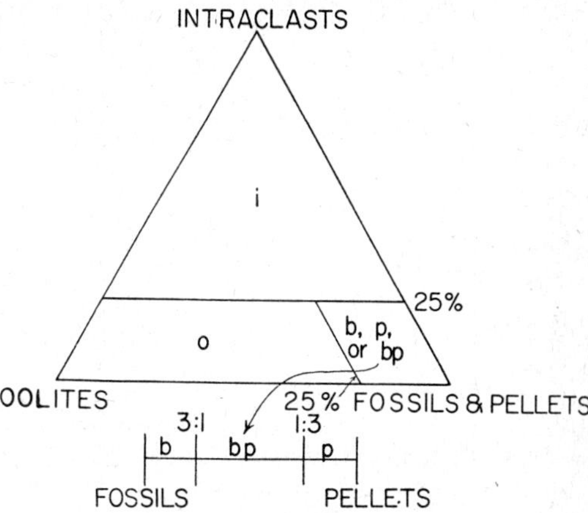

FIG. 2. Triangular diagram to show method of classifying limestones based on volumetric allochem proportion. If allochems consist of more than 25 per cent, by volume, of intraclasts, the rock is *intraclastic* (i) limestone. If there are less than 25 per cent intraclasts, then determine proportion of oölites; if allochems consist of more than 25 per cent oölites, rock is classified as *oölitic* (o) limestone. If rock fits none of these categories, it consists either of pellets or of fossils, and linear scale below triangle is used to name them. If fossil:pellet ratio is more than 3:1, rock is *biogenic* (b) limestone, and if this ratio is less than 1:3, it is *pellet* (p) limestone. Intermediate specimens with subequal pellets and fossils can be termed *biogenic pellet* limestones (bp).

dividual description for each occurrence. If these organic structures are broken up and redeposited, the resulting rock is considered to be made up of biogenic debris, and falls in type I or type II, depending on the interstitial material. The name "biolithite" should be applied only to the rock made of organic structures *in growth position*—not to the debris broken from the bioherm and forming pocket fillings or talus slopes associated with the reef. Study in the field is generally required to ascertain whether a specimen should be termed "biolithite."

SUBDIVISIONS OF MAJOR LIMESTONE FAMILIES

After the main division of limestones into types I, II, and III—based chiefly on amount of winnowing and physical energy of the environment—it is most essential to recognize whether the allochemical part consists of intraclasts, oölites, fossils, or pellets. In terrigenous sandstones, one wants to know not only whether or not the rock has a clay matrix, but also what the composition of the sand is; hence geologists recognize arkoses,

TABLE I. CLASSIFICATION OF CARBONATE ROCKS

Volumetric Allochem Composition	Limestones, Partly Dolomitized Limestones, and Primary Dolomites (see Notes 1 to 6)					Replacement Dolomites[7] (V)	
	>10% Allochems Allochemical Rocks (I and II)		<10% Allochems Microcrystalline Rocks (III)				
	Sparry Calcite Cement >Microcrystalline Ooze Matrix — Sparry Allochemical Rocks (I)	Microcrystalline Ooze Matrix >Sparry Calcite Cement — Microcrystalline Alochemical Rocks (II)	1–10% Allochems (Most Abundant Allochem)	<1% Allochems	Undisturbed Bioherm Rocks (IV)	Allochem Ghosts (Evident Allochem)	No Allochem Ghosts
>25% Intraclasts (i)	Intrasparrudite (Ii:Lr) Intrasparite (Ii:La)	Intramicrudite* (IIi:Lr) Intramicrite* (IIi:La)	Intraclasts: Intraclast-bearing Micrite* (IIIi:Lr or La)	Micrite (IIIm:L); if disturbed, Dismicrite (IIImX:L); if primary dolomite, Dolomicrite (IIIm:D)	Biolithite (IV:L)	Finely Crystalline Intraclastic Dolomite (Vi:D3) etc.	Medium Crystalline Dolomite (V:D4)
<25% Intraclasts; >25% Oölites (o)	Oösparrudite (Io:Lr) Oösparite (Io:La)	Oömicrudite* (IIo:Lr) Oömicrite* (IIo:La)	Oölites: Oölite-bearing Micrite* (IIIo:Lr or La)			Coarsely Crystalline Oölitic Dolomite (Vo:D5) etc.	Finely Crystalline Dolomite (V:D3)
<25% Intraclasts; <25% Oölites; Volume Ratio of Fossils to Pellets >3:1 (b)	Biosparrudite (Ib:Lr) Biosparite (Ib:La)	Biomicrudite (IIb:Lr) Biomicrite (IIb:La)	Fossils: Fossiliferous Micrite (IIIb: Lr, La, or Ll)			Aphanocrystalline Biogenic Dolomite (Vb:Dl) etc.	
<25% Intraclasts; <25% Oölites; Volume Ratio of Fossils to Pellets 3:1–1:3 (bp)	Biopelsparite (Ibp:La)	Biopelmicrite (IIbp:La)	Pellets: Pelletiferous Micrite (IIIp:La)			Very Finely Crystalline Pellet Dolomite (Vp:D2) etc.	
<25% Intraclasts; <25% Oölites; Volume Ratio of Fossils to Pellets <1:3 (p)	Pelsparite (Ip:La)	Pelmicrite (IIp:La)					etc.

NOTES TO TABLE I

* Designates rare rock types.

[1] Names and symbols in the body of the table refer to limestones. If the rock contains more than 10 per cent replacement dolomite, prefix the term "dolomitized" to the rock name, and use DLr or DLa for the symbol (e.g., dolomitized intrasparite, Li:DLa). If the rock contains more than 10 per cent dolomite of uncertain origin, prefix the term "dolomitic" to the rock name, and use dLr or dLa for the symbol (e.g., dolomitic pelsparite, Ip:dLa). If the rock consists of primary (directly deposited) dolomite, prefix the term "primary dolomite" to the rock name, and use Dr or Da for the symbol (e.g., primary dolomite intramicrite, IIi:Da). Instead of "primary dolomite micrite" (IIIm:D) the term "dolomicrite" may be used.

[2] Upper name in each box refers to calcirudites (median allochem size larger than 1.0 mm.); and lower name refers to all rocks with median allochem size smaller than 1.0 mm. Grain size and quantity of ooze matrix, cements or terrigenous grains are ignored.

[3] If the rock contains more than 10 per cent terrigenous material, prefix "sandy," "silty," or "clayey" to the rock name, and "Ts," "Tz," or "Tc" to the symbol depending on which is dominant (e.g., sandy biosparite, TsIb:La, or silty dolomitized pelmicrite, TzIIp:DLa). Glauconite, collophane, chert, pyrite, or other modifiers may also be prefixed.

[4] If the rock contains other allochems in significant quantities that are not mentioned in the main rock name, these should be prefixed as qualifiers preceding the main rock name (e.g., fossiliferous intrasparite, oölitic pelmicrite, pelletiferous oösparite, or intraclastic biomicrudite). This can be shown symbolically as Ii(b), Io(p), IIb(i), respectively.

[5] If the fossils are of rather uniform type or one type is dominant, this fact should be shown in the rock name (e.g., pelecypod biosparrudite, crinoid biomicrite).

[6] If the rock was originally microcrystalline and can be shown to have recrystallized to microspar (5–15 micron, clear calcite) the terms "microsparite," "biomicrosparite," etc. can be used instead of "micrite" or "biomicrite."

[7] Specify crystal size as shown in the examples.

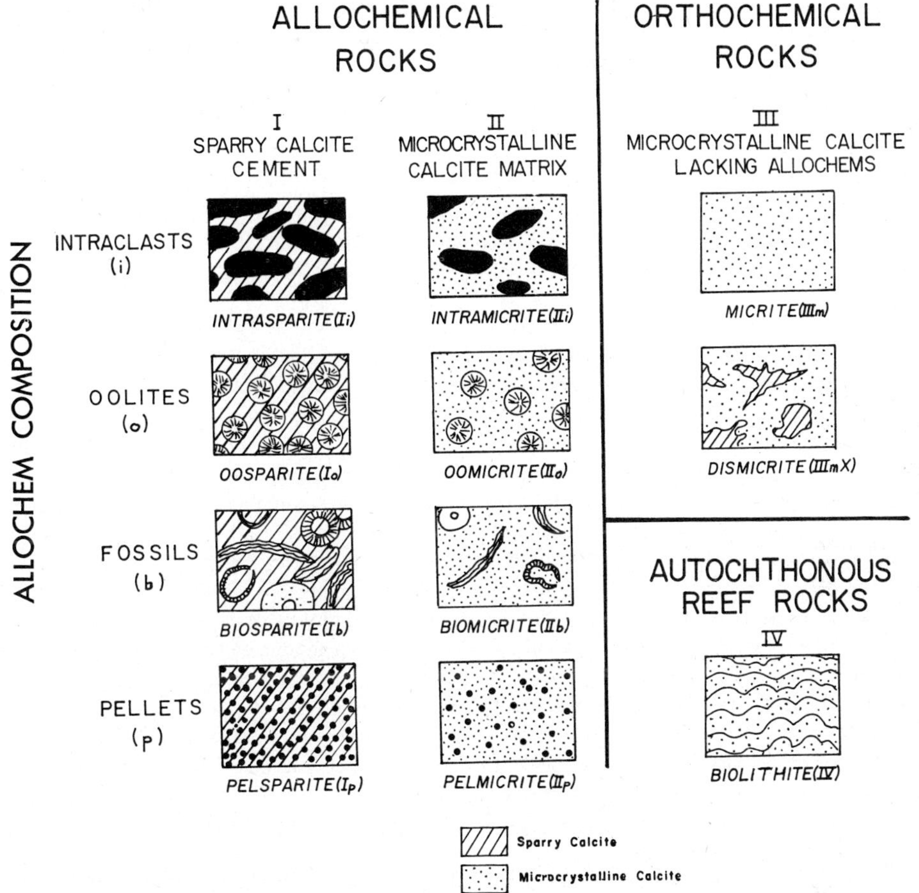

FIG. 3. Graphic classification table of limestones. For determining composition see Fig. 2; for full details of classification, including method of denoting grain size and dolomite content, see Table I.

graywackes, and orthoquartzites, all of which types may or may not contain clay matrix (Fig. 1). It is just as important to recognize the radically different allochem types in limestones, and the scheme for classification is presented in Table I.

Of all the allochemical particles, intraclasts are regarded as the most important because of their implication of shallow water, lowered wave base, or possible tectonic uplift. Therefore, in this classification a rock is called an intraclastic rock if the allochems consist of more than 25 per cent intraclasts by volume (Fig. 2), even if it contains 70 per cent fossils, pellets, or oölites. If the rock has less than 25 per cent intraclasts, next determine the proportion of oölites; if the rock contains more than 25 per cent oölites, it is here called an oölitic rock. If the rock has less than 25 per cent intraclasts and less than 25 per cent oölites, then it consists largely of either fossils or pellets. If the volume ratio of fossils to pellets is greater than 3:1, it is a biogenic rock; if the ratio is less than 1:3, it is a pellet rock; and if the fossil:pellet ratio is between 3:1 and 1:3, it may be called a biogenic pellet rock (Fig. 2).

ROCK NAMES

Rocks are named in this system by combining syllables representing the two major aspects of the rock. The first part of the word refers to allochem composition, and the second part to the character of the interallochem material. Examples are "intrasparite" (intraclasts cemented by sparry calcite); "biomicrite" (fossils in lime mud matrix); "pelmicrite" (pellets in lime mud); and "oösparite" (oölites in spar)—see Table I, and Figure 3. If desirable, "-rudite" can be suffixed if the allochems are of calcirudite size. Some workers prefer to use the longer, uncondensed names, such as "sparry intraclastic calcarenite" for intrasparite, or "microcrystalline biogenic calcirudite" for biomicrite, and that method is quite acceptable, for either way is perfectly adequate in describing the rock. For quick reference, the writer uses the symbolic shorthand described in the earlier paper (Folk, 1959).

Qualification of allochems.—The triangle in Figure 2 is used for determining the main allochem rock name; but in many rocks it is important to recognize admixtures of allochems. For example, it is certainly misleading to call a rock with 40 per cent intraclasts and 40 per cent fossils simply an "intrasparite"; it is much more meaningful to call it a "fossiliferous intrasparite," to call attention to the other allochems abundantly present. In the same way, one finds oölitic biosparite, pelletiferous oömicrite, intraclast-bearing biomicrite, etc. These additional terms can be used depending on the judgment of the individual, as to whether he considers the secondary allochems to be important or not. Main allochem terms can also be treated with considerable freedom, as follows—superficial oösparite (name coined by Don Winston, graduate student, The University of Texas, for rock made of superficial oölites—Illing, 1954); pelecypod-cast intrasparite; algally coated intrasparite; grapestone intramicrite; foram-encrusted algal-plate biomicrite; pisolitic dismicrite; disturbed pelmicrite, etc.

The one or two most important fossils present in biomicrite and biosparite should always be specified, as they are a very important and diagnostic rock constituent and should be considered as a major part of the name. Examples are crinoid biomicrite, brachiopod biosparite, bryozoan-pelecypod biomicrite or pelecypod-foram biosparite. If fossils are diverse and none really dominate, then the rock can be termed a mixed biosparite or biomicrite.

Porous rocks.—Rocks whose original pores have not been filled with spar can be designated simply as porous oölitic calcarenite, porous brachiopod calcirudite, etc. For those with cement other than sparry calcite, names such as the following may be substituted—halite-cemented intraclastic calcirudite, and barite-cemented oölitic calcarenite.

Recrystallization.—This subject was discussed in the earlier paper (Folk, 1959) and will not be touched on here.

MAIN ROCK NAMES AND THEIR MODIFIERS

The basic limestone classification has been described above, and limestones have been classed into eleven main types. One who works with limestones very long, however, soon finds this classification is inadequate to communicate subtle differences, or even some major ones; further specification is necessary, and each of the eleven fundamental types may be subdivided many times, based on the dozens of describable properties that limestones have. Now, such a process *could* lead quickly to a plague of new locality names, as has been grafted onto the igneous rocks. This brings us to a philosophical parting of the ways. One philosophy would have us give specific noun-names to each new variant, such as "spergenite" (Pettijohn, 1957) for a calcarenite containing a subequal mixture of oölites and fossils, with or without intraclasts and quartz sand; or "bahamite" (Beales, 1958) for a rock with bumpy-surfaced intraclasts thought to originate in a specific manner; or "encrinite" for a rock with abundant crinoids, much as the term "granite" in igneous rocks has been split into granitite (biotite-granite), ekerite (arfvedsonite-granite), unakite (epidote-granite), charnockite (hypersthene granite), etc. This we may call the many-nouns philosophy. The other philosophy is to keep the number of major class names as small as possible, but to use various descriptive modifiers. This is the approach used in the writer's scheme, as there are only eleven nouns for the eleven main rock types, and subdivision of these is done by adding qualifying words.

Unfortunately, classifiers (including the writer) often get carried away with a "single-specimen complex," especially if goaded by students or colleagues who ask them, "Now what would you call a rock made of x per cent broken brachiopods, y per cent whole ostracods, z per cent glauconite?" and so on. To the writer this is immaterial. It is pointless to argue whether a boundary line should be set at 10 per cent allochems, 20 per cent, 40 per cent, or 50 per cent. In describing any formation it soon becomes evident that the rocks in the unit pay no attention whatsoever to our arbitrarily chosen boundary lines, and straddle class limits with a fine disregard to our armchair theories. It is thought to be much more preferable when describing a formation to say something like the following—"The limestones of Unit *X* contain 5 to 35 per cent fossils, averaging 20 per cent, and most samples would be classified as brachiopod biomicrite; most of the fossils are whole, but some are badly broken," rather than saying—"Unit *X* contains 2 per cent micrite, 8 per cent fossiliferous micrite, 40 per cent sparse whole-fossil brachiopod biomicrite, 15 per cent packed whole-fossil brachiopod-crinoid biomicrite, and 35 per cent fragmental biomicrite," regarding the names themselves as hallowed entities. In other words, it is certainly desirable to have a good classification which will adequately describe a given single specimen, but let us not forget the more important fact that we deal with formations having assemblages of *many* rock types, and our main purpose is to describe the characteristics of the formation and decipher its environment, not to waste time haggling over the precise name to be given to one particular specimen.

QUALIFICATION BY GRAIN SIZE, TERRIGENOUS ADMIXTURE, MISCELLANEOUS CONSTITUENTS, AND REPLACEMENT PHENOMENA

These qualifications have already been described (Folk, 1959), and will not be discussed here in detail. A grain-size scale based on the divisions of Udden-Wentworth (Wentworth, 1922) becomes the obvious way to describe allochem grain size in carbonates, substituting, for example, "medium calcarenite" for "medium sand" (Table II). This can be combined with petrographic type, as in "coarse biosparite" (for a rock composed of coarse-sand-size fossils) or "medium biosparrudite" (for a rock with 4- to 16-mm fossils). A crystal-size scale (used in describing sparry calcite or dolomite) can also be erected using the same size limits, starting at 1 mm with a constant ratio of 2 between classes. It is critical, in discussing grain-size of limestones, to make clear whether the size of the allochems or of the cement crystals is being described.

If the limestone contains more than 10 per cent of terrigenous sand, silt, or clay, this fact should be mentioned. Rocks containing more than 10 per cent replacement dolomite (or chert, anhydrite, phosphate, or other minerals) should also be specified. Constituents such as glauconite or pyrite should also be listed, if important, though it is unnecessary to set any percentage boundaries. Examples of these various qualifiers follow.

Fine calcarenite: sandy glauconitic foram biosparite.
Coarse calcirudite: pyritic dolomitized intrasparite (or intrasparrudite).
Medium calcarenite: silty micaceous cherty oömicrite.

QUALIFICATION BY FIELD PROPERTIES

Many properties observable mainly in the field are very important in limestone description. Such characters as color, hardness, bedding, and sedimentary structures may be very important in environmental interpretation and should be added adjectivally to the main rock name. Some examples follow.

Black, hard, massive micrite.
White, hard but porous, cross-bedded oösparite.
Light gray, chalky, thin-bedded foram biomicrite.
Bluish gray, laminated, sandy intrasparite.
Pale orange, friable, burrowed oömicrite.

QUALIFICATION BY GENESIS

For many rocks whose precise paleogeographic setting is known, a genetic term may be added to the more purely descriptive main rock name—for example, intrasparite (fore-reef talus); pelecypod biomicrite (inter-reef filling); tidal-channel oösparite; lagoonal dismicrite; tidal-flat intrasparite. Then, if a geologist is given one hand specimen, thin section, or core, he can name the rock immediately using such simple and relatively noncommital terms as intrasparite or biomicrite. If later investigation, usually involving detailed field work, shows that it has originated in a specific locale or by a special process, then that genetic word may be appended to the rock name—this would be a more subjective part of the name, more vulnerable to argument than the main rock name.

As an example of the detail to which genetic

TABLE II. GRAIN-SIZE SCALE FOR CARBONATE ROCKS

	Transported Constituents	Authigenic Constituents	
	Very coarse calcirudite	Extremely coarsely crystalline	
64 mm			
	Coarse calcirudite		
16 mm			
	Medium calcirudite		
4 mm			4 mm
	Fine calcirudite	Very coarsely crystalline	
1 mm			1 mm
	Coarse calcarenite	Coarsely crystalline	
0.5 mm			
	Medium calcarenite		
0.25 mm			0.25 mm
	Fine calcarenite	Medium crystalline	
0.125 mm			
	Very fine calcarenite		
0.062 mm			0.062 mm
	Coarse calcilutite	Finely crystalline	
0.031 mm			
	Medium calcilutite		
0.016 mm			0.016 mm
	Fine calcilutite	Very finely crystalline	
0.008 mm			
0.004 mm	Very fine calcilutite		0.004 mm
		Aphanocrystalline	

Carbonate rocks contain both physically transported particles (oölites, intraclasts, fossils, and pellets) and chemically precipitated minerals (either as pore-filling cement, primary ooze, or as products of recrystallization and replacement). Therefore, the size scale must be a double one, so that one can distinguish which constituent is being considered (e.g., coarse calcirudites may be cemented with very finely crystalline dolomite, and fine calcarenites may be cemented with coarsely crystalline calcite). The size scale for transported constituents uses the terms of Grabau but retains the finer divisions of Wentworth except in the calcirudite range; for dolomites of obviously allochemical origin, the terms "dolorudite," "dolarenite," and "dololutite" are substituted for those shown. The most common crystal size for dolomite appears to be between .062 and .25 mm and for this reason that interval was chosen as the "medium crystalline" class.

subdivision can be carried, let us consider biomicrite, one of the commonest types of limestone, which originates in a great many ways. One of the most important clues to the genesis is the condition of the fossils which may be—

Whole, articulated, in growth position
Whole, articulated, but not in growth position
Whole, disarticulated
Broken (to various degrees)
Broken and rounded (to various degrees).

Whole fossils are, of course, found more commonly in biomicrite, and broken fossils in biosparite, but there are many exceptions. Very common is fragmental biomicrite (broken fossils in micrite—term coined by Don Winston, geology student, The University of Texas). The Buda limestone (Cretaceous, central Texas, Hixon, 1959) is a good example. This consists of extensively fragmented fossil fragments of diverse types, set sparsely in a micrite matrix. How can one explain the seeming paradox of extensively broken fossils, implying a high-energy environment, in lime-mud matrix? In this case, it is apparently due to the activities of burrowing organisms that churned through the mud, crunching up shells in the course of gaining nourishment. These burrowers also left the fossils randomly oriented and patchily distributed through the mud. Many present day calm-water environments, 100 feet or more deep, consist of finely broken shells probably crunched by scavengers.

As a genetic classification of biomicrite, one can set up the following types. In some instances these can be distinguished at the hand specimen or thin section level, but commonly considerable field work is required to determine the precise origin; even then efforts may fail.

1. Biomicrite represents an infiltration between framework fossils, which formed an organic baffle (Ginsburg and Lowenstam, 1958) and caused a local area of sluggish currents. Thus, many "high-energy" reefs have much lime mud and fossils trapped between the branching organisms.
2. Lime mud and fossils trapped by slimy or entangling algal fibers. After the alga rots away, little evidence may be left of its presence unless the algal colony had a characteristic dome-like or columnar shape.
3. Non-framework fossils, living and eventually buried in growth position in lime mud (autochthonous). This would include sessile benthic fauna, and buried burrowing fauna.
4. Vagrant benthos, buried after death without being moved.
5. Plankton or nekton, dying and falling as a gentle rain onto a mud bottom.
6. Organisms living elsewhere, washed into the site of lime mud deposition by currents or storms; may show various stages of breakage or rounding.

Sediment produced by any one of these six processes, or combinations of them, may be either

a. Left undisturbed
b. Attacked by quick waves wash and rapidly reburied, resulting in some sorting, possibly forming poorly washed biosparite or disturbed biomicrite, or producing intraclasts
c. Reworked by burrowers, breaking up the fossils, churning the sediment, disturbing the orientation and distribution of grains.

Combining these two lists (as any of the six formative mechanisms could be affected by any of the three later modifications) would result in at least 18 possible modes of origin of biomicrite, many of which would be indistinguishable! Coining names for all these types would be pointless; the origin could be left to the body of the description or, if one desires, appended parenthetically to the rock name, for example, foram biomicrite (plankton rain); mixed biomicrite (algal-trapped); fragmental pelecypod biomicrite (burrowed); whole-oyster biomicrite (autochthonous).

QUALIFICATION BY TEXTURAL MATURITY: A PROPOSED SCHEME FOR SPECTRAL SUBDIVISION OF THE MAJOR LIMESTONE TYPES

In the former classification of limestones (Folk, 1959) only three textural or "energy" families of limestones were formally recognized—the relatively pure lime muds (micrites); the lime muds with more than 10 per cent allochems; and, finally, the winnowed or mud-free allochems with spar cement. It is, however, possible to subdivide these three families into eight groups (Fig. 4) forming a more complete and gradational spectrum of limestone types, quite similar to the textural maturity scheme proposed for sandstones (Folk, 1951, 1956). The application of this concept to the carbonates was first suggested to the writer in a letter by C. B. Thames, a former student (*see* Thames, 1959), and the idea has been further stimulated as a result of lengthy conversations and letters with Robert J. Dunham, of Shell Development Company. The following scheme has been developed as the result of our discussions and our interchange of ideas, although Dunham has constructed a system of his own using different names and somewhat different boundaries.

This scale is meant to be purely descriptive, although certain genetic implications are inherent. In general, the first-mentioned limestone types in the following sequence represent the lower energy environments, whereas the last-mentioned types represent the higher energy environments. Consequently the sequence could represent the change from a deep marine basin up onto a shallow shelf, and then to the surf and beach zone, or it could represent passage from a protected and very shallow lagoon out to a barrier bar. One can conceive of many exceptions; however, a -micrite could form in a high-energy zone if lime mud were trapped by slimy algae and held firmly from removal by waves, and a -sparite might form in a calm lagoon if fossil fragments accumulated and the chemistry was such that there was no lime mud forming by precipitation or by abrasion in the environment. In the writer's experience these are unusual exceptions to the general rule.

Following is the textural spectrum (Fig. 4).

1. Pure micrite or dismicrite, with less than 1 per cent allochems; these correspond to the pure lithographic limestones. These are not very common rocks because most micritic limestones have a few tiny fossil fragments, pellets, etc., admixed.

2. Micrite or dismicrite with 1 to 10 per cent allochems (for example, fossiliferous micrite, pellet-bearing micrite). Many limestones that appear as pure micrite in the field or under the binocular microscope actually fall in this category when examined in thin section or by acetate peel. Terrigenous rocks analogous to the foregoing two types are the very pure clay shales that form in the middle of many lagoons, or that are found in offshore marine waters.

3. Biomicrite, intramicrite, oömicrite, or pelmicrite with 10 to 50 per cent allochems. It is often useful to subdivide the micritic rocks into two classes—those with really abundant, closely packed allochems; and those with rather sparse allochems floating in lime mud. Leighton (this volume) and the writer independently arrived at the same boundary line of 50 per cent allochems as the most satisfactory, but entirely arbitrary line, as did Wolf (1960), also. It is a line that is quantitatively established, not subject to guesswork in its determination, and thus reproducible between operators; it can be applied both in Recent sediment work and in ancient carbonates. If one wants a specific label for these rocks with 10 to 50 per cent allochems, the writer suggests using such names as "sparse biomicrite," "sparse pelmicrite." These rocks correspond to the sandy shales.

4. Biomicrite, pelmicrite, etc., with more than 50 per cent allochems. These rocks are not as common as the preceding type; they can be termed "packed biomicrite," "packed intramicrite," etc., alluding to the closer packing of the allochems. They correspond to the clayey, texturally immature sandstones.

5. The next step in the textural spectrum is winnowing of lime mud from the allochems. If waves or currents are not very strong, if current action is sporadic, or if too much lime mud is available, all the micrite may not be removed; it will settle out as laminae, irregular patches, or geopetal pore fillings and the rest of the pore space may be later filled with sparry calcite cement. These transitional rocks can be considered as textural type 5; therefore, if the inter-allochem material is subequal spar and micrite such terms as "poorly washed pelsparite," "poorly washed intrasparite," etc., can be applied. These are analogous to many sandstones that hover on the immature-submature boundary because of clayey streaks and patches in an otherwise clean sand.

6. Biosparite, intrasparite, etc., in which all or nearly all of the lime mud has been winnowed out, the

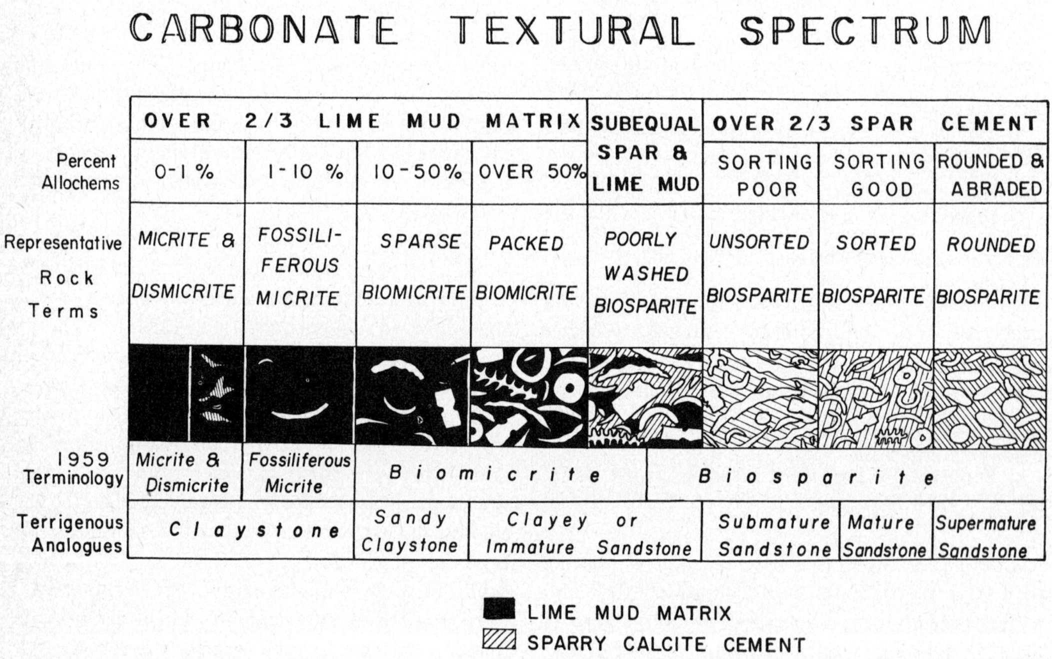

CARBONATE TEXTURAL SPECTRUM

	OVER 2/3 LIME MUD MATRIX				SUBEQUAL SPAR & LIME MUD	OVER 2/3 SPAR CEMENT		
Percent Allochems	0-1 %	1-10 %	10-50%	OVER 50%		SORTING POOR	SORTING GOOD	ROUNDED & ABRADED
Representative Rock Terms	MICRITE & DISMICRITE	FOSSILIFEROUS MICRITE	SPARSE BIOMICRITE	PACKED BIOMICRITE	POORLY WASHED BIOSPARITE	UNSORTED BIOSPARITE	SORTED BIOSPARITE	ROUNDED BIOSPARITE
1959 Terminology	Micrite & Dismicrite	Fossiliferous Micrite	Biomicrite			Biosparite		
Terrigenous Analogues	Claystone		Sandy Claystone	Clayey or Immature Sandstone		Submature Sandstone	Mature Sandstone	Supermature Sandstone

■ LIME MUD MATRIX
▨ SPARRY CALCITE CEMENT

FIG. 4. A textural spectrum for carbonate sediments, showing eight proposed sequential stages. In general, "low-energy" sediments occur to the left, with successively "higher-energy" sediments to the right. These stages are quite analogous to the textural maturity sequence in terrigenous rocks. Because of lack of space, only the biomicrite-biosparite terms are used as representative examples; for these terms, one can substitute the other allochemical limestone types (for example, the cell labeled "packed biomicrite" can equally well stand for packed intramicrite, packed oömicrite, and packed pelmicrite). Comparison with the fourfold division used in Folk, 1959, is also shown.

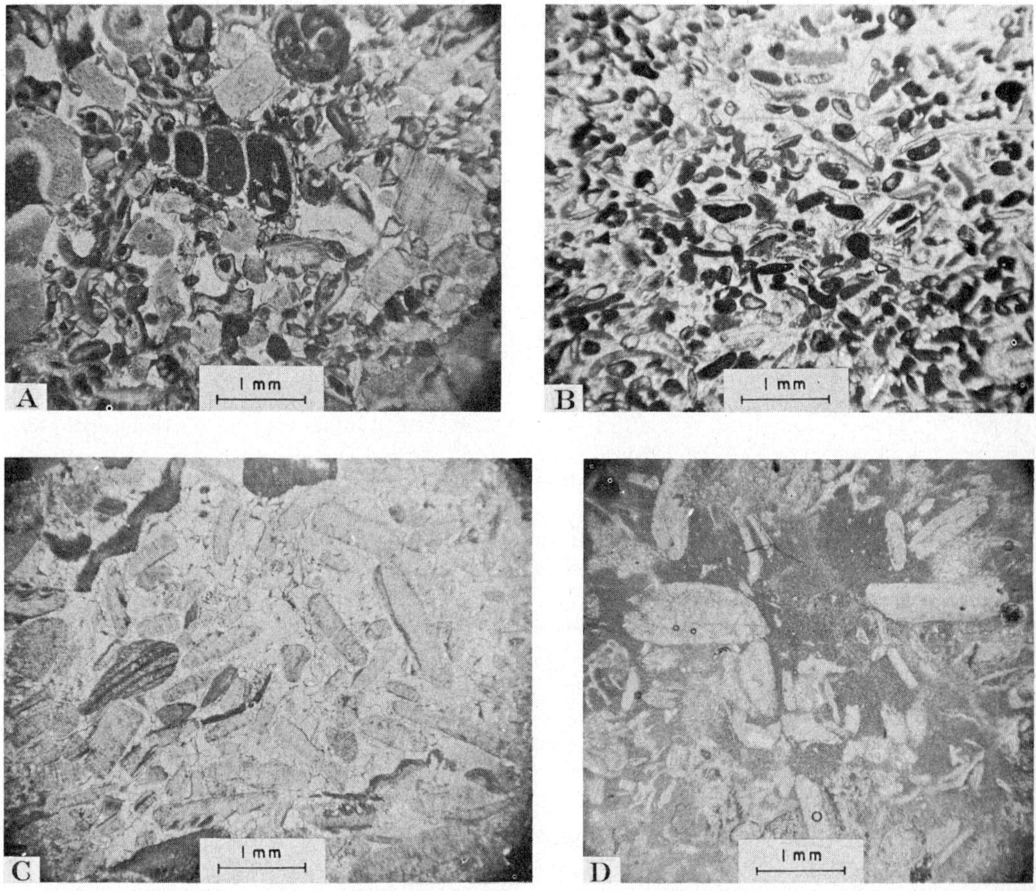

PLATE I. Textural maturity in some limestone specimens.

A. Mississippian limestone, Marion County, Tennessee. Poorly sorted medium calcarenite: crinoid-bryozoan biosparite. This is an unsorted carbonate sand, analogous with the submature stage in sandstones; fossils of diverse sizes are present throughout the slide, ranging from about 0.1 mm (for smallest bryozoan scraps) to 2 mm (for gastropods and largest crinoid columnals). Nevertheless, the rock has been completely winnowed of lime mud. A point count of 100 allochem long axes gave a geometric mean size of 0.42 mm (1.3ϕ), with a standard deviation of 1.45ϕ (poorly sorted).

B. Cretaceous Buda limestone, Culberson County, Texas, collected by S. B. Hixon. Moderately well sorted fine calcarenite: intraclast-bearing mixed biosparite. This is a calcarenite that is rather well sorted for a carbonate rock, and is analogous with the mature stage in sandstones. Diverse fossil fragments, intraclasts, and some pellets have been sorted into laminae of uniform size and there is no micrite matrix. A point count of 100 long axes gave a geometric mean size of 0.24 mm (2.1ϕ) with a standard deviation of 0.65ϕ (moderately well sorted).

C. Cretaceous Austin chalk, facies at Pilot Knob, Travis County, Texas, collected by Rex H. White, Jr. Rounded, sorted coarse calcarenite: pelecypod biosparite. This calcarenite is not only well sorted, but also the pelecypod fragments have been rounded into discs less than 1 mm diameter. It apparently formed as a surf-zone coquina on the windward beach surrounding a Cretaceous volcano.

D. Cretaceous Austin chalk, facies at Pilot Knob, Travis County, Texas, collected by Rex H. White, Jr. This rock, a rounded-pelecypod biomicrite, illustrates textural inversion: pelecypod fragments, rounded and battered in the surf zone around Pilot Knob volcano, were then blown into a calm water, probably lagoonal, environment. Final deposition was thus in a low-energy environment, accounting for the micrite matrix. Similar inversions occur in sandstones and in Recent sediments.

rock cemented with sparry calcite, but the allochems are still poorly sorted (Plate I-*A*). This sixth stage corresponds to the submature stage in sandstones. If names are desired, one can call these rocks "unsorted biosparite," "unsorted intrasparite," etc.

7. Biosparite, oösparite, etc., in which the allochems are by now well sorted but still not much abraded or rounded (Plate I-*B*). These correspond to the mature stage in sandstones, and the analogous carbonates could be called "sorted oösparite," "sorted intrasparite," etc.

8. The final stage of the textural spectrum is intense abrasion of the allochems to rounded grains (Plate I-*C*). This phenomenon, which ordinarily takes place at the surf zone, results in carbonates entirely analogous to supermature sandstones, and the rocks can be called "rounded biosparite," etc.

The foregoing theoretical sequence is very satisfying if we are content to follow the precepts of that famous Roman philosopher, Gluteus Maximus. However, practical difficulties soon arise when we begin to look at this textural spectrum a little bit more closely. Is the spectrum truly evolutionary and sequential? How can we draw precise, reproducible boundaries between classes? Are the boundaries we have drawn really meaningful genetic breaks or are they arbitrary cutoffs in a complete sequence, like the plagioclase divisions? Much research, particularly on Recent carbonates, is needed to answer these questions, and the following discussion is based on inadequate evidence but expresses the writer's opinions as of the moment.

It is believed that the most important single environmental break is between the limestones with a lime-mud matrix and those with a sparry calcite cement, which is a division that reflects the point where wave or current action becomes turbulent enough to wash out the lime mud, keep it in suspension, and carry it into lower energy zones. This is the boundary line between the immature and submature stages in sandstones, and between the -micrites and -sparites in the earlier (Folk, 1959) classification (Fig. 4). Exactly where and how this boundary should be drawn is not quite clear. In the original scheme, the boundary was drawn where the interallochem material was 50 per cent spar and 50 per cent micrite; in the scheme presented here, a transitional class (the "poorly washed" limestones) is formally recognized and defined as containing $\frac{1}{3}$ to $\frac{2}{3}$ spar and $\frac{1}{3}$ to $\frac{2}{3}$ micrite between the allochems. The fundamental break is in the fact that winnowing has taken place; where the precise percentage boundary line between these two families is drawn is of little significance, inasmuch as the whole sequence is transitional.

Sorting—Secondly, consider sorting, the criterion for separating class 6 from class 7 above, corresponding to the submature-mature transition in sandstones (Plate I-*A*, *B*). This division was first suggested to the writer by Robert J. Dunham. Little enough is known about the real meaning of sorting for terrigenous sediments; much less is known about carbonates, for which quantitative and statistical data are meager. Sorting in carbonates, as in sandstones, is a function of mean grain size; beaches of Isla Perez, Alacran reef, Yucatan (Folk and Robles, Ms.), have sorting values that form a sinusoidal trend when plotted against mean grain size, with the best sorted sediments having mean sizes of -3ϕ, 0ϕ, and 2ϕ, and worst sorting shown by sediments with grain sizes midway between these values (Fig. 5). Hence, any meaningful boundary one draws between "well sorted" and "poorly sorted" carbonates should depend on the mean grain size of the sample, and the sorting boundary would be different for different sizes. This fact argues for the principle of describing sorting by a continuous series of adjectives rather than setting up two sharply defined sorting groups, "unsorted" *versus* "sorted."

Next, one must consider the effect of particle type on sorting. If, for example, all the allochems are one kind of fossil, "sorting" would be good regardless of whether there had been any currents or not, because of the inherent size of the animals (Fig. 6). Thus, a chalk consisting of equally sized Foraminifera in micrite certainly does not owe its sorting to current action. Further, fecal pellets in micrite might be all the same size, not because of hydraulic sorting but because of the caliber of the anus extruding them. One can demonstrate *current* sorting in carbonates only if (1) particles of diverse kinds and/or sizes are present in a sequence of beds, and (2) these particles are segregated into layers of varying mean grain size, with each layer being itself well sorted (Fig. 6). In other words, one has to compare the grain size distribution in a particular lamina with the grain size of material offered to the currents, that is, the availability of particles of different sizes. For

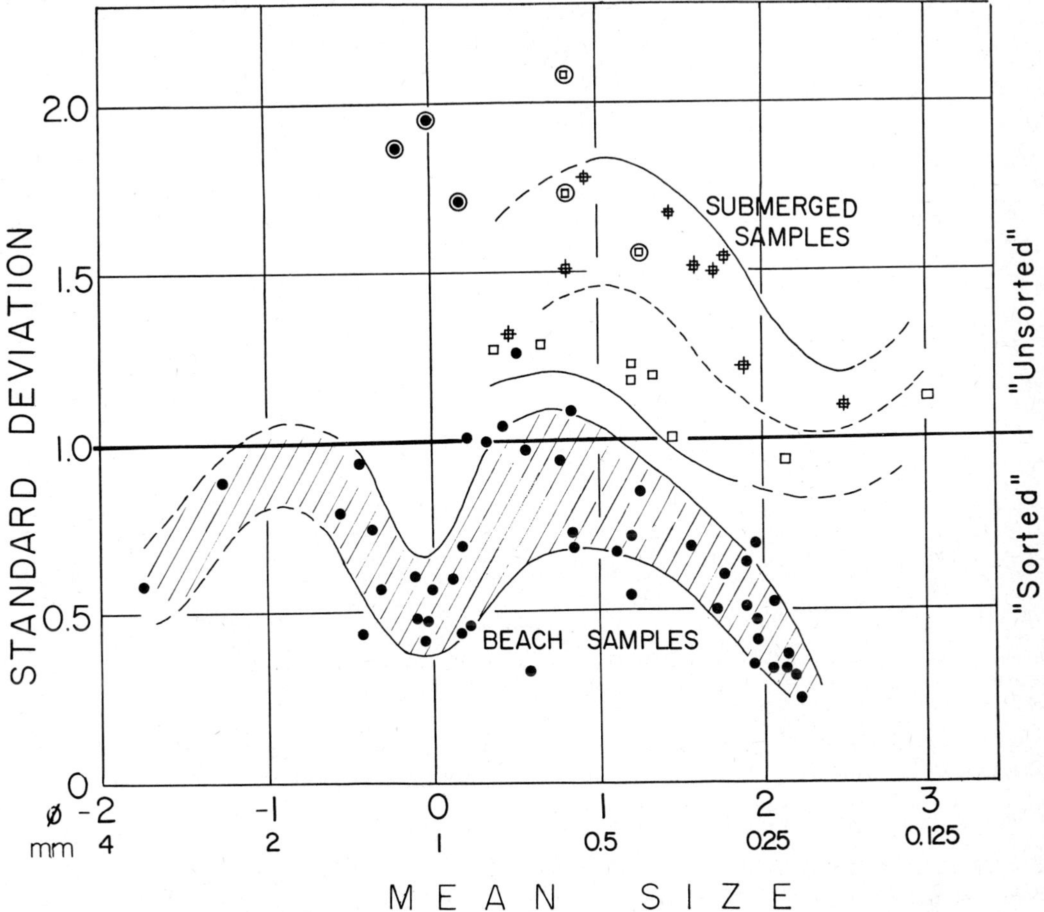

FIG. 5. Mean size (M_z) versus sorting (σ_I) for sediment samples from Isla Perez, Alacran reef, Yucatan Beach samples shown as black dots; subtidal sediments in water from 1 inch to 3 feet deep are shown as squares. Squares with cross indicate samples from submerged grass-covered flats; the others are from submerged bare sand areas. Enclosing circles indicate those samples of all types that contain admixed staghorn coral joints. Most of the beach samples have sorting values below $\sigma_I = 1.0\phi$, which is here proposed as the best boundary to use between "sorted" and "unsorted" calcarenites. Note that sorting is a sinusoidal function of mean grain size in carbonates as well as in terrigenous sediments.

example, if a rock contains crinoid fragments, brachiopod pieces, intraclasts, and Foraminifera, and all these different allochems are between 0.2 and 0.5 mm diameter, one would probably be justified in ascribing the good sorting to current action, especially if layers above and below had allochems of different mean size but similar good sorting. This can be quantitatively established by plotting size versus sorting (Fig. 5).

Rate of supply also strongly affects the sorting. On a beach where large numbers of different organisms are being produced in the vicinity, the rate of production may be so great as to swamp the efforts of waves and currents to sort them out.

Sorting efficiency of currents or waves also varies. For each particle size, there is an optimum strength of waves or currents that will produce best sorting; currents either weaker or stronger produce poorer sorting (Fig. 7). Consider an assemblage of fossil fragments 8 to 64 mm in diameter. We can imagine that very weak waves would accomplish no sorting at all on these parti-

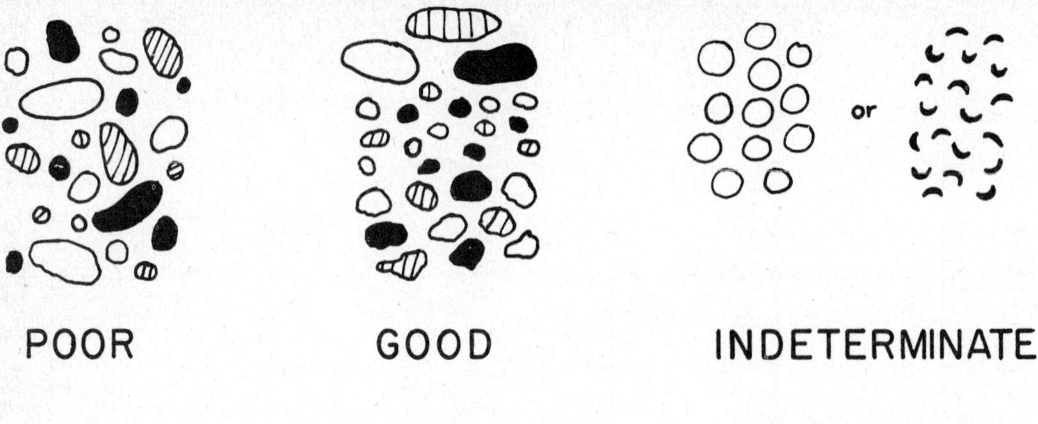

FIG. 6. The meaning of "sorting" in carbonate sediments. Allochems are here idealized, each shading representing a different allochem type; for example, black might represent intraclasts; white, pelecypods; and ruling, crinoids. The left-hand diagram is poorly sorted by any standard. To be able to infer good sorting by currents, one must establish (1) that allochems of different sizes or types were available to the currents, and (2) that these have been segregated into well-sorted layers of differing mean size. The second diagram illustrates this, each lamina or bed being well sorted, although a wide range of sizes and of allochem types was available. In the third diagram current-sorting is indeterminate, because in both cases only one type (and one size) of object is available—perhaps in the first example all crinoid columnals of a given size, and in the second, all ostracod shells. Here the good numerical sorting is simply due to the fact the organisms grew to a certain inherent limiting size; currents need not have had anything to do with producing the visible sorting.

cles, as they might be powerless to move them. Yet very strong storm waves would move them all, in mass, and tend to jumble them up. Waves of some intermediate level could, however, select out the 8 to 16 mm fragments and deposit them in one locality (or one layer), whereas waves at a higher energy level would be able to pick out the 16 to 32 mm, and the 32 to 64 mm shells and sort them into different layers. Consequently, persistent waves or currents of moderate strength (the exact meaning of "moderate" depending on the grain sizes of the particles involved) produce best sorting. On Isla Perez, Alacran reef, the best sorted sediments occur on the lee side, where the waves are gentle.

With all these confusing factors taken into consideration, where should one now draw the line between "well sorted" and "poorly sorted" calcarenites? Considering the present paucity of knowledge concerning sorting of Recent calcarenites it would probably be better to define sorting by an arbitrary, descriptive series of ranked adjectives, rather than by setting up two distinct classes of "well sorted" and "poorly sorted." The geometrical limits in Table III, developed for terrigenous sands, are suggested (slightly modified from Folk and Ward, 1957).

This measure is determined by the formula

$$\sigma_I = \frac{\phi 84 - \phi 16}{4} + \frac{\phi 95 - \phi 5}{6.6},$$

where $\phi 84$ is the phi diameter at the 84th percentile of the distribution, etc. Sorting class limits are based on a constant ratio of $\sqrt{2}$ in the better sorting classes (where most sampies fall), and a ratio of 2 in the higher classes. In the field or in thin section, the simpler formula

$$\sigma = \frac{\phi 84 - \phi 16}{2}$$

can be used readily with a little practice, either by estimation or by counting grains. Thus carbonates can be described texturally as "well-sorted fine calcarenite: foram biosparite" or "poorly sorted medium calcirudite: oölitic intrasparite."

If it is desirable to draw a more definite line to separate the "sorted" from the "unsorted"

TABLE III. SORTING CLASSES

Inclusive Graphic Standard Deviation (σ_I)	*Verbal Sorting Class*	
under 0.35ϕ	very well sorted	Sorted Calcarenite
0.35–0.50ϕ	well sorted	
0.50–0.71ϕ	moderately well sorted	
0.71–1.00ϕ	moderately sorted	
1.00–2.00ϕ	poorly sorted	Unsorted Calcarenite
2.00–4.00ϕ	very poorly sorted	
4.00 and over	extremely poorly sorted	

calcarenites, analogous to the submature-mature boundary in sandstones, it should be drawn at such a line as to separate most effectively the carbonate beach sediments from the subtidal sediments. Work on Alacran reef, Yucatan (Folk and Robles, Ms.), shows that carbonate beaches there have about the same sorting values as terrigenous beaches over a thousandfold range in mean size from 2.5ϕ to -7.5ϕ (0.18 mm to 180 mm), having standard deviations of 0.30–0.60ϕ (Fig. 5). Best separation of beach from subtidal sediments occurs if a σ_I boundary of about 1.0ϕ is used. With these very limited data, then, it is tentatively suggested that the most effective sorting boundary would be the 1.0ϕ limit of the sorting scale given above, considering any car-

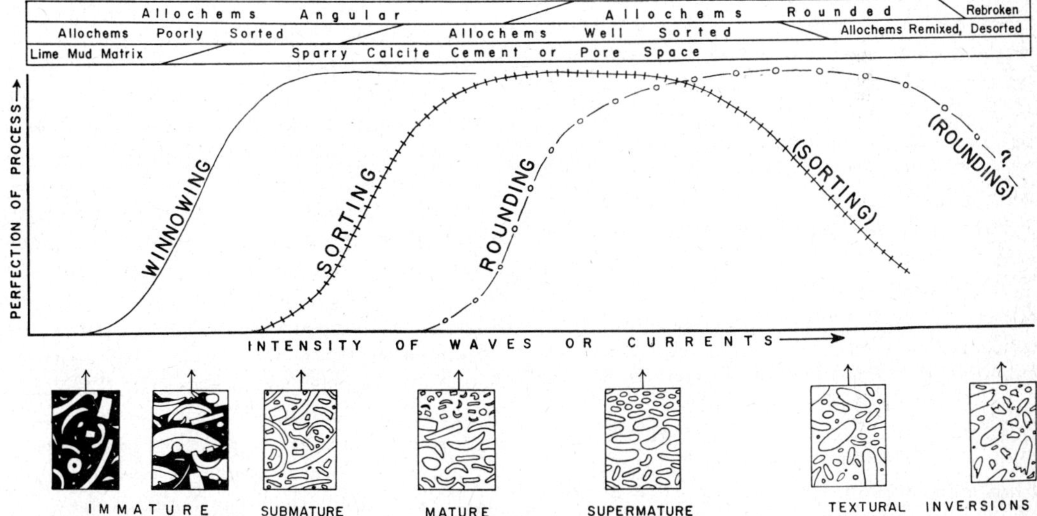

FIG. 7. Winnowing, sorting, and rounding in carbonates. This highly idealized diagram shows how these three textural modifying processes are probably related to the vigor of waves or currents, to produce a textural sequence analogous to the textural maturity sequence in sandstones. Winnowing of lime mud matrix takes place at low energy levels, because the lime mud is so very fine grained and easy to remove. Nonwinnowed rocks with abundant lime mud in them (like the biomicrite shown in 1st figure) normally indicate a low-energy environment (or micro-environment in the case of an organic baffle), and are analogous to the immature or clayey sandstones. In many transitional environments, winnowing is incomplete and a "poorly washed biosparite" (2d figure) is produced. With more intense currents, winnowing may be complete but the allochems remain poorly sorted, resulting in "unsorted biosparite" (3d figure), analogous to a submature sandstone. Further working sorts the allochems into layers of differing mean grain size (4th figure), producing the "sorted biosparite," resembling a mature sandstone. More intense wave action, generally at the surf zone, is required to develop a rounded biosparite (5th figure), like a supermature sandstone. The writer feels that best rounding occurs at energy levels too high for efficient sorting—that is, with waves that are so powerful that they tend to mix the grains in a poorly sorted jumble (6th figure). It is possible that extremely heavy waves may cause breakage of grains that have been rounded under less vigorous conditions, so that rounding, like sorting, would be diminished under excessive energy levels (7th figure). Both processes have an optimum energy level at which they are most efficient, but optimum energy for rounding is thought to be considerably higher than optimum energy level for sorting. Any of these sediments may be remixed with lime mud, if it is available in the environment, by intense storms, activities of burrowers, etc.

bonate sediment falling in the best four sorting classes as being relatively "sorted" and those with σ_I values over 1.0ϕ "unsorted."

Rounding.—Rounding, like sorting, is the result of many complex factors, and is subject to the further handicap that it is almost impossible to quantify in calcarenites. Unfortunately, only fossils are good abrasional indicators. Oölites and pellets are round to begin with, so cannot be counted in evaluating the *abrasional* roundness of a sample. Intraclasts are generally so soft that they round almost immediately, hence also should be discounted. In rocks consisting very largely of oölites, pellets, or intraclasts, nevertheless, the roundness of any associated fossils may be taken as an indicator of the abrasional effectiveness of the environment. But there are many difficulties in evaluating the abrasional roundness of fossils, for many of them are round to begin with (forams and crinoids, for example). It is very likely that different types of fossils round at different rates, even if grain size is constant, because of differences in shell microstructure; they certainly are broken up at markedly different rates as shown strikingly by experiments of Chave (1960). At present, consequently, abrasional roundness of fossil fragments can only be expressed in very subjective terms, and its significance is not surely known. It is probable that rounding of shells takes place only on beaches exposed to surf action, but there are very few quantitative data on this subject. White (1960), for example, found a semicircular rim of beach calcarenite around the northern edge of Pilot Knob, a volcano that existed in the Austin chalk sea near what is now Austin, Texas. Here pelecypod fragments had been battered into tiny, round plates 1 to 2 mm in diameter, superbly sorted (Plate I–*C*). These were found on an atoll-like rim on the north side facing the direction of most vigorous Cretaceous surf action.

On beaches where organisms are very abundant, their rate of supply may be so great as to overwhelm the rounding process, and the bulk of the particles will be nonrounded. Thus, on the islands of Alacran reef, rounded calcarenites are found only on those stretches of beach where large coral fragments are scarce or absent, since the large corals continually break down to provide a supply of new, angular particles. Mean roundness of a calcarenite sample, consequently, is a complicated function of (1) inherent roundness of the particle itself (for example, forams); (2) roundability of the particle, dependent upon the microstructure; (3) grain size, with the coarser particles rounding faster than the finer ones; (4) rate of supply of new material, for example, production rate of the organisms; (5) vigor of surf action; and (6) length of time a given section of beach is exposed to surf action.

TEXTURAL INVERSIONS

Textural inversions (Folk, 1951) are just as common in carbonate rocks as they are in sandstones. Textural inversion results when grains that have attained a certain degree of maturity in one environment or under one regimen, are transferred and finally deposited in an environment of lower maturity.

For example, sand grains may become well sorted in a barrier bar, then blown *in mass* by a hurricane into the lagoon behind, giving a mixture of well sorted sand grains in a clay matrix. Or grains may be laid down in a well-sorted layer by effective current action; then burrowers may churn through the material after burial and mix the well-sorted grains with micrite. Grains may become well rounded and sorted into layers under certain conditions of wave action, and a succession of more violent waves may mix all the sediments up and dump them rapidly so that a mixture of well rounded but poorly sorted grains is laid down. Carbonate grains, being soft, round much more rapidly than quartz grains; the writer has visited an area on Isla Mujeres, Quintana Roo, Mexico, where wave action was so vigorous that the carbonates were well rounded and polished, but sorting of the grains was very poor. In other words, the high wave energy that produced good rounding and polish was too great for optimum sorting to occur; instead, the vigor of surf attack tended to mix abraded grains of all sizes in a confused jumble (this rock, if lithified, could be termed an "unsorted, rounded biosparite," Fig. 7). Hence, the stages of maturity listed previously may not follow sequentially (that is, sorting need not precede rounding), but may develop independently as controlled by different wave conditions.

Intramicrite and oömicrite indicate by their very composition that they should be considered as textural inversions. Most rocks containing intraclasts and oölites are well winnowed and cemented with spar, because the generation of these two allochem types requires vigorous current action, which generally is strong enough to wash out any lime mud in the environment. Oömicrite and intramicrite are much less common because they represent a paradox—allochems are produced in a high-energy environment and then deposited in a low-energy environment. Thus, they are characteristic of a transition belt between environments of these two energy levels, and form, for example, where oölites or intraclasts on a shoal area or bar are washed over into protected lagoonal areas by storms (compare Newell, Purdy, and Imbrie, 1960, p. 485). Rounded, highly abraded fossils may be found in micrite, formed by the same environmental mixing (Plate I–*D*).

Intramicrite and oömicrite can also be produced by burrowing organisms. Consider that alternating beds of lime mud and well-sorted oölites are laid down in cleanly differentiated layers. If, before cementation occurs, worms or pelecypods burrow in these layers and mix the two sediments together, then oömicrite would be produced. Intramicrite in the Cretaceous Buda limestone in central Texas was apparently produced in this manner (Hixon, 1959), because the intraclasts are swirled through the micrite in patches, as would happen by organic churning.

Another way of interpreting textural features of carbonates has been devised by Carozzi (for example, Carozzi and Lundwall, 1959). He measures the size of the largest fossil fragment in a thin section, and equates size of this fragment with bathymetry—the larger the fossil, the shallower the water supposedly is. This, however, leads to some rather strange results. Big oysters in a lagoon mud, or large gastropods crawling along a fairly deep marine shelf, become indicators of shallow, turbulent water; and sand-sized fossils (or presumably oölites also), no matter how well winnowed and sorted they are, become equated with deeper water. In the first place, this sytem is naïve in equating strength of currents with shallowness of water. Sediments in water 20 feet deep on the oceanward side are commonly much coarser than sediments in 2 feet of water inside a protected lagoon. Secondly, it errs in equating size of the largest fossils with current strength. On Alacran reef, Yucatan, beautifully sorted calcarenites with maximum particles about 1-2 mm occur on the beaches, whereas deeper, calmer waters of the lagoon are strewn with huge chunks of broken coral. The criterion for "energy" is certainly not the size of the biggest fossil; rather, it is much more closely correlated with the amount of winnowing, sorting, and rounding.

CONCLUSIONS

There are two approaches to carbonate classification. One is to set up a system of many noun-names based on "type" localities to cover the myriads of carbonate rock types that vary in composition, sorting, color, sandiness, genetic niche, etc. This might be done systematically, so that every conceivable rock type would have its pigeonhole (many of the classes perhaps being vacant) as Johannson did for the igneous rocks. Or the same thing might be done unsystematically, letting a hodgepodge of new noun-names grow like Topsy (Stowe, 1852) every time some worker describes a particular local section, with no order to the nomenclature—examples of such nonsystematic terms being marl, coquina, encrinite, spergenite, vaughanite, edgewise conglomerate, pelletoid limestone, microbreccia, tangue, bituminous limestone, siliceous limestone. This we might call a "random" terminology, as each name develops by itself with no regard for its position or limits in a comprehensive and orderly system of nomenclature.

The other approach is to develop a limestone system consisting of only a handful of major rock types, whose names are determined by descriptive, quantitative means. Then to this universal system, each worker can add as he likes modifiers denoting such characters as grain size, terrigenous content, odd chemical constituents, precise origin (often based on field work), color, hardness, bedding, sedimentary structures, textural maturity, and detailed paleontology. It is very doubtful if any uniformity could be attained in such a modifying system; liberty should be permitted to reign, because each area has its own local problems that need local emphasis but might be unimportant elsewhere. (In the Cretaceous it is important to distinguish the soft, chalky limestones from the hard, nonporous ones; yet both might fall in the same major rock class, for example, both might be foram biomicrite.)

An admirable piece of work in this direction has been published by Weiss and Norman (1960), who describe their limestone types in terms of a few major families (for example, biosparite), but then go on to split each group into several subtypes based on grain size, sorting, fragmentation and orientation of fossils, per cent of insoluble residue, and sedimentary structures (laminated, nodular, etc.). In other geographic provinces, other local subclassifications of biosparite would be found useful, and the system of Weiss and Norman might be inapplicable there. Each area, then, should develop its own subclassification system, based on different sets of properties. It would clearly be pointless to attempt to set up an elaborate noun-terminology for all the vast number of subtypes that would emerge. In conclusion, the writer advocates uniform usage of the eleven major limestone types, as a basic classification system, and individual qualification, by adjectives, for all the other properties.

REFERENCES

Beales, F. W., 1958, Ancient sediments of Bahaman type: Am. Assoc. Petroleum Geologists Bull., v. 42, no. 8, p. 1845–1880.

Bramkamp, R. A., and Powers, R. W., 1958, Classification of Arabian carbonate rocks: Geol. Soc. America Bull., v. 69, no. 10, p. 1305–1318.

Carozzi, A. V., and Lundwall, W. R., Jr., 1959, Microfacies study of a Middle Devonian bioherm, Columbus, Indiana: Jour. Sed. Petrology, v. 29, no. 3, p. 343–353.

Cayeux, Lucien, 1935, Les roches sedimentaires de France, roches carbonates: Paris, Masson et Cie.

Chave, K. E., 1960, Carbonate skeletons to limestones—problems: New York Acad. Sci. Trans., Ser. 2, v. 23, p. 14–24.

Cumings, E. R., and Shrock, R. R., 1928, Niagaran coral reefs of Indiana and adjacent states and their stratigraphic relations: Geol. Soc. America Bull., v. 39, no. 2, p. 579–620.

Folk, R. L., 1951, Stages of textural maturity in sedimentary rocks: Jour. Sedimentary Petrology, v. 21, no. 3, p. 127–130.

——— 1952, Petrography and petrology of the Lower Ordovician Beekmantown carbonate rocks in the vicinity of State College, Pennsylvania: unpub. Ph.D. dissertation, The Pa. State College.

——— 1956, The role of texture and composition in sandstone classification: Jour. Sed. Petrology, v. 26, no. 2, p. 166–171.

——— 1959, Practical petrographic classification of limestones: Am. Assoc. Petroleum Geologists Bull., v. 43, no. 1, p. 1–38.

——— and Robles, Rogelio, Carbonate sands of Isla Perez, Alacran reef, Yucatan, Mexico: ms. in progress.

——— and Ward, W. C., 1957, Brazos River bar—a study in the significance of grain-size parameters: Jour. Sed. Petrology, v. 27, no. 1, p. 3–26.

——— and Weaver, C. E., 1952, A study of the texture and composition of chert: Am. Jour. Sci., v. 250, no. 7, p. 498–510.

Ginsburg, R. N., and Lowenstam, H. A., 1958, The influence of marine bottom communities on the depositional environment of sediments: Jour. Geology, v. 66, no. 3, p. 310–318.

Hatch, F. H., and Rastall, R. H., 1938, revised by Black, Maurice, The petrology of the sedimentary rocks, 3d ed.: London, George Allen and Unwin Ltd.

Hixon, S. B., 1959, Facies and petrography of the Cretaceous Buda limestone of Texas and northern Mexico: unpub. M.A. thesis, Univ. of Texas, 151 p.

Illing, L. V., 1954, Bahaman calcareous sands: Am. Assoc. Petroleum Geologists Bull., v. 38, no. 1, p. 1–95.

Murray, R. C., 1960, Origin of porosity in carbonate rocks: Jour. Sed. Petrology, v. 30, no. 1, p. 59–84.

Newell, N. D., Purdy, E. G., and Imbrie, John, 1960, Bahamian oölitic sand: Jour. Geology, v. 68, no. 5, p. 481–497.

Pettijohn, F. J., 1957, Sedimentary rocks: New York, Harper and Bros.

Sander, Bruno K., 1951 Contributions to the study of depositional fabrics—rhythmically deposited Triassic limestones and dolomites, trans. by E. B. Knopf: Am. Assoc. Petroleum Geologists; orig. pub. in 1936.

Stowe, Harriet Beecher, 1852, Uncle Tom's cabin; or Life among the lowly: Cleveland, Jewett, Proctor and Worthington, 552 p.

Thames, C. B., Jr., 1959, Facies relationships in the Mississippian—effects upon fluid migration (abs.): Am. Assoc. Petroleum Geologists Bull., v. 43, no. 5, p. 1106; also, *in* Geol. Record, Rocky Mtn. Sec. A.A.P.G., Albuquerque, 1959, p. 83–86.

Weiss, M. P., and Norman, C. E., 1960, The American Upper Ordovician standard; IV, Classification of the type Cincinnatian: Jour. Sed. Petrology, v. 30, no. 2, p. 283–296.

Wentworth, C. K., 1922, A scale of grade and class terms for clastic sediments: Jour. Geology, v. 30, no. 5, p. 377–392.

White, Rex H., 1960, Petrology and depositional pattern in the upper Austin group, Pilot Knob area, Travis County, Texas: unpub. M.A. thesis, Univ. of Texas, 133 p.

Wolf, K. H., 1960, Simplified limestone classification (geol. note): Am. Assoc. Petroleum Geologists Bull., v. 44, no. 8, p. 1414–1416.

ENERGY INDEX FOR LIMESTONE INTERPRETATION AND CLASSIFICATION[1]

W. J. PLUMLEY,[2] G. A. RISLEY,[2] R. W. GRAVES, JR.,[3] AND M. E. KALEY[2]
La Habra, California, and Denver, Colorado

ABSTRACT

Limestone genesis is an important consideration in reconstruction of sedimentary basin history. We have designed a genetic classification of limestones based upon the energy that existed in the depositional environment, and one which permits us to construct geologic models of sedimentary history.

The energy spectrum at any depositional site, which is related to wave and current action, may range from quiet water through strongly agitated water. The Energy Index (EI) is an operational device for dividing the continuous energy spectrum into discrete energy levels. These steps are designated as limestone types in the EI classification as follows: Type I—quiet water sediments; Type II—intermittently agitated water sediments; Type III—slightly agitated water sediments; Type IV—moderately agitated water sediments; Type V—strongly agitated water sediments. The grading spectrum of energy and related water agitation is not directly related to depth, as quiet-water, low-energy sediments may be deposited in very shallow water.

We believe limestones are largely of biogenic origin and are comprised of carbonate materials which originate within the depositional basin. Such material may or may not be indigenous to its depositional site. Thus, recognition of energy levels and classification of a limestone in the EI spectrum depend upon evidence for mechanical transport of sedimentary particles by wave or current action. This evidence is found in the textural properties and biotic make-up of the granular components and in the textural properties of the finer grained matrix.

Carbonate sediments are easily altered by postdepositional processes. Thus, alteration textures must be recognized and understood, as they tend to obscure the depositional features we use for interpretation. In most limestones studied, however, primary features are sufficiently recognizable for successful interpretation of the energy spectrum.

A rock classification has a maximum utility if, in addition to its use as a medium of description and communication, it provides a means of constructing geologic models for interpretation of earth history. Our classification has this utility because it allows us to relate limestones genetically on a three-dimensional basis in space and time. Changes in depositional energy at one place as a function of time may be studied by means of an EI log. The change of EI with time at one locality is related to important developments in basin history such as transgression, regression, basin subsidence, or stillstand. Combination of several EI logs permits one to relate these energy-time changes on an areal basis for correlation purposes.

Finally, the limestone types, which essentially are lithofacies, provide a genetic framework for delineation of facies related to geomorphic environments of deposition.

INTRODUCTION

Geologists, like scientists in many other fields, expend considerable effort in classifying natural phenomena. Such classification is an important part of the geological scientific method. Geologists have found that grouping or classifying related phenomena and properties of the earth leads them to a better understanding of earth history. Classification of rocks is the cornerstone upon which the majority of geological concepts rest and is the basis for communication of ideas about earth history.

The purpose of this paper is to describe a classification for limestones. The classification permits interpretations of limestone genesis based primarily upon the energy level in the deposi-

[1] Part of a symposium arranged by the Research Committee, and presented at Denver, Colorado, April 27, 1961, under joint auspices of the Association and the Society of Economic Paleontologists and Mineralogists. Manuscript received, March 24, 1961.

[2] California Research Corporation, La Habra, California.

[3] Lion Oil Company, Denver, Colorado.

The limestone studies and concepts summarized in this paper are the outgrowth of work initiated in 1948 when discovery of the North Snyder and Leduc reef fields in Texas and Canada stimulated renewed interest in carbonate petrology. The classification was developed as an operational tool for use by geologists of the Standard Oil Company of California. Many of these company geologists contributed to our studies and concepts by discussions of specific areas and problems.

Special thanks are due to Mr. J. E. Adams of The Standard Oil Company of Texas for his contributions on carbonate rock problems in West Texas and to Mr. W. Lynch of The California Company for cooperative work on Jurassic carbonates of the Gulf Coast.

We appreciate particularly the valuable assistance provided in the early stages of our work by professor H. A. Lowenstam of the California Institute of Technology.

tional environment and thereby helps us to construct geologic models of sedimentary history. The depositional energy level, which is a function of wave and current action, varies in space and time and leaves its record in the rocks. We divide this record into five major limestone types and fifteen subtypes based upon an interpretation of the energy level primarily, and to a lesser extent upon the biota.

Many limestone classifications have been based upon rock properties that reflect the physical environment. Within the past decade, numerous papers have related limestone textures to the degree of water agitation in the depositional environment. Among the more important papers are those of Pettijohn (1949, 1957), Rittenhouse (1949), Henson (1950), Lowenstam (1950), Wanless (1952), Adams (1953), Bergenbeck and Terriere (1953), Plumley and Graves (1953), Beales (1956, 1958), Myers and others (1956), Carozzi (1957, 1958), Forman and Schlanger (1957), Houbolt (1957), Moretti (1957), Andrichuck (1958a, b), Bramkamp and Powers (1958), Dott (1958), Pray (1958), Teichert (1958), Wolfenden (1958), Folk (1959), and Illing (1959).

Recent papers by Andrichuck (1958a,b), Bramkamp and Powers (1958), and Illing (1959) describe classifications that are very similar to the one presented here. In all the papers cited, the authors recognized the importance of interpreting the response of carbonate sediments to the physical environment. We believe that this recognition is based upon characteristics of limestones that have genetic significance and that may be applied in a useful way for limestone classification.

Danger exists that any classification will be applied indiscriminately as a panacea for all problems in carbonate rocks. We regard our classification as a first step, only, in understanding limestones in relation to petroleum accumulation. Many carbonate petroleum reservoirs owe their favorable porosity and permeability to depositional textural properties; whereas other carbonate reservoirs are favorable because secondary porosity and permeability developed by solution, recrystallization, and dolomitization. Understanding and prediction of carbonate reservoir porosity logically depend, therefore, upon (1) interpretation of depositional facies, and (2) an understanding of limestone alteration processes in relation to depositional textures. Although we recognize the importance of secondary processes in limestones, this paper is concerned only with depositional interpretations.

DEFINITIONS

Many arguments among geologists arise because of the semantic curtain. Rock classifications often tend to aggravate this situation. Although our classification generates no new vocabulary, we have found it necessary to define a number of terms rather precisely because of nonuniformity of usage in the literature.

1. *Wave base.*—Wave base is that water depth below which the movement of the water caused by surface waves does not move the sediment. Wave base ranges widely, depending on oceanographic conditions (for example, wave amplitude and fetch, storms, and bottom topography).
2. *Energy level.*—The energy level is the kinetic energy that exists in the water at the depositional interface and a few feet above. This energy of motion may be due to either wave or current action. Depending upon several oceanographic variables (for example, depth of water, wave amplitude, and storm activity), the energy level at the depositional interface may be fairly constant, or may range within wide limits as a function of time. Quiet-water deposition is equated with an effective zero energy level in terms of the energy of the water mass capable of moving sedimentary particles. Such an energy level, however, does not necessarily imply a complete lack of water movement or stagnant conditions in the depositional environment.
3. *Depositional interface.*—The depositional interface is the interface between the water and the bottom where sediments are deposited in relation to the energy level at the interface.
4. *Clastic carbonate particles.*—We define clastic carbonate particles as grains that have been transported mechanically by current or wave action. Such grains could have originated by mechanical, biochemical, or biological breakup of pre-existing limestone or shell material, or could have formed by chemical precipitation. The essential characteristic is that they have been mechanically transported. Many microcrystalline limestones undoubtedly are of clastic origin in the above sense, but positive criteria for such an origin generally are lacking.
5. *Microcrystalline carbonate.*—Microcrystalline carbonate is composed of carbonate particles less than 0.06 mm diameter, that cannot be recognized as clastic. Microcrystalline textures probably result from either inorganic or biochemical precipitation or post-depositional recrystallization of carbonate mud.
6. *Micrograined carbonate.*—Micrograined carbonate is composed of distinct carbonate particles between 0.0039 and 0.06 mm diameter (silt-size range) which can be interpreted as clastic grains.
7. *Matrix.*—Matrix is defined as the material in which any sedimentary particle is embedded. The

matrix may be either microcrystalline or granular. The crystal size in microcrystalline matrices is uniform. Granular matrices tend to become more poorly sorted as particle size increases.

8. *Nonskeletal grains.*—Nonskeletal grains are carbonate grains, ranging from silt through sand size, and composed of homogeneous microcrystalline carbonate, whose genesis is unknown. Such grains in the geologic record are described by Beales (1958), who has given the name "bahamite" to rocks composed of such grains by analogy to similar carbonate sediments in Recent environments (Illing, 1954). Beales and Illing apparently attribute the genesis of these grains to an accretionary process by carbonate precipitation in shallow, slightly turbulent waters of higher than normal sea-water salinity. Whereas this origin is quite likely for many nonskeletal grains, similar grains undoubtedly are formed by recrystallization of skeletal material, particularly of algae, and by breakup and transportation of early lithified carbonate muds. Whatever the origin of nonskeletal grains, we believe they were deposited in an energy level of slightly to moderately agitated water.

ENERGY INDEX CLASSIFICATION

The classification is genetic and provides a basis for the interpretation of depositional environments of limestones. The primary consideration for the genetic grouping of limestone types is the inferred degree of water agitation in the depositional environment. From this consideration we have designated our classification as the Energy Index (EI) system of classification.

Textural and compositional data are used in grouping limestones into the genetic categories of the classification. The textural data, which are of primary consideration, are size, sorting, and roundness of granular particles, and the nature of the matrix. The compositional data, which are supplemental, are mineralogy and fossil types, abundance, and associations. Textural and compositional data are most easily obtained from thin sections, plastic peels, and polished surfaces. Wet or dry examination of rough limestone surfaces yields considerably less information. Where available from outcrop or core examination, sedimentary structures are useful in augmenting the textural data for interpretation.

Our classification consists of five major limestone types which constitute a grading spectrum between quiet water and strongly agitated water. The major types are—quiet water (Type I), intermittently agitated water (Type II), slightly agitated water (Type III), moderately agitated water (Type IV), and strongly agitated water (Type V). Each type is a pigeonhole with arbitrary boundaries determined by semiquantitative and qualitative analysis of primary textural properties.

Each major limestone type (I through V) is subdivided into three subtypes, which are designated as I_1, I_2, I_3, II_1, etc. The subtypes are used to indicate (1) the genetic similarities among limestones with different textural properties, and (2) genetic differences among limestones with similar textural properties.

The complete classification is shown in Table I.

Type I.—This type represents the end member of minimum water agitation. Quiet-water limestones are characterized by lack of recognizable clastic particles.

They range from nonfossiliferous lime muds (microcrystalline carbonate) to coquinoid limestones (nonclastic shell limestone). Type I_1 limestones (Plate I-*a*) are identified primarily by their argillaceous content. Type I_2 and Type I_3 limestones are relatively pure carbonate; the former (Plate I-*b*) are essentially nonfossiliferous and the latter (Plate I-*c*) are fossiliferous (coquinoid limestone).

The shapes of the fossils represent primarily their original morphology. The skeletal materials are not abraded by transportation, although they may be broken by scavenger activity. If the fossils are broken, the fragments are angular, which implies lack of transportation. Fossil assemblages are simple, consisting of many individuals, but few species. The quiet-water limestone category thus includes several varieties of limestones from the viewpoint of other classifications, but from our viewpoint of physical environment they are considered as one major type.

Type II.—Intermittently agitated-water limestones are mixed types, representing the influences of both quiet- and agitated-water environments.

The characteristic textural feature is a microcrystalline matrix that comprises more than 50 per cent of the rock and represents the quiet-water environment. Admixture of less than 50 per cent clastic particles is considered as evidence for intermittent water agitation. Because of transportation of fossil detritus, the assemblages are more complex than those of quiet-water types. The re-

Table I. Energy Index Classification of Limestones

Limestone Type According to Energy Index	*Limestone Sub-Types*	*Mineralogy*	*Texture* Size	*Texture* Sorting	*Texture* Roundness	*Fossil Abundance and Complexity*	*Characteristic Fossils*[1] *Fossil Associations* *Fossil Preservation*
QUIET I Deposition in quiet water	I_1	Calcite Clay (15 to 50%) Detrital quartz (<5%)	Microcrystalline carbonate (<0.06 mm) or any size fossil fragments in a microcrystalline carbonate matrix (matrix <50%)	Matrix—good Fossils—poor	Original fossil shapes; angular fragments if broken	Barren to moderately fossiliferous Simple assemblages	Crinoids; echinoids; bryozoans (fragile branching types); solitary corals; ostracodes; thin-shelled brachiopods, pelecypods, and gastropods; Foraminifera; sponge spicules; tubular, encrusting, and sediment-binding algae; fecal pellets of bottom scavengers. Common fossil associations are crinoid-bryozoa assemblages, bivalve shell assemblages, Foraminifera assemblages (predominantly planktonic). Many fossils are whole and unbroken and are not mechanically abraded. Any fragmentation of fossil material probably is due to disarticulation upon death, to predatory (boring, opening, and breaking) activity and scavenger activity, or to solution.
	I_2	Calcite (predominant) Clay (<15%) Detrital quartz (<5%)					
	I_3		Any size fossil fragments in microcrystalline matrix (matrix <50%)	Matrix—good Fossils—moderate to good		Moderately to abundantly fossiliferous Simple assemblages (coquinoid limestone)	
INTERMITTENTLY AGITATED II Deposition alternately in agitated water and in quiet water	II_1	Calcite (predominant) Clay (<25%) Detrital quartz (<50%)	Microcrystalline matrix (>50%). Micrograined to medium-grained clastic carbonate and terrigenous material	Matrix—good Clastic material—poor to good	Clastic carbonate material subangular to rounded. Roundness of terrigenous clastics is principally a function of size.	Barren to moderately fossiliferous. Moderately simple assemblages	Characteristic fossils and fossil associations are similar to Type I limestones. Fossil materials are more fragmental than those in Type I limestones and also may be more or less rounded by wave action. Scattered fragments of fossils from rougher water environments may be present.
	II_2		Microcrystalline matrix (>50%). Coarse- to very coarse-grained clastic carbonate and terrigenous material				
	II_3		Interbedded microcrystalline carbonate and any size clastic. Microscale rhythmic bedding	Sorting good within individual lamina	Oölites may be present	Barren to moderately fossiliferous. Moderately complex assemblages	
SLIGHTLY AGITATED III Deposition in slightly agitated water	III_1	Calcite (predominant) Detrital quartz (up to 50%)	Micrograined clastic carbonate (<0.06 mm) predominates	Matrix—good Clastic material—moderate to good	Clastic material subrounded to well rounded. Fine-grained oölites may be present	Barren to sparsely fossiliferous Simple assemblages	Echinoderm, bryozoan, and bivalve shell debris; Foraminifera; encrusting algae. Common fossil associations are Foraminifera-abraded bivalve shell fragment assemblages. Fossil materials comminuted from larger fossil structures are well abraded by wave and current action.
	III_2		Very fine-grained clastic carbonate (0.06 to 0.125 mm) predominates			Barren to moderately fossiliferous Simple assemblages	
	III_3		Fine-grained clastic carbonate (0.125 to 0.25 mm) predominates	Matrix—poor Clastic material—moderate to good		Barren to abundantly fossiliferous Simple to moderately complex assemblages	
MODERATELY AGITATED IV Deposition in moderately agitated water	IV_1	Calcite (predominant) Detrital quartz (up to 50%)	Medium-grained clastic carbonate (0.25 to 0.5 mm) predominates	Matrix—poor Clastic material—moderate to good	Clastic material subrounded to well rounded. Oölites may be present	Moderately to abundantly fossiliferous Simple to moderately complex assemblages	Crinoids, echinoids, bryozoans, brachiopod and pelecypod shell fragments, colonial coral fragments, stromatoporoid fragments (Silurian and Devonian predominantly); tubular algal fragments, colonial algal fragments (rare), encrusting algae. Common fossil associations are similar to associations of Types I, II, and III, or they are mixtures of these associations. Fossil materials are generally broken and abraded.
	IV_2		Coarse-grained clastic carbonate (0.5 to 1.0 mm) predominates				
	IV_3		Very coarse-grained clastic carbonate (1.0 to 2.0 mm) predominates			Moderately to abundantly fossiliferous Moderately complex to complex assemblages	

[1] The occurrence of the different fossil groups is in part a function of geologic age. All groups listed are not necessarily present in the respective limestone types.

TABLE I.—(*continued*)

Limestone Type According to Energy Index	*Limestone Sub-Types*	*Mineralogy*	*Texture*			*Fossil Abundance and Complexity*	*Characteristic Fossils*[1] *Fossil Associations* *Fossil Preservation*
			Size	*Sorting*	*Roundness*		
STRONGLY AGITATED V Deposition and growth in strongly agitated water	V_1	Calcite (predominant) Clay (<5%) Detrital quartz (<25%)	Gravel-size clastic carbonate (rock fragments and fossil material >2.0 mm) predominates	Matrix—poor Clastic material—poor to moderate	Clastic material subrounded to well rounded. Pisolites may be present	Sparsely to moderately fossiliferous Complex assemblages	Crinoids; echinoids; encrusting bryozoans; thick-shelled brachiopods, pelecypods, and gastropods; colonial coral fragments; stromatoporoid fragments (Silurian and Devonian predominantly); colonial algal fragments; rudistid fragments (Cretaceous predominantly). Fossil associations are similar to Type IV associations. Fossil materials are generally broken and abraded.
	V_2		Gravel-size conglomeratic or brecciated carbonate (>2.0 mm) Tectonic breccias excluded	Matrix—poor Clastic material—poor	Clastic material angular to well rounded	Barren to sparsely fossiliferous Complex assemblages	
	V_3	Calcite	Not applicable	Not applicable	Not applicable	Abundantly fossiliferous Simple assemblages (fossil colonial growth in place)	Colonial corals, stromatoporoids, colonial algae (principally the Rhodophyta or red algae and some genera of the Cyanophyta or blue-green algae).

quirement of greater than 50 per cent matrix clearly distinguishes these Type II limestones from the agitated-water types, but some of them may be confused with quiet-water types. Definite evidence of mechanical abrasion of particles or other evidence of "clasticity" are required to make a positive distinction of Type II limestones from Type I limestones. Types II_1 and II_2 are distinguished on the basis of the size of the clastic particles other than the predominant microcrystalline matrix; the former (Plate II-*a*) contain fine- to medium-grained clastics; the latter (Plate II-*b*) coarse- to very coarse-grained clastics. Type II_3 (Plate II-*c*) is characterized by alternating laminae of lime mud and coarser clastic carbonate that reflect alternations of quiet- and agitated-water energy levels.

Type III.—Slightly agitated-water limestones have a particle size range from silt through fine-grained sand.

Type III_1 (Plate III-*a*) could be called a "calcisiltite" and Types III_2 (Plate III-*b*) and III_3 (Plate III-*c*), very fine-grained and fine-grained "calcarenites," respectively. If a matrix is present in these clastic limestones, it is less than 50 per cent of the rock. The sorting of the clastic particles is good, and admixed terrigenous grains may be common. The matrix of the Type III_1 and III_2 limestones, if present, is microcrystalline and homogeneous (on the scale of our observations). In type III_3 the matrix may contain a range of particle sizes from microcrystalline through grain sizes that approach the median grain size of the nonmatrix particles. This implies that the action of agitated water prevents deposition of a carbonate mud matrix. Type III limestones range from nonfossiliferous to coquinoid. The Type III_3 limestones contain more complex biotic assemblages than do the Type III_1 limestones. Nonskeletal or fossil fragments are mechanically rounded.

Type IV.—Moderately agitated-water limestones (Plates IV-*a*, *b*, *c*) have a particle size range from medium-grained sand through very coarse-grained sand. Thus, they are medium-grained to very coarse-grained calcarenites. As one continues up the scale through Type IV and Type V limestones, a poorly sorted matrix is characteristic. Their other characteristics are similar to those of Type III limestones.

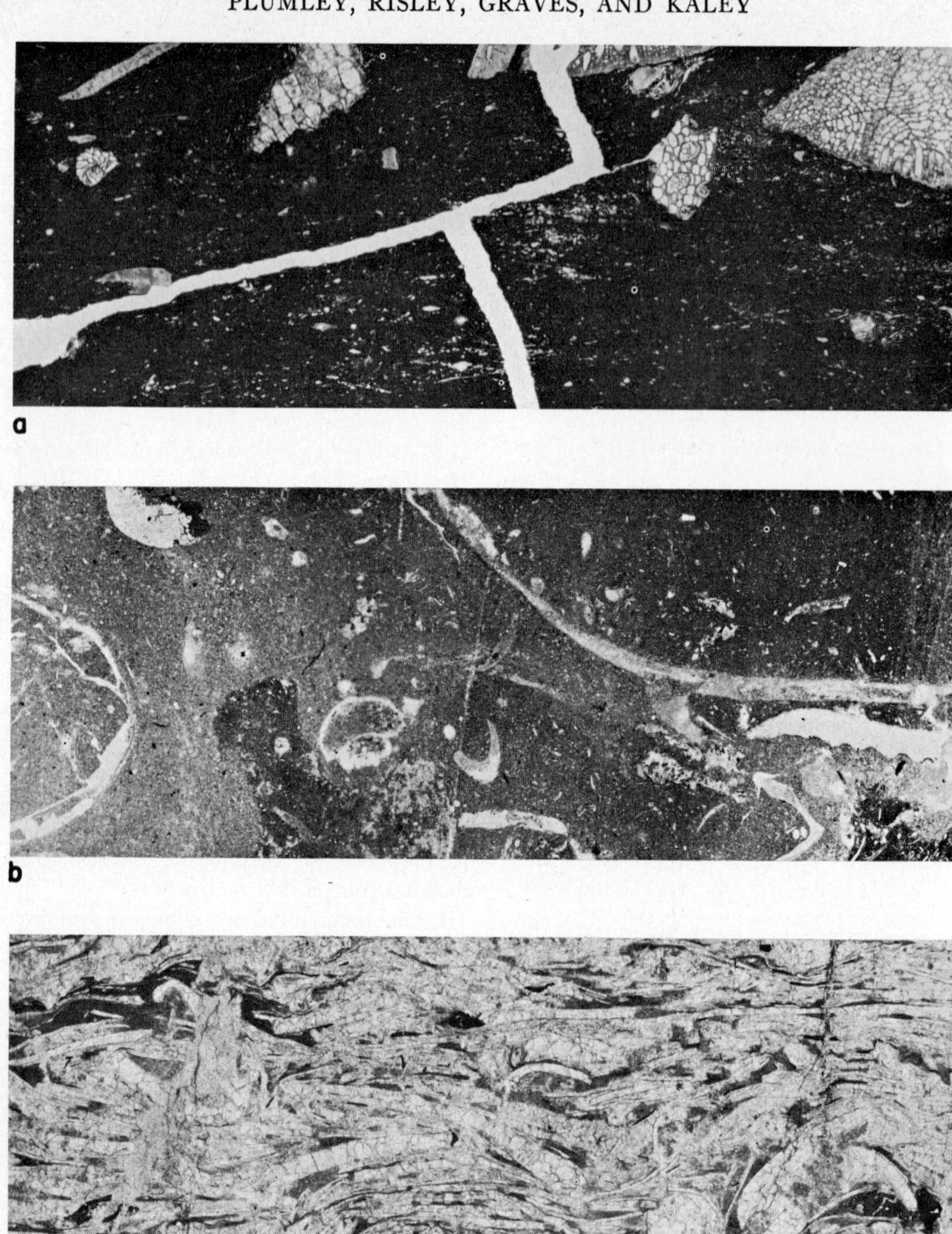

Plate I.—Type I limestones.

Type V.—Strongly agitated-water limestones represent the end member of the increasing scale of water agitation. Fragments of rock or fossil debris are coarser than 2 mm (calcirudites). Type V_1 (Plate V-*a*) is composed of poor to moderately sorted gravel-size fossil and rock fragments; whereas Type V_2 (Plate V-*b*) is poorly sorted, generally, and is composed predominantly of conglomeratic or brecciated rock fragments. Type V_3 (Plate V-*c*) represents in-place framework builders that are typical of reef type limestone accumulations.

The difficulty of placing any sample accurately within one of these categories increases as the individual sample becomes smaller, particularly where the sample size is smaller than the component particle size of the rock (that is, interpretation of Type V limestones from chips). In practice, however, we find that even with thin sections of drilling chips we can obtain a picture of changing conditions of environment, with time, in a carbonate sequence. Definitive criteria for accurate typing of a single sample may be missing. In such an event we examine samples above and below for clues to the general energy level. In general, the evidence of systematic changes of environment (either in time or space) is more important than an absolute pigeonholing of any one sample.

Carbonate sediments are easily altered throughout their postdepositional history. The processes of recrystallization, dolomitization, mineral replacement, solution, and precipitation (cementation) may preserve, modify, or destroy the depositional textures and structures that we use to classify limestones. A complete treatment of limestone alteration is outside the scope of this paper, but we need to discuss briefly the effects of these processes on the depositional characteristics upon which our classification is based.

All the processes of alteration, except some types of cementation, are dependent upon crystal size and mineralogy, other physical and chemical variables being equal. Smaller crystals are more likely to recrystallize because of their greater boundary free energy, are more reactive chemically, and are more easily dissolved. Some minerals—for example aragonite as opposed to calcite—are more soluble or less stable at given temperatures and pressures.

Alteration processes generally modify rather than destroy the depositional characteristics, because the degree of destruction depends largely on the completeness of the process. In some carbonate sequences, complete recrystallization or dolomitization has destroyed the original texture and composition; however, in many, original textures and structures are preserved as relics. Relics are present because either the process has affected only part of the rock—for example, only the matrix may be recrystallized or dolomitized—or the impurities in the original rock are not completely eliminated and the resulting rock retains at least "shadows" of the original texture and structure. All degrees of preservation are possible, and much interpretive information can be gained by comparing more poorly preserved textures with those having better preservation. Comparison will commonly permit almost complete textural reconstruction in samples having very little of the original texture preserved. This is particularly true if the samples to be compared are from the same bed or immediately adjacent beds.

CRITERIA FOR INTERPRETATION OF AGITATED-WATER ENVIRONMENTS

As the primary basis of the classification is degree of water agitation in the depositional environment, one must distinguish sedimentary particles that have been transported from those

---

←

EXPLANATION OF PLATE I

FIG. *a*.—Type I_1, microcrystalline limestone with large bryozoan fragments and about 45 per cent clay. Pennsylvanian, Strawn Series; Sotex Brown 2-5, depth 7,545 feet; Scurry County, Texas.

b.—Type I_2, slightly fossiliferous microcrystalline limestone. Devonian, Woodbend formation; Socony Vegreville 1, depth 3,069 feet; Alberta, Canada.

c.—Type I_3, coquinoid limestone, bivalve shells in a microcrystalline carbonate matrix. Cretaceous, Cogollo formation; Rexco Zulia 26D-2, depth 11,670 feet; Venezuela.

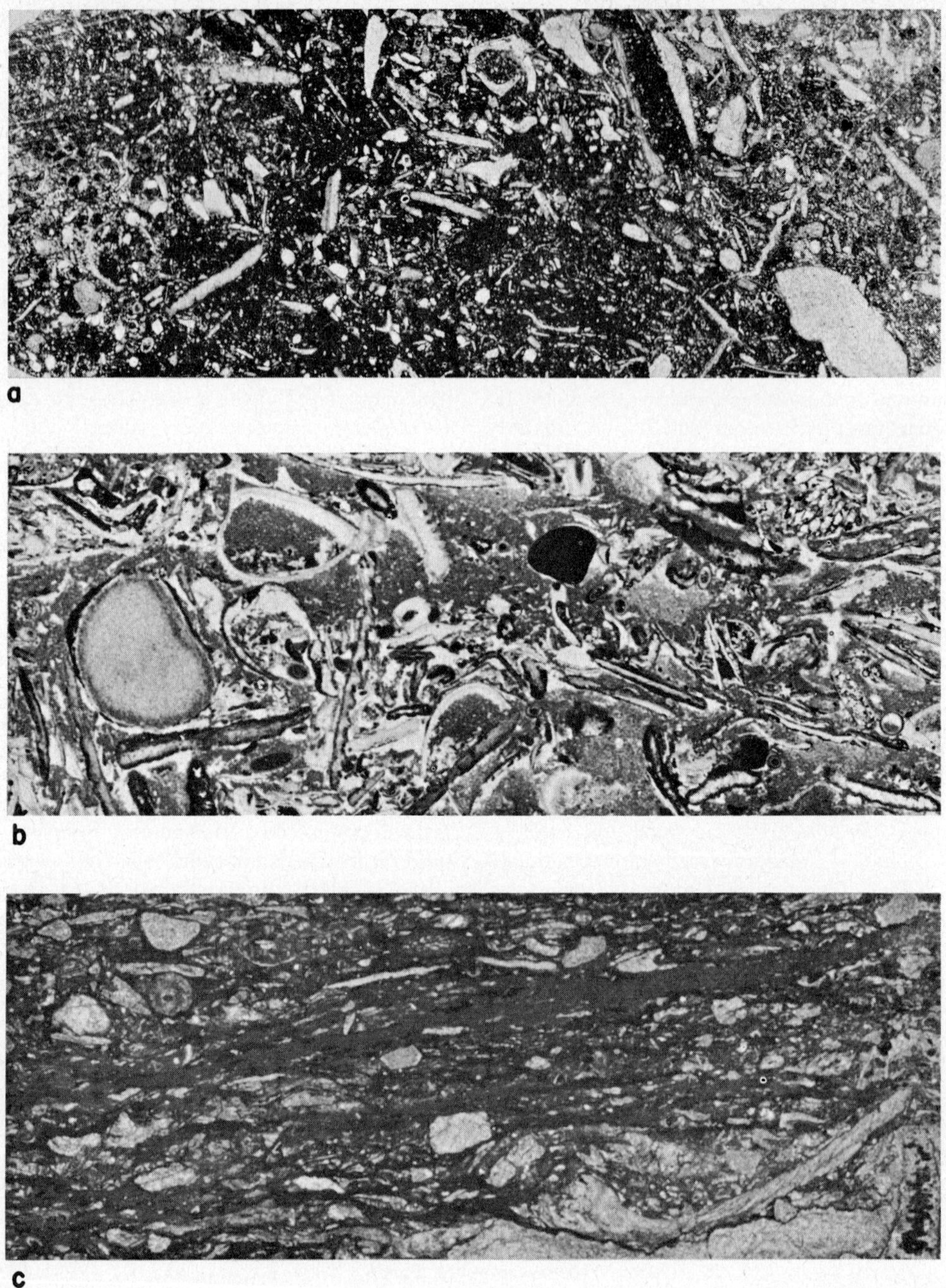

PLATE II.—Type II limestones.

that have not. The distance of transport cannot be estimated, except in special cases of admixed terrigenous particles which have been added from a source beyond the carbonate realm. We consider that the bulk of carbonates originates within the depositional basin by chemical or biochemical means. One also must recognize carbonate sedimentary structures that are resistant to the forces of agitated water and may reflect this environment indirectly. Listed below are criteria that may be used to infer agitated water environments and, in most cases, transportation of carbonate detritus.

1. Fragments of partly indurated sediment or pre-existing rock, ranging in size from silt to boulders, of carbonate or other lithology, angular or rounded.
2. Rounded fragments of fossils that were not originally round.
3. A poorly sorted matrix.
4. Carbonate particles mixed with terrigenous clastics of same size (for example, quartz sand).
5. Mixed faunas and floras, comprising assemblages that are ecologically incompatible.
6. Oölites. Although evidence exists that some oölites may originate as concretionary aggregates in quiet-water environments, most evidence suggests an agitated-water environment. This evidence applies whether the oölites are of chemical or algal origin.
7. Wave-resistant, colonial organisms in place. These include colonial corals, colonial algae, and stromotoporoids primarily, although other framework-building organisms also have been suggested as being wave resistant.
8. Sedimentary structures such as small scale cross-bedding.

PHYSICAL MEANING OF LIMESTONE TYPES

We have stated that the various rock types of the classification are based on an interpretation of the degree of water agitation at the depositional site as inferred from textural and compositional analysis. What does this actually mean in terms of a physical picture or model of the depositional environment? It means that the depositional interface experienced a certain energy level or degree of water agitation during the deposition of any particular type of carbonate sediment.

The energy level at the depositional interface is controlled by waves and currents. Regardless of whether the energy is of wave or current origin, sedimentary particles at the depositional interface will respond as a function of the energy level and the materials available for transport. We cannot distinguish whether sediments are wave or current transported, and therefore our classification interprets only the energy level in the depositional environment.

Energy level is an abstract concept and difficult to translate into a physical picture for geologic interpretation. To increase understanding of this conceptual model as related to classification, therefore, we will discuss reef and associated environments as an example of energy level as influenced by wave action.

In this hypothetical example we can picture a fringing reef situated on a sloping shelf and separating an open marine environment from a lagoonal environment landward. Below a certain water depth on the shelf, wave base is above the depositional interface and the wave-induced energy level is zero. In such an environment quiet water Type I limestones are deposited. Farther up the shelf and toward the reef, the water is shallower and the depositional interface approaches wave base. In such areas of shoaling waters, be they reefs, banks, or shelves bordering land areas, the depositional interface is close to the depth of wave base. Intermittently agitated carbonate sediments (Type II) occur in this transition zone between deep water, where the depositional

←«««

EXPLANATION OF PLATE II

FIG. *a.*—Type II_1, fine- to medium-grained fossil debris in microcrystalline carbonate matrix. Cretaceous, Cogollo formation; Texas Raban 10, depth 8,260 feet; Venezuela.

b.—Type II_2, coarse- to very coarse-grained rock fragments and fossils in microcrystalline carbonate matrix. Devonian, Woodbend formation; Socony Vegreville 1, depth, 3,041 feet; Alberta, Canada.

c.—Type II_3, interlaminated microcrystalline carbonate and fossil debris. Mississippian; Cal Standard West Daly 8-29, depth 2,474 feet; Manitoba, Canada.

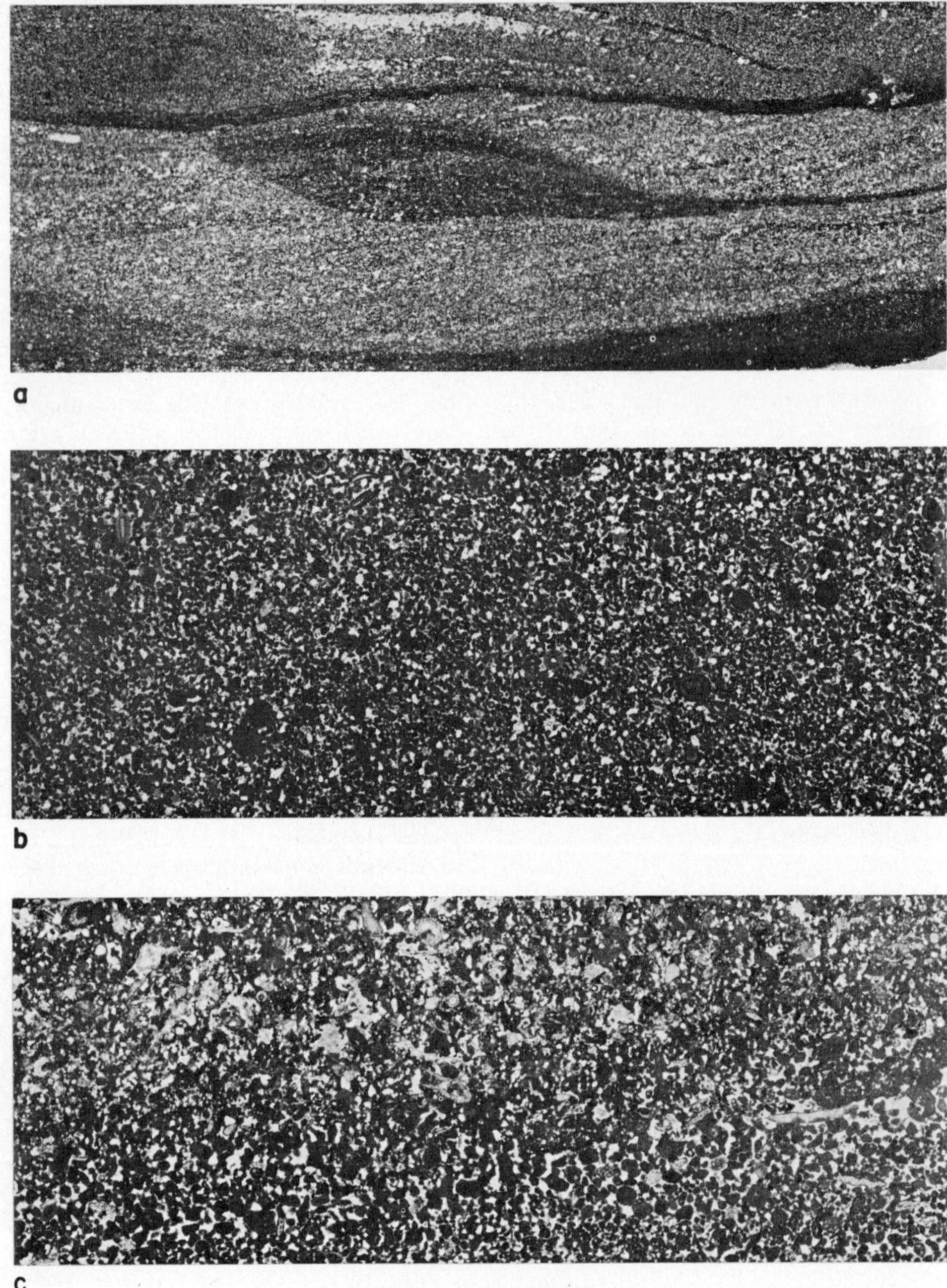

PLATE III.—Type III limestones.

interface always is below wave base, and very shallow water where the interface is constantly above wave base. The average depth of wave base and departures from a mean depth can vary considerably, depending upon oceanographic and climatic variables such as slope of the shelf, amplitude and fetch of the waves, storm paths and cycles. Depending upon the changing depth of wave base, the bottom sediment is alternately stirred up by wave turbulence and allowed to resettle in quiet water. Thus, these sediments are neither products of predominantly quiet nor predominantly agitated water; they have textural and compositional features of both. The quiet-water feature is represented by the microcrystalline matrix (>50 per cent) and some autochthonous fossils. The agitated-water feature is represented by an admixture of transported coarser grained particles (terrigenous grains, oölites, or rounded fossil debris).

Where the depositional interface is slightly above the zone of wave base variation, the bottom is continually subjected to slightly agitated-water conditions. Such an energy level will result in Type III sediments. Farther up the shoaling slope the depositional interface comes successively into more and more agitated water as the sea surface is approached. Thus, the bottom sediments are subjected to moderately agitated and then strongly agitated water in a grading spectrum with deposition of Type IV and Type V sediments, respectively.

At the fringing reef wall itself, Type V sediments would occur. Such sediments would consist of reef framework builders in place, or reef wall fragments torn from the reef and dumped as a debris apron.

In the lagoonal environment behind the reef wall, the energy level at the depositional interface is considerably lower than at the reef wall, which serves as a baffle to dissipate the energy of the incoming waves. In such a protected back-reef environment, we could expect to find a variety of limestone types from the energy viewpoint. Quiet-water (Type I), and in this environment very shallow-water, sediments would be common. During periodic storm activity, the depositional interface in the lagoon environment could be subjected to a variety of energy levels producing Types II, III, IV, and V sediments.

Thus, energy level and the resulting limestone types are not necessarily related to water depth. Quiet-water Type I limestones may occur in either deep or shallow water. Type I limestone may be recognized as being a shallow-water deposit if it contains shallow-water fossils, and the fossils show no evidence of transportation. Agitated-water sediments of Types III, IV, and V are generally typical of shallow water in reef areas, banks, shallow shelves, and coastal areas.

In this conceptual model we have ignored the types of sediments that would result from current activity at the depositional interface. We can only add that in any of the geomorphic environments discussed above (for example, shelf, reef, back-reef), currents at the depositional interface in shallow or deep water can produce agitated-water textures similar to those produced by wave turbulence at the same energy level.

APPLICATION

A rock classification has a maximum utility if, in addition to its use as a medium of description and communication, it provides a means of constructing geologic models for interpretation of earth history. Our classification has certain genetic similarities, from the energy-level viewpoint, to broad groups of terrigenous clastic sediments. Thus, Type I limestones are similar to shales (nonfossiliferous and fossiliferous); Type

---

←

Explanation of Plate III

Fig. *a.*—Type III$_1$, microclastic limestone with well-developed cross-bedding. Mississippian; Canadian Superior Cruikshank 14-4, depth 2,712 feet; Manitoba, Canada.

b.—Type III$_2$, very fine-grained clastic limestone. Jurassic, Smackover formation; Stanolind Bodcaw 1, depth 11,050-51 feet; Lafayette County, Arkansas.

c.—Type III$_3$, fine-grained clastic limestone, Devonian, Woodbend formation; Socony Vegreville 1, depth 3,871 feet; Alberta, Canada.

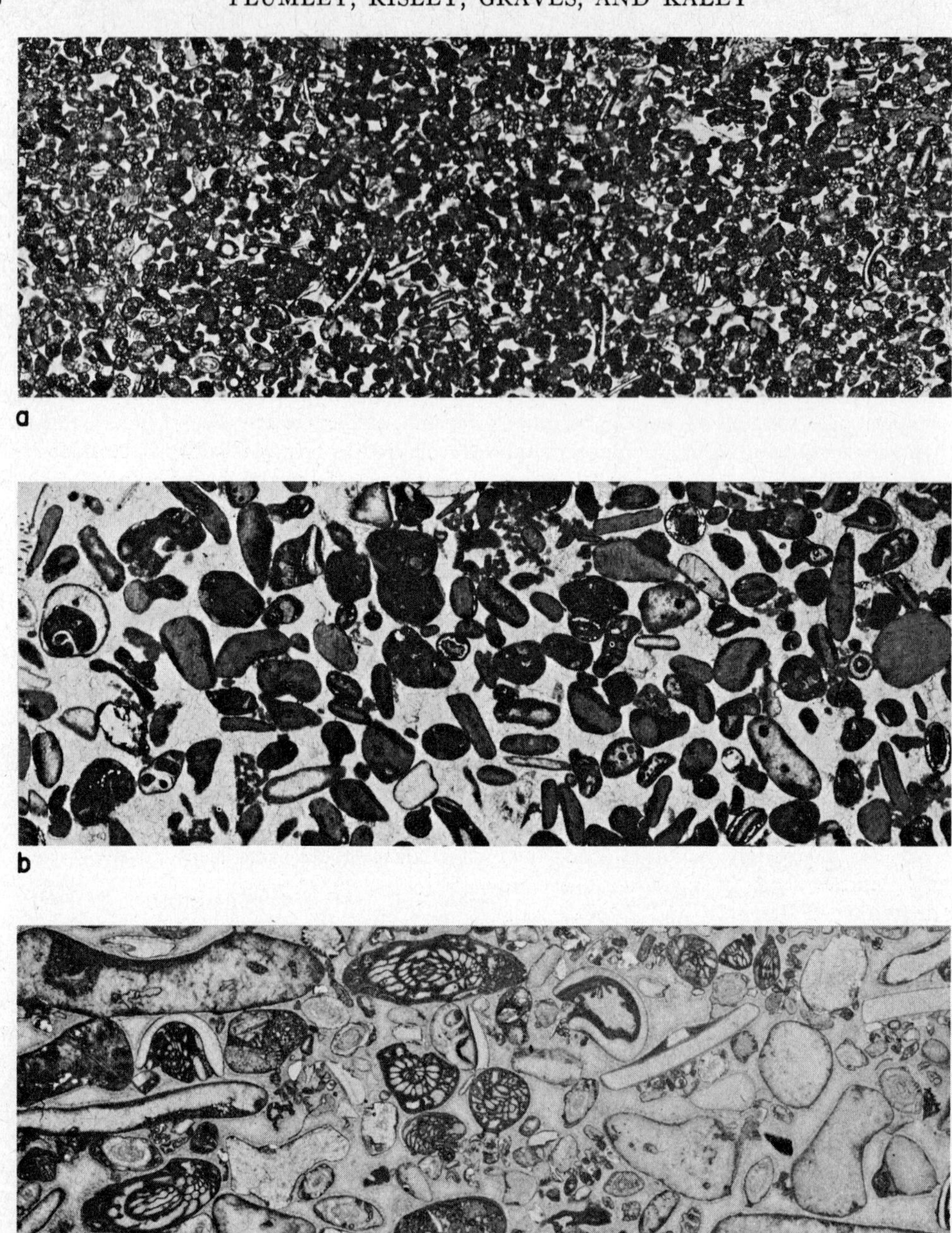

PLATE IV.—Type IV limestones.

III and IV to silts and sands; and Type V to conglomerates. Type II limestones have their counterparts in mixed types such as sandy and conglomeratic shales.

Whereas terrigenous clastic particles are from extrabasinal sources, limestone components preponderantly are from intrabasinal sources. For this reason not all carbonate particles are clastic, and the textural analogy with terrigenous clastic particles has certain boundary conditions as defined in the classification.

Textural characteristics of the terrigenous clastic sediments commonly are interpreted in terms of the energy of the environment. Beaches, offshore surf zones, and breaks in slope are characteristically zones of high energy and coarser grained clastic sediments; whereas shallow-water protected bays, lagoons, and the deeper water offshore areas (turbidite deposition excepted) are zones of low energy and the finer grained clastic sediments.

Carbonate sediments respond to the same energy levels as do the terrigenous clastic sediments. The coarser grained clastic carbonates are found in the higher energy environments at the beach zone and in shoaling waters created by carbonate banks and reefs. The low-energy carbonates are found in shallow back-reef or lagoonal areas or in deep water seaward of carbonate bank or reef buildups.

Our classification, based on the environmental energy spectrum, permits us to reconstruct a three-dimensional model of the depositional history of a carbonate basin. In initial studies, we need not define the environments in terms of shoreline, reef, bank, etc. Indeed, during the early stages of a carbonate study, we cannot define environments in terms of these morphological characteristics. Although a reef complex has zones of high energy, it also has zones of low energy. Thus, before we can reconstruct the morphological picture of such environments, we must determine the three dimensional, space and time picture of the sediments.

The Energy Index classification facilitates such a space-time reconstruction of carbonate depositional history. This reconstruction is a twofold process that analyzes (A) the vertical changes (time-dependent) in sedimentation, and (B) the horizontal changes (space-dependent) in sedimentation. As stratigraphers well know, vertical changes in sedimentation reflect shifting facies as a function of time in response to various processes that result in marine transgressions or regressions, or similar effects. To understand depositional history, facies changes in both time and space must be integrated.

A. *Energy variations in time.*—The vertical change in the energy spectrum of carbonate sedimentation is analyzed by means of the EI log. On such a log the vertical scale is depth in a well, and the horizontal scale is limestone type from I through V. In practice, we translate the I to V scale into Arabic numbers for purposes of computing average energy levels for specific depth intervals. A typical log is shown in Figure 1-*A* (Standard Oil Company of Texas J. Brown 2–5, Scurry County, Texas). This log, which is typical of many other EI logs of carbonate-rock sequences, illustrates a number of points related to application of the classification.

The section portrayed in this log extends from the top of the Pennsylvanian Canyon limestone (Missourian) at 6,240 feet to well down into the Strawn (Desmoinesian) at 7,565 feet. The base of the Pennsylvanian is at 7,800 feet and rests upon Mississippian. Core samples were analyzed at 5-foot intervals through this section. The EI log was constructed by averaging the EI over 100-foot intervals with 50-foot overlaps.

←⋘

Explanation of Plate IV

Fig. *a.*—Type IV_1, medium-grained clastic (algal oölite) limestone. Pennsylvanian, Virgil Series; surface sample; Sacramento Mountains, New Mexico.

b.—Type IV_2, coarse-grained clastic (rock and fossil fragments) limestone, crystalline calcite matrix. Cretaceous, Cogollo formation; Texas Raban 10, depth 7,867 feet; Venezuela.

c.—Type IV_3, very coarse-grained clastic limestone with crystalline calcite matrix. Pennsylvanian, Canyon Series; Sotex Brown 6-6, depth 6,770 feet; Scurry County, Texas.

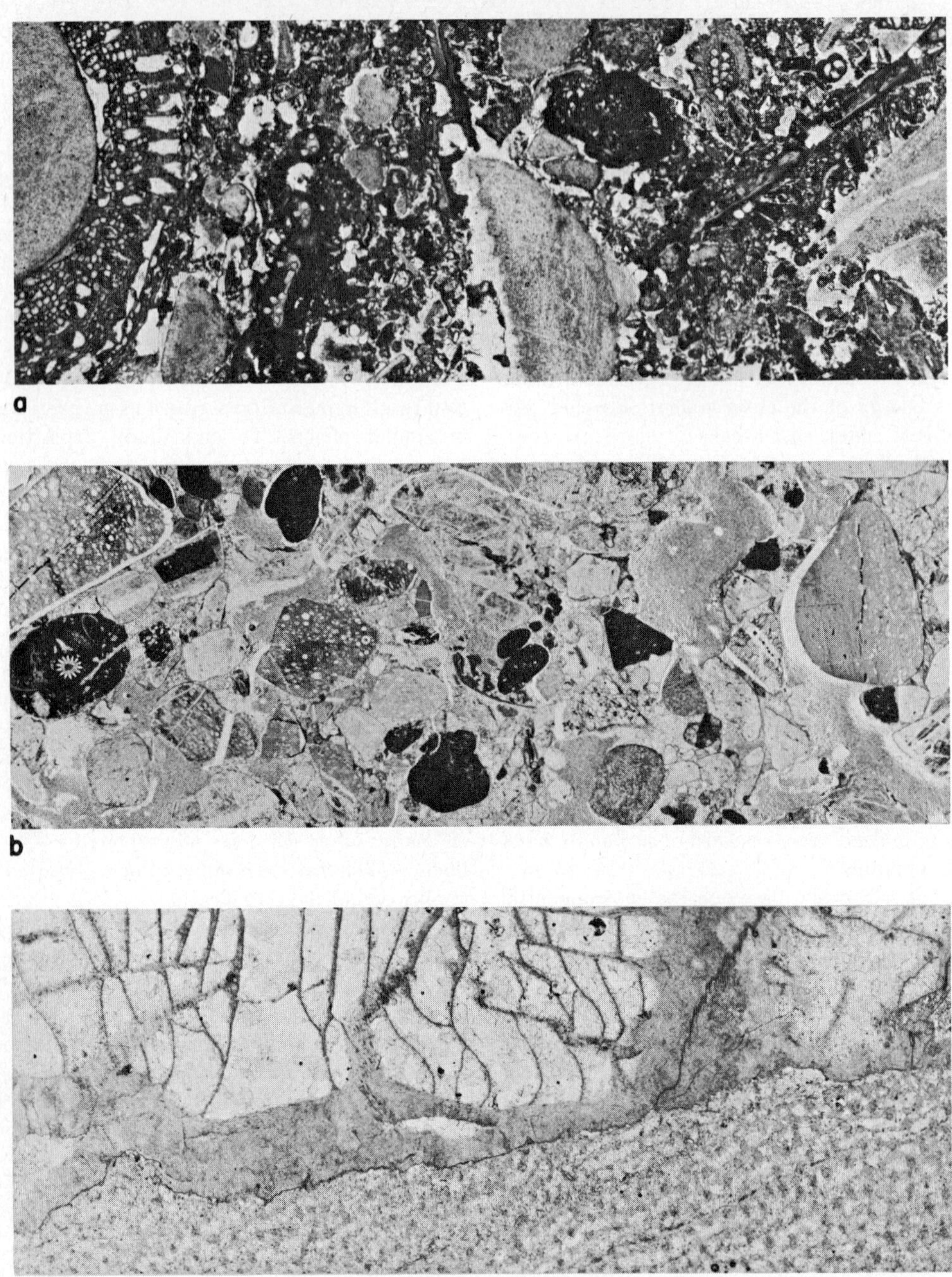

PLATE V.—Type V limestones.

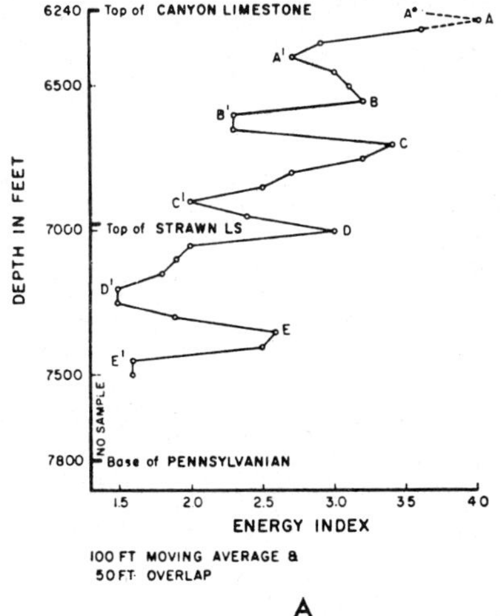

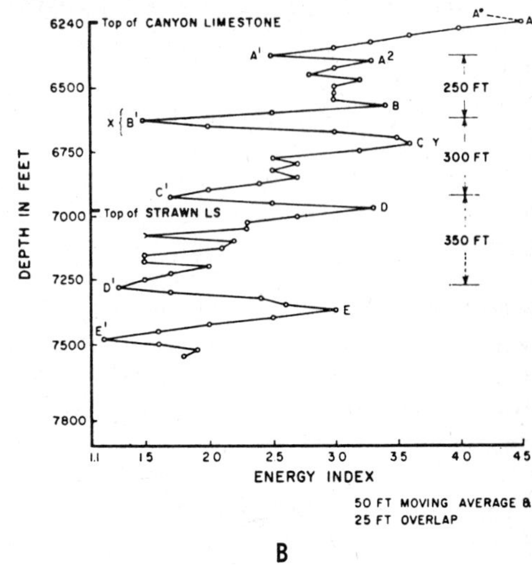

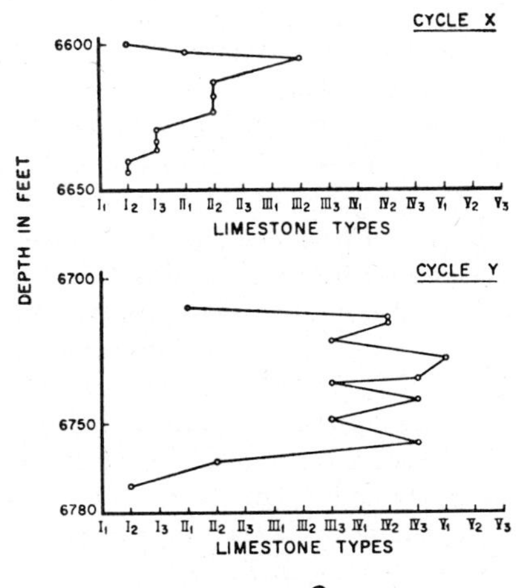

Fig. 1.—Energy Index logs of Pennsylvanian limestone in Standard Oil Company of Texas J. Brown 2-5, Scurry County, Texas.

We see in this example that the depositional energy level fluctuated from quiet to agitated water through several cycles as a function of time. Three major cycles are present in the Canyon (A^0-A-A^1, A^1-B-B^1, B^1-C-C^1) and two in the Strawn (C^1-D-D^1, D^1-E-E^1). The final cycle in the Canyon (A^0-A-A^1) is abruptly terminated at the top of the Canyon limestone at 6,240 feet with a capping of calcareous black shale. The top of the Strawn at 6,975 feet is a paleontologic top. It ap-

---

Explanation of Plate V

Fig. *a*.—Type V_1, gravel-size clastic limestone. Pennsylvanian Canyon Series; Sotex Brown 3-1, depth 6,677 feet; Scurry County, Texas.

b.—Type V_2, conglomeratic limestone. Pleistocene, Ryukyu formation; surface sample; Ie Shima, Ryukyu Islands.

c.—Type V_3, stromatoporoid and colonial coral limestone. Devonian, Woodbend formation; Socony Vegreville 1, depth 3,818 feet; Alberta, Canada.

pears to correspond closely with a period of maximum energy in the environment.

These cycles possibly could be interpreted as cyclic eustatic changes in sea level, which brought the sea bottom alternately into quiet and agitated waters as related to wave base and currents. In this particular example, however, we are inclined to attribute these cycles to alternating periods of stillstand and basin subsidence. In this area of bank and reef development, the intervals of increasing energy (E^1-E, D^1-D, etc.) are interpreted as periods of stillstand, when the bank organisms built the bank surface higher into the zone of water turbulence. These periods were culminated by periods of basin subsidence, when the bank surface was lowered into quieter water near or below wave base. The bank apparently subsided at a rate which could not be compensated by organic productivity. Cessation of subsidence initiated a new cycle.

Although not all carbonate sequences show the cyclic uniformity of this example, most of them are cyclic to a greater or lesser extent, be it on a bed-to-bed or a formation-to-formation basis. Thus, the time changes in the energy spectrum can provide important information on the time changes of carbonate sedimentation.

The details of cyclic sedimentation depend upon the scale of observation and averaging procedures. This is shown in Figures 1-*B* and 1-*C*. In Figure 1-*B* the same data were analyzed with 50-foot moving averages (25-foot overlap) rather than 100-foot average as in Figure 1-*A*. The major cycles are still evident, but the limbs of the cycles have more character and are composed of smaller scale cycles. This character is important for correlation purposes described later.

On the scale of averaging in Figure 1-*B*, the major cycles show a regular decrease in thickness in the upper Strawn and through the Canyon. Cycle D^1-D-C^1 encompasses 350 feet of section; C^1-C-B^1, 300 ft; and B^1-B-A^1, 250 ft. If this sequence continued, we would expect A^1-A-A^0 to encompass 200 feet rather than 135 feet as it actually does. The incompleteness of this last cycle may be due to subaerial erosion of the reef surface, as upper Pennsylvanian Cisco (Virgilian) sediments are missing from the section and the Canyon limestone in this well is capped by Permian Wolfcamp shales (personal communication, J. E. Adams, Standard Oil Company of Texas). These calculations of cycles would indicate that about 65 feet of Canyon limestone had been eroded from the reef crest during Cisco time.

In Figure 1-*C* we have analyzed two examples of the smallest scale cycle possible on the basis of our sampling interval. Each point represents one sample. Another difference is the use of subtypes (for example, I_1, I_2, I_3, II_1). Cycle X shows the variation in rock type in a 45-foot interval near a minimum energy point (B′ on Fig. 1-*B*); whereas cycle Y shows the variation in a 60-foot interval near a maximum energy point (C on Fig. 1-*B*). Cycle X is predominantly one of quiet to intermittently agitated water; whereas cycle Y is predominantly one of slightly to moderately agitated water. In both cycles a progressive increase in water agitation is followed by a decrease. Thus, the energy spectrum variation follows a cyclic pattern which is independent of the scale.

The cycles shown in the preceding illustrations are typical of sequences in limestone bank and reef areas. For comparison we have illustrated energy cycles in a carbonate shelf environment (Fig. 2). This EI log is of the Canadian Superior Cruickshank 14-4 well, Manitoba, Canada. Core samples were analyzed at 2-foot intervals from the top of the Mississippian unconformity at 2,388 feet to the base of the Mississippian at 2,726 feet. EI values are averaged over 20-foot intervals with 10-foot overlap. On the scale used, the Mississippian shows a general increase in energy level in its lower half, followed by pronounced energy cycles in the upper half of the section. For comparison with similar limestone thicknesses in the Pennsylvanian examples, this EI log on the same scale and same averaging basis as the Brown 2–5 well (Fig. 1-*B*) is shown in the insert of Figure 2.

B. *Energy variations in space.*—We have seen that energy fluctuations are time-dependent. We might expect, therefore, that at any one time the energy conditions would be the same over an area of the sea floor; the smaller the area the more similar would be the energy level, with decreasing departure from similarity as a function of distance from the point of comparison. For example, a nearshore area is exposed to high wave energy in

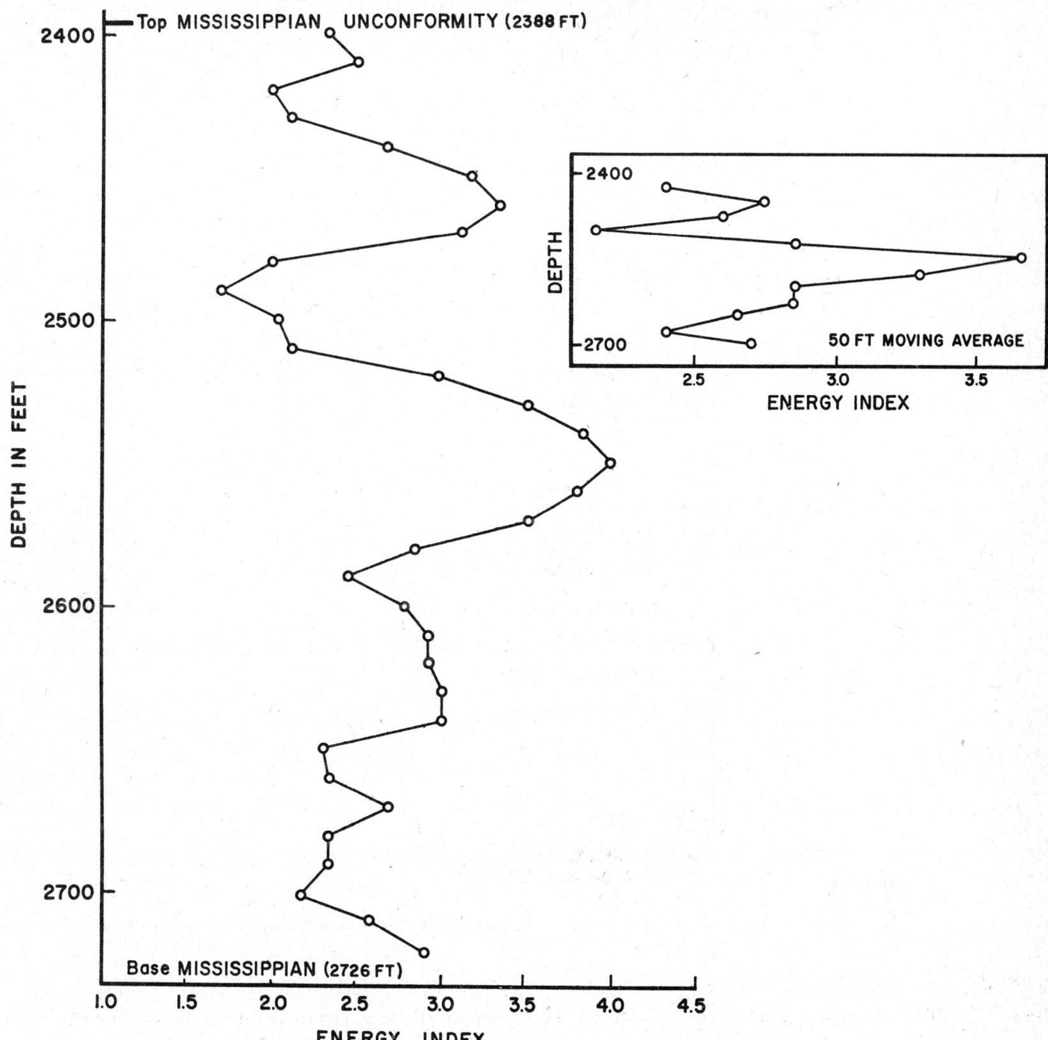

FIG. 2.—Energy Index log of Mississippian limestone in Canadian Superior Cruickshank 14-4, Manitoba, Canada. (20-foot moving averages with 10-foot overlap.)

comparison to one farther offshore where the wave turbulence is less effective and the energy at the sea bottom is less. If a hurricane moves through the area the energy level is raised at both locations and is reflected in higher energy sediments. Thus, as a function of time, the increase in energy is reflected in the sedimentary record at both locations, although the absolute scale of this reflection is different.

We can use this principle for correlating EI logs by means of the energy cycles as reflected in the rock types. By correlating cycles we effectively are establishing time lines in carbonate sequences. An example of this application is shown in Figure 3, where we have shown suggested time correlations among three closely spaced wells in the North Synder area of Scurry County, Texas. Because the bank environment in this area contains so

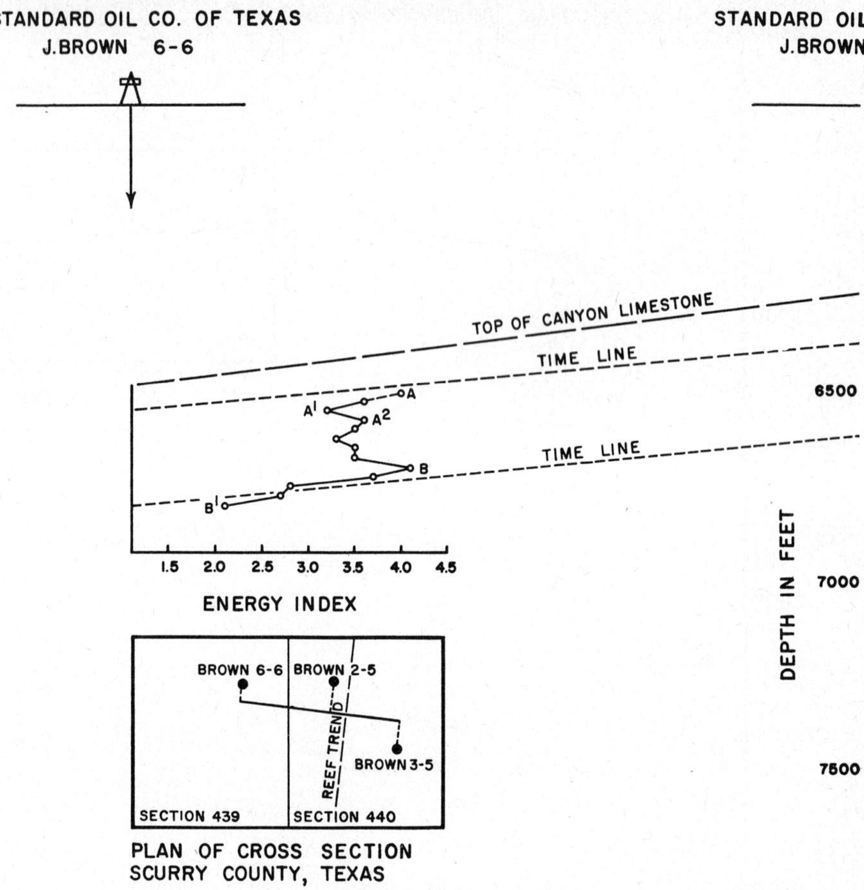

FIG. 3.—Energy Index correlation cross section through crest

many different varieties of limestone, and they change so rapidly laterally, it is impractical to correlate bed for bed. On the other hand, it is entirely feasible to obtain logical correlations of depositional energy cycles.

Continuous cores were available from the upper part of the Canyon limestone to the east and west of the Standard of Texas Brown 2-5 well. Thus, the correlation section is roughly transverse to the regional strike of Scurry County limestone buildup. The Standard of Texas J. Brown 3-5, to the east of 2-5, penetrates about 200 feet of Canyon limestone; the Standard of Texas J. Brown 6-6, to the west, about 320 feet. In this cross section the three wells are projected into a section which is transverse to the trend of the limestone buildup (insert of Fig. 3). The highest point on the limestone buildup is estimated to be about 600 feet east of Standard of Texas Brown 2-5 (J. E. Adams, personal communication). Sample depths are corrected for differences in surface elevations of wells and a regional dip to the west of 40 feet per mile. Vertical exaggeration is two.

The most obvious and most reliable correlation is between Brown 2-5 and Brown 6-6 to the west. The cycle B^1-B-A^1 in Brown 2-5 can be closely duplicated in Brown 6-6. If the calculations on post-Canyon erosion can be extended to the west, it appears that an even greater thickness of Canyon limestone was eroded in the area of Brown 6-6 in Cisco time. The depositional surface immediately to the west of the reef crest, as shown by the cyclic time datum A^1, slopes about 240 feet per mile (drops 180 feet in 3,950 feet). This deposi-

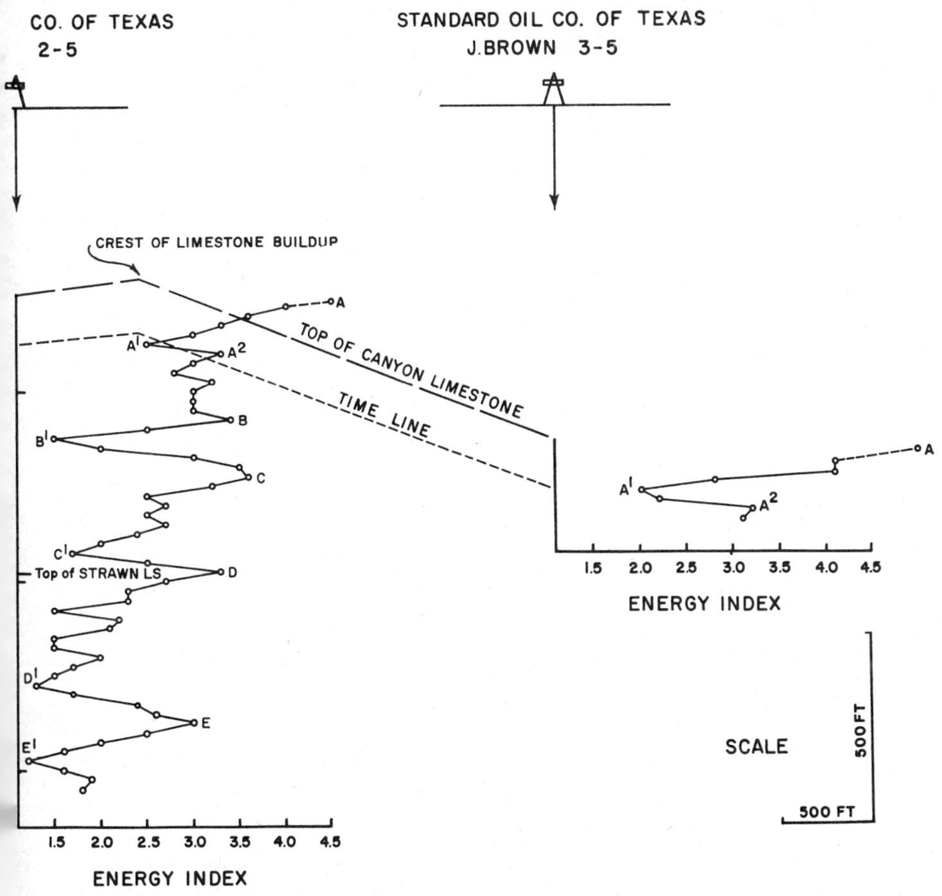

of Pennsylvanian Canyon reef, Scurry County, Texas.

tional slope is less than the eroded? Canyon limestone surface, which has a slope of 334 feet per mile.

Immediately to the east of the crest, however, the depositional surface may have approached a slope of 985 feet per mile (420 feet in 2,250 feet). This estimate is obtained by correlating the inverse cycle A^2-A^1-A of well Brown 2-5 with the energy sequence in well Brown 3-5. The A^1-B leg shown in the 2-5 and 6-6 wells is missing in well 3-5. Therefore, the energy increase shown in well 3-5 must correlate either with A^1-A or B^1-B in Brown 2-5. We prefer the former time correlation because of the character of the higher energy sediments and regional considerations. The limestone types at the top of the Canyon limestone in Brown 3-5 are Type V conglomeratic limestones, similar to those in well Brown 2-5. The regional picture of the Midland basin seaward (to the east) of the Scurry County limestone buildup is one of a starved basin with a minimum of terrigenous clastic sedimentation during Pennsylvanian time (Adams and others, 1951). Thus, the eastern flank of the limestone buildup would be expected to have a steeper slope than the western flank. The correlation of Brown 2-5 with Brown 3-5 as shown in Figure 3 is consistent with these local and regional geologic considerations.

The time correlations shown in Figure 3 are important for local detailed studies. Although long-range correlations by this method are not shown for this area, such correlations are possible where the causes of the cyclic changes in energy of the environment are regional in scope. As the

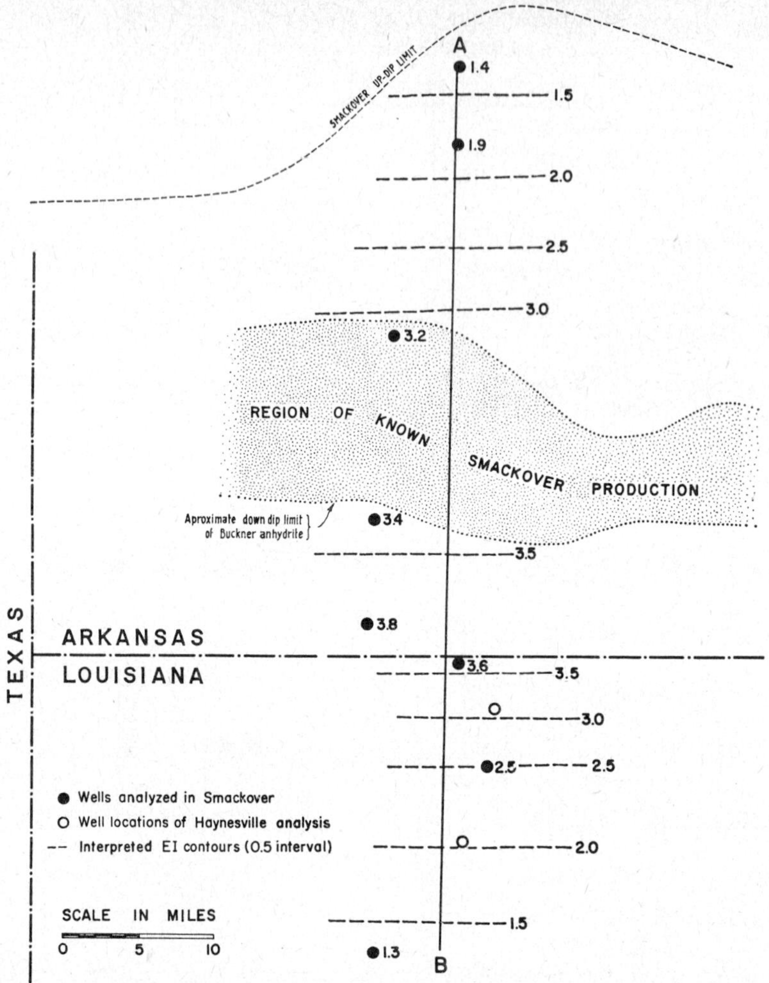

FIG. 4.—Energy Index map of Jurassic Smackover formation.

area of correlation increases, however, the correlatable details decrease and one must be content with major cycles of energy change.

Another application of the energy concept is in the construction of areal contour maps of average EI for selected stratigraphic intervals. An example of this application is shown in Figure 4, where contours of EI are drawn between wells in a reconnaissance-type study of a north-south traverse in Arkansas and Louisiana. The stratigraphic interval used in this analysis is the Jurassic Smackover formation and consists essentially of the Reynolds oölite member (and assumed facies equivalents), which occurs in the upper part of the Smackover. Because sampling was much less complete than in the Pennsylvanian examples, these EI contours are only semiquantitative. Nevertheless, they show an energy gradient from low energy at the north near the updip Smackover limit to a maximum energy zone north of the Arkansas-Louisiana border. The energy gradient reverses near the border and decreases southward into northern Louisiana.

The area of Smackover petroleum reservoirs trends east-west in southern Arkansas. This producing area is bordered on the south by a high EI trend and on the north by an EI gradient toward quiet water. The high EI zone south of production is believed to be related to development of an upper Smackover barrier, which separated basinal

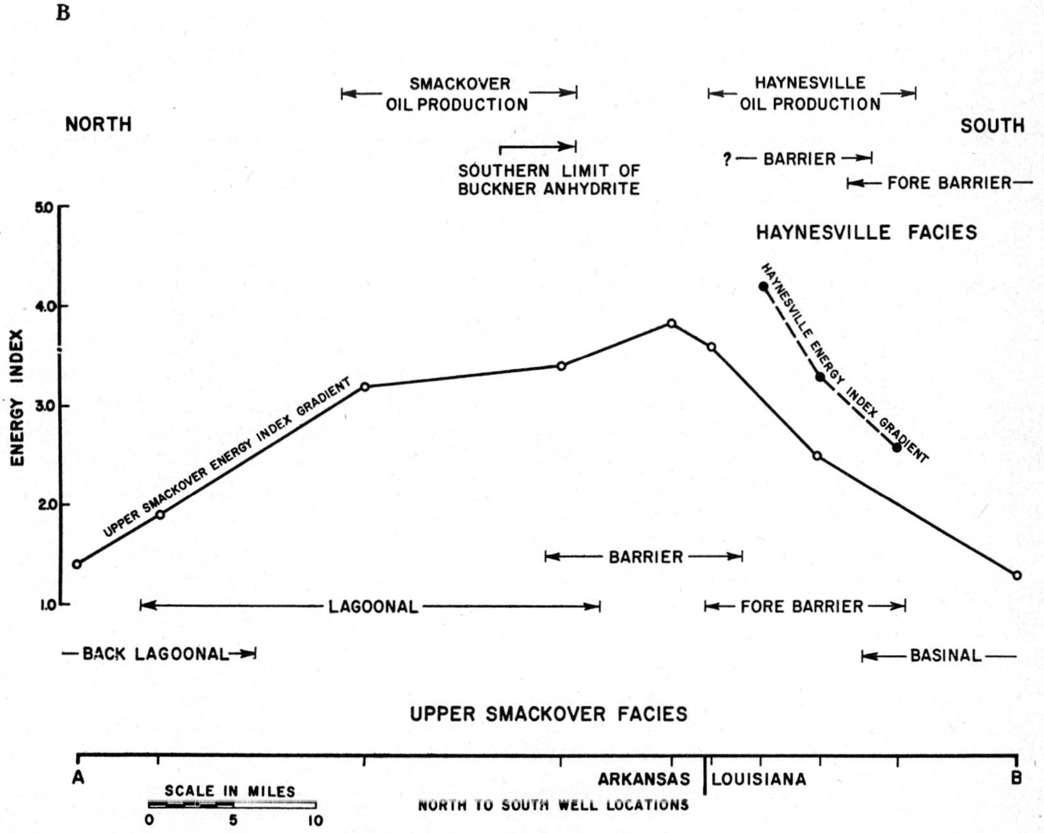

A

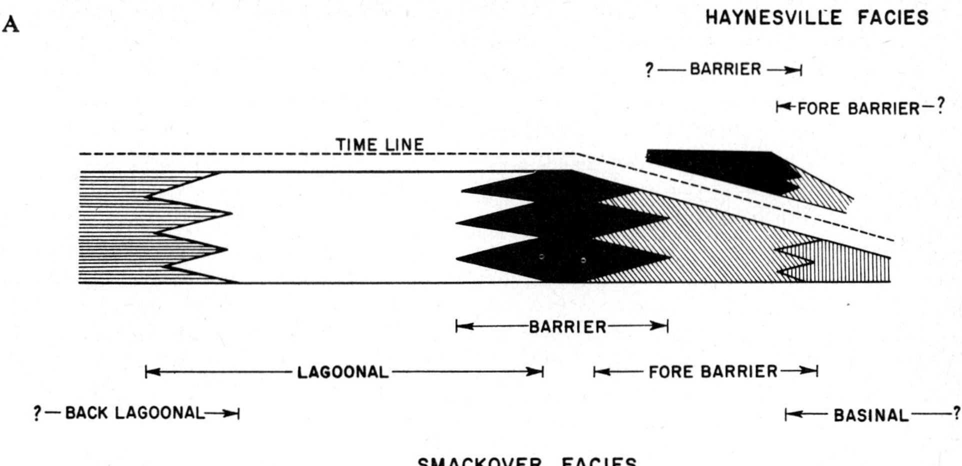

B

FIG. 5-*A*.—Schematic relations of Smackover and Haynesville facies. *B*—Energy Index cross section of Smackover and Haynesville limestones. Data points are from well locations in Fig. 4.

deposition from a back-bar or lagoonal environment. In the postulated barrier zone the upper Smackover limestones examined contain fragments of colonial coral and colonial algae that may have been part of a barrier-reef assemblage. The barrier finally caused sufficient restriction to circulation of marine waters that evaporite deposition occurred (Buckner anhydrite; down-dip limits shown in Fig. 4).

This picture of the Smackover is greatly simplified, as will be appreciated by geologists working in the area. Major complicating factors in any interpretation of the area are graben faults and salt-dome structures which were contemporaneous with Smackover deposition. These structural complexities particularly obscure the stratigraphic relationships south of the Arkansas-Louisiana line. In this region an oölitic facies occurs above the strata considered by many geologists as Smackover. This upper oölitic facies is considered to be part of the Haynesville formation and younger than the Smackover. The Haynesville oölitic facies is productive along an east-west belt just south of the Arkansas-Louisiana line. Like the Smackover, the Haynesville also is interpreted to have developed a barrier facies south of the postulated Smackover barrier. Also like its older counterpart, the Haynesville barrier resulted in anhydrite deposition to the north, although the evaporites are present as anhydritic shales rather than massive anhydrite typical of the Buckner.

The interpreted stratigraphic and time relationships between the Smackover and Haynesville are shown diagrammatically in Figure 5-*A* and in an EI cross section in Figure 5-*B*. Data points in Figure 5-*B* are those from the well locations shown in Figure 4.

Finally, the limestone types of the EI classification are useful for facies analysis. The limestone types are basically lithofacies, as defined by Moore (1949, p. 32) ". . . the rock record of any sedimentary environment, including both physical and organic characters." Thus, the limestone types may be used as the basic building blocks for facies analysis, as according to Moore (1949, p. 17), "A sedimentary facies comprises one or more lithofacies, and any facies differs from others adjacent to it in having one or more lithofacies constituents which are absent in the others."

We can illustrate these facies concepts by typical limestone type associations near the extremes of the energy scale. In carbonate sequences which lie immediately above the initial sediments of a marine transgression, we commonly find a sequence of quiet-water, Type I limestones interbedded with minor amounts of Type II and III limestones. This facies (group of lithofacies) was deposited in moderately deep water offshore.

In contradistinction to this quiet-water offshore facies, we can assemble rock types into facies characteristic of high energy environments such as reefs. Reefs are complex assemblages of morphological environments, characteristically high in Type IV and V limestones, although Types I, II, and III also are present in the overall reef facies.

In the present example from the Smackover, the refinement of a facies analysis is controlled by the limited sampling of the stratigraphic interval, the size of the interval, and the use of five principal rock types rather than a large number of subtypes. Thus, the analysis is a reconnaissance broad-brush approach.

In Figure 5-*B* the limits of several facies are shown by arrows. On the scale of our observations and study, all facies are shown as transitional by overlapping arrows. The barrier facies consists predominately of Type III oölitic limestones, followed by Type IV, Type II, and Type V oölitic limestones in decreasing amounts. The southernmost well in this facies group contains sand and silt, which is transitional into the silty Type III limestones of the fore-barrier facies. The basinal facies is predominately Type I limestone. In a shoreward direction the barrier facies interfingers with the lagoonal facies, which contains abundant Type II limestones consisting of oölites in a carbonate mud matrix. To the north in this facies, the percentage of Type I limestones increases and they eventually interfinger with a back lagoon facies which contains only Type I limestones and no oölites.

In the Haynesville wells it appears that the two northernmost wells are in a barrier facies, which grades southward into a fore-barrier facies.

SUMMARY

We have described a genetic classification of limestones based on the energy that existed in the depositional environment. The energy spectrum, which is related to wave and current action, ranges from quiet water through strongly agitated water, as a function of time. Our classification divides this continuous energy spectrum into five main levels and into fifteen sublevels, which comprise discrete genetic limestone types.

Criteria for identifying limestone types are based primarily upon evidence for the clastic *versus* nonclastic origin of particles which comprise the rock. The matrix and granular components have textural and compositional characteristics that are related to the energy level of the depositional environment.

We regard our classification as a first step, only, in understanding limestone in relation to petroleum accumulation. Carbonate-reservoir porosity is related to both depositional and postdepositional textures. Although we recognize the importance of secondary processes in limestones, this classification deals only with depositional interpretations.

The utility of a rock classification is enhanced if, in addition to its use as a medium of description and communication, it provides a means of constructing geologic models for interpretation of earth history. The Energy Index concept permits us to understand the time-dependent changes in carbonate deposition at one place, and the spatial distribution of assemblages of limestone types (facies) at one time. Thus, time-rock correlations of limestones are facilitated by the use of a classification based upon an index of depositional energy.

REFERENCES

Adams, J. E., 1953, Non-reef limestone reservoirs: Am. Assoc. Petroleum Geologists Bull., v. 37, no. 11, p. 2566–2569.

——— and others, 1951, Starved Pennsylvanian Midland basin: Am. Assoc. Petroleum Geologists Bull., v. 35, no. 12, p. 2600–2607.

Andrichuk, J. M., 1958a, Stratigraphy and facies analysis of Upper Devonian reefs in Leduc, Stettler, and Redwater areas, Alberta: Am. Assoc. Petroleum Geologists Bull., v. 42, no. 1, p. 1–93.

——— 1958b, Cooking Lake and Duvernay (Late Devonian) sedimentation in Edmonton area of central Alberta, Canada: Am. Assoc. Petroleum Geologists Bull., v. 42, no. 9, p. 2189–2222.

Beales, F. W., 1956, Conditions of deposition of Palliser (Devonian) limestone of southwestern Alberta: Am. Assoc. Petroleum Geologists Bull., v. 40, no. 5, p. 848–870.

——— 1958, Ancient sediments of Bahaman type: Am. Assoc. Petroleum Geologists, Bull., v. 42, no. 8, p. 1845–1880.

Bergenback, R. E., and Terriere, R. T., 1953, Petrography of Scurry reef, Scurry County, Texas: Am. Assoc. Petroleum Geologists Bull., v. 37, no. 5, p. 1014–1029.

Bramkamp, R. A., and Powers, R. W., 1958, Classification of Arabian carbonate rocks: Geol. Society America Bull., v. 69, no. 10, p. 1305–1318.

Carozzi, A., 1957, Contribution a l'etude des proprietes géométriques des oölithes: Inst. Natl. Genevois Bull., v. 58, p. 1–51.

——— 1958, Micro-mechanisms of sedimentation in the epicontinental environment: Jour. Sed. Petrology, v. 28, no. 2, p. 133–150.

Dott, R. H., Jr., 1958, Cyclic patterns in mechanically deposited Pennsylvanian limestones of northeastern Nevada: Jour. Sed. Petrology, v. 28, no. 1, p. 3–14.

Folk, R. L., 1959, Practical petrographic classification of limestones: Am. Assoc. Petroleum Geologists Bull., v. 43, no. 1, p. 1–38.

Forman, M. J., and Schlanger, S. O., 1957, Tertiary reef and associated limestone facies from Louisiana and Guam: Jour. Geology, v. 65, no. 6, p. 611–627.

Henson, F. R. S., 1950, Cretaceous and Tertiary reef formations and associated sediments in Middle East: Am. Assoc. Petroleum Geologists Bull., v. 34, no. 2, p. 215–238.

Houbolt, J. J. H. C., 1957, Surface sediments of the Persian Gulf near the Qatar Peninsula: The Hague, Mouton and Co., p. 1–113.

Illing, L. V., 1945, Bahaman calcareous sands: Am. Assoc. Petroleum Geologists Bull., v. 38, no. 1, p. 1–95.

——— 1959, Deposition and diagenesis of some Upper Paleozoic carbonate sediments in Western Canada: 5th World Petr. Cong., New York, Proc. Sec. I, p. 23–52.

Lowenstam, H. A., 1950, Niagaran reefs of the Great Lakes area: Jour. Geology, v. 58, no. 4, p. 430–487.

Moore, R. C., 1949, Meaning of facies, *in* Sedimentary facies in geologic history: Geol. Soc. America Mem. 39, p. 1–34.

Morretti, F. J., 1957, Observations on limestones: Jour. Sed. Petrology, v. 27, no. 3, p. 282–292.

Myers, D. A., Stafford, P. T., and Burnside, R. J., 1956, Geology of the late Paleozoic Horseshoe atoll in West Texas: Univ. Texas Pub. No. 5607, p. 1–113.

Pettijohn, F. J., 1948, A preface to the classification of the sedimentary rocks: Jour. Geology, v. 56, no. 2, p. 112–117.

Plumley, W. J., and Graves, R. W., Jr., 1953, Virgilian reefs of the Sacramento Mountains, New Mexico: Jour. Geology, v. 61, no. 1, p. 1–16.

Pray, L. C., 1958, Fenestrate bryozoan core facies, Mississippian bioherms, southwestern United States: Jour. Sed. Petrology, v. 28, no. 3, p. 261–273.

Rittenhouse, Gordon, 1949, Petrology and paleogeography of Greenbrier formation: Am. Assoc. Petroleum Geologists Bull., v. 33, no. 10, p. 1704–1730.

Teichert, Curt, 1958, Cold- and deep-water coral banks: Am. Assoc. Petroleum Geologists Bull., v. 42, no. 5, p. 1064–1082.

Wanless, H. R., 1952, Cyclic sedimentation in the marine Pennsylvanian of the southwestern United States: Cong. pour l'Advancement des Études de Stratigraphie et de Géologie Carbonifère, 3d, Heerlen, 1951, Comptes rendus, v. 2, p. 655–664.

Wolfenden, E. B., 1958, Paleoecology of the Carboniferous reef complex and shelf limestones in northwest Derbyshire, England: Geol. Soc. America Bull., v. 69, no. 7, p. 871–898.

CLASSIFICATION OF CARBONATE ROCKS ACCORDING TO DEPOSITIONAL TEXTURE[1]

ROBERT J. DUNHAM[2]
Houston, Texas

ABSTRACT

Three textural features seem especially useful in classifying those carbonate rocks that retain their depositional texture (1) Presence or absence of carbonate mud, which differentiates muddy carbonate from *grainstone;* (2) abundance of grains, which allows muddy carbonates to be subdivided into *mudstone, wackestone,* and *packstone;* and (3) presence of signs of binding during deposition, which characterizes *boundstone.* The distinction between grain-support and mud-support differentiates packstone from wackestone—packstone is full of its particular mixture of grains, wackestone is not. Rocks retaining too little of their depositional texture to be classified are set aside as *crystalline carbonates.*

INTRODUCTION

The increasing use of thin sections and oiled slabs has shown that most limestone and much dolomite retain their depositional texture, in a more or less ghostly fashion, despite diagenesis. A descriptive classification based on depositional texture is thus a generally helpful adjunct to other classifications, particularly to those based on genetic kind of particles and to those based on mineralogic composition. It will not substitute for further description and classification, nor will it produce ready-made interpretations, but it will focus attention on whichever few textural properties are chosen as particularly significant for interpretation of depositional environment, and it will provide the convenience of class names based only on depositional texture.

Ideally, one could confidently divide unaltered carbonate rocks into two main groups, which Grabau (1904) termed clastic and biogenic. According to the ideal, one group is controlled mainly by hydraulic conditions. Origin of particles is relatively insignificant, and subdivision is according to particle size. Calcirudite thus is distinguished from calcarenite. The other group is controlled mainly by the biologic or biochemical processes responsible for producing carbonate. Here, particle size is relatively insignificant, and subdivision is made according to origin of particles. Crinoidal limestone thus is distinguished from coral limestone. As it turns out, most samples are neither clearly in one group nor clearly in the other. Instead, they fall in the middle ground where hydraulic conditions and biologic or biochemical processes are in joint control.

Focusing attention on whether or not the larger particles are transported (fragmented or disarticulated) does not re-establish the sharp boundary between the two groups. Too often one is forced to conclude that a carbonate sediment was transported a little but not far, or that some components were transported and others were not,

[1] Part of a symposium arranged by the Research Committee, and presented at Denver, Colorado, April 27, 1961, under joint auspices of the Association and the Society of Economic Paleontologists and Mineralogists. Manuscript received, April 23, 1961.

[2] Shell Development Company, Exploration and Production Division. I am deeply indebted to R. L. Folk, who shared his knowledge of carbonates and classification prior to publication, and repeatedly contributed to the evolution of the present concepts; to R. N. Ginsburg, whose studies of Recent carbonates clarified problems in ancient carbonates; and to D. L. Amsbury, K. J. Hsu, S. D. Kerr, O. P. Majewske, P. F. Moore, R. C. Murray, J. M. Parks, B. F. Perkins, G. Rittenhouse, C. I. Smith, B. W. Wilson, and J. L. Wilson, who gave encouragement and stimulating criticism.

EXPLANATION OF PLATE I

Looser packing would require mud-support. Samples were impregnated on the beach in such a way as to preserve natural packing and were then reimpregnated in the laboratory and sliced. All samples were from Cayo Centro, Cayos Arcas, Campeche Banks, Mexico.

a. Coral lime gravel, ×1, reflected light. South side of island, AC-64.
b. Coral-red algae lime sand, ×25, transmitted cross-polarized light. Northeast side of island, AC-47.
c. Red algae lime sand, ×5, transmitted cross-polarized light. Southeast side of island, AC-83.

PLATE I.—Grain-support in beach deposits.

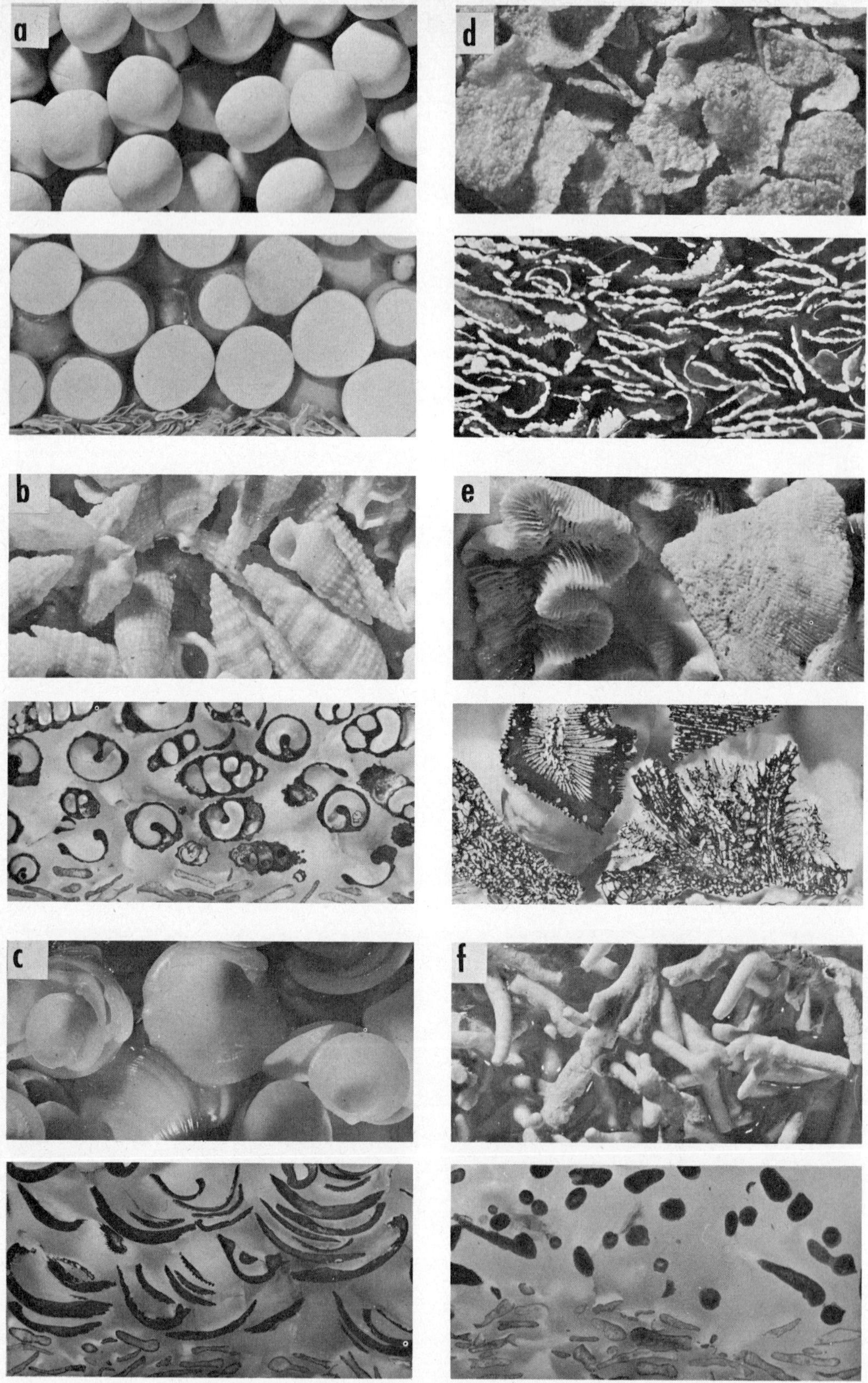

PLATE II.—Grain-support influenced by grain shape.

or that degree of transportation is indeterminate. Indeed, the outstanding differences between land-derived sediment and carbonate sediment stem from the simple fact that, as a rule, land-derived sediment is produced by destruction far from the site of deposition, whereas carbonate sediment is produced by destruction and construction at or near the site of deposition. The recognized usefulness of classifications based on origin of particles attests to the idea that carbonate grains are unlike land-derived sediment in distance of transport; if grains did not generally remain near where they were produced, such classifications would lack the environmental significance they are known to have. Possibly, the ease with which carbonate grains are destroyed, or cemented, accounts for their relatively short transport.

SIGNIFICANCE OF MUD

The distinction between sediment deposited in calm water and sediment deposited in agitated water is fundamental. Evidence bearing on this problem thus deserves to be incorporated in class names. This can be accomplished in several ways. One is to focus attention on average or predominant size, which erroneously assumes that all sizes in a sample are equally significant hydraulically. Another is to focus attention on the size, abundance, and condition of the coarse material brought to the site of deposition. This emphasis on what might be called currents of delivery has long been successful in dealing with land-derived sediments, but does not work well in lime sediment because of the local origin of many coarse grains. A third way is to focus attention on the fine material that was able to *remain* at the site of deposition. This emphasis on what might be called currents of removal seems advisable if we wish to characterize carbonate sediment systematically in terms of hydraulic environment.

Inasmuch as calm water is characterized by mud being able to settle to the bottom and remain there, it seems that the muddy rocks deserve to be contrasted with mud-free rocks, regardless of the

←

EXPLANATION OF PLATE II

Looser packing would require mud-support. Aggregates were made by sedimenting wet grains in quiet water onto a bed of previously deposited grains (*Halimeda* plates visible at base of aggregate), drying, impregnating with clear plastic, slicing, then staining. Plate II-*d* was sedimented dry.

Per cent grains is expressed in two ways, both values being rounded to the nearest 5 per cent. Per cent grain-solid, which is measured by water displacement, refers to the volume of solid matter in the grains divided by the volume of the aggregate. Per cent grain-bulk, which is measured by point-counting, differs in that openings and deep indentations in grains are conventionally counted as grain instead of as pore.

a. Well sorted, well rounded, highly spherical porcelain balls, ×1, 65 per cent grain-bulk, 60 per cent grain-solid.

b. High-spired snails, ×1½, 45 per cent grain-bulk, 25 per cent grain-solid.

c. Small clams, ×1½, 30 per cent grain-bulk, 25 per cent grain-solid.

d. Corn flakes, ×1, 30 per cent grain bulk.

e. Rose corals, ×¾, 70 per cent grain-bulk, 20 per cent grain-solid.

f. Branching red algae broken to ¾-inch lengths, ×1¾, 20 per cent grain-bulk, 15 per cent grain-solid.

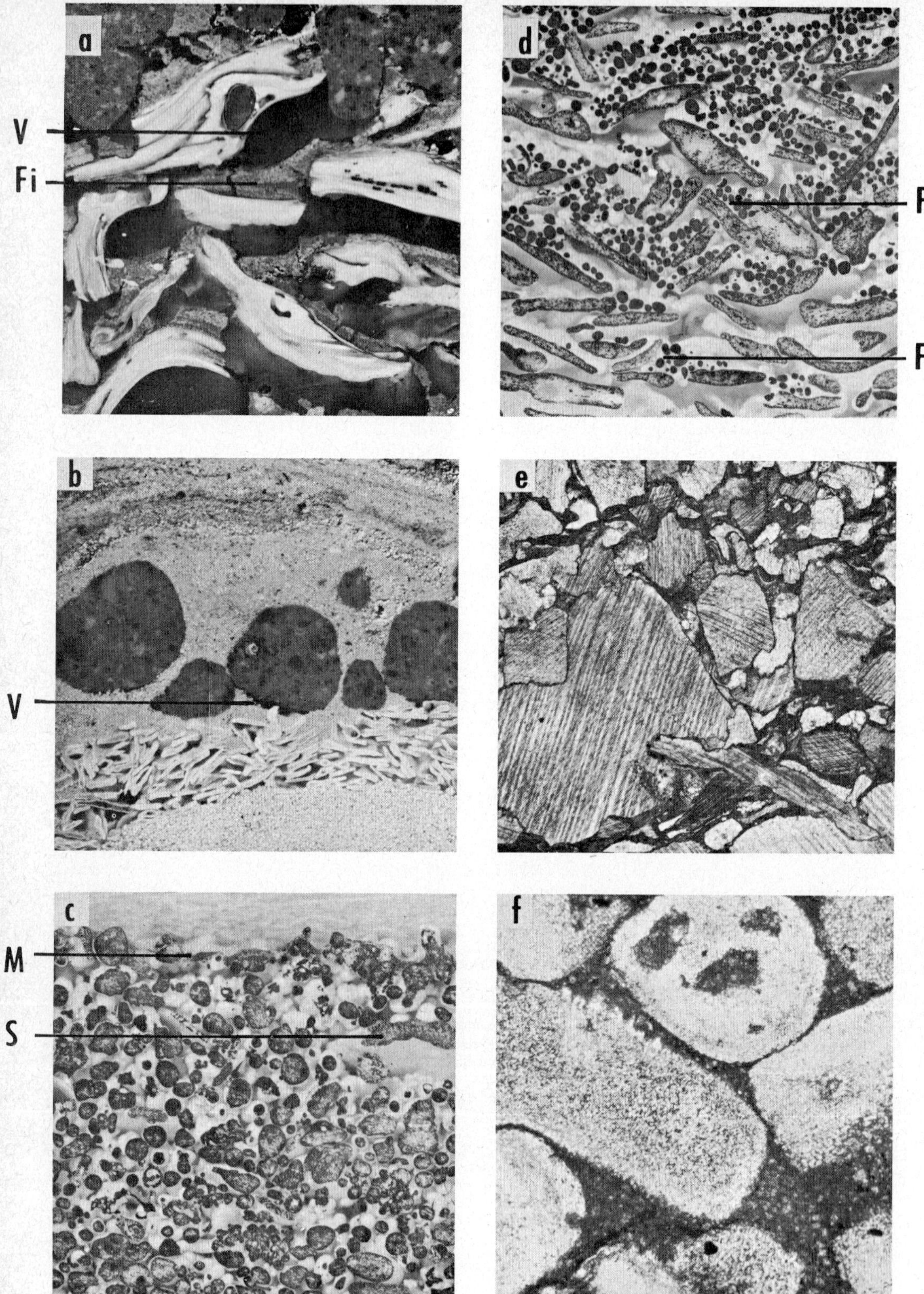

Plate III.—Indications of grain-support.

amount and size of included coarse material. Folk (1959) and Bramkamp and Powers (1958) in their new classifications of carbonate rocks have much the same viewpoint. The terms mud and grains are used variously by different authors. Usage here is based on particle size, grains being larger than 20 microns and mud being smaller than 20 microns. The distinction thus parallels the distinction between matrix and grains in sandstone (Pettijohn, 1957, p. 284). Freedom from mud is taken to mean virtual absence—less than 1 per cent.

GRAIN-SUPPORT AND MUD-SUPPORT

Rocks bearing carbonate mud constitute the bulk of many carbonate sequences and therefore require subdivision. The most useful textural subdivision of such rocks seems to be on the basis of abundance of grains. Such subdivision allows mapping of gradients in rate of production of grains relative to rate of accumulation of mud.

Three degrees of abundance can be recognized. In the most common case, grains are abundant enough to be prominent, say more than 10 per cent, but are not so abundant as to support one another. In such a texture, the grains are sometimes said to be "floating." Here they will be called "mud-supported." Rocks in which grains are less abundant than 10 per cent constitute a second category. Rocks in which grains are so abundant as to support one another, just as they do in mud-free rocks, which are necessarily "grain-supported," are a third category.

The distinction between mud-support and grain-support seems to be more meaningful than

←

Explanation of Plate III

Floored interstices, shelter effects, embayed contacts, and overly close packing indicate grain-support.

a–d—Floored interstices are produced by fine sediment filtering into coarser sediment, and by concurrent deposition of fine and coarse sediment. Marine infiltering reaches deeply only if the size difference is large, and even then does not fill interstices to the roof.

a. Oyster shells infiltered by lime mud in the laboratory, ×1, reflected light. Mud floors (*Fi*) are layered, and drape over irregularities. Shrinkage during drying reduced the amount of mud in the interstices, but voids (*V*) were beneath the shells before drying.

b. Gravel, *Halimeda*, and oöliths infiltered by very fine sand in the laboratory, ×1, reflected light. Sand largely fills interstices in the gravel layer, reaches part way through the *Halimeda* layer, and does not enter the oölith layer. The voids (*V*) beneath the pebbles are original shelter effects—the sediment did not shrink during drying.

c. Beach sand infiltered by lime mud in the laboratory, ×5, reflected light. Infiltering (*M*) is negligible except in the top layer of grains. Note the shelter effects at the large grain (*S*).

d. Floored interstices (*Fd*) produced by concurrent deposition of oöliths and *Halimeda* in the laboratory, in volume ratio of 3:1, ×3, reflected light. Oöliths making floors (*Fi*) in lower quarter of picture filtered into interstices in previously deposited bed of pure *Halimeda*.

e. Embayed contacts, ×20, transmitted unpolarized light. Lake Valley limestone, Mississippian, Sacramento Mountains, New Mexico, AGN.

f. Overly close packing, ×50, transmitted unpolarized light. Mission Canyon formation, Mississippian, Shell Richey NP-1, Richey field, Dawson County, Montana, NP 1-7312.

any alternative percentage boundary. A grain-supported rock is full of its particular mixture of grains, whereas a mud-supported rock is not. In land-derived sediments, the figures 65 per cent grains, 35 per cent porosity or interstitial debris, have been used to mark the boundary between grain-support (framework) and mud-support (disrupted framework). If all carbonate grains were as equidimensional as oöliths, a percentage boundary might equally well be substituted for visual distinction between mud-support and grain-support in carbonate rocks; but carbonate grains commonly are shaped like potato chips and twigs instead of like marbles. Because of this, a grain-supported rock whose grains are *Ivanovia*, a platy alga shaped rather like a cornflake, or *Halimeda*, would contain a far smaller percentage of grains than would a grain-supported rock whose grains are crinoid ossicles. A 65 per cent boundary, or a 50 per cent boundary, would put the *Ivanovia* rock in one group and the crinoid rock in another group; yet both rocks would contain as much of their particular mixture of grains as their volume allows them to hold.

Objection may arise that differentiating mud-supported from grain-supported rocks is impossibly subjective because of the need to envision a three-dimensional arrangement of irregular shapes by looking at a two-dimensional view. The difficulty is real but not so bad as it at first seems. (The errors are not much greater than those encountered in attempting to measure or estimate per cent grains in rocks having hollow or indented grains.) Experience gained in examining mud-free carbonates, which are necessarily grain-supported is an aid in determining what the kind of support is in muddy carbonates. Other aids are the floored interstices, embayed grains, overly close packing, and sheltering effects seen in grain-supported rocks and not in mud-supported rocks. Illustrations of these and of grain-supported natural and artificial aggregates are shown in Plates I–III.

The phenomenon of grain-support has the added importance of bearing on the postdepositional history of the sediment. Soluble grains that are grain-supported are in contact with each other, and thus have a chance of forming a connected network of molds (or incomplete molds) unlike the relatively disconnected molds in mud-supported rocks. Furthermore, compaction affects grain-supported sediment differently than it does mud-supported sediment. The grains in grain-supported sediment carry the weight of the overburden. This tends to cause weak grains to brecciate. It also tends to protect from compaction

---

»»→

Explanation of Plate IV

(×5, transmitted unpolarized light)

a. Coral lime *boundstone.* Toronto limestone, Pennsylvanian Virgil, Greenwood County, Kansas, L-38-8b.

b. Laminated lime *boundstone* (stromatolite). Cabbage-head structure in West Spring Creek limestone, Ordovician, Arbuckle Mountains, ADN-1.

c. Floored lime *boundstone.* Floored openings (*F*) constructed by intergrown complex (*C*) of encrusting Foraminifera, algae, and hydrozoans? Permian Wolfcamp. Shell State ETA-5, Townsend field, Lea County, New Mexico, ETA5-10368.2.

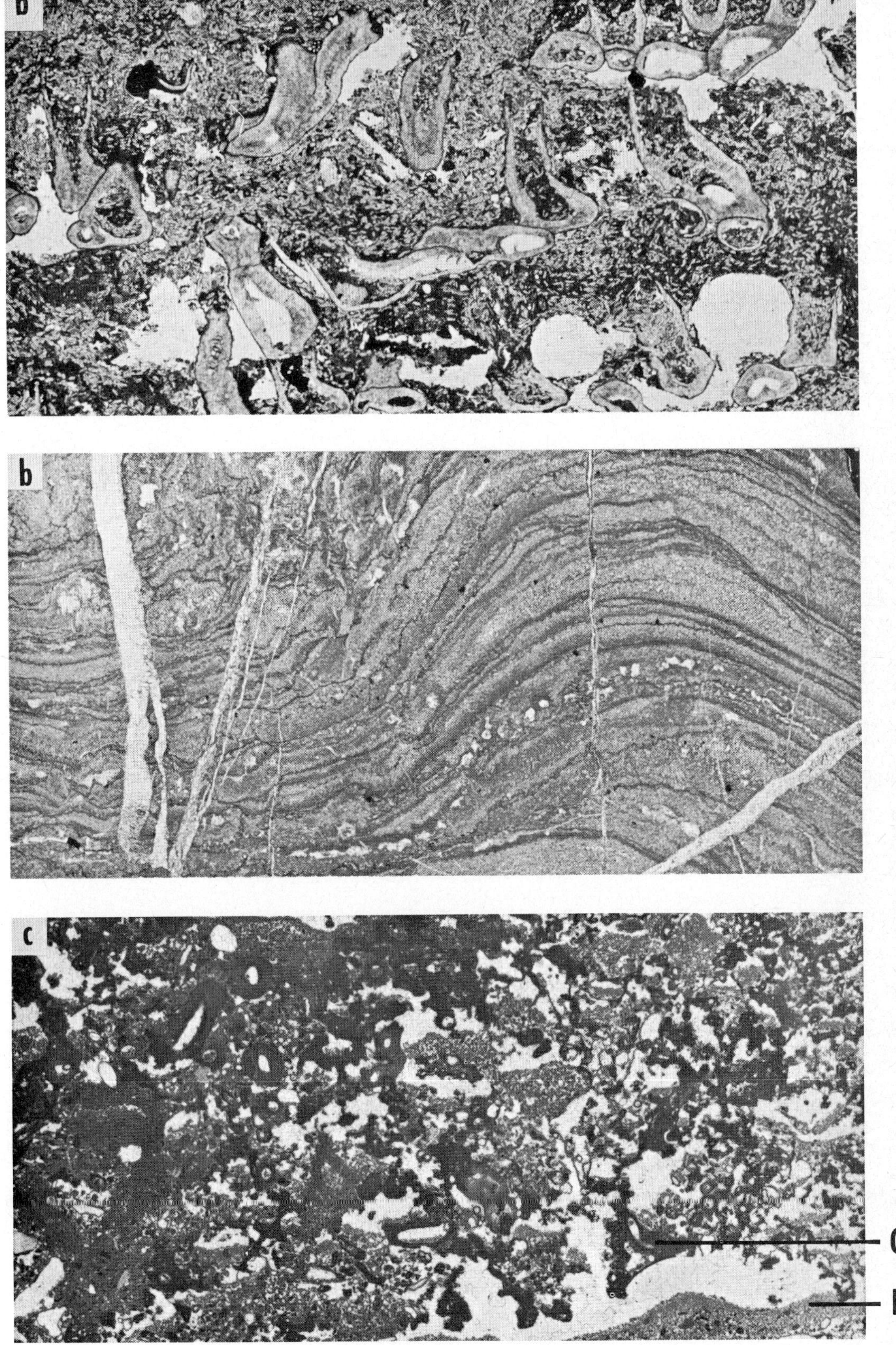

PLATE IV.—Binding in boundstone.

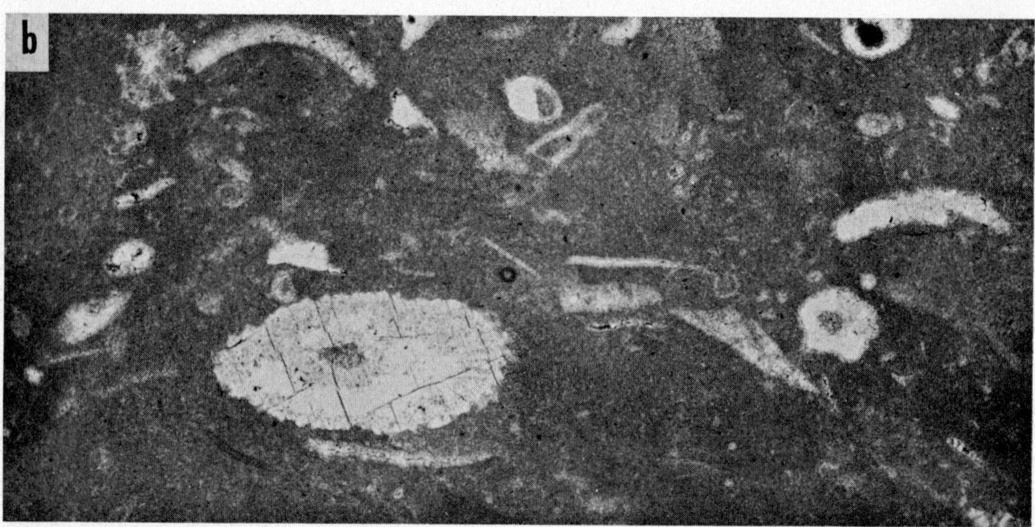

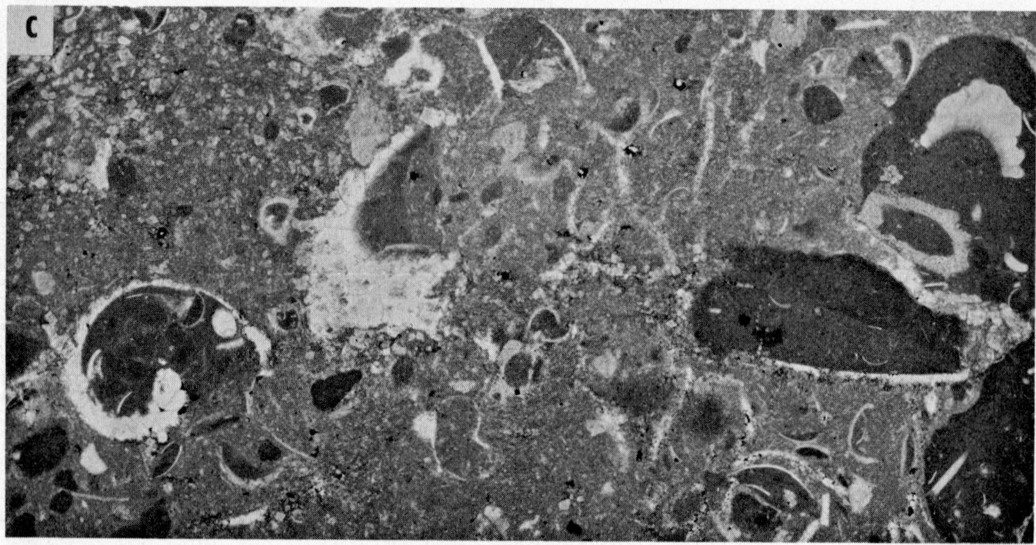

PLATE V.—Mudstone and wackestone.

Table I. Classification of Carbonate Rocks According to Depositional Texture

<table>
<tr><td colspan="5">DEPOSITIONAL TEXTURE RECOGNIZABLE</td><td rowspan="5">DEPOSITIONAL TEXTURE NOT RECOGNIZABLE

Crystalline Carbonate

(Subdivide according to classifications designed to bear on physical texture or diagenesis.)</td></tr>
<tr><td colspan="4">Original Components Not Bound Together During Deposition</td><td rowspan="4">Original components were bound together during deposition... as shown by intergrown skeletal matter, lamination contrary to gravity, or sediment-floored cavities that are roofed over by organic or questionably organic matter and are too large to be interstices.</td></tr>
<tr><td colspan="3">Contains mud
(particles of clay and fine silt size)</td><td rowspan="3">Lacks mud and is grain-supported</td></tr>
<tr><td colspan="2">Mud-supported</td><td rowspan="2">Grain-supported</td></tr>
<tr><td>Less than 10 percent grains</td><td>More than 10 percent grains</td></tr>
<tr><td>Mudstone</td><td>Wackestone</td><td>Packstone</td><td>Grainstone</td><td>Boundstone</td><td></td></tr>
</table>

any sheltered mud beneath strong grains, perhaps making the mud more susceptible to leaching. Collapse brecciation improved permeability in muddy grain-supported limestone composed mostly of *Ivanovia* in the Paradox formation of the Desert Creek field, Utah (Murray, 1960, p. 66). Leaching of mud from interstices in muddy grain-supported limestone composed mostly of crinoids caused the porosity in some of the Devonian reservoirs in Andrews County, Texas (F. J. Lucia, personal communication).

BINDING

Most carbonate rocks retaining their depositional texture are lithified sediment made of clearly discrete and originally loose particles. The rocks that differ by showing signs of being bound during deposition are scarce, but are worth special attention. Three signs of binding during deposition are recognized (Pl. IV). One is interconnected skeletal matter, such as occurs where colonial corals or encrusting Foraminifera grow one on the other. Another is lamination contrary to gravity, such as occurs in the crinkly lamination of stromatolites. The third is sediment-floored cavities that are too large to be interstices and are roofed over by organic or questionably organic matter, such as the large and small tunnels and grottoes in coral reefs.

CLASSES AND NAMES

The concepts outlined above allow five textural classes to be recognized (Table I). The names tentatively attached to these classes are fairly

---

←

Explanation of Plate V

(×25, transmitted unpolarized light)

a. Ostracod lime *mudstone*, less than 1 per cent grain-bulk. Duperow formation, Late Devonian, Brown's Gulch section, Blaine County, Montana, BG-17.

b. Mixed-fossil dolomite *wackestone*, 20 per cent grain-bulk. The rock contains no calcite. San Andreas Permian, Shell D. Roberts No. 15, 5,121 feet, Wasson field, Yoakum County, Texas, I-300.

c. Ostracod-lithiclast lime *wackestone*, slightly dolomitized, 40 per cent grain-bulk. Duperow formation, Late Devonian, Shell Richey NP-1, 8,900 feet, Richey field, McCone County, Montana, 1.562.

short, meaningful English nouns that apply only to texture. They can be combined with names for grain-kind classes and mineralogic classes, as shown in the figure captions, and they also can stand alone where mineralogy and grain-kind are not at issue.

Mudstone.—Muddy carbonate rocks containing less than 10 per cent grains (10 per cent grain-bulk as defined in Pl. II) are termed mudstone Pl. V). The name mudstone is synonymous with calcilutite, except that it does not specify mineralogic composition and thus avoids such ambiguities as dolomite calcilutite, and it does not specify that the mud is of clastic origin. The significance of mudstone, aside from the implication of calm water, is the apparent inhibition of grain-producing organisms.

Wackestone.—Mud-supported carbonate rocks containing more than 10 per cent grains (10 per cent grain-bulk) are termed wackestone (Pl. V). The name has much against it, but it does have the advantage of calling to mind a mixture of mud and grains similar to that seen in some sandstones, and it is less awkward than expressions such as calcarenitic calcilutite or calcarenitic limestone.

Packstone.—Grain-supported muddy carbonate rocks are termed packstone (Pl. VI). Grain-support is generally a property of rocks deposited in agitated water, and muddiness is generally a property of rocks deposited in quiet water. A rock exhibiting both properties is peculiar, and it is well to have it isolated for further study. It may record simple compaction of wackestone, as is suggested where interstices are completely filled with mud. It may record early or late infiltering of previously deposited mud-free sediment, or prolific production of grains in calm water, as is suggested where interstices are floored with mud. It may record mixing by burrowers or incomplete winnowing or partial leaching of mud, as is suggested by patchily distributed mud.

Grainstone.—Mud-free carbonate rocks, which are necessarily grain-supported, are termed grainstone (Pl. VII). Grainstones are not all of the same hydraulic significance. Some are current laid; some are the product of mud being bypassed while locally produced grains accumulate, or of mud being winnowed from previously deposited muddy sediment; and some, conceivably, are the product of locally produced grains accumulating too rapidly to be contaminated by mud. Commonly, origin cannot be definitely known from

---

→

EXPLANATION OF PLATE VI

(×5, transmitted unpolarized light)

a. Crinoid lime *packstone* overlying lens of lime mudstone. Overly close packing (75 per cent grain-bulk) suggests that grain-support was acquired during compaction. Mission Canyon formation, Mississippian, Shell Richey NP-1, Richey field, Dawson County, Montana, NP 1-7312.

b. Hydrozoan? lime *packstone.* Floored interstices (*F*) indicate that grain-support is original and suggests infiltering. Permian Wolfcamp, Shell Hilburn No. 1, Townsend field, Lea County, New Mexico, SH-1-10,556.

c. Coated-grain lime *packstone.* Abraded nuclei of grains indicates turbulent water; presence of mud indicates quiet water; patchy distribution of mud suggests that burrowers mixed originally interbedded sand and mud together. Toronto limestone, Pennsylvanian Virgil, Kansas, Bed A.

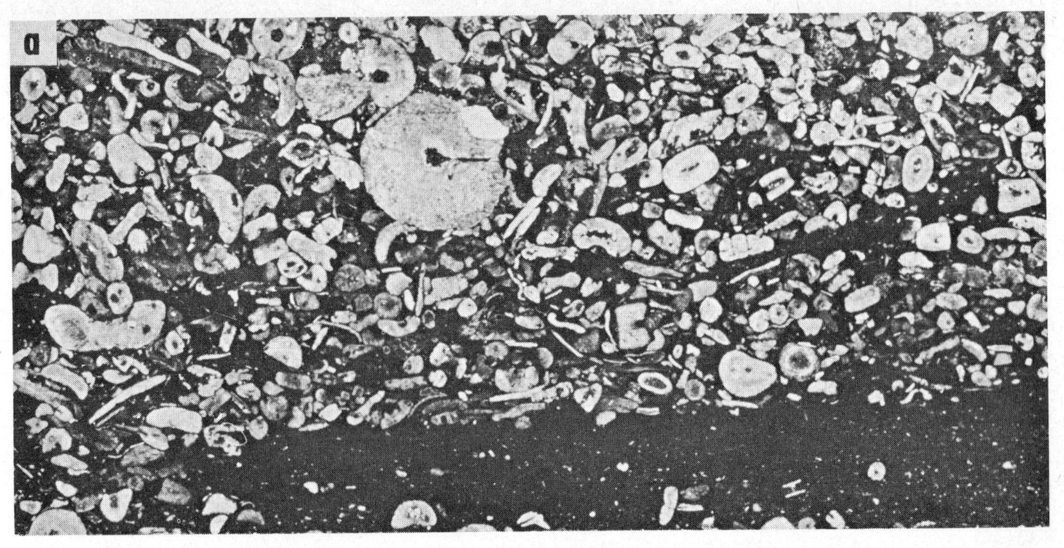

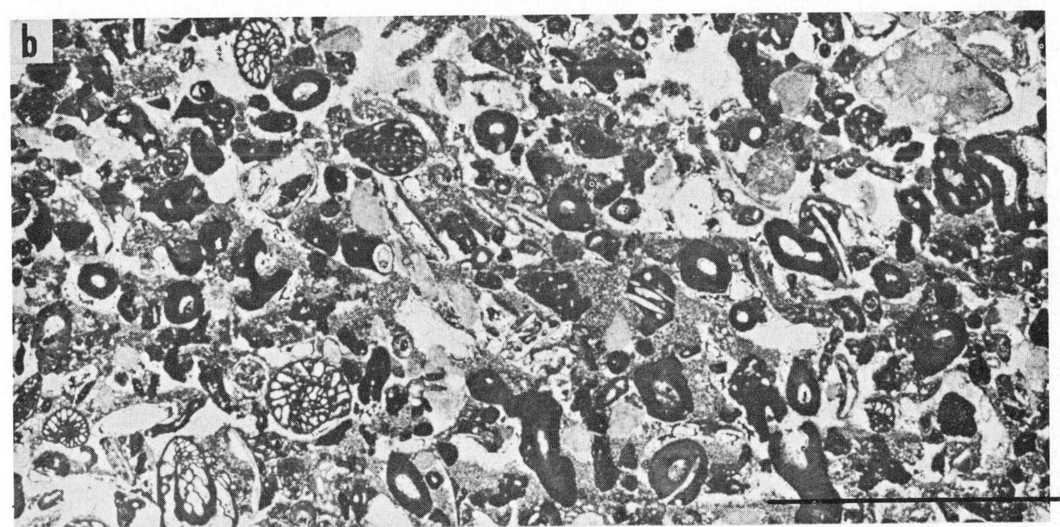

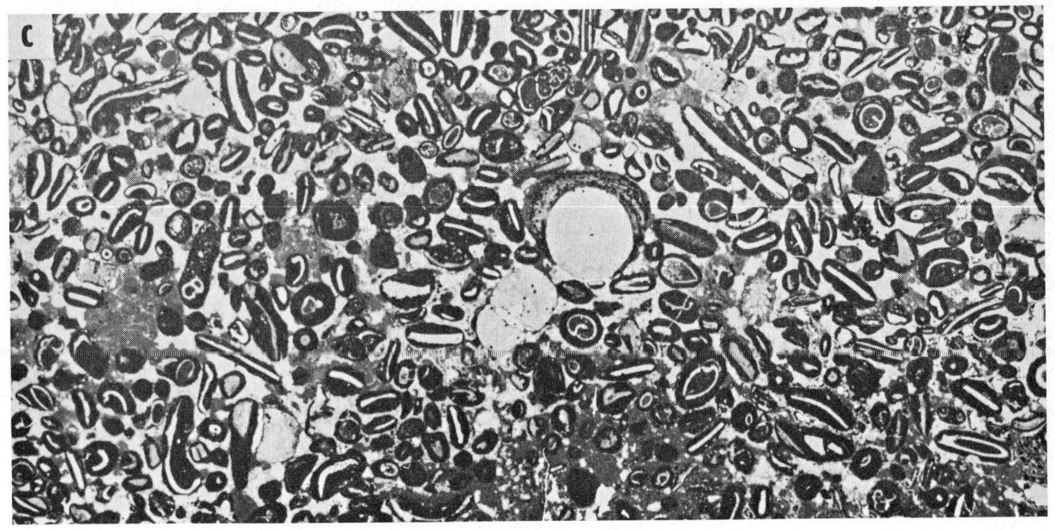

PLATE VI.—Packstone.

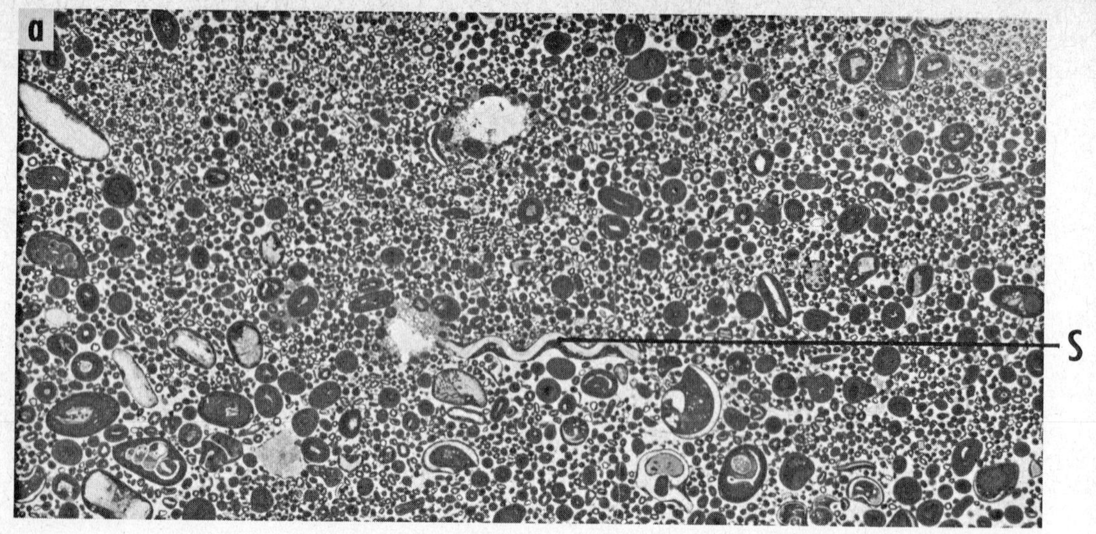

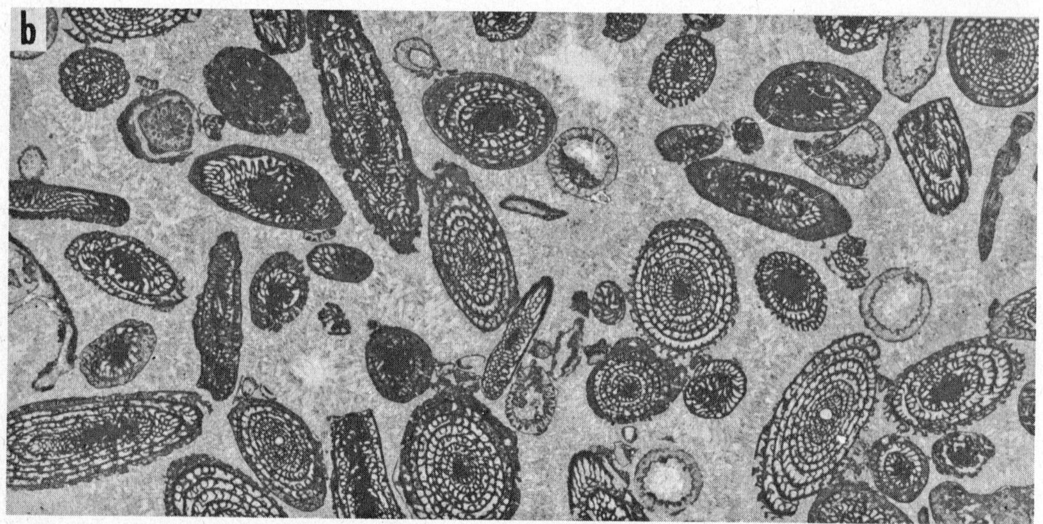

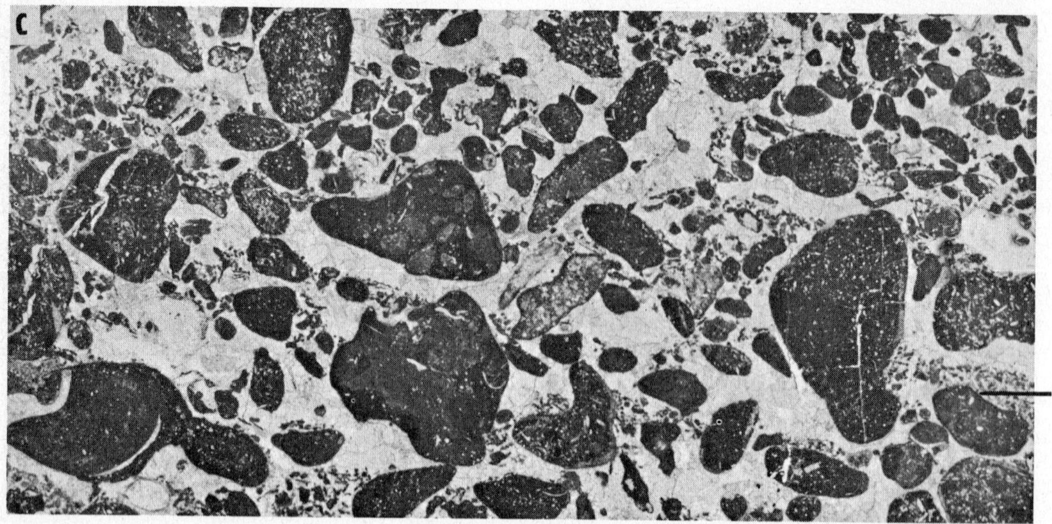

PLATE VII.—Grainstone.

the single sample that is being classified. The class name thus denotes merely the absence of mud, and, of course, the corollary that the grains are supported by each other. If the grains were not self-supporting, the former presence of now-recrystallized mud would be indicated. Subdividing grainstone, so as to include more evidence in class names, is a temptation. Many possible subdivisions suggest themselves. Grain size is, of course, one possibility. Sorting is another, for the well-sorted grainstones are scarce enough to be noted. Wear is another. Names such as *calcirudite*, *sortedstone*, and *wornstone* are useful in studying some suites of rocks, but, at present, none of these properties seems of wide enough application to warrant being incorporated in a general classification.

Boundstone.—Carbonate rocks showing signs of being bound during deposition are termed boundstone (Pl. IV). The signs of binding are specific, and they occur within the sample being classified. Except for that, the concept of boundstone plays the same role as the reefoid carbon te, biohermal carbonate, constructed biogenic carbonate, klintite, and biolithite of other classifications.

Crystalline carbonates.—Inasmuch as this classification is concerned with depositional environments, the rocks retaining too little of their depositional texture to be classified must be set aside. Such rocks are here termed crystalline carbonates (specifically, crystalline dolomite, crystalline limestone). Although depositional texture is lacking, relics or ghosts of grains commonly allow classification according to origin of grains; for example, crinoid-bearing crystalline dolomite.

REFERENCES

Bramkamp, R. A., and Powers, R. W., 1958, Classification of Arabian carbonate rocks: Geol. Soc. America Bull., v. 69, no. 10, p. 1305–1318.

Folk, R. L., 1959, Practical petrographic classification of limestones: Am. Assoc. Petroleum Geologists Bull., v. 43, no. 1, p. 1–38.

Grabau, A. W., 1904, On the classification of sedimentary rocks: Am. Geologist, v. 33, p. 228–247.

Murray, R. C., 1960, Origin of porosity in carbonate rocks: Jour. Sed. Petrology, v. 30, no. 1, p. 59–84.

Pettijohn, F. P., 1957, Sedimentary rocks, 2d ed.: New York, Harper and Bros.

←

Explanation of Plate VII

(×5, transmitted unpolarized light)

a. Oölith lime *grainstone* (oölite). Note the sheltering done by the coated brachiopod shell (*S*) near the center —grains are smaller and more numerous above the shell than below the shell; compare Plate III-*c*. Wapanucka limestone, Pennsylvanian Morrow, Bromide, Oklahoma, W-23.

b. Fusulinid lime *grainstone*, druse-cemented. Seemingly loose packing is due to fusulinids being unusually elongate. Uniform orientation (long axis perpendicular to page) and breakage indicate that the grains are current-laid. Back-reef limestone of Capitan reef, Permian Guadalupe, Pinery Canyon, Guadalupe Mountains, Texas, PN-6-A.

c. Lithiclast lime *grainstone*. Note the sand-floored interstices (*F*); compare Plate III-*d*. El Paso limestone, Ordovician, Franklin Mountains, Texas, AGE.

ARABIAN UPPER JURASSIC CARBONATE RESERVOIR ROCKS[1]

R. W. POWERS[2]
Dhahran, Saudi Arabia

ABSTRACT

Jurassic carbonate reservoir rocks of northeastern Saudi Arabia contain productive oil at several levels. For more than 20 years, samples and other data have been collected on the main oil reservoir—the Upper Jurassic Arab-D zone. Diamond cores from 12 wells with high Arab-D recovery were selected for detailed petrologic examination as part of the present study. Nearly 4,000 thin sections have been cut at closely spaced intervals and examined in detail; of these, 1,200 were analyzed by point counting. Particle size, particle type, authigenic constituents, and visual porosity were recorded. Calcareous algae, stromatoporoids, and Foraminifera proved to be the main skeletal elements; aggregate pellets, "algal" nodules, and "fecal" pellets are the most important nonskeletal particles.

Examination of Arab-D cores, equivalent rocks on outcrop, and modern calcareous Persian Gulf sediments has shown that these carbonates can best be understood by considering them to be products of mechanical deposition with certain environments being characterized by specific particle sizes and types. Arabian carbonates can be divided according to original particle size and sorting or obliteration of original texture into five groups—(1) aphanitic or fine-grained limestone, (2) calcarenitic limestone, (3) calcarenite, (4) coarse carbonate clastic, and (5) dolomite. Classification of Arab-D rocks according to this scheme has permitted (a) recognition of distinctive stratigraphic units for correlation and reservoir zonation, (b) delineation of original environment-sedimentation patterns, and (c) relation of reservoir properties to original textures and secondary changes.

Arab-D rocks represent the transition from continuous carbonate deposition to precipitation of nearly pure anhydrite. The lower part of the reservoir consists of mixed mud and nonskeletal sand. Near the middle, a thin persistent unit of aphanitic limestone records an episode of muddy deposition over a wide area. Widespread shallow-water conditions during upper Arab-D time are suggested by a pronounced increase in skeletal sand and clean-washed calcarenite derived in large part from dasyclad algae and stromatoporoids. Many features known to be persistent on outcrop have proved equally continuous in the subsurface, indicating that changes which affected sedimentation must have operated on a large scale.

Regionally, reservoir units show gradual lateral change. The picture to emerge is that of a broad shelf with finer lagoonal sediments being deposited in the west, dominantly calcareous sand in the form of offshore bars accumulating near the present coast, and presumably deeper water mud with sparse sand being laid down in the east. The sediment patterns cut across and are apparently unrelated to modern structure.

Of the original textural elements, carbonate mud matrix exerts a dominant control on reservoir rock behavior. As mud content increases relative to sand content, porosity and permeability uniformly decrease. Original rock textures have been altered in at least six ways. Addition of dolomite (which exhibits strong affinity for mud-size particles, little for calcarenites) has the most pronounced effect on reservoir properties. In any textural group, porosity and permeability (a) progressively decrease as dolomite increases from 10 to 80 per cent, (b) increase where dolomite forms 80 to 90 per cent of the rock, and (c) again decrease as dolomite exceeds 90 per cent.

INTRODUCTION

During recent years, as a result of the discovery of prolific limestone oil reservoirs in Canada, the Middle East, and elsewhere, increased emphasis has been placed on the study of carbonate rocks and modern calcareous sediments. Since 1938, when commercial oil was first discovered in Saudi Arabia, the Arabian American Oil Company

[1] Part of a symposium arranged by the Research Committee, and presented at Denver, Colorado, April 27, 1961, under joint auspices of the Association and the Society of Economic Paleontologists and Mineralogists. Manuscript received, April 12, 1961.

[2] Arabian American Oil Company.

This paper was presented as a dissertation to the Faculty of the Graduate School, Yale University, in candidacy for the degree of Doctor of Philosophy. The writer wishes to express his thanks to officers of the Arabian American Oil Company for the use of materials on which this study is based. Particular thanks are due P. H. Arnot, D. M. Brown, O. A. Seager, and Burt Beverly, Jr., for their help during all phases of the investigation. Critical suggestions and assistance received from S. D. Bowers and E. L. Maby, Jr., proved invaluable as the study progressed.

J. E. Sanders, who directed the research, gave unstintingly of his time, encouragement, and capable advice. Thanks are also extended to K. K. Turekian and K. M. Waage for their critical reading of the manuscript.

This acknowledgment would be incomplete if special mention were not made of the late R. A. Bramkamp, who suggested the study and initiated preparation of the thin sections. Many of the basic principles used in the study of Arab-D carbonates have evolved directly from his work on Arabian limestones and the nature of their sedimentation.

(Aramco) has collected data on its Upper Jurassic producing intervals. Present Upper Jurassic production is exclusively from carbonate members of the Arab formation, which consists of four normal marine carbonate units, each separated by thin, laterally persistent anhydrite members. The carbonate units, recognizable over much of northeastern Saudi Arabia, have been informally designated from top to bottom as the -A, -B, -C, and -D members of the Arab formation. The Arab-D member has proved on widespread exploration to be the most important reservoir; it contains productive oil in six widely scatt red fields. Cores from four of these fields—Ghawar, Abqaiq, Khursaniyah, and Khurais—have been thin sectioned and examined in detail as part of the present study (Fig. 2).

The productive structures of Ghawar and Abqaiq are north-south elongated anticlines located just inland from the western shore of the Persian Gulf. Abqaiq is some 40 miles long; Ghawar production is continuous over 140 miles. The folds are generally symmetrical with flank dips of 5°–10° at the oil zone. Khursaniyah, about 70 miles north of Ghawar and on the same line of folding, is slightly oval shaped, averaging about 7 miles in diameter. Khurais, 70 miles west of Ghawar, is in an intermediate position between Upper Jurassic surface exposures in Central Arabia and equivalent rocks in coastal oil wells. The structure, sharply elongated north-south, is about 20 miles long and 6 miles wide.

Highest productivity is obtained where the Arab-D consists predominantly of calcarenite. Normally, the oil-saturated interval extends about 250 feet below the base of the lower anhydrite, which separates the C and D zones.

To make a more cohesive document, the major sections of this report following the introduction have been placed approximately in the sequence in which the work itself was done; that is, thin-section petrography and description, classification, correlation, stratigraphy, reservoir characteristics, and finally, some general conclusions regarding paleogeography and paleoecology.

OBJECTIVES

The study consists primarily of a petrographic analysis of Arab-D carbonates; the main objective is the reconstruction of original environmental conditions and sedimentation patterns that were associated with D-member deposition. Thin-section examination is used to—(1) determine origin and relative proportions of constituent particles; (2) classify rock types present and outline their vertical and horizontal distribution; (3) establish detailed intramember correlation and zonation; (4) relate original rock types, particle types, and diagenetic changes to reservoir characteristics; (5) reconstruct physical and chemical conditions prevailing during Arab-D time; (6) note relation between diagenetic alteration and specific particle type; and (7) establish sequence of cementation, recrystallization, and dolomitization.

PREVIOUS WORK

References to the geology of Saudi Arabia prior to the start of surface mapping in 1933 in connection with the oil search, are scarce. Camel trips across the interior escarpment region by Philby, during World War I and later years, provided the first concrete evidence that Jurassic marine rocks in carbonate facies crop out extensively in Central Arabia (Philby, 1922, 1928, 1933, 1939). Collections made on these early travels indicated the presence of Lower Kimeridgian (Newton, 1921) and Callovian (Cox, 1933). Systematic investigation of the outcrop belt by oil company geologists led finally in 1952 to the publication of a summary of Arabian Jurassic stratigraphy based dominantly on the contained ammonites (Arkell, Bramkamp, and Steineke). Arkell (1956) included a similar summary in his monumental work on the Jurassic geology of the world. As these two publications contain an essentially complete list of references up to that time, their citations will not be repeated here unless pertinent.

Although several regional studies of Middle East tectonics and stratigraphy have been reported (Lamare, 1936; Picard, 1939; von Wissmann, 1943; Lees, 1950; Henson, 1951), none contains other than the most general lithologic descriptions (Fig. 1). In 1954, Daniel described the Qatar sequence, including a general account of the Arab formation. More detailed descriptions of Arab rocks in Saudi Arabia and adjacent countries appeared during the last half of the 1950's.

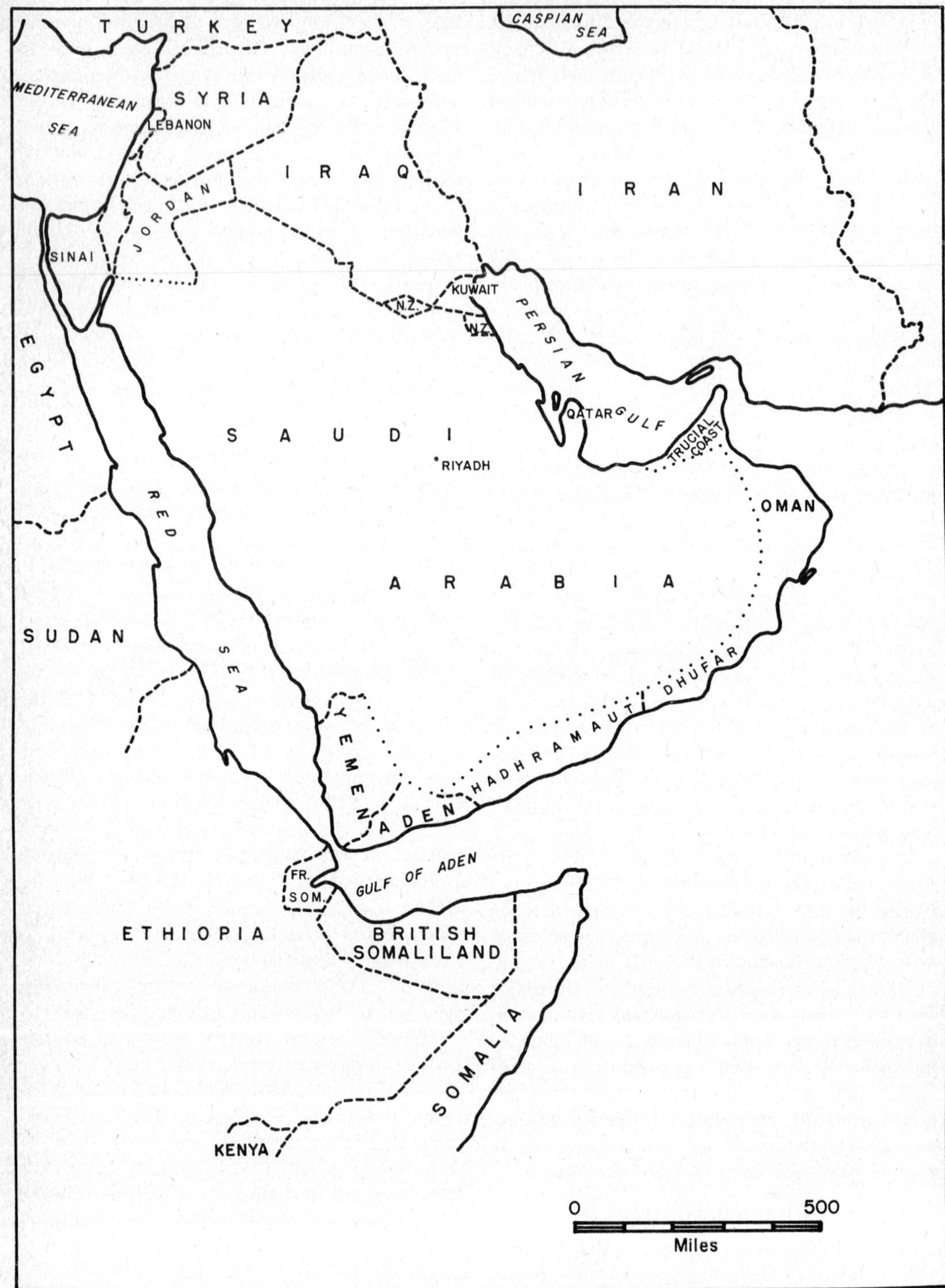

FIG. 1.—Index map—Middle East and adjacent countries.

Steineke, Bramkamp, and Sander (1958) discussed the stratigraphic relations of Arabian Jurassic oil and made very sound inferences from textural relationships regarding the paleogeography governing Arab formation deposition. They considered a broad shelf to be the most likely control on sedimentation patterns, a concept that has received striking confirmation from the present study.

Owen and Nasr (1958) indicated that in Kuwait, rocks probably equivalent to the Arab formation occur in massive anhydrite and salt facies with carbonates absent. Stratigraphic relationships between Arabia and Northern Iraq are incompletely understood; however, Dunnington (1958) shows that Upper Jurassic rocks are again admixed carbonate and anhydrite. In the extreme southeast, in Oman, strong evidence exists that rocks at least partially equivalent to the Arab formation are in typical clastic facies (Hudson and Chatton, 1959). The Arab formation, its general lithology, and reservoir characteristics, were discussed by the Aramco geological staff (1959). Sugden[3] (in press) gives a detailed account of the Qatar sequence, including the paleontology and lithology of strata undoubtedly equivalent to the Arab formation. The units and fossil content are remarkably similar to those encountered in Arabian coastal wells.

Detailed studies of the stratigraphy, petrography, and paleontology of the Arab formation or its individual members have not previously been made.

JURASSIC PALEOGEOGRAPHY

Marine Jurassic rocks, dominantly in carbonate facies, are extensively exposed in the Middle East. Well developed ammonite faunas indicate that several areas contain essentially complete sequences from Toarcian to Kimeridgian. One incompletely known section in southern Iran now appears to extend from Sinemurian through highest Tithonian and pass uninterruptedly into Lower Cretaceous (Arkell, 1956). The system varies little in thickness over much of the basin of deposition and averages about 3,300 feet.

Regional structure.—The tectonic framework controlling Jurassic sedimentation can readily be generalized into three positive elements—the Arabo-Nubian and Arabo-Somali massifs on the west and south, and the Russian platform of Paleozoic rocks on the north. Around these stable land masses Jurassic rocks were deposited in the southern continuation of the Tethys sea. The zone of thickest Jurassic sediments forms a great arc which wraps around the Arabo-Nubian shield and passes east through Lebanon, Syria, and Turkey; southeast across northern Iraq; then parallels the modern Persian Gulf trend. During much of Jurassic time, the Tethys must have been a broad neritic sea extending from central and southern Arabia across Iran.

Relationship to adjacent systems.—The passage from Triassic to Jurassic is everywhere represented either by unconformity or nonmarine sedimentation. Around the margin of the crystalline massifs, marine Jurassic beds are separated from undoubted Triassic by generally unfossiliferous sandstone. These nonmarine clastics are tentatively assigned a Liassic age on the basis of stratigraphic position and rare occurrences of fish teeth, molluscs, and plant scraps (Clapp, 1940; Clift, 1956; Renouard, 1955; Arkell, 1956). Some of the fossils are of questionable Hettangian age.

Except in the central part of the geosyncline, the Jurassic-Cretaceous boundary is marked by hiatus. Unquestioned highest Jurassic is absent in all areas except northern Iraq, Iran, and Oman, where Tithonian passes without visible interruption into Berriasian (Clapp, 1940; Kent and others, 1951; Hudson and others, 1954; Arkell, 1956; Dunnington, 1958; Hudson and Chatton, 1959).

Upper Jurassic stratigraphy.—The lower Upper Jurassic (Oxfordian) is mostly limestone, although the dominant lithology is shale in British Somaliland (Macfayden, 1933); sandstone in Wadi Raman, Palestine (Arkell, 1956); and possibly anhydrite in Kuwait (Owen and Nasr, 1958).

The most widely distributed Jurassic beds in the Middle East are Lower Kimeridgian. Normally they conformably overlie Oxfordian, but in Yemen (Arkell, 1956), the Hadhramaut (Little, 1925), and coastal Arabia (Steineke and others, 1958) they lie unconformably on Rhaetic, crystal-

[3] The writer is indebted to Mr. Sugden through whose courtesy a copy of the Lexique Stratigraphique International manuscript for the Qatar Peninsula was made available.

line basement, and Bathonian, respectively. Lower Kimeridgian rocks are almost everywhere carbonate, with the possible exception of Kuwait and northern Iraq, where the equivalent may be anhydrite and salt.

Above the Lower Kimeridgian, Jurassic deposits become progressively more restricted and undergo a definite change in lithic character. Younger rocks take on a more clastic aspect with regard to both silicates and carbonates. Sandstone, shale, and mudstone are common in East Africa (Arkell, 1956), whereas various types of calcarenite appear in Arabia (Steineke and others, 1958), Qatar (Sugden, in press), Oman (Hudson and Chatton, 1959), and Lebanon (Renouard, 1955). Essentially equivalent current-washed deposits probably occur elsewhere, for example, western Iran, but available lithologic descriptions are too vague to be certain.

The highest definitely dated Jurassic is restricted to Oman, Iran, and northern Iraq, where Tithonian-Berriasian transition takes place without apparent break. Post-Kimeridgian beds may also occur in Arabia, Qatar, and Kuwait in the form of anhydrite, but the absence of fossils makes age determination of these evaporites impossible.

This pattern of sedimentation indicates that following widespread deposition of carbonate muds in the Lower Kimeridgian the Tethys contracted and shoaled; Arab formation calcarenite and anhydrite were deposited and the period closed with the precipitation of massive saline units west of the present Persian Gulf axis. Normal marine conditions prevailed to the east.

THIN-SECTION PETROGRAPHY

Previous knowledge of the Arab-D member had been based on examination of cuttings, cores, logs (electric and radiation), and chemical and physical measurements. The early phase of reservoir-rock analysis, that of routine sample examination, description, classification, and graphic presentation, has progressed rapidly. A fairly detailed picture of Arab-D rock textures and their relationship to original depositional conditions had been reconstructed, using a standard binocular microscope. This instrument, which can often resolve such textural characteristics as grain size and shape, is commonly inadequate for differentiating more detailed rock aspects such as specific particle type or mode of diagenesis. Thin-section analysis was considered to offer the next logical step toward understanding the processes associated with Arab-D deposition and its subsequent history.

More than 80 suites of diamond cores, many in which recovery exceeds 90 per cent, are available from the Arab-D. Each core has been plugged at approximately six-inch intervals throughout and tested for porosity and permeability. Usually, plugs are alternately cut parallel to and normal to the long axis of the core. Standard-thickness thin sections were cut from the discarded ends of each plug in seven high-recovery wells in Ghawar and three in Abqaiq. Thin sections from two critical fields in adjacent areas (Khursaniyah and Khurais) were also prepared (Fig. 2). Examination of slides from these wells forms the framework of the present study. A total of nearly 4,000 slides was cut and examined; some 1,200 of these, representing four key wells spaced uniformly through Ghawar and Abqaiq, were analyzed by point counting.

METHOD

The initial phase of the study consisted of point counting slides from Haradh No. 3 well, 'Uthmaniyah No. 45, Fazran No. 1, and Abqaiq No. 71 to determine as accurately as possible the volumetric proportions of the various components contributing to the reservoir rock. These wells were selected for two reasons—namely, their uniform spacing through Ghawar and Abqaiq, and their nearly 100 per cent core recovery from the Arab-D. Average distance between thin sections from these wells is slightly more than 6 inches. Each slide, prepared from the discarded end of a core plug, is 25 mm diameter and, where rock cohesiveness permitted, ground as nearly as possible to standard thickness (0.03 mm).

Chayes (1949 and 1956) outlined the point-count method for petrographic modal analysis where, to determine relative area and volume, a series of parallel, equally spaced point-grid traverses are substituted for continuous line integration. Krumbein (1935) and others (Greenman, 1951b; Pelto, 1952; Packham, 1955) have shown

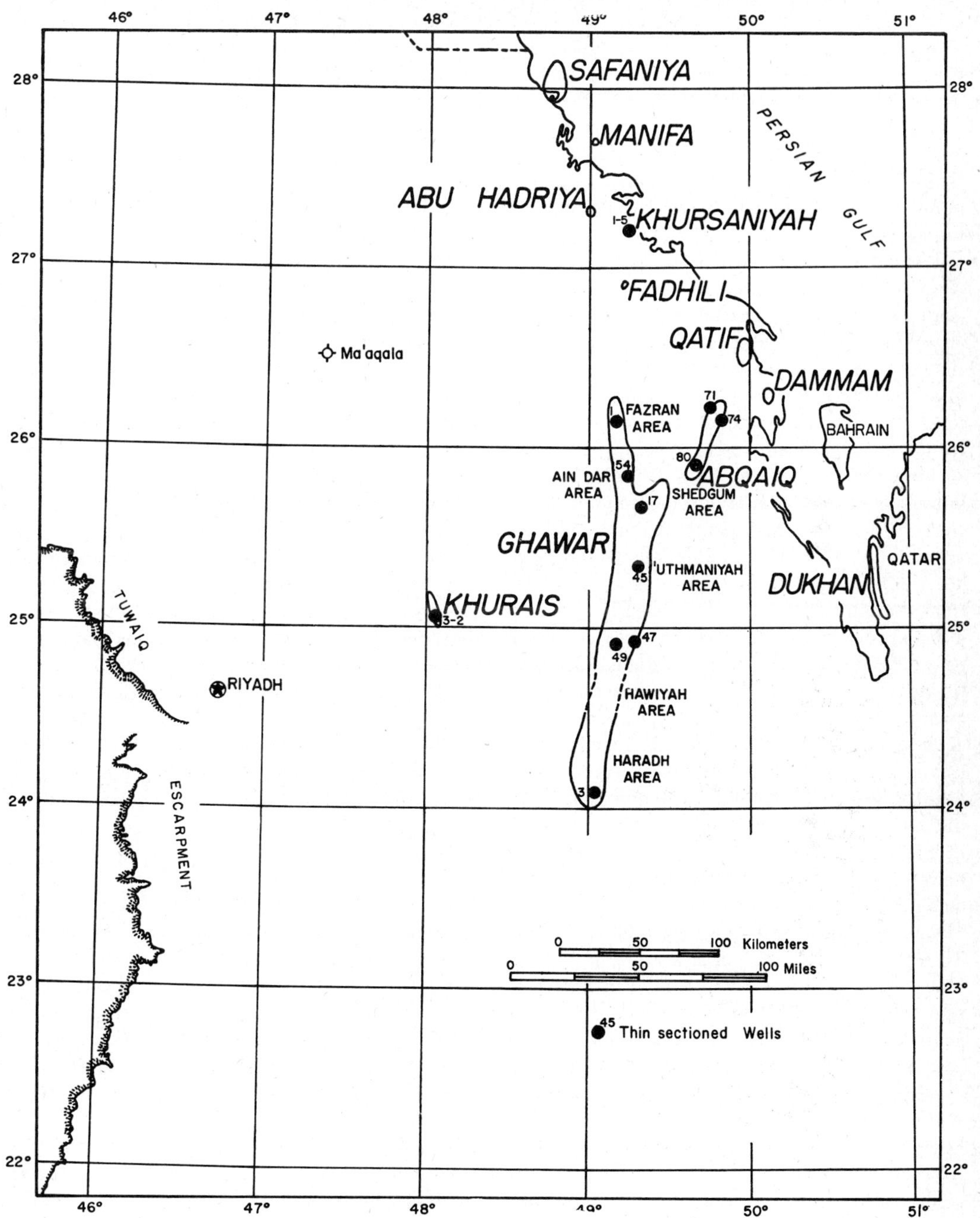

FIG. 2.—Index map—northeast Saudi Arabia.

that the results of such analyses cannot be directly compared to mechanical sieve measurements of dissaggregated rocks or modern sediments. As pointed out by Rosenfeld and others (1953), however, it is possible to compare thin-section measurements with one another, for rock parameters can be as adequately defined by consistent slide measurements as by mechanical methods.

A standard Leitz mechanical stage was converted to a point-count stage by addition of a spring clip to engage notches filed in one of the traversing wheels. These notches were spaced to allow a linear slide motion of 0.8 mm between stops. Distance between point-count lines was controlled by the second traversing wheel. Numerous experiments were tried to determine an ideal spacing between lines of points for obtaining acceptable results in a minimum of time. Initially, a pattern with points 0.8 mm and lines of points 1.0 mm apart was used (about 600 points per slide). Compared with line integration results from the same slides, this point density gave no difference for any one constituent greater than 2 per cent. Using a 0.8 by 2.0 mm grid on slides with irregular particle shapes and poor sorting, the maximum difference was 4 per cent. The difference increased progressively as distance between traverses increased. Most slides were finally counted on a pattern of 0.8 by 2.0 mm (about 300 points); uniformly textured rocks such as aphanitic limestone with scattered dolomite rhombs, however, could be processed with equal accuracy on a 0.8 by 4.0 mm grid.

Figure 3 shows the data recorded for each slide. To record this information, a battery of 24 individual hand counters was mounted in lines corresponding to size classes and types of components. For each stop of the point-count stage, a counter appropriate to the component or pore type appearing under the cross hairs was punched. At the same time, the apparent long axis of each originally sedimented grain was measured with a micrometer ocular and the proper size grade recorded by counter. At the completion of each count, all components which contribute to the volume of the rock, with the exception of intragranular elements (porosity or authigenic constituents) were set equal to 100 per cent and the volumetric proportion of each calculated. Occurrences of intragranular elements are recorded in a separate column, but the original particle which encloses them is used to calculate volumetric proportions. This is done to permit a closer comparison with recent carbonate sediment studies where particles are essentially unaltered.

Following the point-count examination of slides from 4 wells, constituent proportions in thin sections representing 8 other wells were estimated (Abqaiq 74 and 80, 'Uthmaniyah 47 and 49, Ain Dar 54, Shedgum 17, Khurais 3 and 2, and Khursaniyah 1 and 5).

A Leitz Dialux-Pol binocular polarizing microscope was used for examination of all thin sections. With this instrument, textural differences difficult to resolve with monocular or standard binocular stereoscopic systems were readily apparent. Staining methods for differentiating dolomite and calcite were found to be unnecessary, as the shape and light-brown color of dolomite was sufficiently distinctive. Spot insoluble residue checks indicate that Arab-D carbonates are essentially pure, generally containing less than 1 per cent noncarbonate fraction which commonly consists of clay, pyrite, or very fine-grained quartz sand.

The data recorded for each slide include—particle size, particle type, authigenic constituents, and visual porosity. Diagenetic effects and the order in which authigenic changes occurred, were also noted.

PARTICLE SIZE

Arab-D rock particles show considerable size variation, ranging from mud- to sand- and gravel-size grains. The particles were graded according to a simplified version of the Wentworth scale in order to obtain at least an approximation of grain-size distribution for comparison with other studies. The standard grade limits between mud and sand (0.06 mm) and between sand and gravel (2.00 mm) have been preserved, but are subdivided into class intervals with a ratio of 3.2 between successive classes (Fig. 4). The terms mud, sand, and gravel as used in this paper have no mineralogical significance but refer only to particle size.

Aphanitic limestone proved on detailed exami-

Well Fazran Well 1

Slide				1350		1351		1352		1353		1354		1355		1356		1357		1358		1359	
Depth				7038.6		7039.1		7039.5		7040.1		7040.6		7041.0		7041.4		7042.0		7043.8		7044.3	
Plug				7V		8H		9V		10H		11V		12H		13V		14H		15V		16H	
Original Particle Size - mm.	Clay-silt		<0.06	40		5						55		76		74		69					
	Sand	fine	0.06-0.20	18		2				3		3		3		2		6		21		22	
		med.	0.20-0.60	9	31	33	53			9	21		3	5	8	3	5	6	15	28	59	24	54
		cse.	0.60-2.00	4		18				9								3		10		8	
	Gravel		>2.00	21		15				64										4		4	
Original Particle Type (larger than 0.06 mm.)	Skeletal	Calcareous algae				32				58						1		1		48		45	
		Foraminifera		5		2				2		1				tr		tr		tr		tr	
		Stromatoporoid		20		13				11													
		Echinoderm		1		tr				1		2		2		1							
		Mollusca								5				1		3		1		tr		1	
		Brachiopod																					
		Coral								1													
		Indeterminate												3									
		Total skeletal		26		47				73		3		6		5		2		49		46	
	Non-skeletal	Angular aggregate		1		1				3								2					
		Rounded aggregate (pellet)		25		13				9				2				10		4		3	
		'Algal' nodule				8														9		8	
		'Faecal' pellet																					
		Superficial oolith																					
		True oolith																					
		Total non-skeletal		26		22				12				2				12		13		11	
	Indeterminate																						
Authigenic Constituents	Crystalline cement			*1	+						1									1			
	Drusy coating			4	1	7				8	14							1		19	1	19	2
	Mosaic calcite					6												5		4		6	
	Dolomite					2		90				34		15		18		1		4		7	
	Anhydrite							1												tr			
Porosity	Visual Porosity	Granular		2	2	11	tr			6	9	8		1			1	2		10	4	11	3
		Secondary void																					
		Channel														3		7					
		Disrupted																					
		Intercrystalline						9										1					
		Total		4		11		9		15		8		1		4		10		14		14	
	Measured porosity			19		26		9		27		21		14		19		17		14		24	
	Measured permeability			17		274		7		796		106		7		2		2		4		139	
Rock type				2C		3A		4B		51AR		11BD		11CD		11CD		21AR		31AR		31AR	
Remarks								Photo												Photo			

*Intergranular
+Intragranular

RWP-July 1959

FIG. 3.—Basic-data sheet for thin-section analysis.

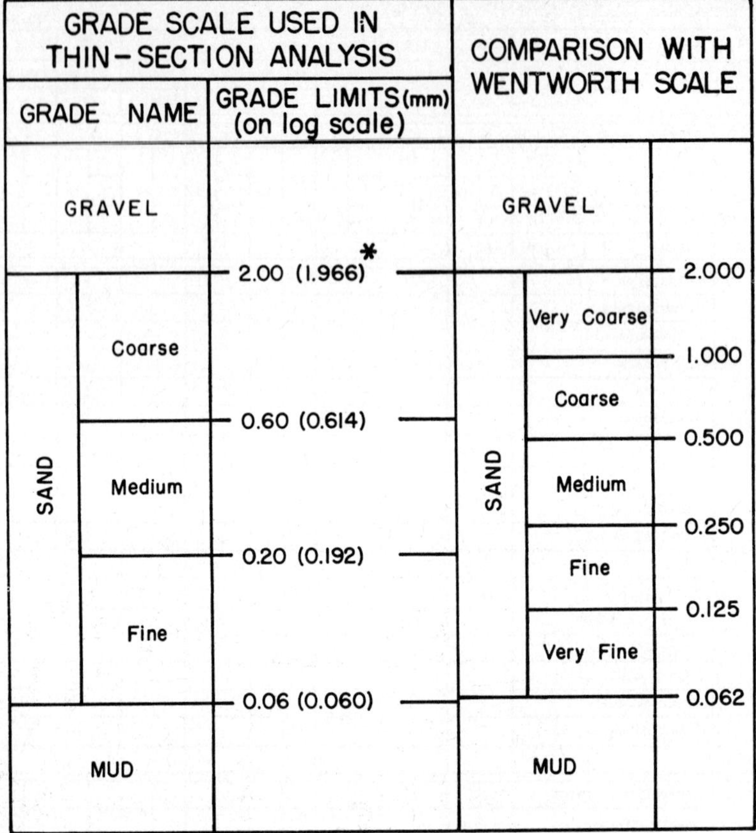

FIG. 4.—Grade limits used in thin-section analysis.

nation to consist of individual grains that have been lithified by rim cementation to a uniform textural mosaic. Original particle size rarely exceeds 10 microns and generally is near the clay-silt limit, or about 4 microns. Specific particle types show considerable size variation; however, some correlation exists between particle size and type—for example, "fecal" pellets are generally fine grained; calcareous algae, Foraminifera, and aggregate pellets are normally fine to coarse grained; and stromatoporoid and "algal" nodules are dominantly medium grained to gravel size. Individual particles on occasion are larger than 25 mm in diameter and cover an entire slide.

ORIGINAL PARTICLE TYPE

Particle type can be deciphered with any certainty only where the grain was originally sand or gravel size. In this range, it is generally easy to determine the source of various rock particles except where replacement by dolomite has obliterated the original texture. Calcareous sand and gravel fall naturally into two main genetic groups—skeletal and nonskeletal. Illing (1954) first proposed these terms to designate carbonate fragments described by earlier workers as "organic" and "inorganic." They have been adapted in this paper for ease of comparison with Illing's work, other carbonate-sediment studies (Ginsburg,

1956; Daetwyler and Kidwell, 1959), and recent investigations of ancient limestones (Beales, 1956, 1957; Illing, 1959).

SKELETAL PARTICLES

Calcareous algae, Foraminifera, and stromatoporoids proved to be the main skeletal elements in the Arab-D; echinoderms, molluscs, brachiopods, sponges, and corals occur only in limited amounts.

Calcareous algae.—The upper part of the Arab-D reservoir contains the remains of calcareous algae in surprising abundance (Pl. I, Fig. 1). Although they are slightly more susceptible to recrystallization than other particle types, their preservation is generally adequate for identification of genera and, in some instances, species. Identifications were made by comparison with figured works on Upper Jurassic algae and Foraminifera of the Middle East (Elliott, 1955, 1956, 1957, 1958) and Europe (Carozzi, 1955; Dufaure, 1958; Gianotti, 1958). Most forms described by Elliott from the Arab-D equivalent in Qatar were recognized in Arabian strata.

One family of green calcareous algae, the Dasycladaceae, is well represented; members of the red algae family Corallinaceae are less common. Identifiable dasyclad forms include—*Clypeina jurassica* Favre, *C.* cf. *hanabatensis* Yabe and Toyama, *C.* sp., *Salpingoporella* sp., and *Cylindroporella arabica* Elliott. Coralline algae include *Polygonella incrustata* Elliott, and a few rare, poorly preserved specimens of *Solenopora?* Of these forms *Clypeina jurassica, C.* cf. *hanabatensis*, and *Polygonella incrustata* are the most common. *Clypeina* is readily distinguished by the radiating, spoke-like arrangement of the branches around a central stem (Pl. I, Fig. 2). The incrusting coralline genus *Polygonella* is characterized by a single layer of cells which show a polygonal honeycomb appearance in transverse section and are rectangular in vertical section (Pl. I, Fig. 3).

The occurrence of different calcareous algae is sharply controlled by environment. Dasyclads thrive best in mud-free sediment, and the hardy *Polygonella* occurs even in lime mud, only slightly sandy.

Foraminifera.—Foraminifera rarely form more than 5 per cent of the reservoir rock. Some of the calcareous algae are apparently restricted to the Arab-D, but many of the Foraminifera in the Arab-D occur also in the underlying Jubaila formation and extend upward without apparent break. Jubaila Foraminifera have been studied in detail by Sander (1954) and reference to his excellent photomicrographs and thin sections of type specimens permitted identification of the important Arab-D forms—*Valvulinella jurassica* Henson, *Nautiloculina oolithica* Mohler, *Pseudocyclammina* sp., *Cyclammina* sp., *Textularia* spp., and various Miliolidae. All forms with the exception of *Pseudocyclammina* sp. and *Cyclammina* sp. occur throughout the Arab-D. *Cyclammina* sp. has been found only in the lower part of the Arab-D *Pseudocyclammina* sp., in the upper part.

Stromatoporoidea—Hydroids of the order Stromatoporoidea are, along with calcareous algae, the most important skeletal rock-builders in the Arab-D. Skeletal fragments range from medium sand to gravel size and are commonly larger than 25 mm. Recognition is simplified by the trabecular appearance of the walls, which give wavy extinction in polarized light, transverse and radial lamellae which outline rectangular interspaces, and light-yellow color in ordinary light (Pl. I, Fig. 4). Well-rounded fragments of stromatoporoids commonly comprise more than 50 per cent of the upper half of the reservoir. Identification below the ordinal level was not attempted.

Echinodermata.—Echinoderm fragments occur through the entire Arab-D, but almost universally form less than 2–3 per cent of the total rock volume, and in only rare instances exceed 5 per cent. Debris from members of this phylum, represented by random slices through skeletal plates and spines, are easily recognized by their unit extinction in polarized light. Echinoderm grains are commonly surrounded by a corona of clear calcite cement deposited in optical continuity with the original plate (Pl. I, Fig. 5). They appear to be less susceptible to complete replacement by dolomite than most other particle types. In some instances, where nearly complete dolomite replacement has occurred, echinoderm fragments form the last remaining vestige of original texture.

Mollusca and Brachiopoda.—With few excep-

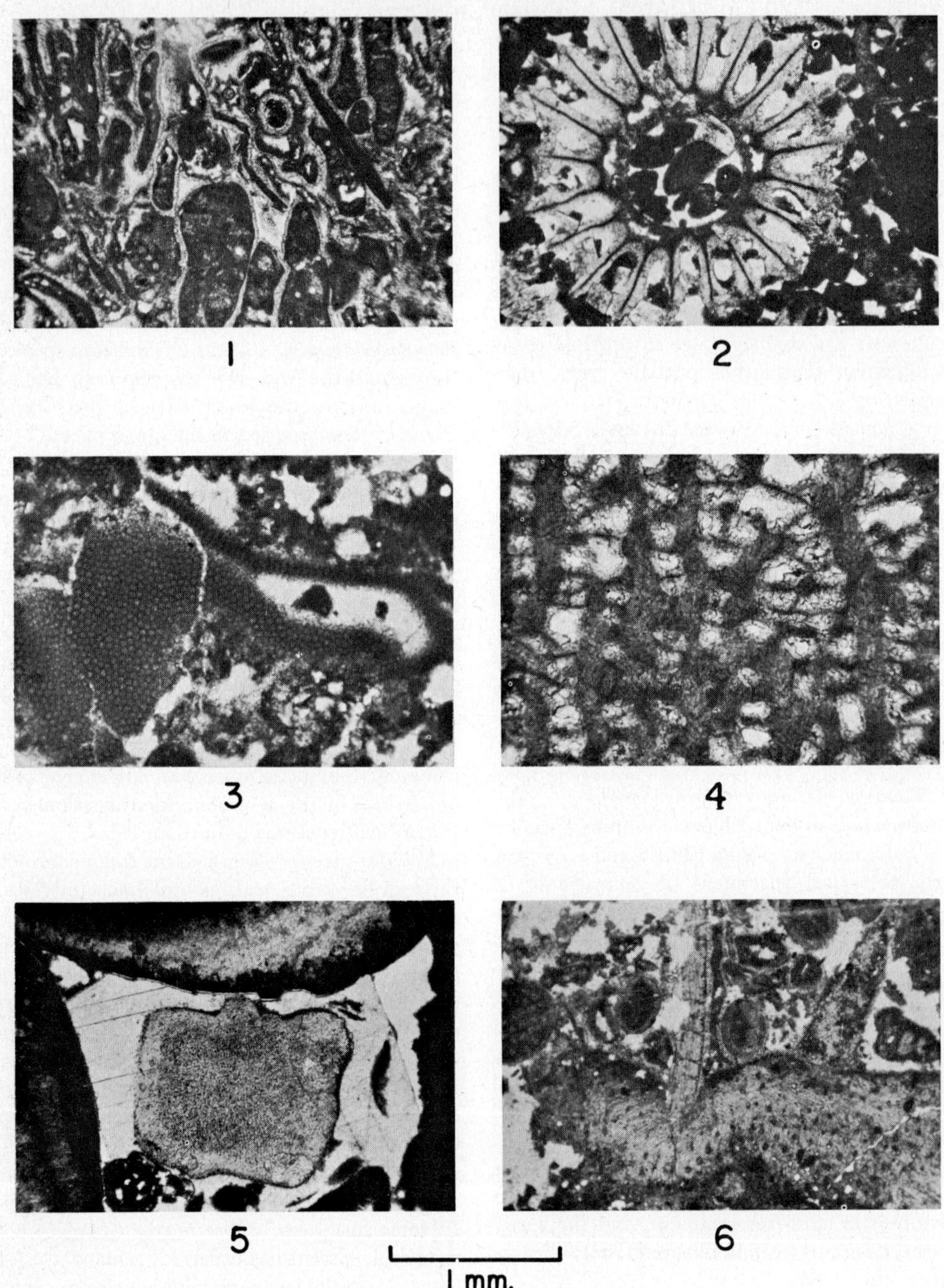

PLATE I.—Skeletal particles.

tions, brachiopod and molluscan fragments are scarce. The two can normally be separated on the basis of differences in preservation. Molluscan shells are commonly altered to a clear, fine- to medium-crystalline calcite mosaic, whereas in brachiopod shells the internal structure, including punctae, is generally preserved in considerable detail (Pl. I, Fig. 6). Neither brachiopods nor molluscs occur in significant amounts in the Arab-D, although gastropods do become more common in the upper part where transition from carbonate to anhydrite deposition takes place.

Sponge.—In rare instances, some aphanitic limestones contain hollow or calcite-filled external molds of what originally must have been siliceous monaxon sponge spicules. Nowhere in the Arab-D was original sponge debris recognized. The perfect, tapered, needle-like molds, and the presence in several instances of cherty dolomite in immediately adjacent beds, however, are considered presumptive evidence of their original presence.

Coral.—Scleractinian coral proved surprisingly rare in the Arab-D and, along with sponges, is volumetrically the least important skeletal contributor to the interval. Where recognized, the coral skeleton is generally poorly preserved, presumably as a result of its original aragonitic composition.

NONSKELETAL PARTICLES

The most important nonskeletal particles are "fecal" pellets, angular aggregates, aggregate pellets, and "algal" nodules. Superficial and true oöliths are rare to absent.

"Fecal" pellets.—Particles considered to be of fecal origin are abundant in the lower, more muddy part of the Arab-D. They are smaller than fecal pellets reported from the Bahama Banks (Illing, 1954), and normally occur in the fine sand range (0.06–0.20 mm); only rarely are they larger. The pellets are oval in longitudinal section and commonly show some distortion—probably as a result of compaction while still incompletely lithified (Pl. II, Fig. 1). Proof that these pellets result from organic activity is lacking. Their uniform size, shape, and excellent sorting, together with their restriction to muddy sediments, however, suggest that they result from the reworking of weakly compacted lime mud by bottom-dwelling organisms.

Angular aggregates.—Discrete angular sand- and gravel-size fragments aggregated from mud, or in rare instances from mud and sand grains, are common in some parts of the Arab-D (Pl. II, Fig. 2). These fragments appear to originate in two ways—(1) from the destruction of incompletely consolidated bottom sediment during time of intense current activity with deposition following before edges and corners become rounded, and (2) growth in place by cementation of originally aragonite particles to sand size, as described by Illing (1954). Although detailed evidence is missing, a gradational sequence may occur beginning with angular aggregates, passing through well-rounded aggregate grains (pellets), and ending, where conditions are favorable, with the precipitation of concentric oölitic layers on the rounded grains.

Rounded aggregates (pellets).—Rounded aggregates or aggregate pellets formed by accretion of mud-size, and rarely mud- and sand-size grains, are common in the Arab-D. These internally structureless, nonskeletal particles are normally well rounded and range from fine to coarse sand.

←

EXPLANATION OF PLATE I

FIG. 1.—Algal debris. Calcarenite composed almost entirely of tabular fragments of calcareous algae. Note lineation. Khursaniyah No. 5 well, slide 4229, depth 6,661 feet. *Calcarenite.*

FIG. 2.—*Clypeina jurassica* Favre. Transverse section showing spoke-like arrangement of branches around a central stem; typical of this dasyclad genus. Ain Dar No. 54 well, slide 766, depth 7,381 feet. *Calcarenite.*—porosity 20%, permeability 48 md.

FIG. 3.—*Polygonella incrustata* Elliott. Transverse and vertical sections. Fazran No. 1 well, slide 1425, depth 7,086 feet. *Calcarenite.*—porosity 26%, permeability 1,144 md.

FIG. 4.—Stromatoporoid. Oblique section. Abqaiq No. 71 well, slide 162, depth 7,434 feet. *Calcarenitic limestone.*—porosity 14%, permeability 3 md (low permeability is due to surrounding mud matrix not visible on figure).

FIG. 5.—Echinoderm. Section of echinoderm fragment with clear calcite cement in crystallographic continuity. 'Uthmaniyah No. 45 well, slide 599, depth 6,779 feet. *Coarse carbonate clastic.*—porosity 29%.

FIG. 6.—Brachiopod. Oblique sections of punctate brachiopod shells. 'Uthmaniyah No. 45 well, slide 399, depth 6,502 feet. *Calcarenite.*—porosity 21%, permeability 84 md.

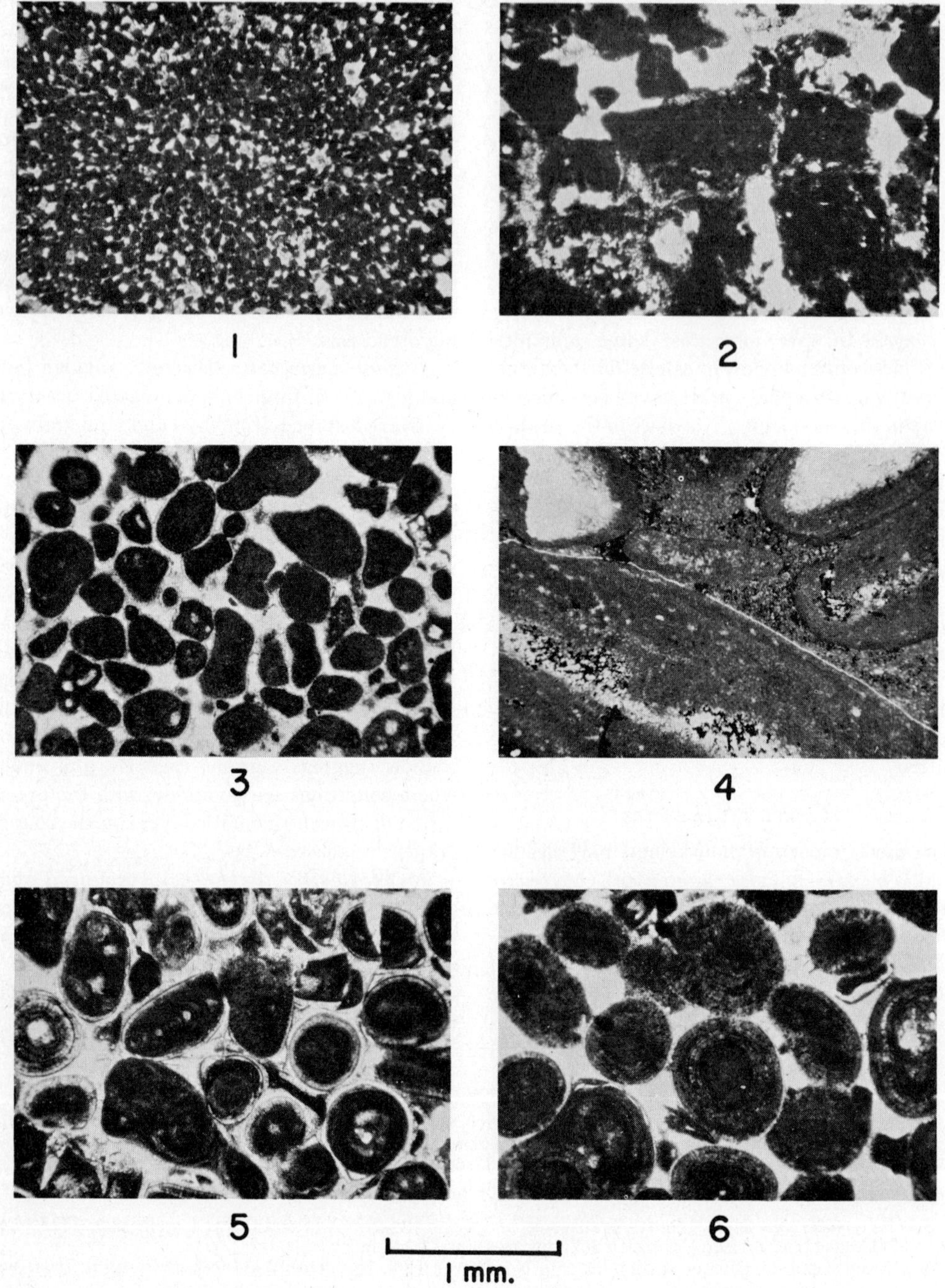

PLATE II.—Nonskeletal particles.

They rarely exceed 2.0 mm in diameter (Pl. II, Fig. 3). At least two modes of origin are considered likely for these pellets. In the first, weakly consolidated muddy bottom is ripped up, abraded, and then deposited as rounded sand grains; in the second, calcareous silt particles are cemented *in place* into lumps of medium-grained sand. That the first process occurs, is indicated by discrete, sharply angular gravel, made up of sand-size particles in a mud matrix. Aggregation by the second process in modern sediments is undoubted, and apparently played a major role in Arab-D pellet formation. Whether the two methods of particle formation can be distinguished in most instances is doubtful, for both are products of mud cementation, transport, and later deposition as an individual grain.

"Algal" nodules.—In this study, the term "algal" nodule is used for dominantly gravel-size aggregates of fine particles showing poorly developed, concentric layering but containing no evidence of a rigid skeletal framework (Pl. II, Fig. 4). These nodules are considered nonskeletal as their present composition appears to result exclusively from the aggregation of mud grains, although it is likely that algae originally were active in particle collection and cementation. Commonly, the nodules are constructed around a fragment of brachiopod or mollusc shell which serves as a nucleus for the collection of fine calcareous sediment. These nodules are present throughout the reservoir, commonly forming more than 50 per cent of some beds and, along with stromatoporoids, are the main gravel-size grains.

Superficial oöliths.—Oöliths or rounded carbonate bodies which show concentric structure in cross section, are rare in the Arab-D. Grains with incomplete or single layers, however, do occur and are here considered as superficial oöliths, in the manner of Carozzi (1957) (Pl. II, Fig. 5). Superficial oöliths are normally medium grained and rarely exceed 0.5 mm diameter. Various particle types including Foraminifera, aggregate pellets, echinoderm fragments, and algae, serve as nuclei around which the oölite layer is deposited.

True oöliths.—Grains which could definitely be regarded as true oöliths, that is, with two or more well-developed concentric layers, were seen only rarely in the Arab-D. The single well (Khursaniyah No. 1 well), from which some thin sections are available for the Arab-C member, however, did contain true oöliths (Pl. II, Fig. 6). In these slides, the oöliths average about 0.5 mm diameter.

AUTHIGENIC CONSTITUENTS

Original Arab-D rock textures have been altered in at least six ways—(1) addition of a drusy coat of acicular calcite around calcarenite particles; (2) recrystallization to mosaic calcite; (3) cementation by clear calcite; (4) growth of tabular anhydrite crystals; (5) dolomitization; and (6) silicification. The sequence in which authigenic changes occur is approximately in the order listed.

Drusy coating.—Calcarenite grains, regardless of origin, are commonly surrounded by a thin layer of needle-like calcite crystals that grew normal to the grain surface. The coat, composed of tightly packed scalenohedral crystals projecting outward into the intergranular pore space, forms a rind generally not more than 100 microns thick (Pl. III, Fig. 1). Although not present in all Arab-D calcarenites, about half the clean-washed beds are coated to some degree. Near the top of the reservoir, shortly before change to anhydrite deposi-

---

EXPLANATION OF PLATE II

FIG. 1.—"Fecal" pellets. Abqaiq No. 71 well, slide 214, depth 7,474 feet. *Calcarenite.*—porosity 14%, permeability 13 md.

FIG. 2.—Angular aggregates. Abqaiq No. 71 well, slide 156, depth 7,430 feet. *Calcarenitic limestone.*—porosity 17%, permeability 43 md.

FIG. 3.—Rounded aggregates (pellets). Abqaiq No. 74 well, slide 2069, depth 7,682 feet. *Calcarenite.*—porosity 17%, permeability 780 md.

FIG. 4.—"Algal" nodules. Note skeletal fragment nuclei and mud matrix. 'Uthmaniyah No. 45 well, slide 632, depth 6,817 feet. *Calcarenitic limestone.*—porosity 5%, permeability 0 md.

FIG. 5.—Superficial oöliths. Particles of various types serve as nuclei for single, commonly discontinuous oölitic layer. Khursaniyah No. 5 well, slide 4191, depth 6,642 feet. *Calcarenite.*

FIG. 6.—True oöliths. Both radial and concentric structure is visible. Note pressure-solution effects presumably as a result of compaction. Khursaniyah No. 1 well, slide 1013, depth 6,159 feet (Arab-C) *Calcarenite.*—porosity 27%, permeability 1,312 md.

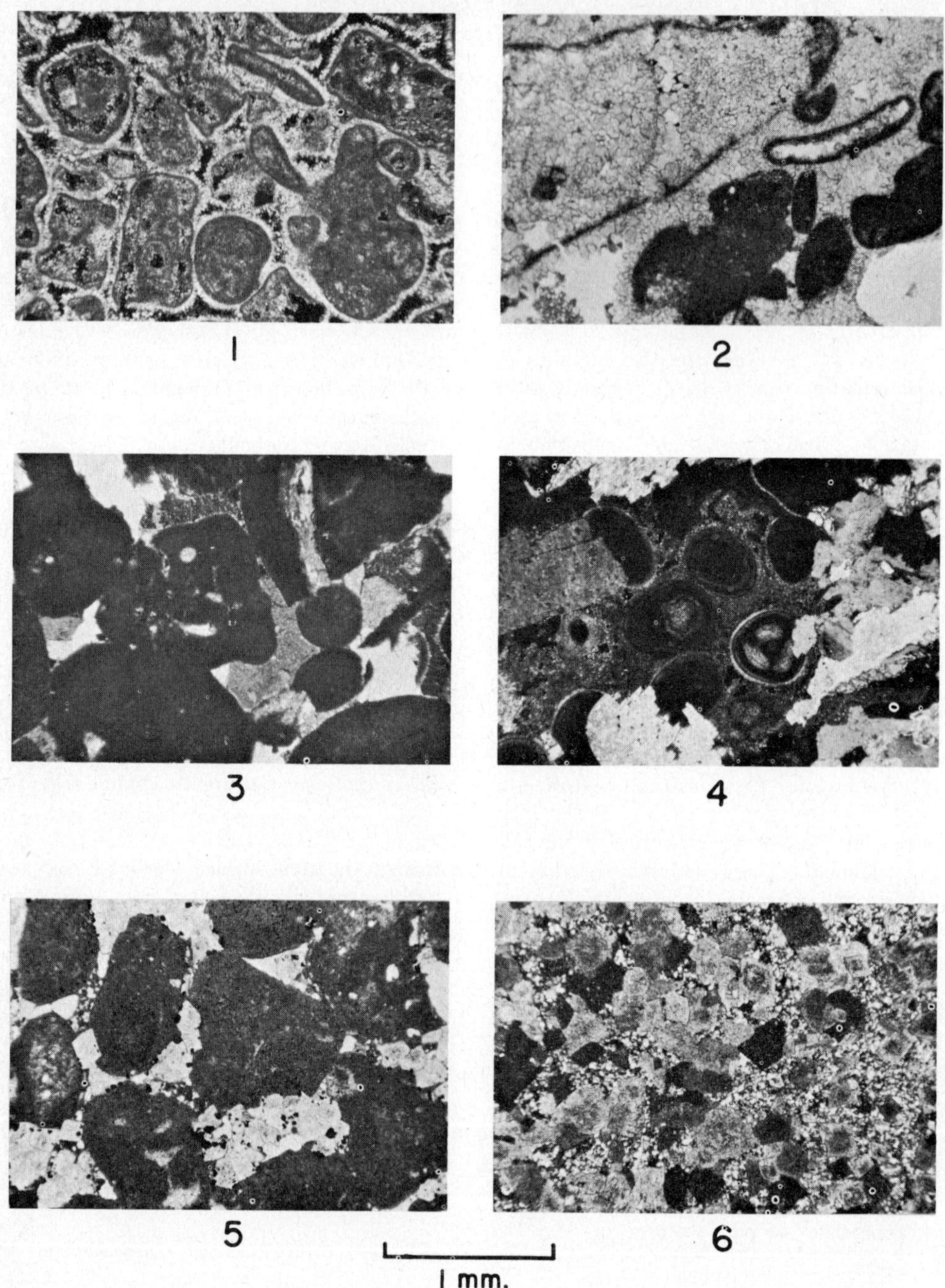

PLATE III.—Authigenic constituents.

tion, drusy calcite is better developed and in some instances makes up 15–20 per cent of the rock volume—decreasing original pore space an equal amount.

The absence of a drusy coat where particles are in direct contact with one another suggests that the acicular layer is added after deposition. The calcite may well be an outgrowth of the drusy aragonite coating noted in Recent sediments (Illing, 1954). In these, individual aggregate pellets are cemented by densely packed aragonite prisms, some of which are as long as 50 microns. The growth of aragonite crystals certainly represents an early stage in the consolidation of these sedimentary particles into a lithified rock.

Mosaic calcite.—Recrystallization of original rock particles to a coarser but still finely crystalling calcite mosaic is rare but does occur commonly enough to require description. Calcareous mud is most susceptible to this type of alteration, and only in rare instances was the recrystallization of sand-sized particles to mosaic calcite noted (Pl. III, Fig. 3). Mosaic textures appear to result mainly from the enlargement of mud grains (whose diameter probably was originally less than 10 microns) into an interlocking network of crystals 50 microns or larger.

Crystalline cement.—Calcarenites cemented with clear crystalline calcite have proved surprisingly rare in the Arab-D reservoir. Of the 4,000 slides examined, less than 5 were strongly cemented—that is, where original pore space was nearly or completely filled with secondary calcite cement. Many more slides contained traces of cement but normally in amounts less than 5 per cent, thus little affecting original porosity. Where present, the cement consists of several interlocking crystals whose length ranges from 0.1 mm to commonly larger than 1.0 mm (Pl. III, Fig. 3). Only one particle type—echinoderm—shows strong affinity for calcite cement which is invariably precipitated as a secondary corona in optical continuity with the original fragment (Pl. I, Fig. 5).

The occurrence of cement in aphanitic limestone where originally discrete mud grains have been welded together by rim cementation (Bathurst, 1958), is commonly overlooked, probably because of the small size involved. Although on a different scale than carbonate sand cementatation, it would seem that the two processes are more closely comparable than is generally considered.

Anhydrite.—Coarse anhydrite[4] crystals crosscutting original textural elements are common through the Arab-D. Individual crystals sometimes exceed 2 mm in length (Pl. III, Fig. 4), but normally make up less than 1 per cent of the rock bulk. Although present in association with calcarenite and calcarenitic limestone made up of all particle types, authigenic anhydrite shows a definite preference for stromatoporoid fragments. Tabular anhydrite crystals with perfect orthorhombic outline randomly transect the reticulate stromatoporoid skeleton.

Dolomite.—Partial or complete replacement of

[4] K. K. Turekian suggested (personal communication) that these crystals might be the strontium sulfate celestite which has been reported occurring under similar circumstances in association with scleractinian coral and rudistid skeletons (Andrieux, 1960). Later X-ray analysis (by P. E. Biscaye and the writer) showed the crystals to be definitely anhydrite.

←««

Explanation of Plate III

Fig. 1.—Drusy coating. Algal debris and aggregate pellets with well-developed layer of drusy calcite crystals· Coat is absent where plane of section cuts grain contacts. Khursaniyah No. 5 well, slide 4216, depth 6,654 feet. *Calcarenite.* Crossed nicols.

Fig. 2.—Mosaic calcite. Partial recrystallization of gastropod and other particle types to anhedral calcite mosaic. Abqaiq No. 71 well, slide 74, depth 7,371 feet. *Coarse carbonate clastic.*—porosity 17%, permeability 69 md.

Fig. 3.—Calcite cement. "Algal" nodules (black grains) tightly cemented by clear secondary calcite (white and light-gray). Khurais No. 2 well, slide 4082, depth 5,504 feet. *Coarse carbonate clastic.* Crossed nicols.

Fig. 4.—Anhydrite. Superficial oöliths and aggregate pellets cut by authigenic anhydrite. Khursaniyah No. 5 well, slide 4191, depth 6,642 feet. *Calcarenite.* Crossed nicols.

Fig. 5.—Dolomite. Mud matrix is almost completely replaced by dolomite; aggregate pellets and other sand-size grains are little altered. Black spots are pyrite. Fazran No. 1 well, slide 1613, depth 7,216 feet. *Calcarenitic limestone.*—porosity 9%, permeability 63 md.

Fig. 6.—Chert. Dolomite (black to medium-gray, finely crystalline rhombs) and chert (white to dark-gray, microcrystalline equant grains). Fazran No. 1 well, slide 1512, depth 7,150 feet. *Crystalline dolomite.*—porosity 3%, permeability 0 md. Crossed nicols.

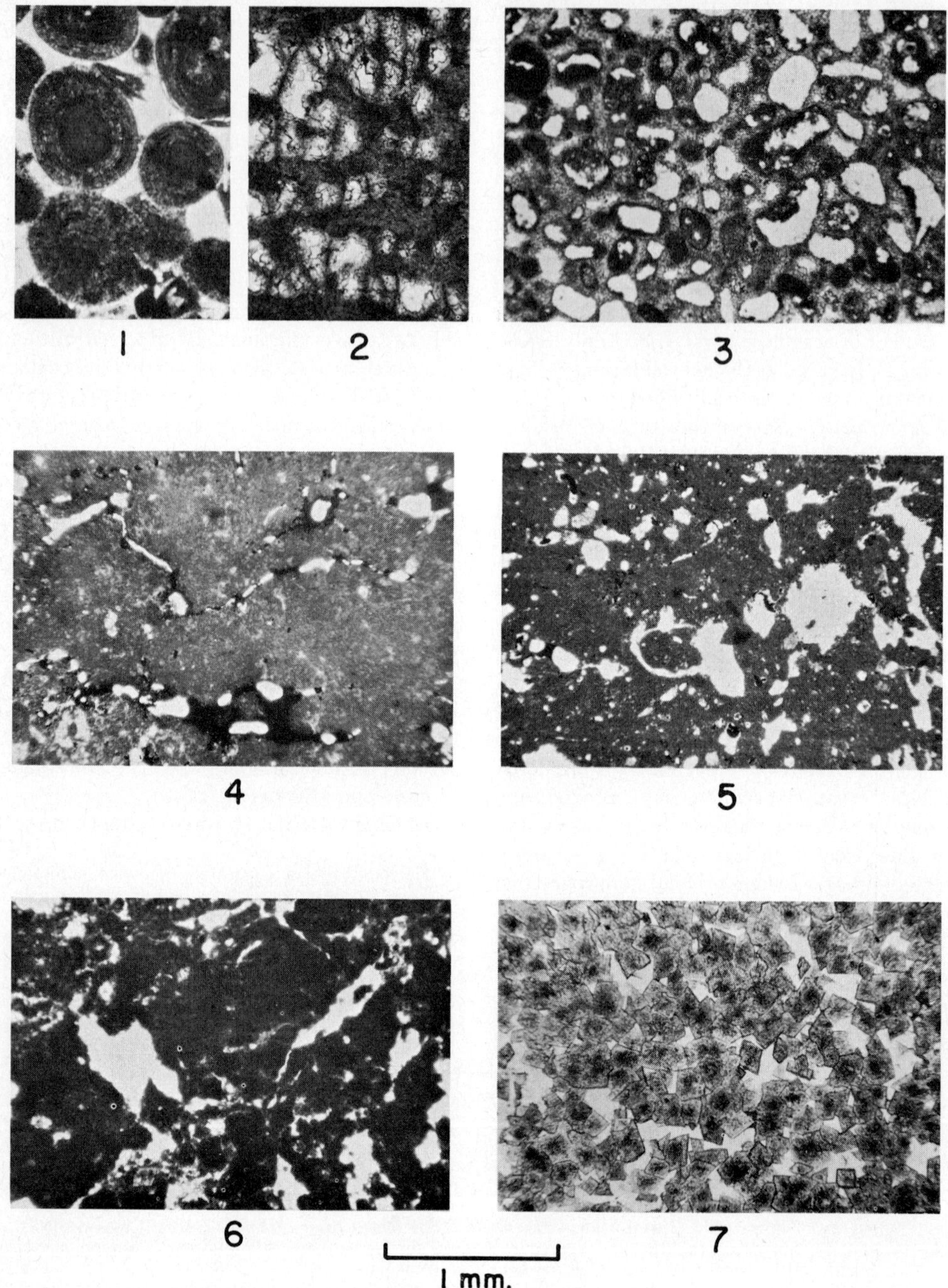

PLATE IV.—Visual porosity.

Arab-D carbonates by dolomite is common throughout the reservoir. Evidence is overwhelming that the dolomite is secondary. A primary origin is considered possible but not certain for scattered discrete rhombs occurring in the anhydrite separators. Where individual rhombs occur (Pl. VII, Fig. 1) they are normally between 0.1 and 0.3 mm. Where dolomite completely replaces original texture, crystals commonly impinge on one another and a coarse mosaic results with individual anhedral crystals as large as 0.6 mm (Pl. V, Fig. 6).

Chert.—At several levels dolomite or partially dolomitized aphanitic limestone has been incompletely replaced by chert. Though these zones are generally lenticular, one thin bed, whose thickness generally does not exceed 3 feet, can be traced laterally over much of Ghawar and Abqaiq. The chert associated with Arab-D rocks is of the variety microcrystalline quartz which consists of minute equant interlocking grains in random orientation (Pl. III, Fig. 6). Average grain size is about 30 microns but individual crystals range up to 300 microns in diameter. In polarized light each grain shows undulose extinction. Evidence from this and other studies (Folk and Weaver, 1952; Biggs, 1957) shows that chert of this type forms as a replacement of the original carbonate rock.

VISUAL POROSITY

Void space which can be resolved and point counted under low-power magnification (×60 or less) is here considered as visual porosity. In well-sorted calcarenite and crystalline dolomite, visual porosity agrees closely with true measured values. Where rocks contain mud, however, porosity measurements determined by the two methods differ. Mud and sandy mud apparently have considerable submicroscopic pore space, and true porosity exceeds visual measurements in some rocks of this type by as much as 10–15 per cent. Arab-D visual porosity is of six types—(1) intergranular, (2) intragranular, (3) void, (4) channel, (5) disrupted, and (6) intercrystalline.

Intergranular porosity.—Void space between grains or intergranular porosity is volumetrically the most important for storage of oil in Arab-D rocks (Pl. IV, Fig. 1). The outline of intergranular voids is exceedingly variable; it depends on particle shape, sorting, and secondary alteration. The porosity of clean-washed, well-sorted calcarenite commonly amounts to as much as 15–20 per cent, and in some instances as much as 25 per cent. Pore shape is controlled in large part by particle type; it is uniform where well-rounded grains are dominant and very irregular where algal debris or other angular fragments occur (Pl. I, Fig. 1). The pore pattern is reduced and complicated by the addition of authigenic constituents such as drusy coating and calcite cement.

Intragranular porosity.—Intragranular pore space or voids within individual particles such as Foraminifera are generally of limited importance except in stromatoporoids where an open skeletal network may create as much as 15 per cent effec-

---

←

EXPLANATION OF PLATE IV

FIG. 1.—Intergranular porosity. Khursaniyah No. 1 well, slide 1013, depth 6,159 feet (Arab-C). *Calcarenite.*—porosity 27%, permeability 1,312 md.

FIG. 2.—Intragranular porosity. Pore space is outlined by open reticulate network of stromatoporoid skeleton. Abqaiq No. 71 well, slide 162, depth 7,434 feet. *Calcarenitic limestone.*—porosity 14%, permeability 3 md (low permeability is due to surrounding mud matrix not visible on photomicrograph).

FIG. 3.—Secondary void porosity. Space originally occupied by grains is now voided, presumably as result of solution. Khursaniyah No. 1 well, slide 999, depth 6,133 feet (Arab-C). *Calcarenite.*—porosity 26%, permeability 74 md.

FIG. 4.—Channel porosity. Black filling in parts of channels is impregnating plastic. Abqaiq No. 71 well, slide 91, depth 7,385 feet. *Aphanitic limestone.*—porosity 21%, permeability 39 md.

FIG. 5.—Disrupted porosity. Reworking of muddy bottom sediment by burrowing organisms, entrapped gases, and solution may all play a part in formation of porosity of this type. Abqaiq No. 71 well, slide 43, depth 7,350 feet. *Calcarenitic limestone.*—porosity 24%, permeability 14 md.

FIG. 6.—Disrupted porosity. Incompletely separated, sharply angular fragments are believed to have been formed by in-place brecciation of semiconsolidated bottom, possibly during periods of intense current activity or slumping. Khursaniyah No. 1 well, slide 1010, depth 6,152 feet. *Calcarenitic limestone.*—porosity 36%, permeability 136 md.

FIG. 7.—Intercrystalline porosity. Fazran No. 1 well, slide 1483, depth 7,130 feet. *Crystalline dolomite.*—porosity 18%, permeability 416 md.

tive intragranular porosity (Pl. IV, Fig. 2). Like intergranular porosity, this type of pore space is adversely affected by diagenetic processes.

Secondary void porosity.—Some Arab-D rocks have undergone a unique type of alteration in which clastic particles have been voided presumably as a result of solution (Pl. IV, Fig. 3). The sequence of events leading to the development of void porosity appears to be—(1) a complete welding of individual grains and filling of intergranular pore space by drusy calcite, (2) removal of original grains, leaving only a drusy calcite framework. Porosity of this type is rare in Arab-D.

Channel porosity.—Owing to scale, only rarely is solution channel porosity recognizable in thin section. Vugs measured in centimeters and cavities several meters across have been reported from cores and drilling records. Some thin sections of crystalline dolomite do contain chert-filled vugs up to 3 and 4 mm in diameter. Channels in some aphanitic limestones are commonly 0.5 mm wide and can be traced continuously along an irregular path for 10–20 mm (Pl. IV, Fig. 4). The quantitative importance of channels or reservoir rock fractures with respect to total pore space is unknown.

Disrupted porosity.—Some aphanitic limestones in the lower Arab-D exhibit porosity of uncertain origin. Disrupted porosity is used as a general term to include voids which are of irregular shape and result from diverse but unknown causes. Void outline is generally sharp and, in some instances, the openings have been filled with clear calcite cement. Apparently porosity of this type is rarely interconnected, for permeability is rarely greater than in undisturbed muds. The varied character of disrupted porosity suggests that no single agent is responsible for its formation, but rather that different factors are involved, including burrowing organisms (Pl. IV, Fig. 5), entrapped gas, incomplete buckling and tearing of semiconsolidated mud (Pl. IV, Fig. 6), and slumping.

Intercrystalline porosity.—Well developed intercrystalline porosity is most common in dolomite where crystals are widely spaced and joined mostly at the apices (Pl. IV, Fig. 7). The porosity of open network dolomite ranges from 10 to 25 per cent, and only rarely exceeds this figure.

DIAGENESIS

Diagenesis is commonly defined as post-depositional and pre-lithification changes occurring in a sediment. However, as this distinction cannot generally be made, the term is used here for all alterations occurring at low temperatures and pressures (Correns, 1950). Compaction and authigenic changes (mostly brought about by reaction between sediment and contained fluids) are the principal diagenetic processes recorded in Arab-D rocks. Dissolution of original particles at unknown and possibly different times has produced channels in lime mud, vugs in dolomite, and voids in place of clastic particles in calcarenite.

Compaction.—Evidence of compaction in Arab-D rocks is only rarely observable at thin-section scale. Some rigid calcarenite grains such as oöliths (Pl. II, Fig. 6) show pressure-solution effects in which some grains have been pressed into others. "Fecal" pellets, presumably soft at time of deposition, commonly show effects of squeezing and bending due to compaction. Tabular carbonate grains produced by fragmentation of mollusc shells and calcareous algae are commonly broken to adjust to irregularities in surrounding grains as overburden increases.

Carbonate mud must also undergo considerable compaction prior to lithification. A preliminary study of relatively undisturbed cores of lime mud from the floor of a Persian Gulf lagoon shows a nearly 50 per cent decrease in the column of mud during the first few days of settling. On the other hand, Pray (1960) cites evidence such as absence of crushing of delicate shells, as indication of minor compaction of lime mud during formation of aphanitic limestone. Additional work is required to resolve the two sets of data.

Sequence of authigenesis.—Original Arab-D rock textures have been altered by at least five and possibly six generations of authigenic changes. In approximate order of occurrence these are—(1) addition of a drusy calcite coat around calcarenite particles, (2) recrystallization to mosaic calcite, (3) cementation by clear calcite, (4) growth of anhydrite crystals, (5) dolomitization, and (6) silicification. Evidence concerning relative times of authigenic events, although scarce for documenting some of the changes, is not contradictory and indicates that alterations took place in the following order.

1. In calcarenite and coarse carbonate clastic, a thin layer of needle-like calcite crystals covers the free surface of individual grains (Pl. V, Fig. 1). Considerable evidence from modern studies (Illing, 1954; Ginsburg, 1957) and the present thin-section work suggest that this drusy coat uniformly covers exposed particle surfaces shortly after deposition and is probably the first step toward lithification in many cases.

2. Where clear coarsely crystalline calcite cement and drusy coat occur together, cement fills the voids outlined by the needle-like surfaces (Pl. V, Fig. 2).

3. Anhydrite crystals, many with perfect orthorhombic outline, cut uninterruptedly across original textural elements to give indisputable proof of their secondary nature (Pl. V, Fig. 3; Pl. III, Fig. 4). In addition, where the relationship can be observed, authigenic anhydrite transects drusy coating and calcite cement (Pl. V, Fig. 1).

4. Where the time relation between dolomite and authigenic anhydrite is demonstrable, dolomite has universally been introduced later than the anhydrite (Pl. V, Fig. 3). A number of clearcut examples show dolomite cutting across all original textural elements and authigenic constituents described above.

5. Chert (variety microcrystalline quartz) can be shown in several instances to follow dolomite in the sequence of alteration. One slide in particular (Pl. V, Fig. 4) clearly demonstrates the relationship between original mud, dolomite, and chert. In this slide, the original rock was an aphanitic limestone which was later altered by the addition of a small percentage of dolomite in the form of discrete euhedra. Still later, some of the aphanitic limestone was replaced by chert, leaving "islands" of unaltered mud along with dolomite rhombs "floating" in the silica. Chert is associated normally with crystalline dolomite and very rarely with aphanitic limestone. Time relations exhibited by the chert-dolomite rocks are generally inconclusive; however, two lines of evidence suggest that the chert was introduced later than the dolomite. First, perfect dolomite euhedra are surrounded by chert much as if a partially dolomitized aphanitic limestone had been replaced. Second, most dolomites appear to have had only their intercrystalline pore space filled with silica (Pl. III, Fig. 6) and in a few of these, small islands and fingers of chert break up the regular dolomite crystal outline. This order of replacement—aphanitic limestone-dolomite-chert—is in close agreement with other studies on the subject (Folk and Weaver, 1952; Biggs, 1957).

6. Recrystallization of original textures to a mosaic calcite probably by the growth of larger crystals at the expense of smaller ones has not been accurately placed in the sequence of authigenesis. Little doubt exists that this type of alteration takes place later than the formation of a drusy coat, for the acicular crystals commonly serve as a base for the outward growth of mosaic calcite crystals. The relative time at which recrystallization terminates cannot be placed with any degree of certainty. In Arab-D rocks, mosaic calcite occurs dominantly in patches and rarely covers a complete slide area. Lime mud, *Solenopora?* algae, and stromatoporoids appear to be more susceptible to recrystallization than other particles.

Secondary openings.—Channels in aphanitic limestone, chert-lined vugs in crystalline dolomite, and voids in place of original calcarenite grains have been observed in cores and thin sections. These secondary openings are described in the section on visual porosity. In some areas, the sudden drop of drilling tools proves the existence of relatively large cavities. Thin-section data throw little light on the actual mechanism(s) responsible for these openings or the time(s) of their origin. Presumably, the dissolving out of calcium and carbonate ions by passing fluids plays some part in their formation. The voiding of calcarenite and coarse carbonate clastic particles appears to have occurred after the cementation of original grains by a well developed drusy coat of calcite crystals (Pl. IV, Fig. 3). The stage(s) at which limestone channels and dolomite vugs originated is unknown.

CLASSIFICATION OF CARBONATE ROCKS

A number of classifications have been proposed for the carbonate rocks. A common tendency in the past has been to treat them as a unique suite of rocks somehow divorced from normal sedi-

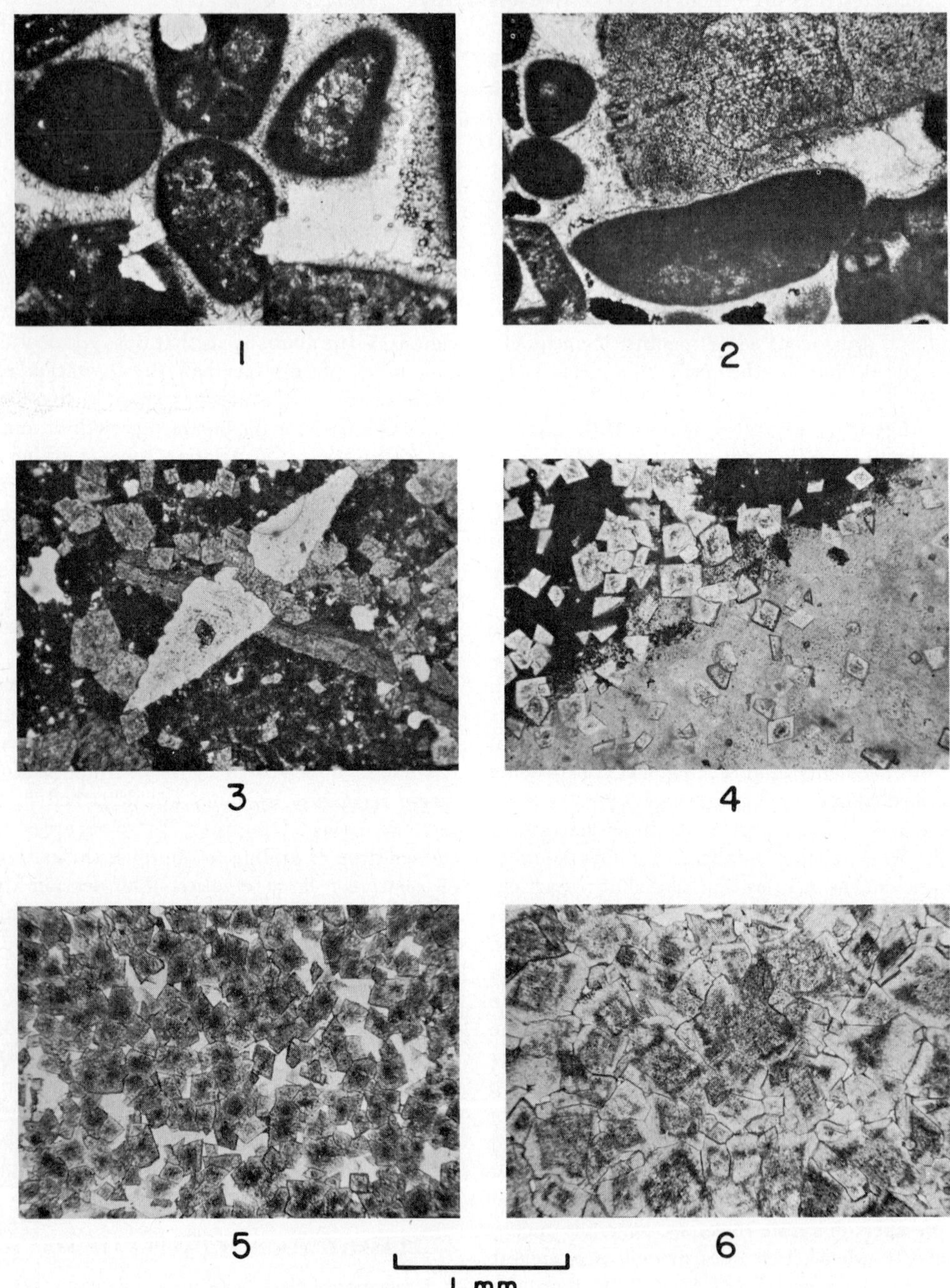

PLATE V.—Sequence of authigenesis and dolomite porosity.

mentary mechanics. An exhaustive study of Arabian carbonates on outcrop, from deep wells and in the modern Persian Gulf, has shown that carbonate grains behave basically as sediments and as such are subject to the same mechanics of deposition as siliceous particles. Their transport, sorting, and deposition differ little from those of the materials which form shale, sandstone, and conglomerate. This is apparently true regardless of whether calcareous particles are derived from older rock or precipitated chemically or biochemically. Source will merely determine the type and composition of material available; hydrodynamic properties and currents, their final resting place. It is obvious that clay- and silt-size particles, regardless of origin, cannot normally come to rest in current-swept areas, and that sand and gravel require current for their concentration. Once this apparently rather formidable barrier in thinking has been breached, the systematic classification of the limestones is a relatively simple matter. The clastic nature of most carbonates has long been recognized (Sorby, 1879; Evans, 1900; Grabau, 1903), but its application to the classification and interpretation of carbonates has not been fully exploited.

The problem of reconstructing depositional conditions associated with noncarbonate rocks is simplified owing to durability of particles and mineralogical differences between particles. On the other hand, the carbonate rocks, at the time of deposition are composed predominantly of one chemical compound—calcium carbonate. Consequently, texture alone generally furnishes the basis for understanding and reconstructing conditions which controlled their deposition. Accordingly, careful descriptive study and classification of these textural differences are required before interpretation can be made of critical environmental relations. After classification of the rocks according to particle size the next logical subdivision appears to be to break them down further according to the degree to which their original texture has been altered by diagenetic processes. Thus, two continua are established—one grading from fine to coarse particles, another between unaltered and obliterated original textures (Fig. 5).

Obviously, no scheme can be considered entirely satisfactory, for in practice complete gradational series exist between end-member rock types. The classification in both a horizontal and vertical direction is gradational, and the percentages used to separate the various groups imply a degree of accuracy not attainable by visual examination. It is essential for the purpose of discussion, however, to give some general quantitative values for subdividing the various types. This practice, tempered with experience, has allowed different individuals to classify limestones with a high degree of uniformity.

The classification presented here is based on empirical evidence and is known to be functional for Arabian carbonates. Discussions and correspondence with other geologists, an extensive search of the literature, and examination of chips

---

←

EXPLANATION OF PLATE V

FIG. 1.—Drusy coating-anhydrite. Addition of drusy calcite crystals to free grain surfaces is earliest recognized phase of authigenesis. Note anhydrite crystals cutting both drusy coat and grains. Khursaniyah No. 1 well, slide 1016, depth 6,166 feet (Arab-C). *Calcarenite.*—porosity 21%, permeability 49 md.

FIG. 2.—Calcite cement-drusy coating. Calcite cement rimmed with drusy coat indicates that cement is introduced at a later date. Abqaiq No. 71 well, slide 80, depth 7,369 feet. *Calcarenite.*—porosity 5%, permeability 2 md.

FIG. 3.—Anhydrite-dolomite. Figure shows anhydrite crystal cutting shell fragment and in turn is transected by dolomite. Other slides including Fig. 1 show anhydrite is introduced later than drusy coat and calcite cement. Fazran No. 1 well, slide 1470, depth 7,121 feet. *Calcarenitic limestone.*—porosity 14%, permeability 7 md.

FIG. 4.—Chert-dolomite-lime mud. Rock, originally aphanitic limestone, has been partially dolomitized (Pl. VII, Fig. 1). Still later, chert (lower right) has selectively replaced mud, leaving behind "floating" dolomite rhombs and small "islands" of aphanitic limestone. Khurais No. 3 well, slide 3001, depth 5,491 feet. *Aphanitic limestone.*—porosity 11%, permeability 25 md.

FIGS. 5, 6.—Dolomite porosity. Dolomite changes from finely crystalline, commonly euhedral, porous network in Fig. 5 (82% dolomite; porosity 18%, permeability 416 md) to tightly packed, medium to coarsely crystalline, anhedral mosaic in Fig. 6 (98% dolomite; porosity 2%, permeability 0 md). See Pl. VII, Fig. 6 for intermediate state (90% dolomite; porosity 10%, permeability 6 md). Fig. 5.—Fazran No. 1 well, slide 1483, depth 7,130 feet. Fig. 6.—Abqaiq No. 80 well, slide 3351, depth 6.092 feet.

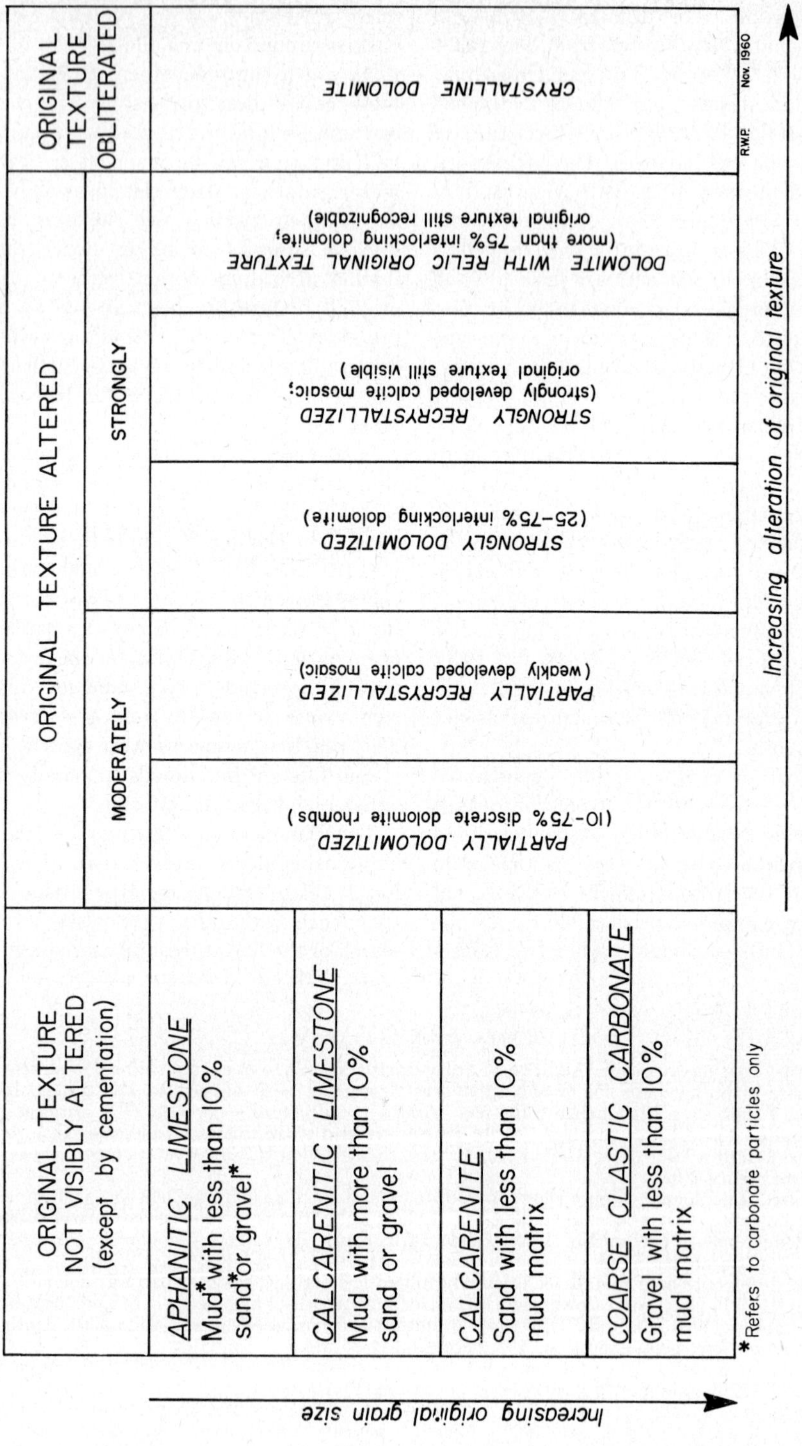

<table>
<tr><th rowspan="2">ORIGINAL TEXTURE NOT VISIBLY ALTERED (except by cementation)</th><th colspan="5">ORIGINAL TEXTURE ALTERED</th><th rowspan="2">ORIGINAL TEXTURE OBLITERATED</th></tr>
<tr><th colspan="2">MODERATELY</th><th colspan="3">STRONGLY</th></tr>
<tr><td><u>APHANITIC LIMESTONE</u>
Mud* with less than 10% sand* or gravel*</td><td rowspan="4">PARTIALLY DOLOMITIZED
(10–75% discrete dolomite rhombs)</td><td rowspan="4">PARTIALLY RECRYSTALLIZED
(weakly developed calcite mosaic)</td><td rowspan="4">STRONGLY DOLOMITIZED
(25–75% interlocking dolomite)</td><td rowspan="4">STRONGLY RECRYSTALLIZED
(strongly developed calcite mosaic; original texture still visible)</td><td rowspan="4">DOLOMITE WITH RELIC ORIGINAL TEXTURE
(more than 75% interlocking dolomite; original texture still recognizable)</td><td rowspan="4">CRYSTALLINE DOLOMITE</td></tr>
<tr><td><u>CALCARENITIC LIMESTONE</u>
Mud with more than 10% sand or gravel</td></tr>
<tr><td><u>CALCARENITE</u>
Sand with less than 10% mud matrix</td></tr>
<tr><td><u>COARSE CLASTIC CARBONATE</u>
Gravel with less than 10% mud matrix</td></tr>
</table>

*Refers to carbonate particles only

R.W.P. Nov. 1960

Increasing original grain size (↓)

Increasing alteration of original texture (→)

FIG. 5.—Generalized classification of Arabian carbonate rocks.

and thin sections from the Swabian Jurassic and the Permian carbonates of Texas and New Mexico indicate that it may have as wide an application as any scheme yet proposed. Rare types not extensively represented in Arabia, such as clastic dolomite sands and organic reef complexes, can readily be included with no modification of the basic classification framework. The principal criteria, accompanied by illustrative photomicrographs, used to class the Arabian carbonates are outlined below. For a more complete discussion see Bramkamp and Powers (1958).

ORIGINAL SEDIMENTARY TEXTURE

Using original particle size and sorting, the carbonate rocks may be divided into four main groups—(1) aphanitic limestone, (2) calcarenitic limestone, (3) calcarenite, and (4) coarse carbonate clastic. A fifth group, crystalline dolomite, is defined where original texture has been obliterated.

Aphanitic limestone.—Aphanitic rocks are composed dominantly of calcareous mud (less than 0.06 mm) and contain less than 10 per cent sand- or gravel-size carbonate grains (Pl. VI, Fig. 1).

Calcarenitic limestone.—Calcarenitic limestone is essentially an aphanitic limestone to which more than 10 per cent sand or gravel has been added (Pl. VI, Fig. 2). The important feature of this rock type is the presence of significant amounts of original mud matrix. As will be shown later, the presence or absence of original matrix is especially critical from both an environmental and reservoir point of view.

Calcarenite.—Calcarenite is composed dominantly of lime sand grains (0.06 to 2.0 mm) and contains less than 10 per cent mud matrix (Pl. VI, Fig. 3). Although arbitrary, the 10 per cent limit on matrix has proved extremely functional for grouping these clean-washed rocks.

Coarse carbonate clastic.—The coarse carbonates include rocks whose dominant particle size exceeds 2 mm diameter and contain less than 10 per cent original mud matrix (Pl. VI, Fig. 4). Calcarenite and coarse carbonate clastic are on occasion cemented with clear crystalline calcite and care must be taken not to confuse this with original mud matrix; this distinction is rarely difficult.

Other carbonate rocks.—Two other groups of carbonates not encountered in the Arabian oil reservoirs should be mentioned to make the classification broadly applicable. These carbonates—residual organic[5] and chemically precipitated limestone—can be included as separate groups.

The residual organic class would be restricted to include only the original framework of organic reefs and biostromes formed by permanently attached organisms and shell-covered bottoms. The remainder of the reef complex including the clastic fan, lagoonal deposits, and debris lodged in the reef-core is all mechanically distributed (Hadding, 1941; Newell and others, 1953) and can be arranged according to particle size. Presumably, residual organic rocks would undergo the same type of alteration as other carbonates.

Residual organic rocks are most applicable to direct ecologic analysis. They are essentially a "frozen" record particularly useful in the interpretation of ancient environments. On the other hand, the use of transported rock types as environment indicators is complicated by such factors as movement of rock constituents from their natural habitat and admixture of grains from diverse sources.

The chemical limestone class would include presumably primary carbonates associated with evaporite sequences and miscellaneous nonmarine limestones such as tufa and travertine.

ALTERATION IN ORIGINAL TEXTURE

Any primary carbonate rock texture may remain essentially unaltered or be subjected to diagenetic modification and consequent change in texture and composition. Two main types of alteration have been noted associated with Arabian carbonates—the first is actual replacement of original grains or matrix by dolomite, which results in changes both in texture and composition; the second is recrystallization which involves the growth of some calcite crystals at the expense of others; in recrystallization, texture alone is altered. Of these two alteration processes, dolomitization is by far the more common. In no instance was original texture rendered unrecognizable through recrystallization alone; in many

[5] Term suggested by J. E. Sanders.

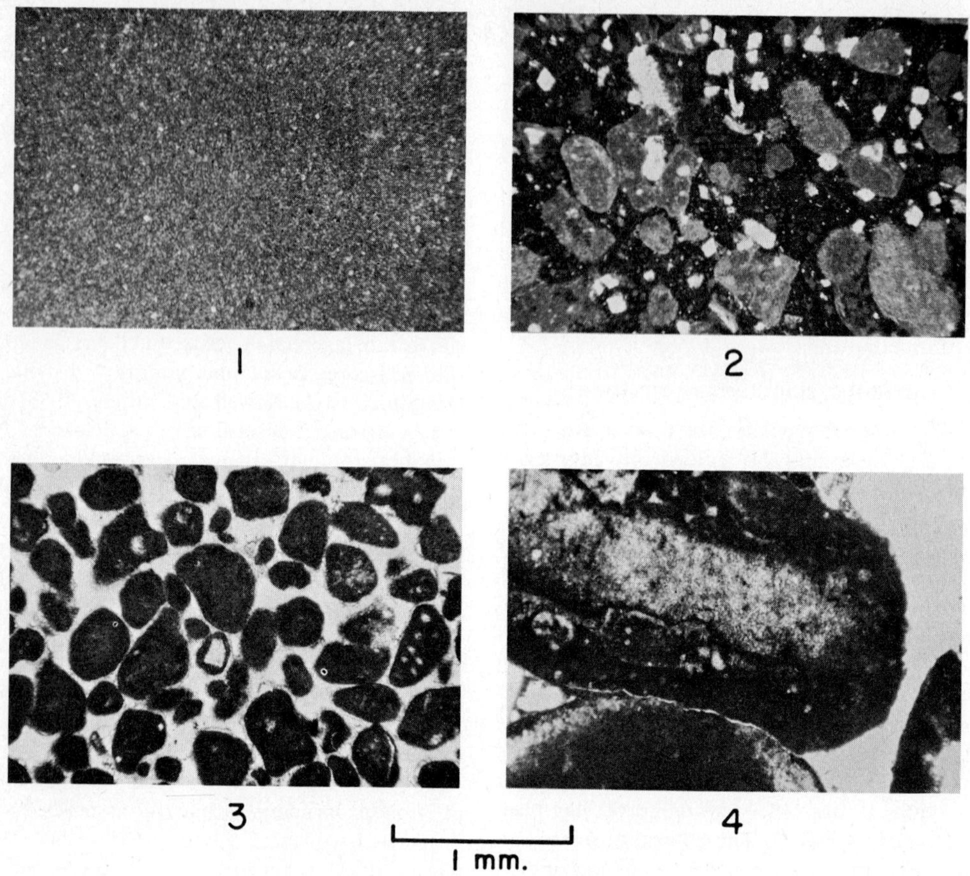

PLATE VI.—Original sedimentary texture.

FIG. 1.—Aphanitic limestone. Sediment originally lime mud with little or no calcareous sand. Haradh No. 3 well, slide 4386, depth 6,464 feet. *Aphanitic limestone.*—porosity 2%, permeability 0 md.

FIG. 2.—Calcarenitic limestone. Aggregate pellet sand with original mud matrix. Note scattered dolomite rhombs (white euhedra). Abqaiq No. 80 well, slide 3394, depth 6,137 feet. *Calcarenitic limestone.*—porosity 5%, permeability 0 md.

FIG. 3.—Calcarenite. Clean washed aggregate pellet sand with some Foraminifera. Abqaiq No. 80 well, slide 3299, depth 6,065 feet. *Calcarenite.*—porosity 27%, permeability 2,118 md.

FIG. 4.—Coarse carbonate clastic. "Algal" nodules. 'Uthmaniyah No. 45 well, slide 599, depth 6,779 feet. *Coarse carbonate clastic.*—porosity 29%.

Note: Figures 1–4 illustrate main groups in Arabian carbonate rock classification which are based on original particle size and sorting. Another group, crystalline dolomite, occurs where any of the above textures are completely replaced and obliterated by dolomite.

rocks, however, replacement by dolomite is complete. All evidence indicates that the dolomite associated with normal Arabian carbonate rocks is a result of replacement rather than primary precipitation. Primary dolomite may be present in unknown, perhaps considerable, quantities in the anhydrite stringers.

Based on the lack or intensity of alteration of the original texture the carbonate rocks are divided into four types (1) unaltered, (2) partially or moderately altered, (3) strongly altered, and (4) obliterated.

UNALTERED TEXTURE

Rocks of this type have not been visibly altered except by compaction and cementation. Where present, dolomite does not exceed 10 per cent; the composition and textural make-up are essentially that which characterized the rock following deposition (Pl. VI).

PARTIALLY OR MODERATELY ALTERED TEXTURE

In rocks considered partially altered, the original texture is readily recognizable but shows obvious evidences of some secondary changes.

Partially dolomitized.—When more than 10 per cent of the original rock has been replaced by dolomite in the form of discrete euhedral rhombs or porphyroblasts, the rock is considered to be partially dolomitized (Pl. VII, Fig. 1). Individual rhombs are readily visible, generally against a background of little-altered original texture.

Partially recrystallized.—Partial recrystallization is brought about by alteration of original components to a weakly developed and patchy calcite mosaic (Pl. VII, Fig. 2). The limited degree of alteration does not interfere with recognition of the original rock texture.

STRONGLY ALTERED TEXTURE

A carbonate rock is strongly altered if the original texture, though still recognizable, shows considerable change by recrystallization or dolomite replacement.

Strongly dolomitized.—Strongly dolomitized rocks contain 25–75 per cent dolomite most commonly in patches with individual crystals closely packed or interlocked (Pl. VII, Fig. 3). Thin-section study shows that crystals commonly do not interlock unless at least 25 per cent dolomite is present. Original textures tend to be obscured more by this type of replacement than by the addition of discrete dolomite rhombs (partial dolomitization). The interlocking character of the dolomite and the consequent difference in destruction of original texture distinguish the strongly from the partially dolomitized rocks, although the percentage of dolomite present in each case may be the same. Sufficient remnants of original texture are retained, however, so that the rock can be classified with a fair degree of certainty.

Strongly recrystallized.—Notable changes in original texture may be brought about by the rearrangement of calcium and carbonate ions through solution and reprecipitation. Rocks are considered to be strongly recrystallized if this occurs with sufficient intensity largely to obscure original texture by alteration to a mosaic of finely to coarsely crystalline calcite (Pl. VII, Fig. 4). Strongly recrystallized rocks rarely contain more than 10 per cent dolomite.

Relict texture.—Textures are termed relict when a carbonate has been subjected to very intense alteration, for example, by the addition of 75 per cent or more dolomite; but vestiges of original texture sufficient for identification are retained (Pl. VII, Fig. 5). Normally only "ghosts" of original textural elements are still visible but, in some instances, the texture is well preserved even though replacement is complete.

OBLITERATED ORIGINAL TEXTURE

All traces of original rock texture are generally destroyed where dolomite replacement exceeds 75 per cent. This gives rise to the fifth main carbonate rock group—crystalline dolomite, in which original texture is obliterated (Pl. VII, Fig. 6).

ORIGINAL PARTICLE TYPE

Routine, low-power examination of rock chips is generally adequate to distinguish original textural differences and subsequent textural changes; specific particle types can rarely be recognized. Individual particles can be identified, however, in modern sediment or thin-section studies and should, therefore, be considered in any comprehensive classification.

As stated previously, lime-mud components are generally of uncertain origin. The source of the larger carbonate grains can commonly be determined; four types are recognized—(1) skeletal remains, (2) aggregate grains, (3) oöliths, and (4) detritus from older limestones. Skeletal grains and oöliths need little clarification. "Aggregate grain" is a general term used for all discrete, penecontemporaneous, sand- and gravel-size particles formed on the sea floor by (1) the tearing-up, movement, and redeposition of fragments of semiconsolidated bottom sediment, or (2) the aggregation of finer particles by cementation (Illing, 1954). Specific aggregate types include angular aggregates, pellets (rounded aggregates), "fecal" pellets, and "algal" nodules. Carbonate detritus, formed by the mechanical disintegration of older, well-consolidated limestones, can be transported and redeposited as part of a younger

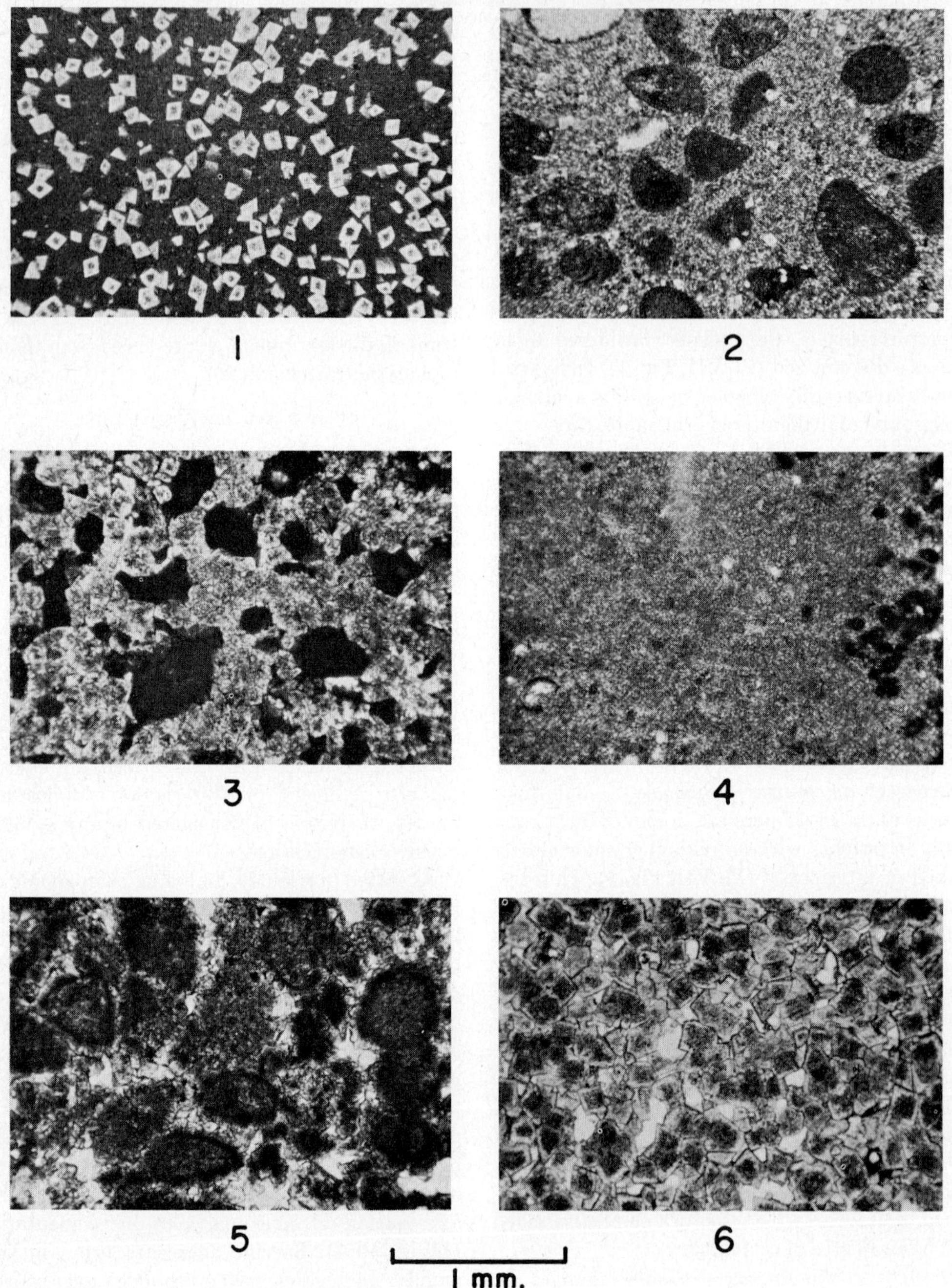

PLATE VII.—Alteration in original texture.

sediment in the same manner as other terrigenous grains. They are commonly distinguished by their "inappropriate" fossils, color, lithology, and other features. Where any specific particle type makes up more than 25 per cent of a rock, the main rock name is so qualified—that is, oölite calcarenite or foraminiferal-pellet calcarenitic limestone.

The introduction of noncarbonate mud and sand (particularly land-derived or terrigenous elements) into the carbonate basin of deposition adds yet another factor which must be accounted for in any systematic classification of the limestones. The terms impure and sandy are used as main rock group modifiers where 10–50 per cent noncarbonate mud or sand is present.

Thus, when sufficiently detailed data are available, carbonate rocks can be considered in terms of four parameters (1) original texture (either clastic or residual), (2) original carbonate particle type, (3) original noncarbonate particle type, and (4) degree of alteration in original texture. A classification of the carbonate rocks which incorporates these parameters is shown in Table I.

GENERAL DISCUSSION

Work on Arabian carbonates, both modern and ancient, indicates that four main rock types can be distinguished on the basis of original textural differences, and a fifth is defined when original texture has been completely replaced by dolomite. The four textural groups—aphanitic limestone, calcarenitic limestone, calcarenite, and coarse carbonate clastic can be recognized and divided accurately in hand specimen, core and ditch sample, or thin section. In connection with this, considerable basic data concerning correlation, original environment-sedimentation patterns, and reservoir rock behavior can be obtained from routine examination and classification of all types of samples. More exhaustive methods, including thin-section analysis, can be reserved for detailed studies of other factors such as paleoecology and diagenesis. Consideration of carbonates in the light of their original textural differences lends itself remarkably well to establishing a general framework into which the results of more rigorous studies can be readily placed. Graphic well logs, whether compiled from drilled samples, core chips, surface exposures, or thin sections, can be used with equal facility to delineate regional correlations and stratigraphic units (Figs. 15–16).

Demonstration of the separate but complementary nature of information derived from two methods of examination—rock chip and thin section—can best be seen in the illustrations accompanying this report. Double columns were drafted for point-counted wells (Figs. 7, 9, 11, 13) to show the relation between original textural groups and the specific particle types contributing to these groups in the different slides. These logs strikingly illustrate the fact that whereas source determines the specific particles available for deposition, the interplay between individual particle hydraulic properties and currents determines the site of deposition. For example, calcarenites at different levels are composed of various types of particles from diverse sources mixed in all proportions; the only common factor is their sand size.

The concept of using original texture to sub-

←

EXPLANATION OF PLATE VII

FIG. 1.—Partially dolomitized. Discrete dolomite rhombs replacing lime mud. Haradh No. 3 well, slide 4381, depth 6,459 feet. *Aphanitic limestone.*—porosity 1%, permeability 0 md.

FIG. 2.—Partially recrystallized. Mud matrix and some parts of aggregate pellets are incompletely recrystallized to calcite mosaic. Haradh No. 3 well, slide 4350, depth 6,428 feet. *Calcarenitic limestone.*—porosity 3%, permeability 0 md.

FIG. 3.—Strongly dolomitized. Mud matrix and parts of individual sand grains are replaced by interlocking dolomite crystals. Abqaiq No. 71 well, slide 94, depth 7,387 feet. *Calcarenitic limestone.*—porosity 17%, permeability 20 md.

FIG. 4.—Strongly recrystallized. Grains and matrix have in large part been altered to anhedral calcite mosaic. Abqaiq No. 71 well, slide 4431, depth 7,298 feet. *Calcarenitic limestone.*—porosity 14%, permeability 4 md.

FIG. 5.—Relict original texture. Original texture is still recognizable although particles have been completely replaced by dolomite. Khursaniyah No. 1 well, slide 1052, depth 6,205 (Arab-C). *Calcarenite.*—porosity 7%, permeability 0 md.

FIG. 6.—Original texture obliterated. Rock has been completely replaced by dolomite. Fazran No. 1 well, slide 1561, depth 7,182 feet. *Crystalline dolomite* (90%).—porosity 10%, permeability 6 md.

Table I. Carbonate Rock Classification

	ORIGINAL TEXTURE NOT VISIBLY ALTERED (except by cementation)						ORIGINAL TEXTURE ALTERED					ORIGINAL TEXTURE OBLITERATED
	ORIGINAL PARTICLE TYPE						MODERATELY		STRONGLY			
ORIGINAL TEXTURE	MORE THAN 25% SKELETAL[2] REMAINS	MORE THAN 25% AGGREGATE[3] GRAINS	MORE THAN 25% OOLITHS	MORE THAN 25% DETRITUS[4] FROM OLDER LS.	10–50% NONCARBONATE SAND	10–50% NONCARBONATE MUD	WEAKLY DEVELOPED CALCITE MOSAIC (<10% DOLOMITE)	MORE THAN 10% DISCRETE DOLOMITE RHOMBS	STRONGLY DEVELOPED CALCITE MOSAIC (<10% DOLOMITE)	25–75% INTERLOCKING DOLOMITE	MORE THAN 75% DOLOMITE WITH RELIC TEXTURE	MORE THAN 75% DOLOMITE
APHANITIC LIMESTONE (Lime mud with less than 10% sand- or gravel-size clastic carbonate grains.) Pl. 6, fig. 1	Origin of mud-size particles generally indeterminate (chalk)				*Sandy*	(marl) *Impure*	*Partially recrystallized* Pl. 7, fig. 2	*Partially dolomitized* Pl. 7, fig. 1	*Strongly recrystallized* Pl. 7, fig. 4	*Strongly dolomitized* Pl. 7, fig. 3	*Aphanitic* dolomite	**CRYSTALLINE DOLOMITE** Pl. 7, fig. 6. Where recrystallization (not involving dolomite) obliterates original texture, rock is termed CRYSTALLINE LIMESTONE.
CALCARENITIC LIMESTONE (More than 10% sand- or gravel-size clastic carbonate grains set in more than 10% original mud-size matrix.) Pl. 6, fig. 2	*Skeletal*[2] calcarenitic limestone	*Aggregate*[3] calcarenitic limestone Pl. 2, figs. 2,4	*Oolite* calcarenitic limestone	*Detrital*[4] calcarenitic limestone							*Calcarenitic* dolomite	
CALCARENITE (Sand-size clastic carbonate grains dominant; contains less than 10% original mud-size matrix.) Pl. 6, fig. 3	*Skeletal* calcarenite Pl. 1, fig. 1	*Aggregate* calcarenite Pl. 2, figs. 1,3	*Oolite* calcarenite Pl. 2, fig. 6	*Detrital* calcarenite							*Calcarenite* dolomite Pl. 7, fig. 5	
COARSE CARBONATE (Gravel-size clastic carbonate grains dominant; contains less than 10% original mud-size matrix.) Pl. 6, fig. 4	Coarse *skeletal* carbonate (coquina)	Coarse *aggregate* carbonate Pl. 6, fig. 4	Coarse *oolite* carbonate (pisolite)	Coarse *detrital* carbonate							*Coarse carbonate* dolomite	
RESIDUAL ORGANIC (Rocks composed dominantly of attached reef-building organisms still in growth position.)	*Residual* algae, *residual* coral, etc.										*Residual organic* dolomite	

RWP

1. Chart shows main rock groups in UNDERLINED CAPITAL LETTERS; modifiers of main rock groups in *italics*. For example: sandy, oolite calcarenite or impure, partially dolomitized, foraminiferal calcarenitic ls.
2. Skeletal is used here as a general modifier; specific modifiers include: foraminiferal, crinoidal, algal, coral, etc.
3. 'Aggregate grain' is a general term used for all discrete, penecontemporaneous, sand- and gravel-size grains formed on the sea floor by (1) the tearing-up, movement, and redeposition of fragments of semi-consolidated bottom sediment or (2) the aggregation of finer particles by cementation (Illing, 1954). Specific types are: angular aggregate, pellet (rounded aggregate), 'faecal' pellet, and 'algal' nodule.
4. The detrital carbonates contain more than 25% grains which have been (a) formed by the mechanical disintegration of older, well-consolidated limestones, (b) transported and, (c) redeposited as part of a younger sediment. Detrital grains are commonly distinguished by their 'inappropriate' fossil content, color, lithology, etc.

divide the carbonates was independently arrived at by Folk (1959). The principles on which his classification is based are remarkably similar to the ideas presented here, but differences exist in several areas. For example, Folk uses textural kind to separate the limestones into three major families; these, in turn, are divided according to the relative proportions of different particle types. Special significance is attached to intraclasts because of their presumed indication of lowered wave base or possible tectonic uplift. The term "intraclast" is used by Folk "to embrace the entire spectrum of sedimented, aggregated, and then reworked particles, regardless of degree of cohesion or time gap between deposition of the original layer of sediment and later reworking of parts of it." Where intraclasts make up 25 per cent or more of the detrital grains, a rock is considered an intraclastic rock even though the remaining three-fourths of the particles are fossils or oöliths. This would seem to emphasize unduly the importance of intraclasts, for the environmental significance of oöliths, fossils, and pellets in many cases rivals that of intraclasts, whether considering position of effective wave base or site of deposition. Arabian practice has been to subdivide the carbonates into the four main textural groups and then, where data permit, include in the rock name any particle type exceeding 25 per cent; for example, foraminiferal calcarenite or aggregate pellet calcarenitic limestone. This retains a completely descriptive classification from which genetic conclusions may be drawn as warranted.

A second minor difference between the two classifications is the assignment to secondary calcite cement a rank equal to that of original lime mud and lime sand. This is not necessary to the classification, for the break between calcarenite and muddy calcarenite can be based solely on the presence or absence of mud matrix. Further, a clean-washed calcarenite, with or without secondary cement, is indicative of active currents. Disregarding terrigenous particles, most Arabian Upper Jurassic carbonates at the time of deposition consisted wholly of mud- to conglomerate-size particles uniformly sorted or admixed in any proportion. Calcite cement is only one of several important constituents that may be secondarily added to these original elements.

METHOD OF ILLUSTRATION

The data derived from point-count analysis and classification of Arab-D rocks have been presented in several forms in the illustrations accompanying this report. The general approach used in preparation of the figures has been to keep the individual well logs as factual as possible so that they in effect serve as basic data summary sheets. Their value for later interpretative work of all kinds is thus not impaired.

Single column graphic logs (not included here), showing original sedimentary sequence were prepared for 6 of the 8 wells in which percentage of constituent particles was estimated. Information from two wells ('Uthmaniyah No. 47 and Shedgum No. 17) was not plotted in final form owing to gaps in core recovery at several critical levels and their marked similarity to adjacent wells with a more complete sequence.

Double-column graphic logs (Figs. 7, 9, 11, 13) as well as individual constituent particle curves (Figs. 8, 10, 12, 14) were prepared for the four wells in which thin sections were point counted. The left column of the double graphic logs shows the original sedimentary sequence or the occurrences of the five main carbonate rock groups in the Arab-D. A master explanation of the symbols used is contained in Fig. 6. Each slide, assigned to one of the five main rock types, was considered to represent an interval halfway from itself to the slides on either side. No slide was allowed to represent more than 2 feet of section—that is, 1 foot above and below. Intervals not covered in this manner are labeled "not sectioned." Position of thin sections is shown immediately to the right of the main column.

The right column depicts the relative proportions of all constituents of the reservoir rock. The width of the column equals 100 per cent, and whatever particles occur at any given level in amounts greater than 2.5 per cent are shown to the nearest 5 per cent. As the close spacing of thin sections prohibits illustration on all but the most magnified scale, the column was vertically marked off in 1-foot intervals and the proper proportion of each slide component contributing to that interval calculated. For the most part, the combined results from one to two slides are represented in each foot.

Abundance and range of identified microfossils are also included on the logs. These have been divided into two sections, one for calcareous algae, the other for Foraminifera. Actual occurrences are shown by lines alone and do not include the intervals covered by the names of specimens. A single line indicates that the slide contained 1–10 specimens (rare), an open double line 10–100 (common), and a filled double line more than 100 (abundant).

A series of individual curves, one for each of the more important reservoir elements, has been compiled for the point-counted wells (Figs. 8, 10, 12, 14). Data derived from each slide are shown exactly as measured and at the proper level. The basic function of these curves is to permit easy visualization and comparison of individual rock characters in a single well and between wells.

Well logs included in the regional correlation charts (Figs. 15 and 16) are compiled from all types of samples as noted on the index map of each chart. No generalization is involved in their construction and all rocks occurring in a 5-foot interval are shown in proper proportion.

POSSIBLE ENVIRONMENTAL SIGNIFICANCE OF ORIGINAL SEDIMENTARY TEXTURE

Although the Arabian limestone classification is purely descriptive, being based on textural differences and alteration in texture, it should be possible—with a reasonable degree of safety—to make some rather general genetic inferences concerning the main rock groups. Reference is made here to the "transported" carbonates only; "residual organic" limestones are excluded. Just as with the siliceous suite of rocks, particle size and sorting offer the obvious first clues of the regimen in which deposition took place.

The relation between particle size and processes of deposition and transportation are complex; however, several broad generalizations are possible. The first is that size, shape, and specific gravity will, in large part, control particle reaction to fluid mechanics and exert in this manner a marked influence on sediment distribution. Source will determine the type and composition of material available for deposition. Once introduced into the environment of deposition, however, loose fragments will be moved (or lie where they fall if they are too big to be moved by existing currents) and finally come to rest only when their respective hydrodynamic properties are in equilibrium with operating waves and currents. Thus, sand and gravel are considered to accumulate in exposed areas; mud in sheltered areas. Though obvious, the fundamental control exerted by current activity on the final sediment texture is commonly overlooked. Protection against the sweeping action of currents can be afforded in a number of ways with similar result on the final deposit. Mud accumulating in shallow water on the lee side of an island, trapped in a grass-covered bottom, or settling in a depression, indicates a fundamental relationship—that is, where sufficient shelter is available, fine particles come to rest.

A second important generalization is that processes of carbonate deposition are more closely related to siliceous sedimentation than commonly suspected. Other studies bear this out—for example, Krumbein and Griffith (1938), in their work on the limestone beach gravels of Little Sister Bay, Wisconsin, found that toward the center of the bay, the gravels are mixed with finer fragments and a complete gradation to sand, both carbonate and quartz, occurs. Stetson (1939), in his discussion of continental shelf sedimentation, points out that in the vicinity of Cape Hatteras, quartz sand grades south into sand in which shell detritus and oöliths are 50–80 per cent of the deposit. Stetson explains that although a physical change in the material has taken place the sediment remains texturally constant.

In a study of Barataria Bay following that of Krumbein and Aberdeen (1937), Caldwell (1940) worked out the areal variations in calcium carbonate. The depositional pattern of the carbonate, most of which is in the finer size range, closely parallels that shown by the size distribution of other grain types. Other investigations of modern carbonate sediments in the Florida-Bahama-Cuba area including those by Thorp (1939), Newell and others (1951), Illing (1954), Newell and Rigby (1957), and Daetwyler and Kidwell (1959), all indicate that the calcareous grains are mechanically distributed and deposited.

In terms of the classification, aphanitic and calcarenitic limestone will normally be indices of relatively quiet water. The presence of significant

(Text continued on page 170)

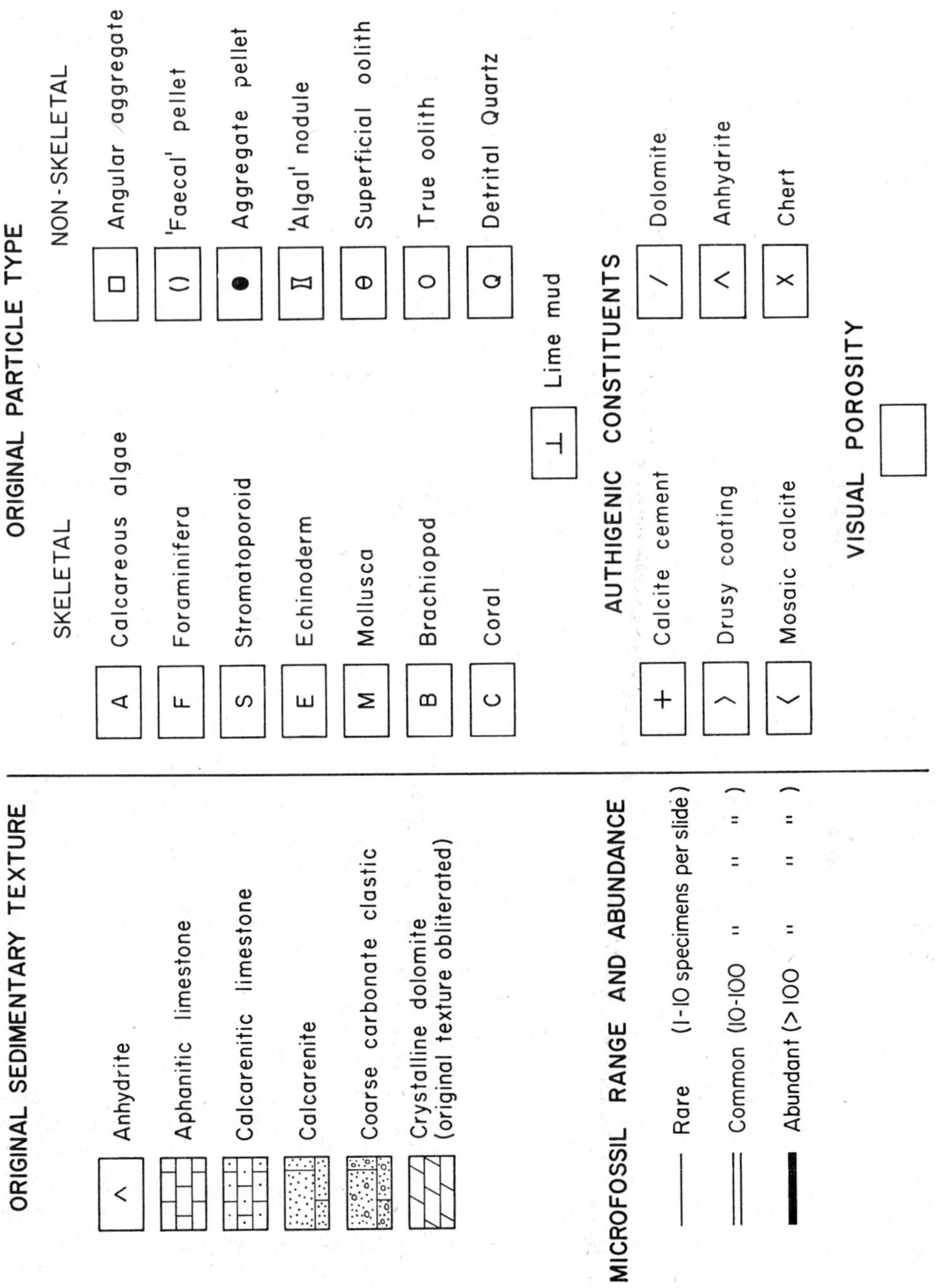

ORIGINAL SEDIMENTARY TEXTURE

^ Anhydrite

Aphanitic limestone

Calcarenitic limestone

Calcarenite

Coarse carbonate clastic

Crystalline dolomite (original texture obliterated)

MICROFOSSIL RANGE AND ABUNDANCE

Rare (1-10 specimens per slide)

Common (10-100 " " ")

Abundant (> 100 " " ")

ORIGINAL PARTICLE TYPE

SKELETAL

A Calcareous algae

F Foraminifera

S Stromatoporoid

E Echinoderm

M Mollusca

B Brachiopod

C Coral

NON-SKELETAL

□ Angular aggregate

() 'Faecal' pellet

● Aggregate pellet

Ɪ 'Algal' nodule

ϴ Superficial oolith

O True oolith

Q Detrital Quartz

⊥ Lime mud

AUTHIGENIC CONSTITUENTS

+ Calcite cement

〉 Drusy coating

〈 Mosaic calcite

/ Dolomite

^ Anhydrite

X Chert

VISUAL POROSITY

FIG. 6.—Master explanation for graphic symbols used in Figs. 7, 9, 11, and 13.

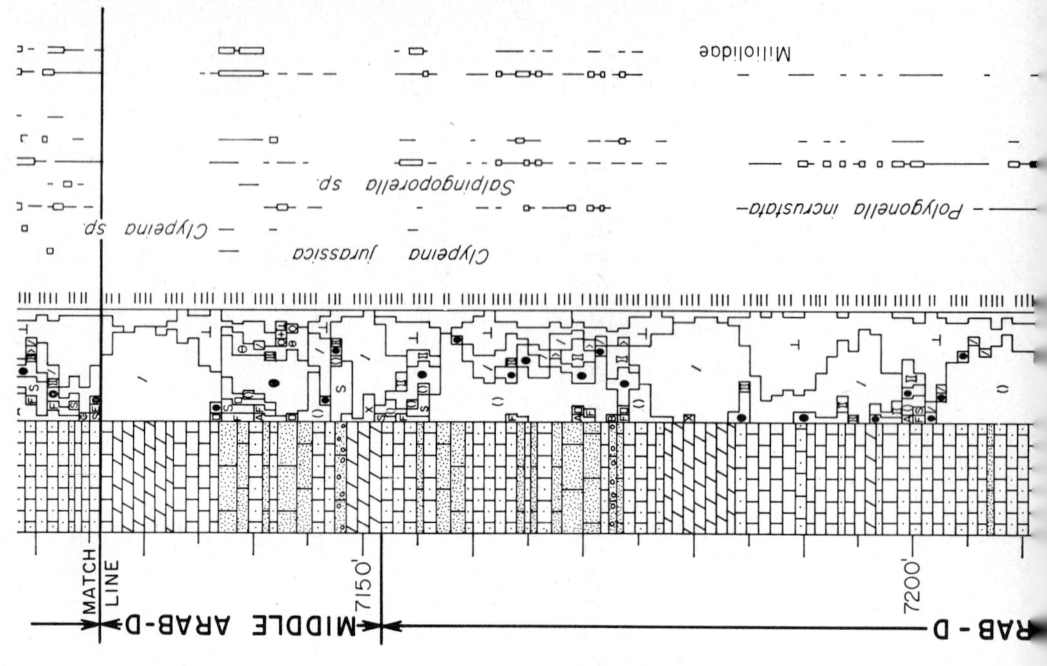
Miliolidae
Salpingoporella sp.
Polygonella incrustata
Clypeina sp.
Clypeina jurassica
MATCH LINE
MIDDLE ARAB-D
7150'
7200'
RAB-D

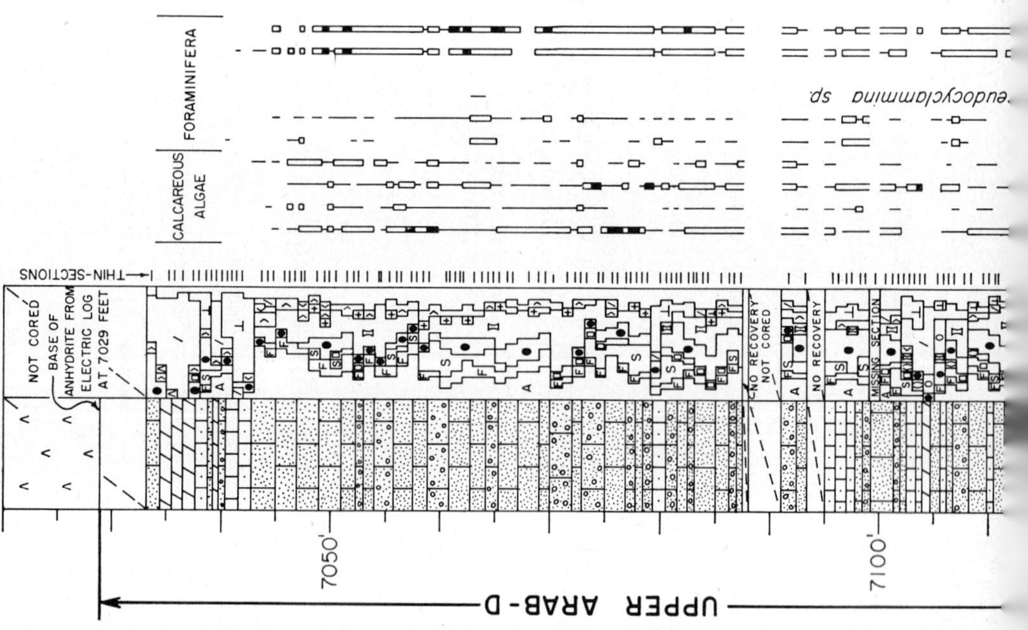
CALCAREOUS ALGAE
FORAMINIFERA
THIN-SECTIONS
NOT CORED
BASE OF ANHYDRITE FROM ELECTRIC LOG AT 7029 FEET
NO RECOVERY NOT CORED
NO RECOVERY
MISSING SECTION
7050'
7100'
UPPER ARAB-D

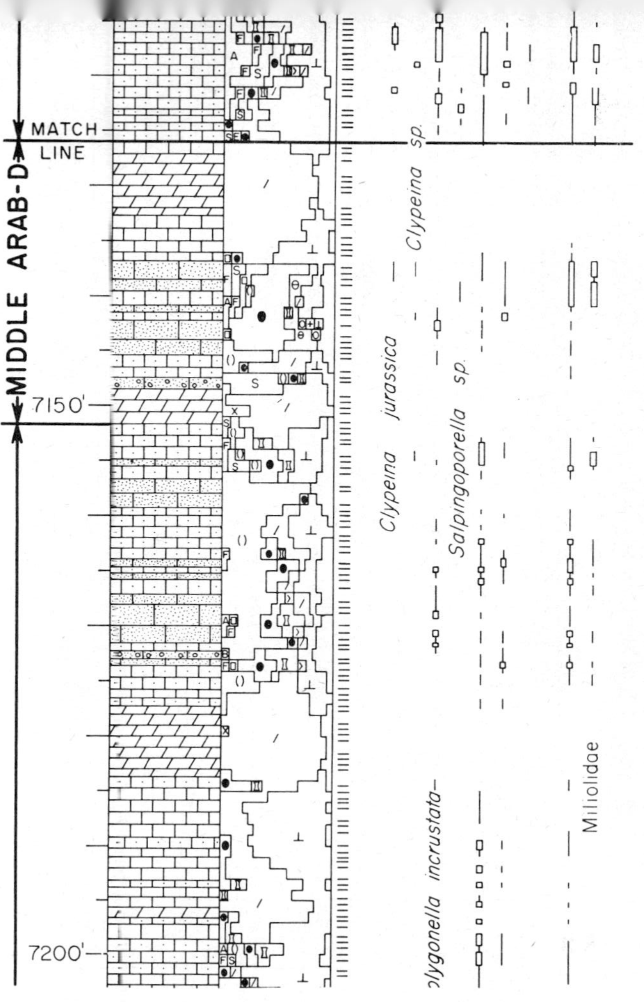

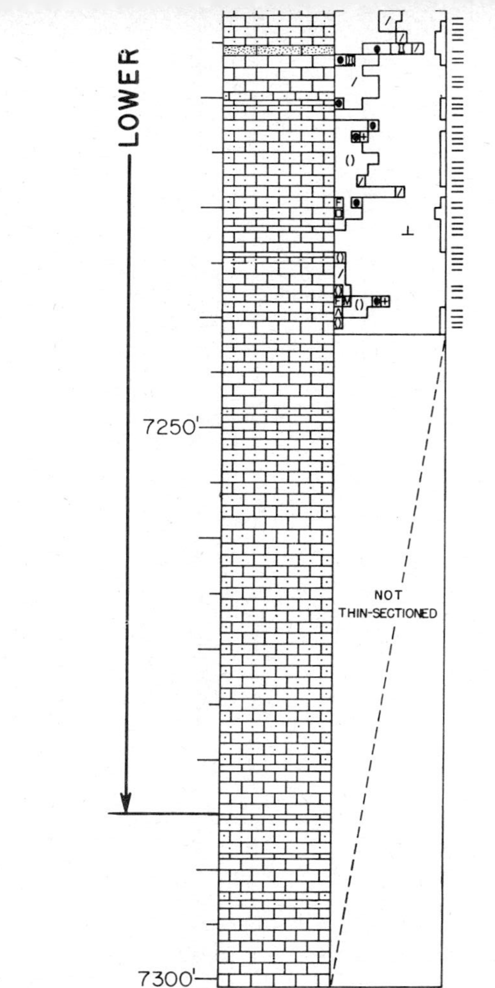

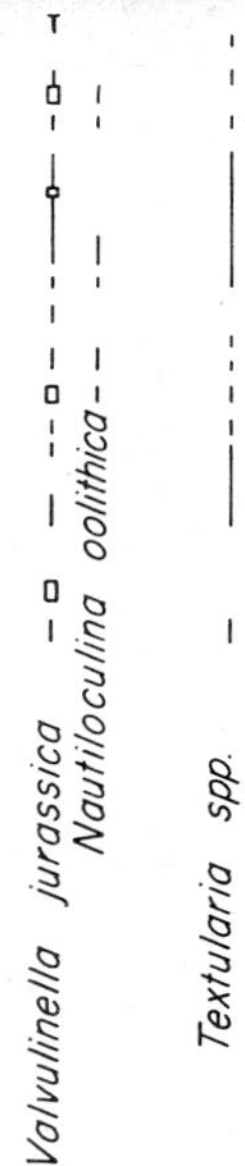

FIG. 7.—Fazran No. 1 well graphic log, showing sedimentary sequence and specific rock constituents associated with the Arab-D. See Fig. 6 for lithologic symbols.

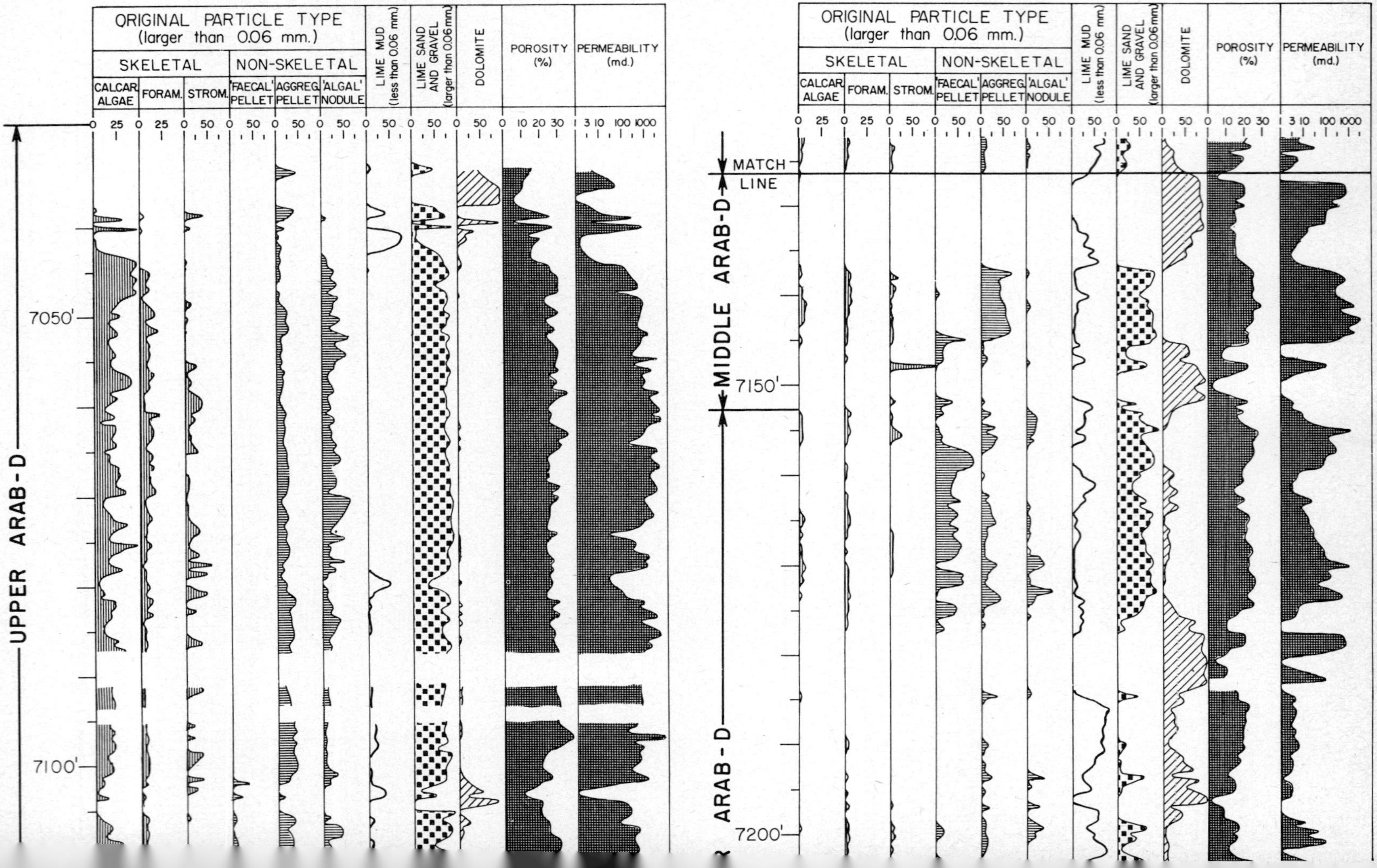

ORIGINAL PARTICLE TYPE
(larger than 0.06 mm.)
SKELETAL
NON-SKELETAL
CALCAR ALGAE
FORAM.
STROM.
'FAECAL' PELLET
AGGREG. PELLET
'ALGAL' NODULE
LIME MUD (less than 0.06 mm.)
LIME SAND AND GRAVEL (larger than 0.06 mm.)
DOLOMITE
POROSITY (%)
PERMEABILITY (md.)
0 25 0 25 0 50 0 50 0 50 0 50 0 50 0 50 0 50 0 10 20 30 3 10 100 1000
7050'
7100'
UPPER ARAB-D
ORIGINAL PARTICLE TYPE
(larger than 0.06 mm.)
SKELETAL
NON-SKELETAL
CALCAR ALGAE
FORAM.
STROM.
'FAECAL' PELLET
AGGREG. PELLET
'ALGAL' NODULE
LIME MUD (less than 0.06 mm.)
LIME SAND AND GRAVEL (larger than 0.06 mm.)
DOLOMITE
POROSITY (%)
PERMEABILITY (md.)
0 25 0 25 0 50 0 50 0 50 0 50 0 50 0 50 0 50 0 10 20 30 3 10 100 1000
MATCH LINE
MIDDLE ARAB-D
7150'
ARAB-D
7200'

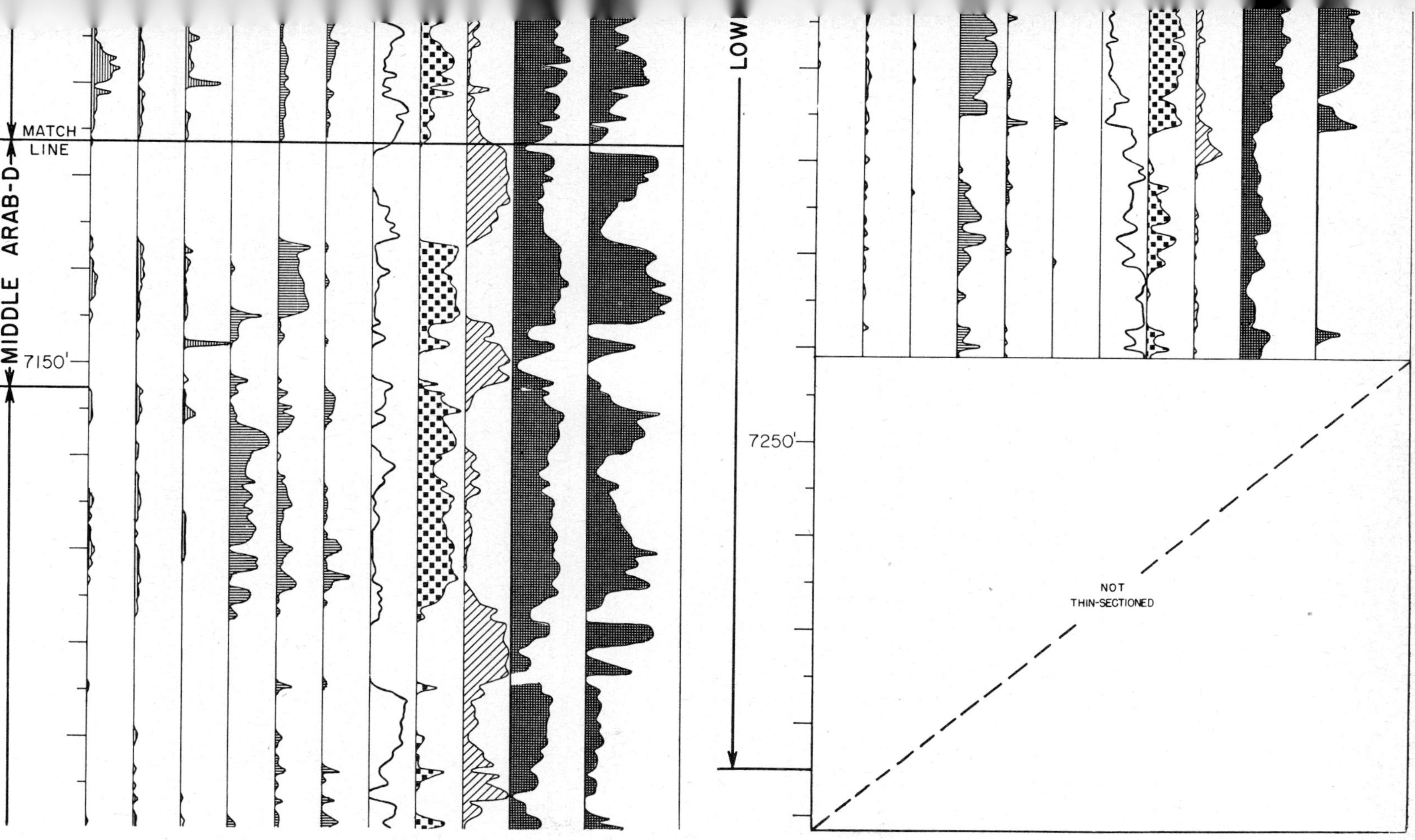

FIG. 8.—Fazran No. 1 well percentage (and permeability) curves showing relationship between important Arab-D rock factors.

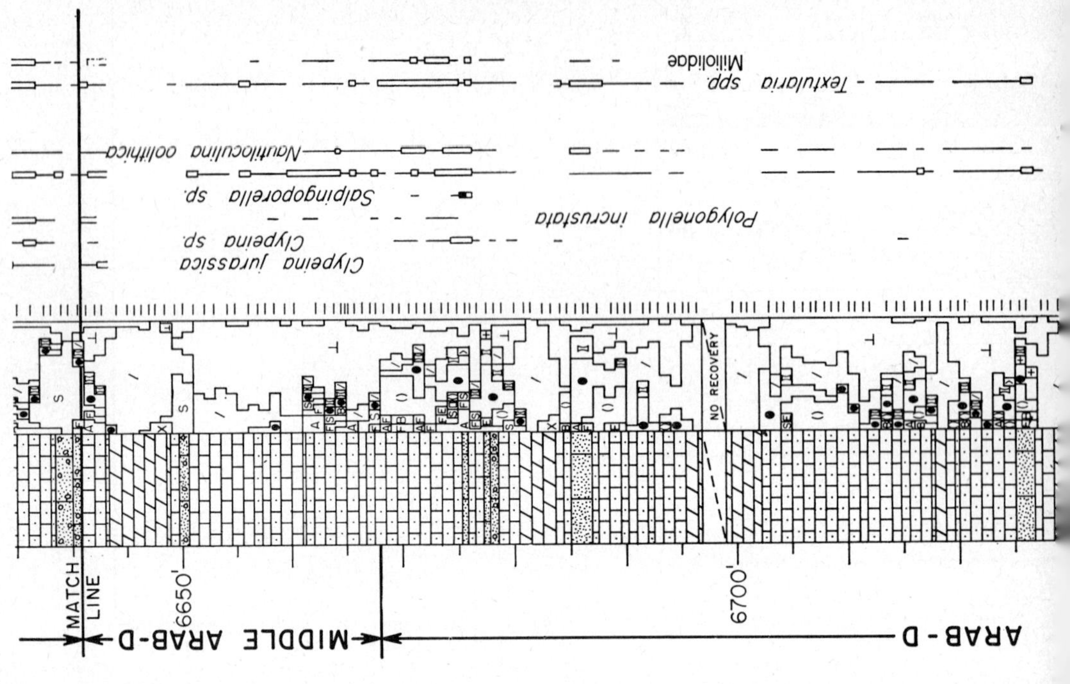
Clypeina jurassica
Clypeina sp.
Salpingoporella sp.
Nautiloculina oolithica
Polygonella incrustata
Textularia spp.
Miliolidae
NO RECOVERY
MATCH LINE
6650'
6700'
MIDDLE ARAB-D
ARAB-D

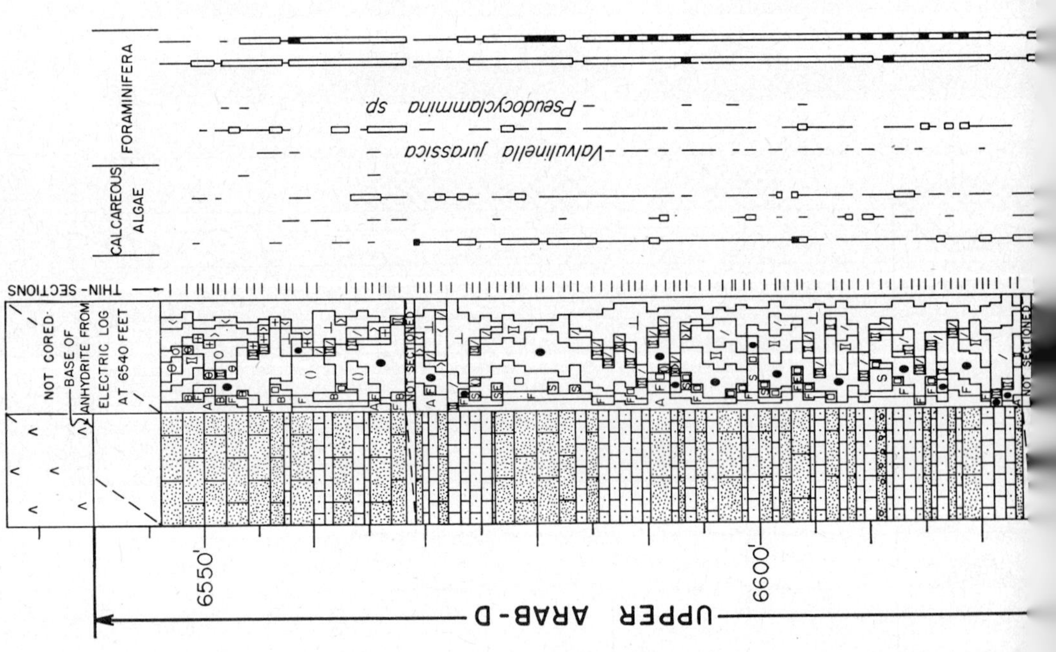
CALCAREOUS ALGAE
FORAMINIFERA
Pseudocyclammina sp.
Valvulinella jurassica
THIN-SECTIONS
NOT CORED
BASE OF ANHYDRITE FROM ELECTRIC LOG AT 6540 FEET
NOT SECTIONED
6550'
6600'
UPPER ARAB-D

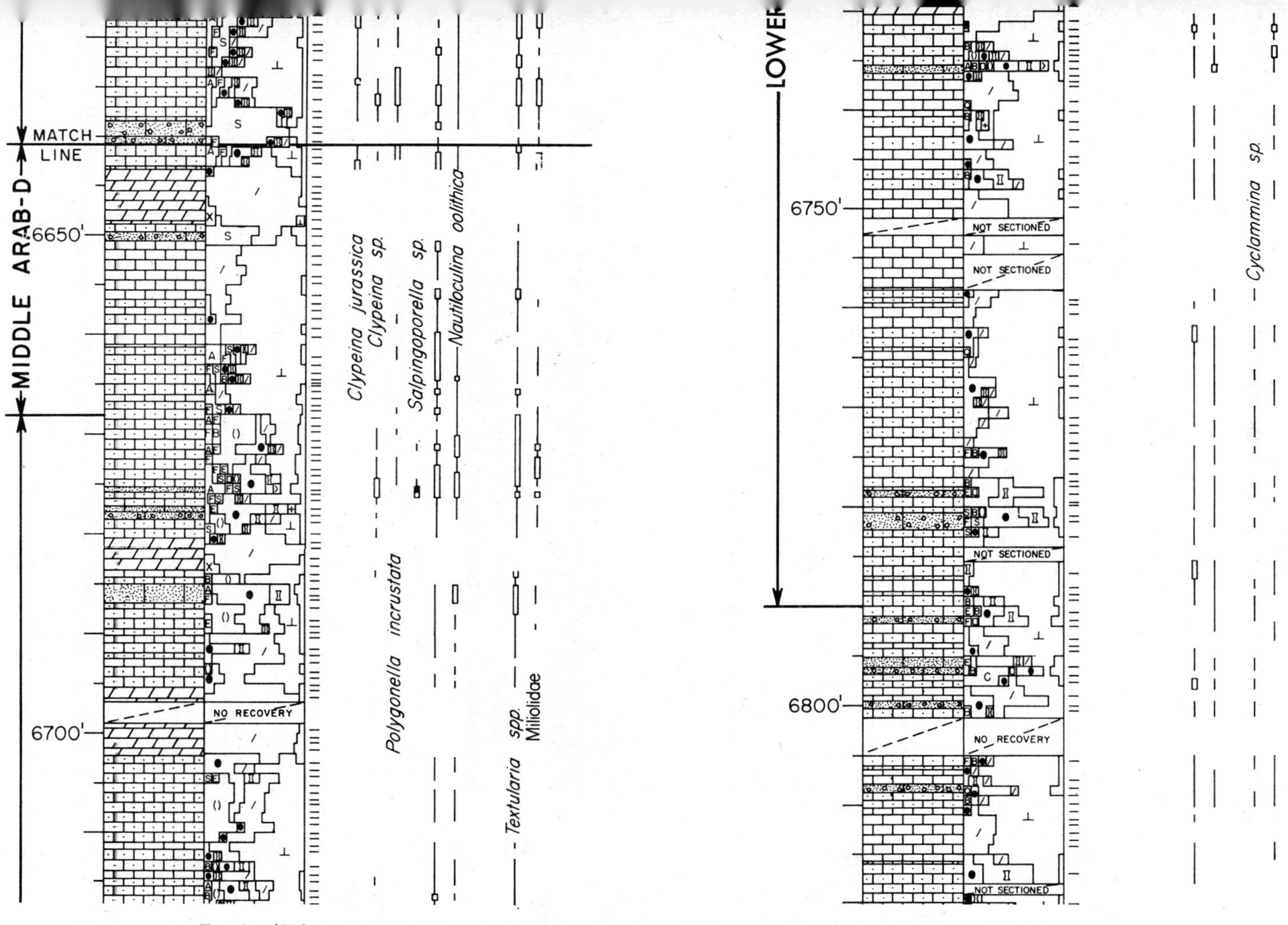

FIG. 9.—'Uthmaniyah No. 45 well graphic log, showing sedimentary sequence and specific rock constituents associated with the Arab-D. See Fig. 6 for lithologic symbols.

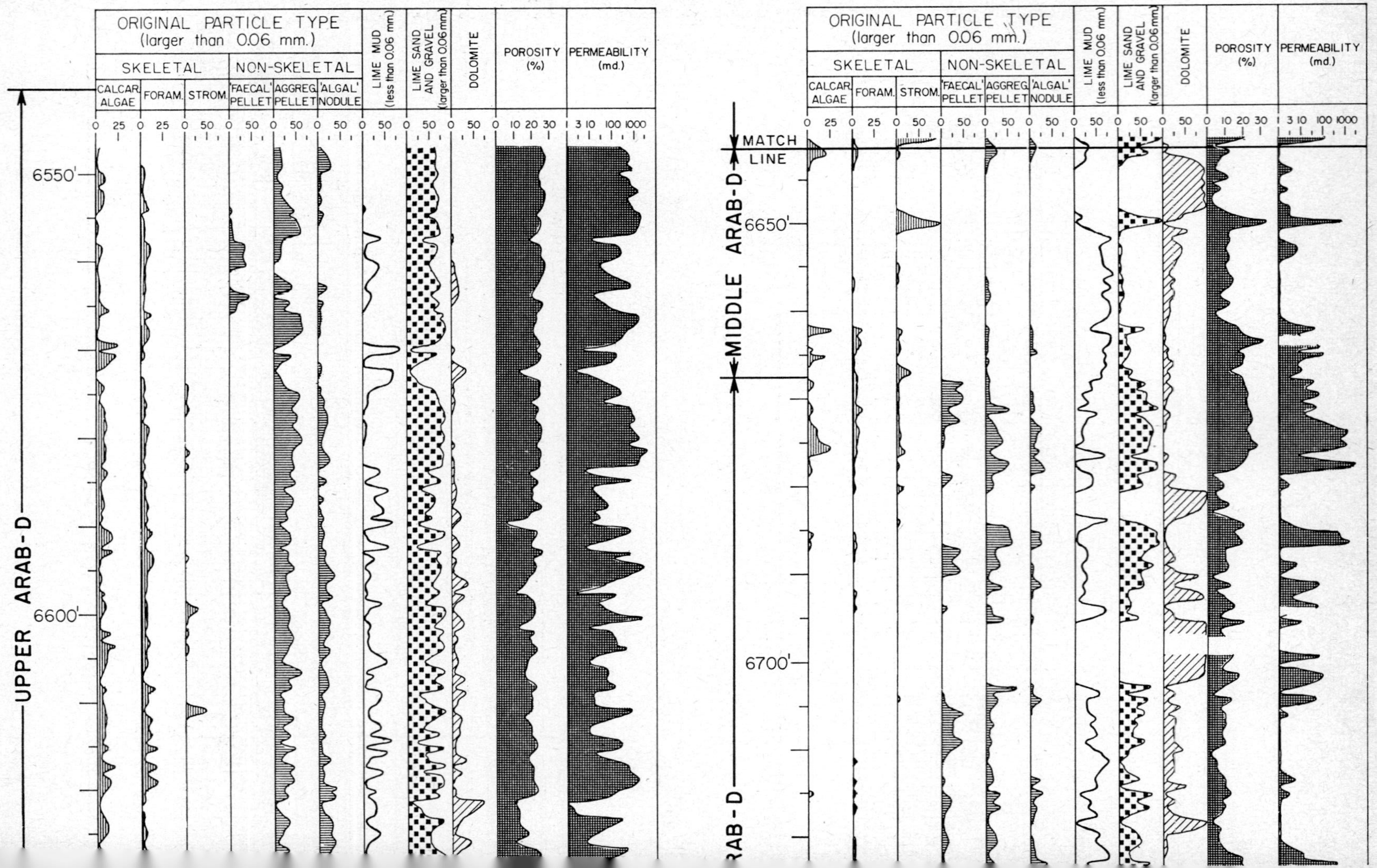

ORIGINAL PARTICLE TYPE (larger than 0.06 mm.)
SKELETAL
NON-SKELETAL
CALCAR. ALGAE
FORAM.
STROM.
'FAECAL' PELLET
AGGREG. PELLET
'ALGAL' NODULE
LIME MUD (less than 0.06 mm.)
LIME SAND AND GRAVEL (larger than 0.06 mm.)
DOLOMITE
POROSITY (%)
PERMEABILITY (md.)
0 25 0 25 0 50 0 50 0 50 0 50 0 50 0 50 0 50 0 10 20 30 1 3 10 100 1000
6550'
6600'
UPPER ARAB-D
ORIGINAL PARTICLE TYPE (larger than 0.06 mm.)
SKELETAL
NON-SKELETAL
CALCAR. ALGAE
FORAM.
STROM.
'FAECAL' PELLET
AGGREG. PELLET
'ALGAL' NODULE
LIME MUD (less than 0.06 mm.)
LIME SAND AND GRAVEL (larger than 0.06 mm.)
DOLOMITE
POROSITY (%)
PERMEABILITY (md.)
0 25 0 25 0 50 0 50 0 50 0 50 0 50 0 50 0 50 0 10 20 30 1 3 10 100 1000
MATCH LINE
6650'
6700'
MIDDLE ARAB-D
RAB-D

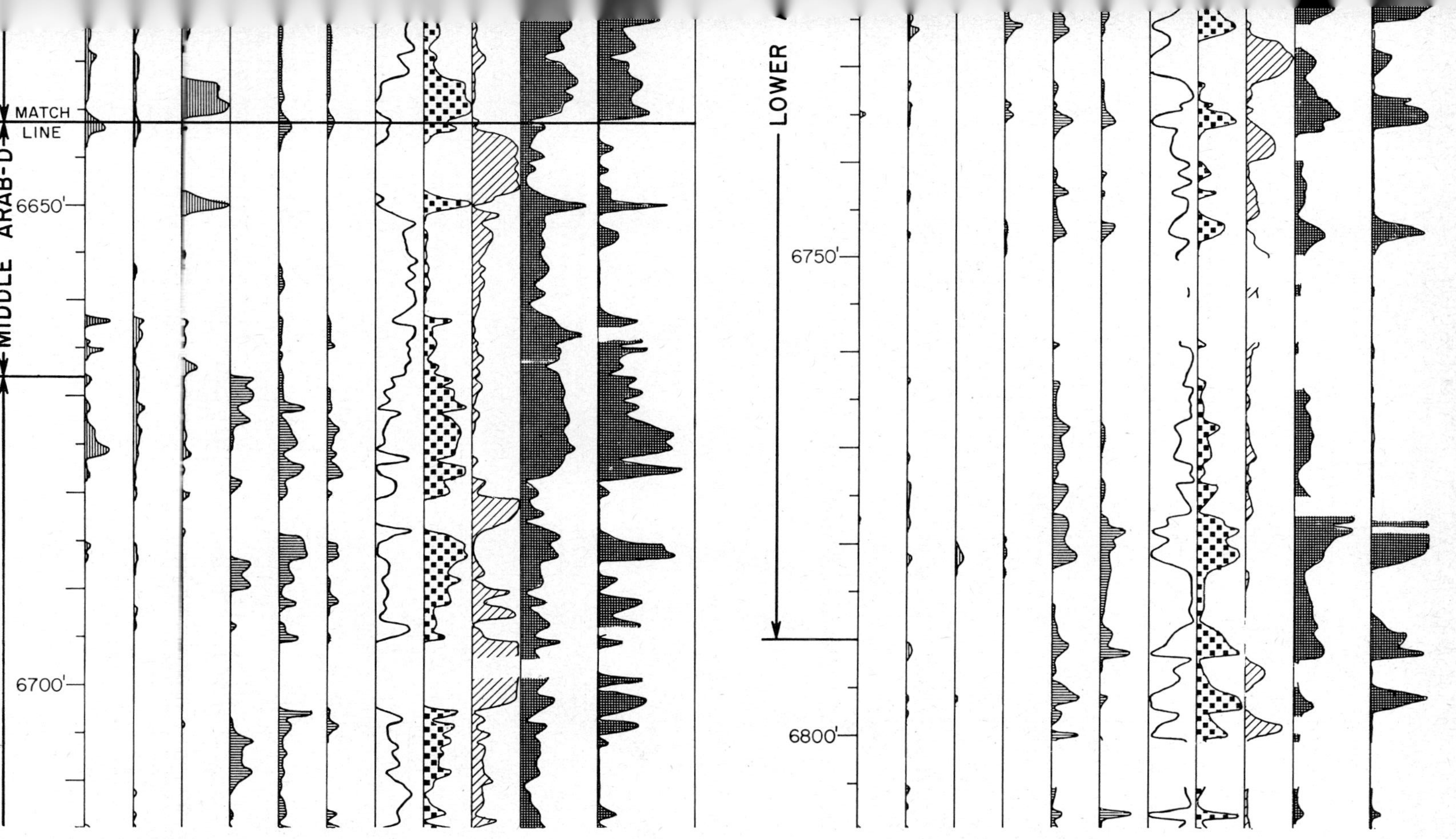

FIG. 10.—'Uthmaniyah No. 45 well percentage (and permeability) curves showing relationship between some important Arab-D rock factors.

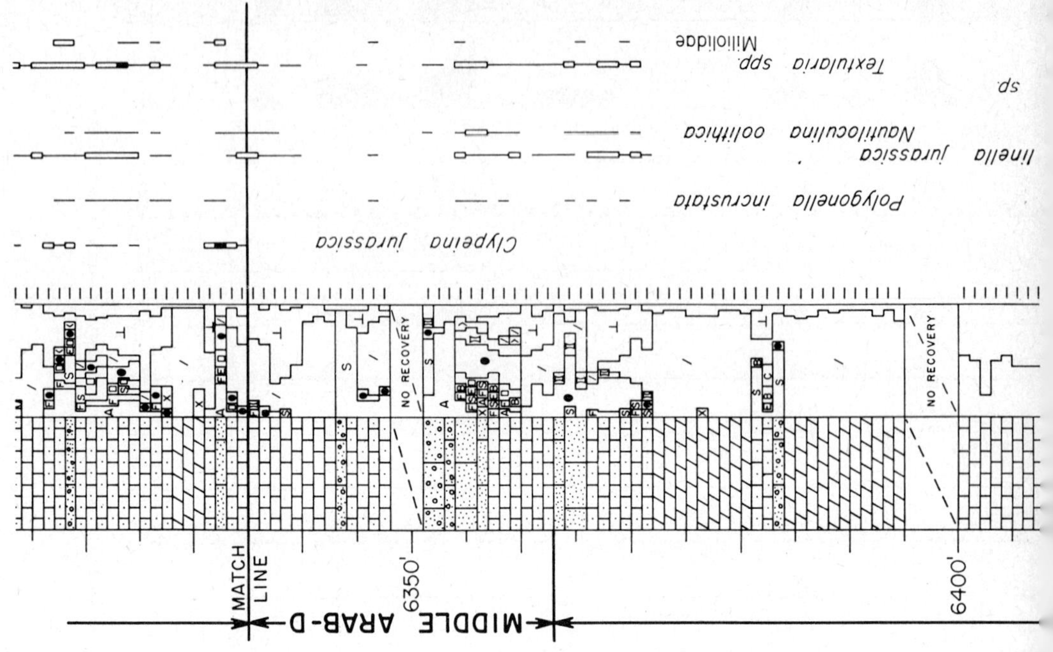
Miliolidae
Textularia spp.
Nautiloculina oolithica
Polygonella incrustata
Clypeina jurassica
NO RECOVERY
MATCH LINE
6350'
6400'
MIDDLE ARAB-D

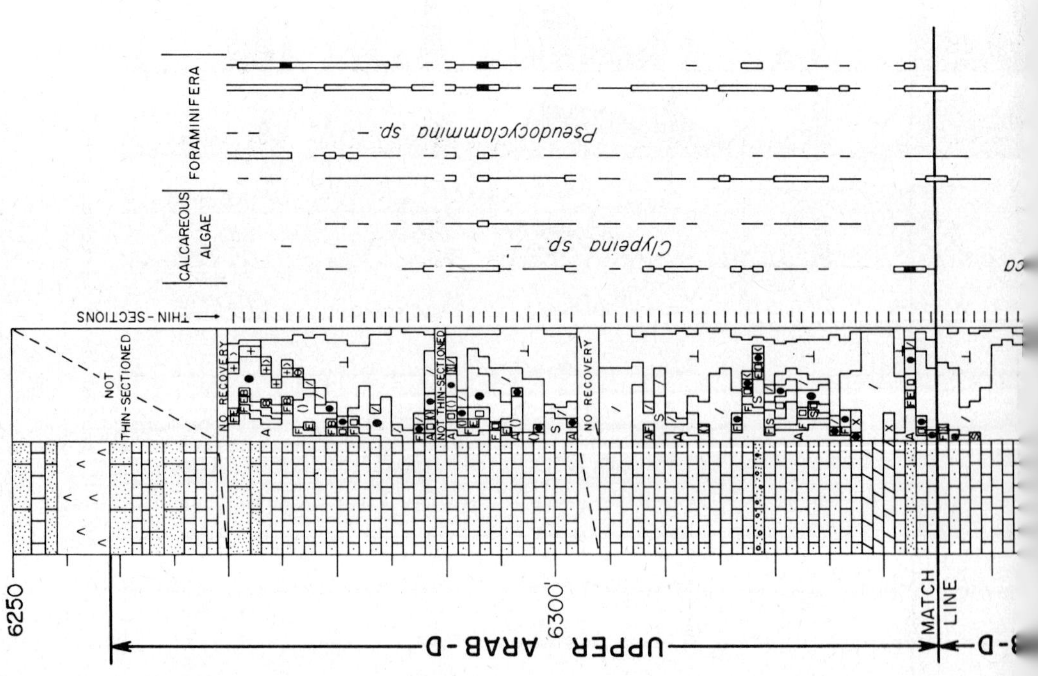
FORAMINIFERA
CALCAREOUS ALGAE
Pseudocyclammina sp.
Clypeina sp.
THIN-SECTIONS
NOT THIN-SECTIONED
NO RECOVERY
6250
6300'
MATCH LINE
UPPER ARAB-D

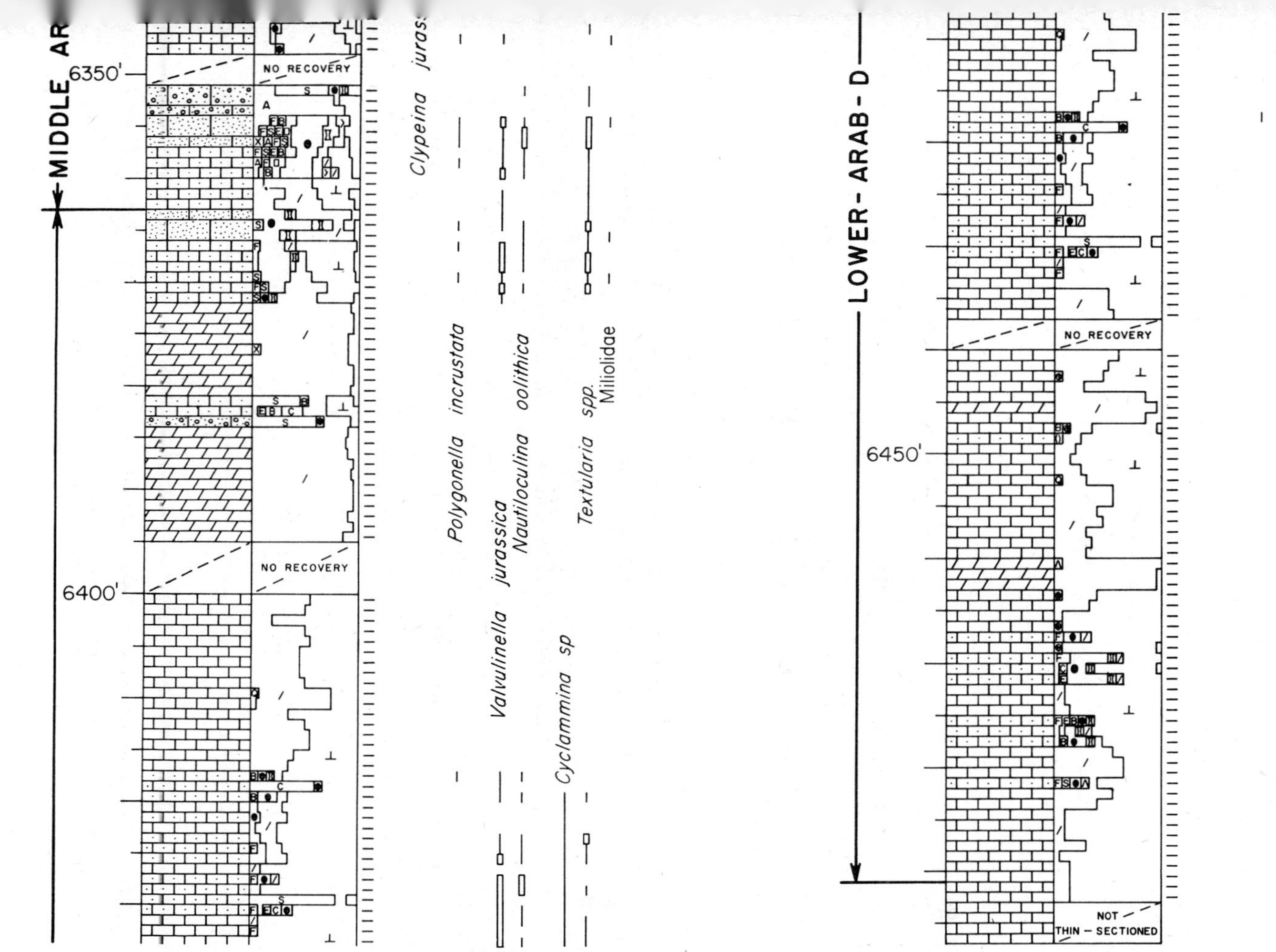

FIG. 11.—Haradh No. 3 well graphic log showing sedimentary sequence and specific rock constituents associated with Arab-D. See Fig. 6 for lithologic symbols.

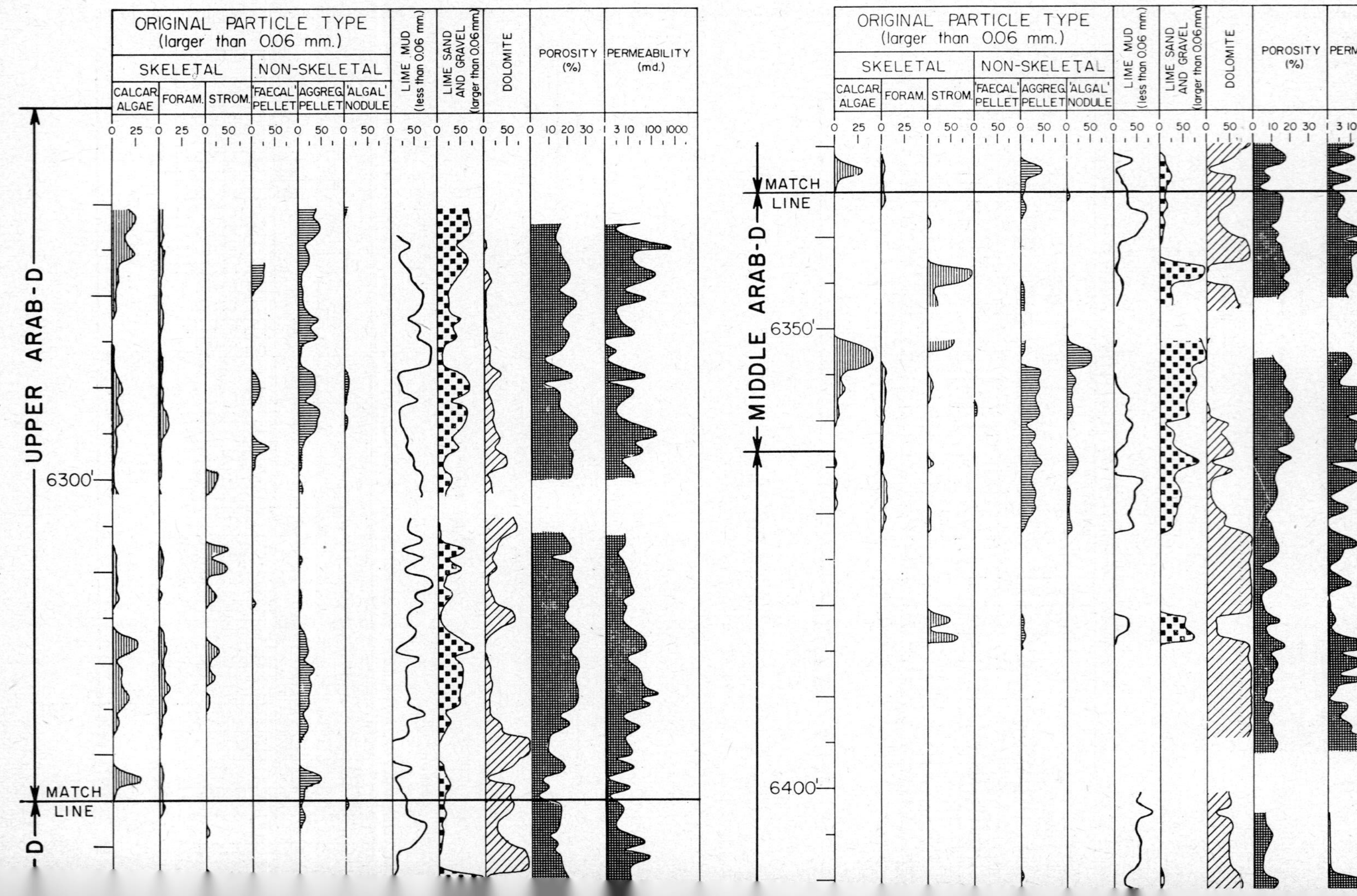
ORIGINAL PARTICLE TYPE
(larger than 0.06 mm.)
SKELETAL
NON-SKELETAL
CALCAR. ALGAE
FORAM.
STROM.
'FAECAL' PELLET
AGGREG. PELLET
'ALGAL' NODULE
LIME MUD (less than 0.06 mm.)
LIME SAND AND GRAVEL (larger than 0.06 mm.)
DOLOMITE
POROSITY (%)
PERMEABILITY (md.)
UPPER ARAB-D
6300'
MATCH LINE
MIDDLE ARAB-D
6350'
6400'

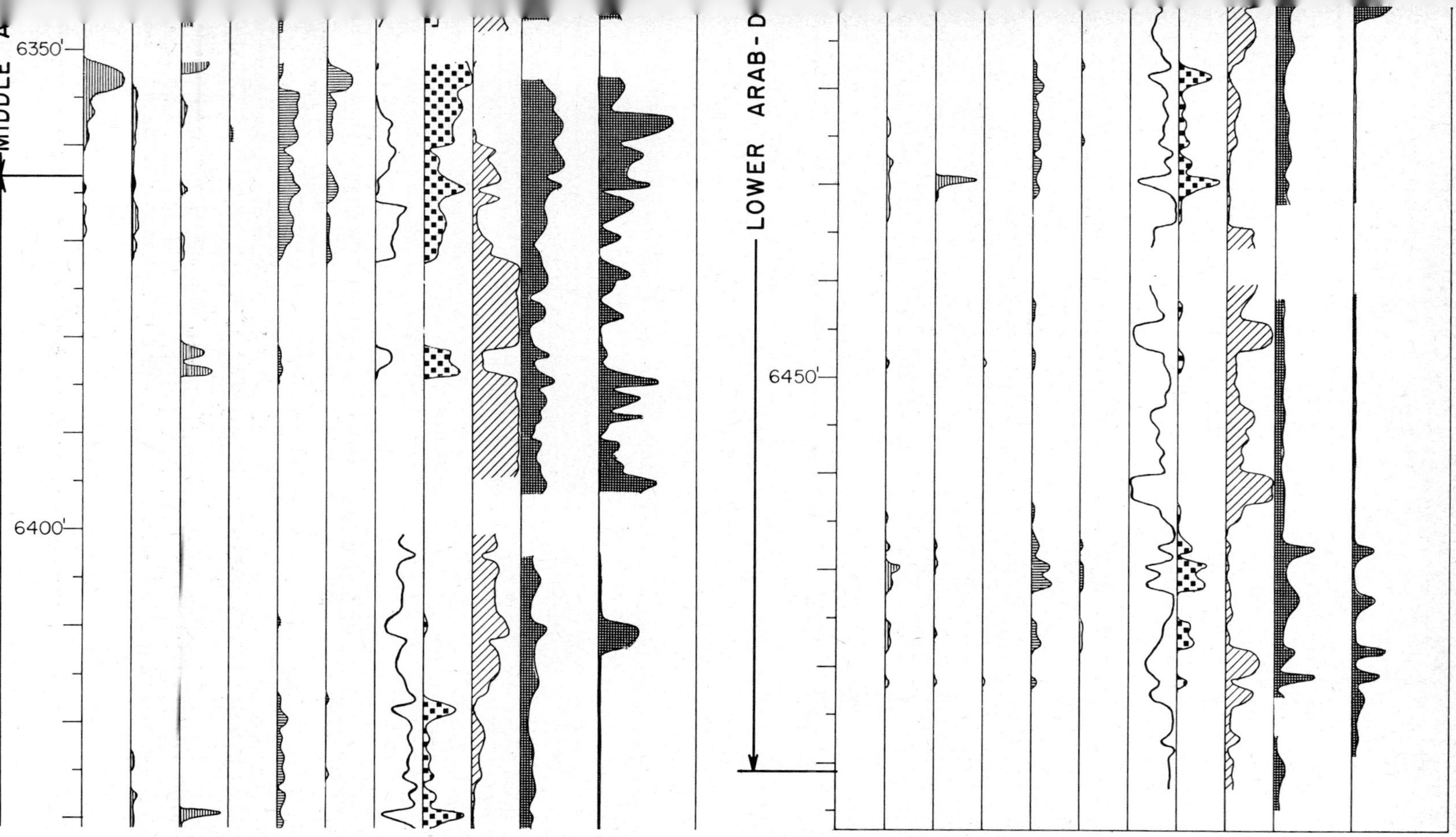

Fig. 12.—Haradh No. 3 well percentage (and permeability) curves showing relationships between some important Arab-D rock factors.

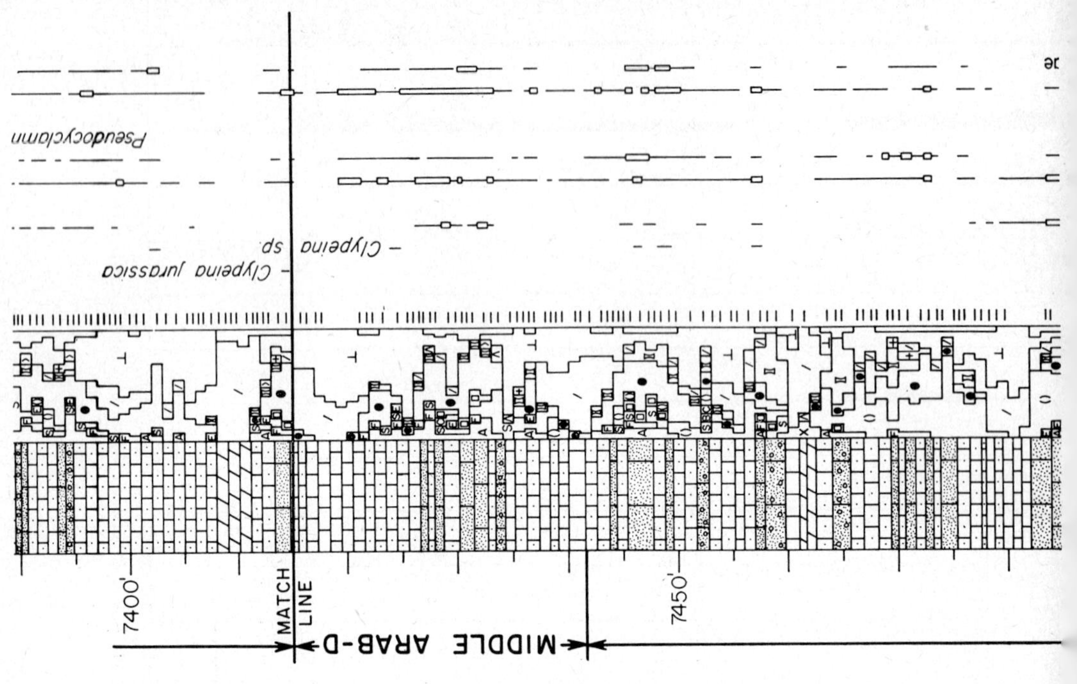

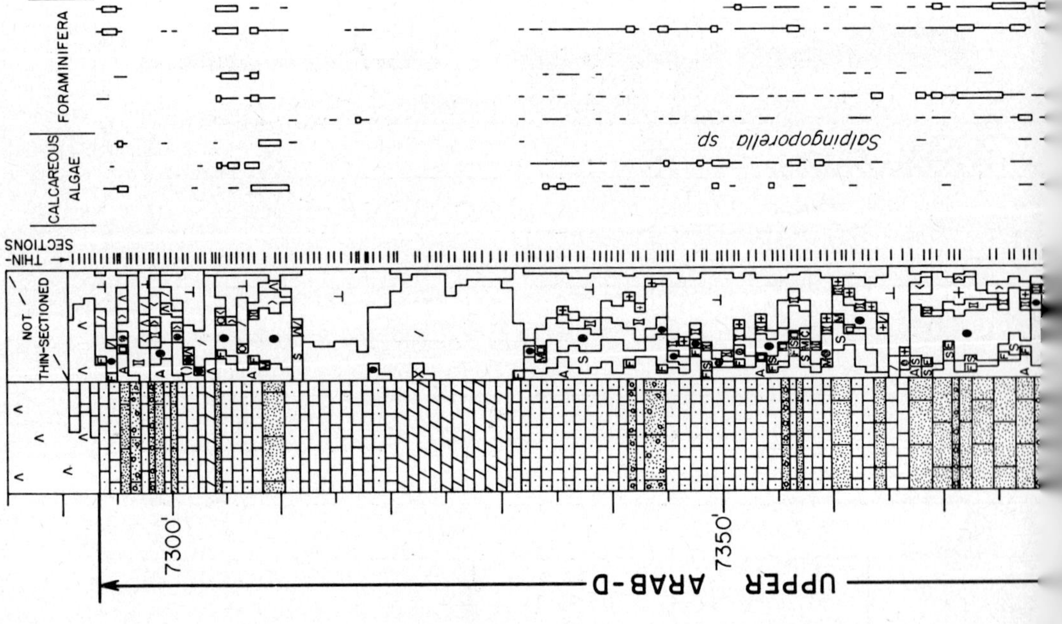

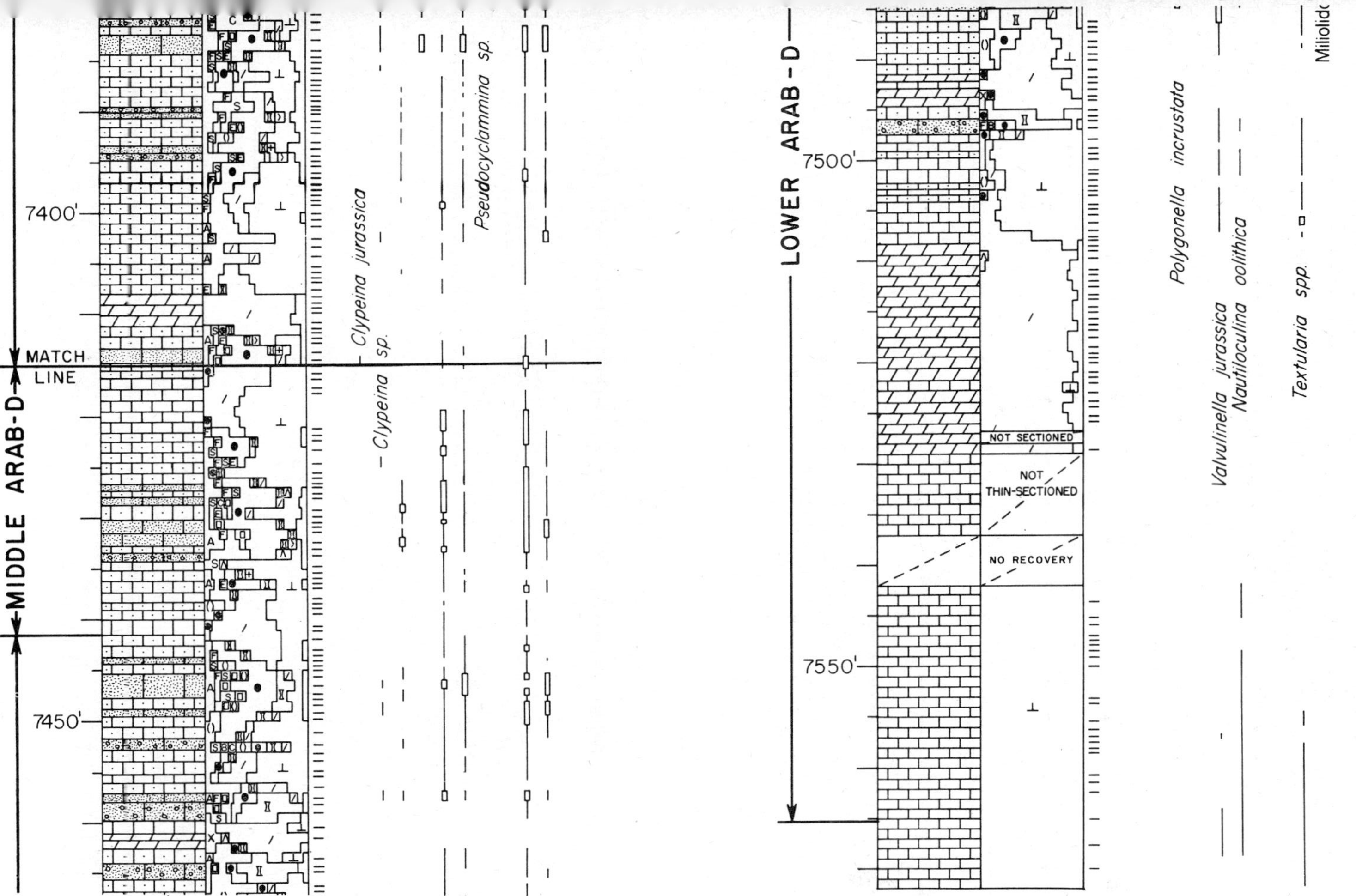

FIG. 13.—Abqaiq No. 71 well graphic log showing sedimentary sequence and specific rock constituents associated with the Arab-D. See Fig. 6 for lithologic symbols.

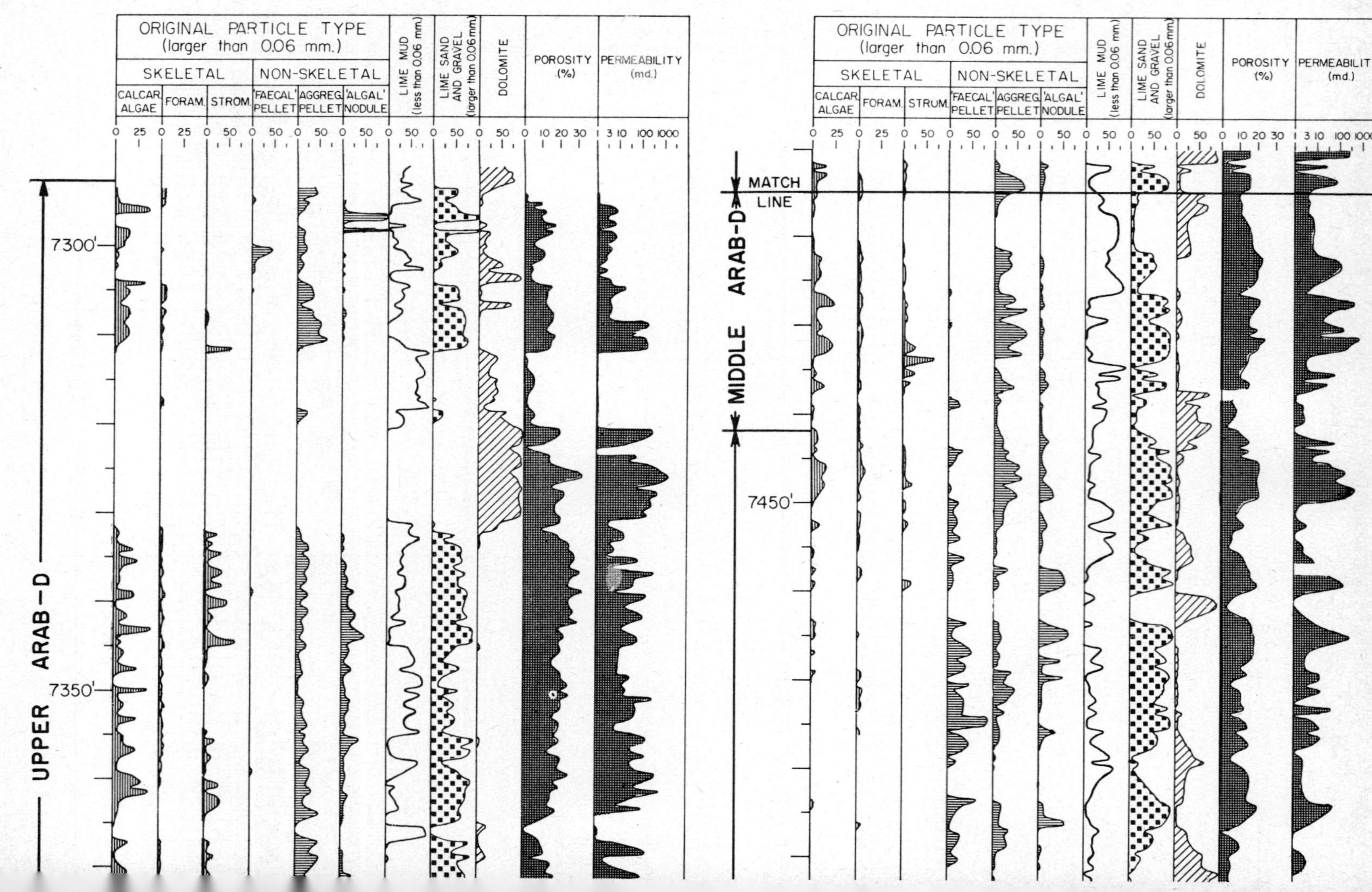
ORIGINAL PARTICLE TYPE
(larger than 0.06 mm.)
SKELETAL
NON-SKELETAL
CALCAR. ALGAE
FORAM.
STROM.
'FAECAL' PELLET
AGGREG. PELLET
'ALGAL' NODULE
LIME MUD (less than 0.06 mm.)
LIME SAND AND GRAVEL (larger than 0.06 mm.)
DOLOMITE
POROSITY (%)
PERMEABILITY (md.)
7300'
7350'
UPPER ARAB-D
MATCH LINE
MIDDLE ARAB-D
7450'

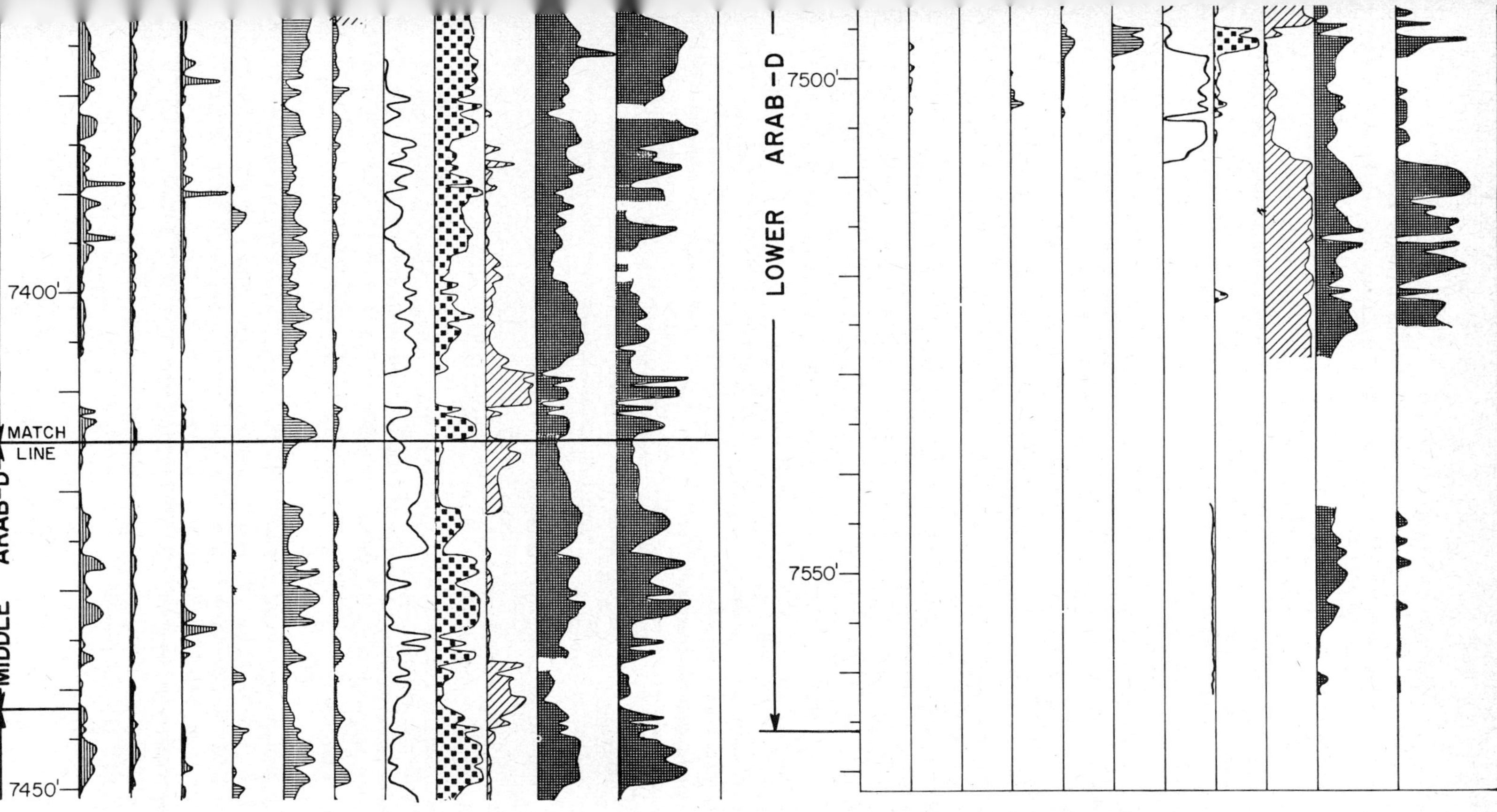

Fig. 14.—Abqaiq No. 71 well percentage (and permeability) curves showing relationships between some important Arab-D factors.

amounts of mud matrix indicates that current action is insufficient to winnow out or bypass the finer fractions or that currents strong enough to move only mud are mixing it with sand from another origin. Thus, rocks with original aphanitic matrix indicate deposition in sheltered areas near shore or quiet water further basinward.

A striking example that aphanitic limestone and calcarenitic limestone are products of similar environments is afforded by the study of modern Persian Gulf lagoons. The distribution of bottom sediments in one of these—Dohat es Saih—has now been adequately mapped (Bramkamp and Powers, 1955). The longest dimension of the lagoon, which is essentially coincident with the fetch, is just under 1 kilometer and the maximum depth slightly less than 1.5 meters. The sediments show essentially a "textbook" continental shelf depositional pattern progressing from clean quartz beach sands outward through admixed quartz and lime sand to muddy calcarenite and lime mud. Lateral changes are gradational, with the exception of the area where clean-washed lime sand is in sharp contact with lime mud, which commonly contains more than 50 per cent calcareous sand. The sandy mud, in turn, grades within a few meters to mud in which no sand occurs. The sharp sand-mud contact, readily visible on aerial photographs and bottom sediment maps, marks the lower limit of wave action effective enough to move sand in the lagoon.

Although calcarenitic limestone forms a thin zone between clean sand and mud in Dohat es Saih, possible exceptions to this certainly occur. Pellets, in the sense of Illing (1954), can form in muddy sediments far from current-washed areas. In other instances, floating shells will be carried out to accumulate with mud—for example, organic oozes. In these deposits, as in those bordering clean-washed sand, the presence of mud affords the clue to process of deposition.

It is worth noting briefly that textural rock types cannot be directly related to water depth at time of deposition. Recent sediment studies show carbonate as well as silicate mud being deposited almost in contact with the shore (Newell and others, 1951; van Straaten and Kuenen, 1958; Ellis, 1960); underwater photographs show current-rippled calcareous sand accumulating on the ocean bottom at a depth of 6,600 feet. One of these underwater photos taken by C. J. Shipek, U. S. Navy Electronics Laboratory, on the southwest slope of Eniwetok Atoll appears in Gilluly, Waters, and Woodford (1959, p. 77). Shipek (1960) indicates that other, still unpublished, photos taken in the same area also show similar ripple marks.

CORRELATION

Contacts between the Arab-D member and bracketing units can be traced through Ghawar and Abqaiq oil fields with little difficulty. The upper limit, marked by the generally sharp change from calcarenite to massive anhydrite, is equally distinctive in adjacent areas such as Khurais, Ma'aqala, Abu Hadriya, Khursaniyah, Dammam, and Fadhili. In Ghawar and Abqaiq, the lower contact is marked by a change from tight lithographic limestone below to less tight, somewhat sandy mud above. This change, which commonly corresponds to the base of the oil-saturated interval, imparts a marked signature pattern to the electric resistivity log. Away from Ghawar and Abqaiq the signature becomes less definite and its equivalent in adjacent fields is tentative.

The Arab-D member is a rock-stratigraphic unit; however, when the overlying C–D anhydrite is added the two together may closely approximate a time-rock unit. The close parallelism between the base of the Arab-C member (top of C–D anhydrite) and the base of the D member and its intramember horizons strongly suggests this possibility.

Subdivision of Arab-D rocks from outcrops and deep wells in accordance with their original sedimentary texture has permitted the definition of intramember units. Accompanying paleontologic and electric log data confirm these subdivisions and correlations.

LITHOLOGIC CORRELATION

Data from ten of the thin-sectioned wells were plotted on graphic logs to bring out original sedimentary textures. In addition, a second column depicting constituent elements in their proper proportions was compiled for the four point-counted wells (Figs. 7, 9, 11, 13). Appropriate colors were used to bring out rock-type and particle-type patterns. Pattern matching of these logs defines three main intramember units which, for the purpose of this report, have been informally designated as the lower, middle, and upper units of the Arab-D member. The lower Arab-D consists of mixed mud and nonskeletal sand; the middle unit is dominantly mud; and the upper Arab-D is mostly sand admixed with subordinate amounts of mud. The upper sand, in large part skeletal, is commonly formed of clean-washed calcarenite.

Two horizons within the lower Arab-D show considerable lateral persistence and can be used in many areas to confirm the main intramember boundaries. In Ghawar and Abqaiq, a thin zone of chert occurs near the top of the lower Arab-D. It was first identified in thin sections, and has now been recognized in intermediate cored wells and on electric logs. The lower half of the lower Arab-D is almost exclusively mud with few layers of calcarenitic limestone or calcarenite; the upper part, though still dominantly mud, contains some thin, well-developed calcarenite units. Where distinguishable, the two parts of the lower Arab-D have been separated by a horizon informally designated as "top of lower mud."

In addition to matching specific rock types, several of the individual components, as might be expected, were also easily related from well to well. The individual curves on Figures 8, 10, 12, and 14, showing percentage of calcareous algae, stromatoporoids, mud, sand-gravel, and dolomite, were particularly useful for this type of correlation. Comparison of these curves between wells shows a remarkable coincidence involving both occurrence and quantity.

An important feature of the three main Arab-D units is the lateral variation between principal rock types—for instance, in the upper Arab-D, beds of calcarenite commonly grade into calcarenitic limestone; nonsandy beds are virtually absent. The influx of sand starting at the base of the upper unit appears to be regional in scope. The change from dominantly sand to dominantly mud sedimentation at different levels has been used with considerable success in correlation.

Logs compiled from routine core examination show the three divisions with equal clarity and can be readily correlated with the thin-sectioned wells. Graphic well logs compiled from core plug data alone have been reduced in scale without generalization and inserted in the correlation framework, as indicated on Figures 15 and 16. The core logs and descriptions from which these reduced versions were compiled by the writer were independently made by Aramco geologists G. R. Ball, H. A. Kimball, C. S. Morse, and J. B. Sheehan.

PALEONTOLOGIC CORRELATION

Only one form—that is, the dasyclad alga *Clypeina jurassica*—appears to be stratigraphically restricted and widely distributed horizontally. Beginning in the upper part of the middle Arab-D, *Clypeina jurassica* extends without apparent interruption, and commonly in large numbers, through the entire upper sandy unit. The foraminifer *Cyclammina* sp. occurs only in the lower part of the lower Arab-D; its lateral occurrence, however, is sporadic.

A feature of particular interest from a paleogeographic, ecologic, and reservoir point of view is the marked influx of skeletal debris at the base of the upper unit, which continues to the base of the C-D anhydrite. Increase in abundance of individual Foraminifera and algae as well as stromatoporoids at this level is apparent from examination of Figures 7–14. Presumably the increase in skeletal elements is a response to the same shoaling conditions which produced the accompanying marked increase in clean-washed calcarenite beds.

A second weakly defined zone in which skeletal elements occur in limited amounts, brackets the contact between the lower and middle Arab-D. Paleontologic patterns coupled with lithologic matches give a consistent intramember zonation probably accurate within a few feet.

ELECTRIC-LOG CORRELATION

Following correlation by lithologic and paleontologic methods, all logs were reduced without generalization and matched to the respective electric-log resistivity curve. Earlier correlations based solely on lithologic and paleontologic considerations were strikingly confirmed by electric-log relations. A close correspondence between the resistivity curve and rock type is also apparent. Particularly evident is the signature pattern that accompanies the chert zone; it can be followed with fidelity over much of the area studied. High-resistivity rocks include anhydrite, dolomite, and aphanitic limestone; calcarenite and some porous calcarenitic limestones show low resistivity.

Arab-D limits and intramember units are thus defined on all types of evidence now available—that is, lithologic, paleontologic, and electric or radioactive logs. Use of this multiple approach has defined three units within the Arab-D of considerable importance for interpreting reservoir history and behavior.

STRATIGRAPHY

GENERAL

The Arab-D member together with the overlying anhydrite seems to represent the opening cycle of four main cycles of deposition, each of which started with normal marine carbonates and closed with anhydrite. Each of the four carbonate members is separated by a thin, laterally persistent anhydrite unit; they have been informally designated from top to bottom as the -A, -B, -C, and -D members of the Arab formation. The much thicker upper or closing anhydrite unit (500 feet in Ghawar) is considered a separate formation—the Hith anhydrite.

The Jubaila formation, which immediately underlies the Arab-D member, is generally penetrated only a few feet during routine well completion. Where completely drilled, the Jubaila is primarily aphanitic limestone with some interbedded calcarenitic limestone. Few true clean-washed calcarenites are present and the formation is dominantly mud. Presumably Jubaila rocks were deposited mostly below effective wave base; shallow-water conditions sufficient to concentrate calcareous sand occurred only infrequently. The Jubaila phase of mud sedimentation gave way to typical Arab-D rocks, which appear to have accumulated under more agitated conditions.

That the Arab-D is considerably more sandy than the underlying Jubaila has long been recognized, but only recently, and particularly with this study, have sufficient data become available to show strong differentiation both vertically and laterally within the Arab-D itself. The reservoir consists of mixed aphanitic limestone, calcarenitic limestone, calcarenite, and coarse carbonate clastic which have remained essentially unaltered or have undergone varying degrees of secondary change. In some instances, original rock types have been completely replaced by dolomite; however, gaps in the original sedimentary record from causes such as this are generally not large. Furthermore, this study has demonstrated that, at least in Arabian rocks, dolomite shows strong preference for lime mud. It appears reasonable to assume that where dolomite now exists, aphanitic or calcarenitic limestone has been replaced. The distribution of these rock types, coupled with specific particle-type occurrence, permits the logical separation of the Arab-D into three units which, when studied separately, give considerable insight into the paleogeography, paleoecology, and fluid behavior of the -D member reservoir.

LOWER ARAB-D

Lithology.—Lower Arab-D rocks form a gradational sequence from the underlying tight lithographic limestone which characterizes the Jubaila, through mud with some sandy mud to dominantly sandy mud in which some clean-washed sand occurs. The change from mud or aphanitic limestone to sandy mud and calcarenite is sufficiently distinct to be used as a horizon to separate the lower Arab-D into two smaller units. This break has been designated on the accompanying stratigraphic and correlation cross sections as the "top of the lower mud." The lower half of the lower Arab-D shows little lithic variation either laterally or vertically. Aphanitic limestone is the main rock type; calcarenitic limestone follows, and calcarenite occurs only sporadically. Although these rocks are oil-saturated, their permeability is negligible except in the thin, apparently lenticular, calcarenites.

The upper part of the lower Arab-D, still composed largely of mud, shows an important increase in percentage of admixed sand and calcarenite. Regionally, the unit shows the first significant paleogeographic differentiation. Calcarenite and calcarenitic limestone form an irregular belt that extends across 'Uthmaniyah, Shedgum, and Ain Dar. As would be expected, an increase in porosity and permeability coincides with the presence of these rock types. Available information suggests that sand and muddy sand diminish outward in all directions from a maximum development in these areas. Significantly, equivalent rocks in south Abqaiq are in muddy facies, but current-washed sand again occurs in north Abqaiq.

A thin zone of chert generally associated with dolomite occurs 10–20 feet below the top of the lower Arab-D. The zone, whose thickness nowhere exceeds 5 feet, can be traced with certainty from Haradh in southern Ghawar through 'Uthmaniyah and Shedgum to north Abqaiq. The zone is also present in Fazran-north Ain Dar and in south Ain Dar, but appears to be missing in some central Ain Dar wells. The widespread continuity of the silica-bearing dolomite has not previously been appreciated owing to difficulty of recognition in core chips and core plugs. The chert (variety microcrystalline quartz) normally fills in between, and in some instances replaces, dolomite crystals.

Lower Arab-D sand consists almost exclusively of nonskeletal particles of which "fecal" and aggregate pellets and "algal" nodules are the most numerous. Foraminifera, though relatively scarce, are the most common skeletal element. Stromatoporoids are very rare, and algae are essentially absent except in the very highest part of the lower Arab-D (above the chert zone) where calcareous algae, Foraminifera, and stromatoporoids occur in some quantity—that is, 3–10 per cent.

The thickness of the lower Arab-D varies little from an average of 120 feet in Ghawar and Abqaiq, where the limits can be recognized with a fair degree of certainty. Some thinning is apparent in Khursaniyah and Abu Hadriya where the unit contacts are tentative.

Paleontology.—A single foraminifer, *Cyclammina* sp., appears to terminate at approximately the same stratigraphic level in the lower Arab-D. Unfortunately, this arenaceous form was noted only in Khurais, 'Uthmaniyah, south Ghawar, and south Abqaiq. Longer ranging forms recognized in the lower Arab-D include—*Valvulinella jurassica*, *Nautiloculina oolithica*, *Textularia* spp., and various Miliolidae.

Calcareous algae occur only rarely below the chert zone; these consist almost exclusively of the incrusting form *Polygonella incrustata*, which has more tolerance for mud than the branching algae that appear higher in the section. Above the chert zone, small poorly preserved *Clypeina* sp. similar to *Clypeina parvula* Carozzi were seen.

MIDDLE ARAB-D

Lithology.—The middle Arab-D member, which marks an episode of widespread mud deposition, can be traced with a high degree of certainty over much of northeastern Saudi Arabia. The unit in the subsurface maintains an almost constant thickness of 30 feet but appears to thin to 20 feet in one well—Khursaniyah 1. The subsurface lithologic pattern so characteristic of the middle Arab-D and bracketing beds, can be recognized with little doubt on outcrop. In surface exposures a pattern which persists for more than 400 miles starts at the base with a thin calcarenite (probably equivalent to the uppermost lower Arab-D calcarenite) and is overlain by a unit of tight aphanitic limestone 20 feet thick which represents the middle Arab-D. The sequence above this is similar to the upper Arab-D.

Middle Arab-D rocks, both at surface and in subsurface, are dominantly aphanitic limestone with some admixed calcarenitic limestone and rare, laterally discontinuous, calcarenite. In most areas the top of the middle unit marks the highest occurrence of nonsandy mud. Recognition of the unit was long masked by irregular dolomite replacement. This addition of dolomite obscures not only the lithologic pattern but also the electric-log signature. Increased understanding of dolomite behavior through thin-section study shows that in Arab-D rocks lime mud and not sand is altered in almost all cases. Using this key, dolomitization does not now present serious difficulties to matching lithologic and electric-log patterns.

Middle Arab-D rocks are mostly mud and show little lateral textural differentiation. The sheet-like concentration of mud over such an extensive area is considered presumptive evidence of deposition below the level of effective wave and current activity. Mud of undetermined origin and its altered equivalent dolomite constitute the bulk of the middle Arab-D. Where sand occurs, it consists of both nonskeletal and skeletal particles. Calcareous algae, stromatoporoids, aggregate pel-

(*Text continued on page 178*)

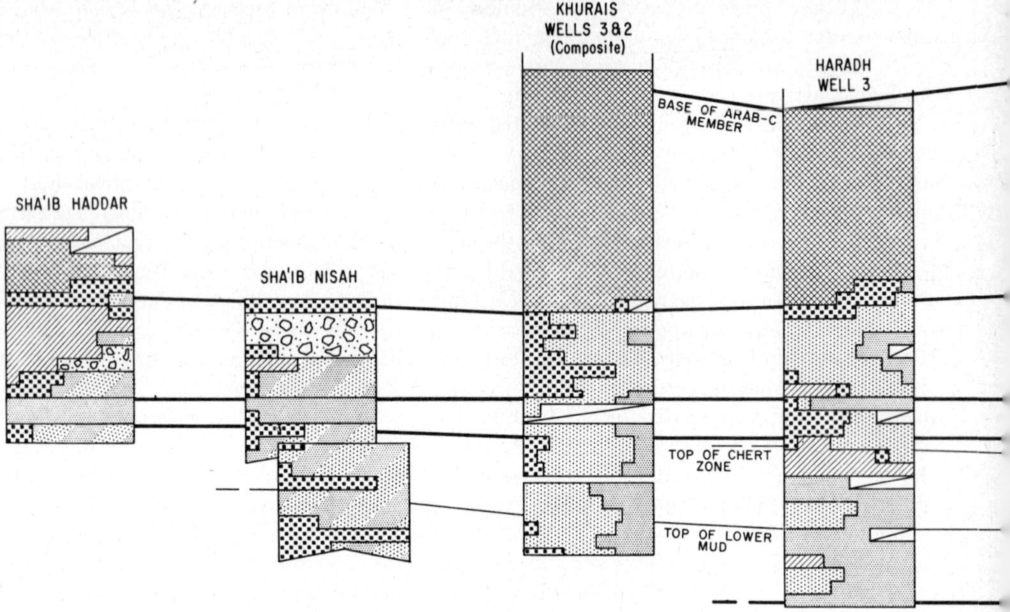

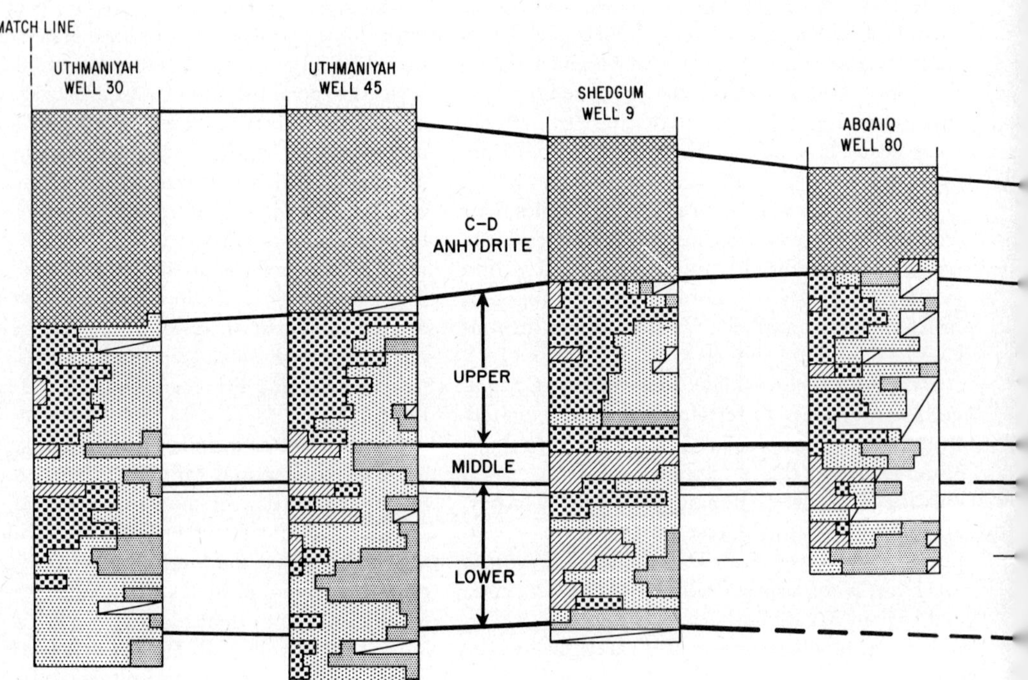

FIG. 15.—Regional correlation and stratigraphy of

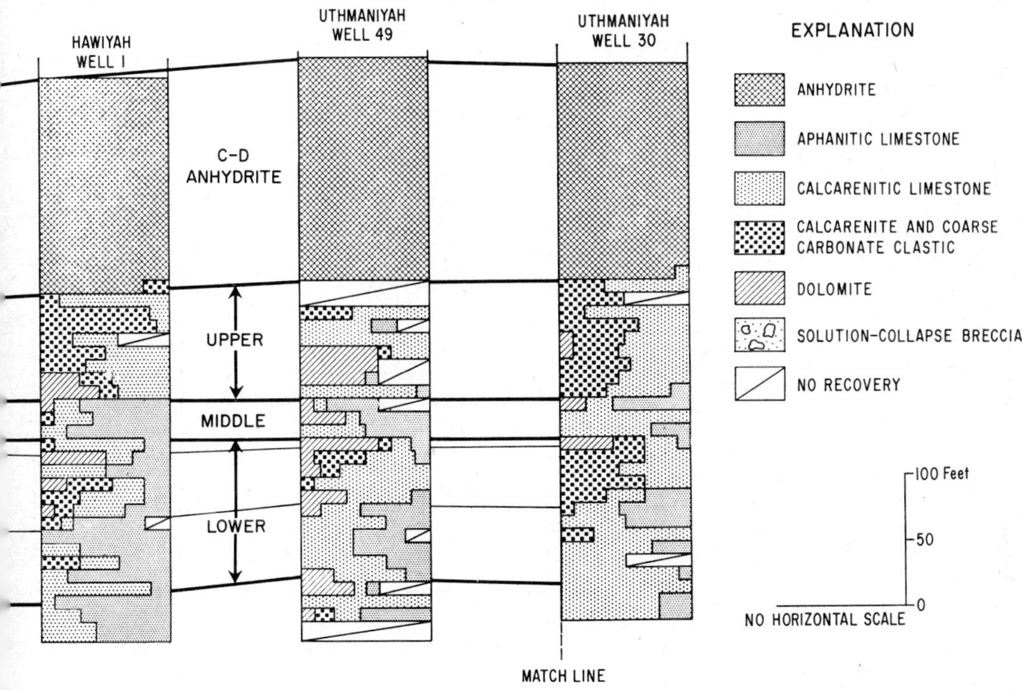

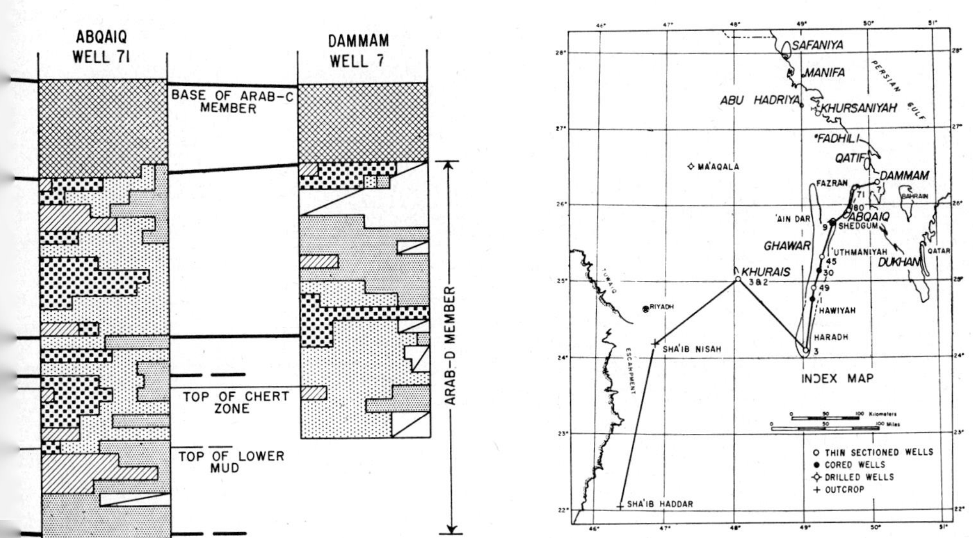

Arab-D member. Datum is top of middle Arab-D.

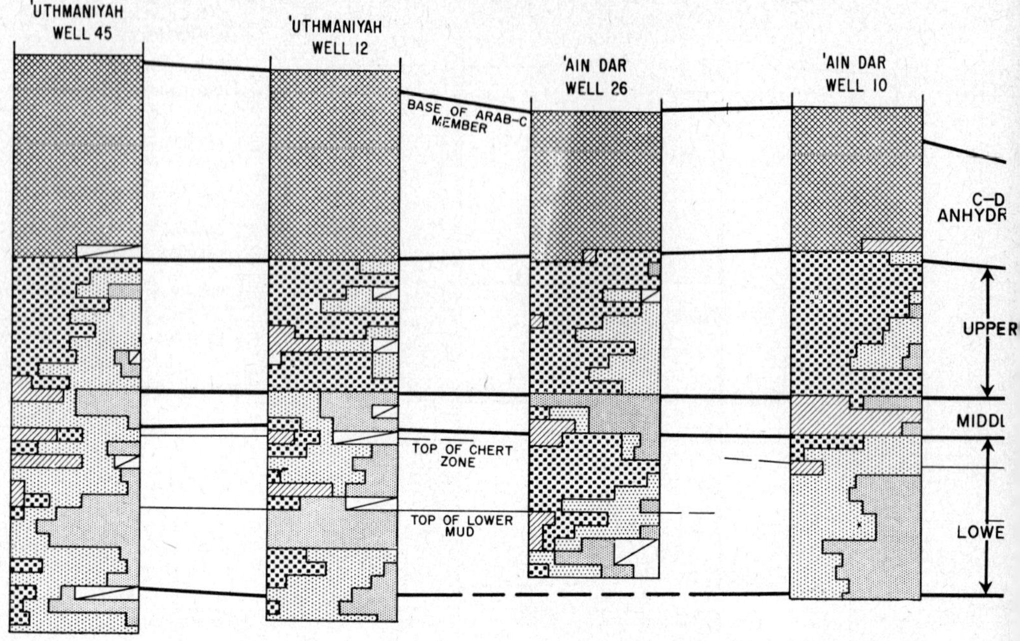

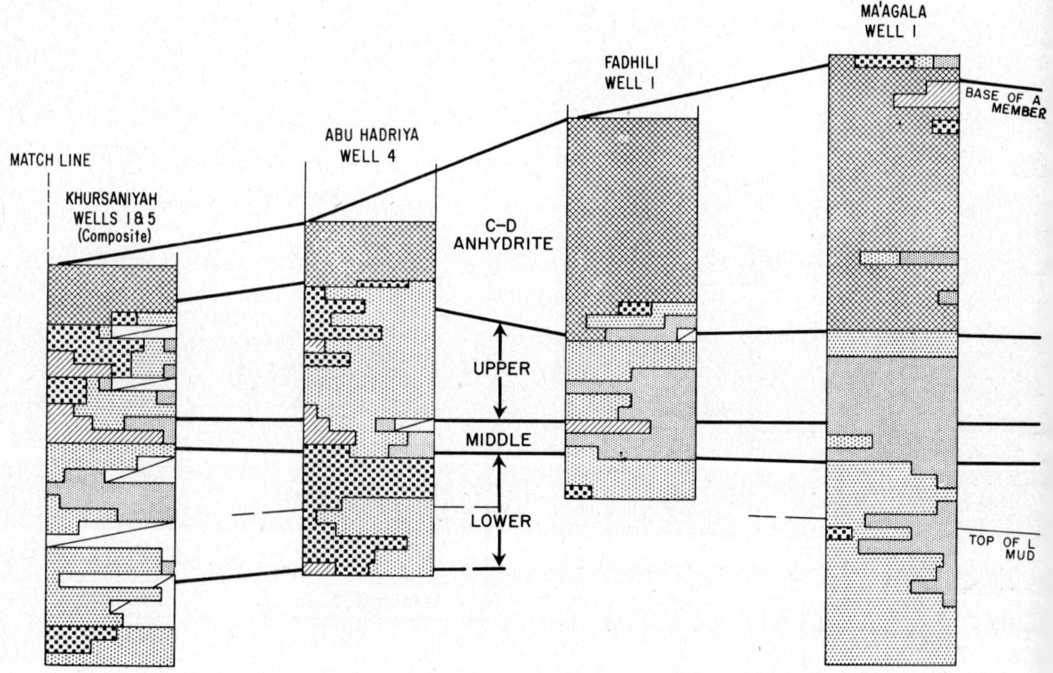

FIG. 16.—Regional correlation and stratigraphy of

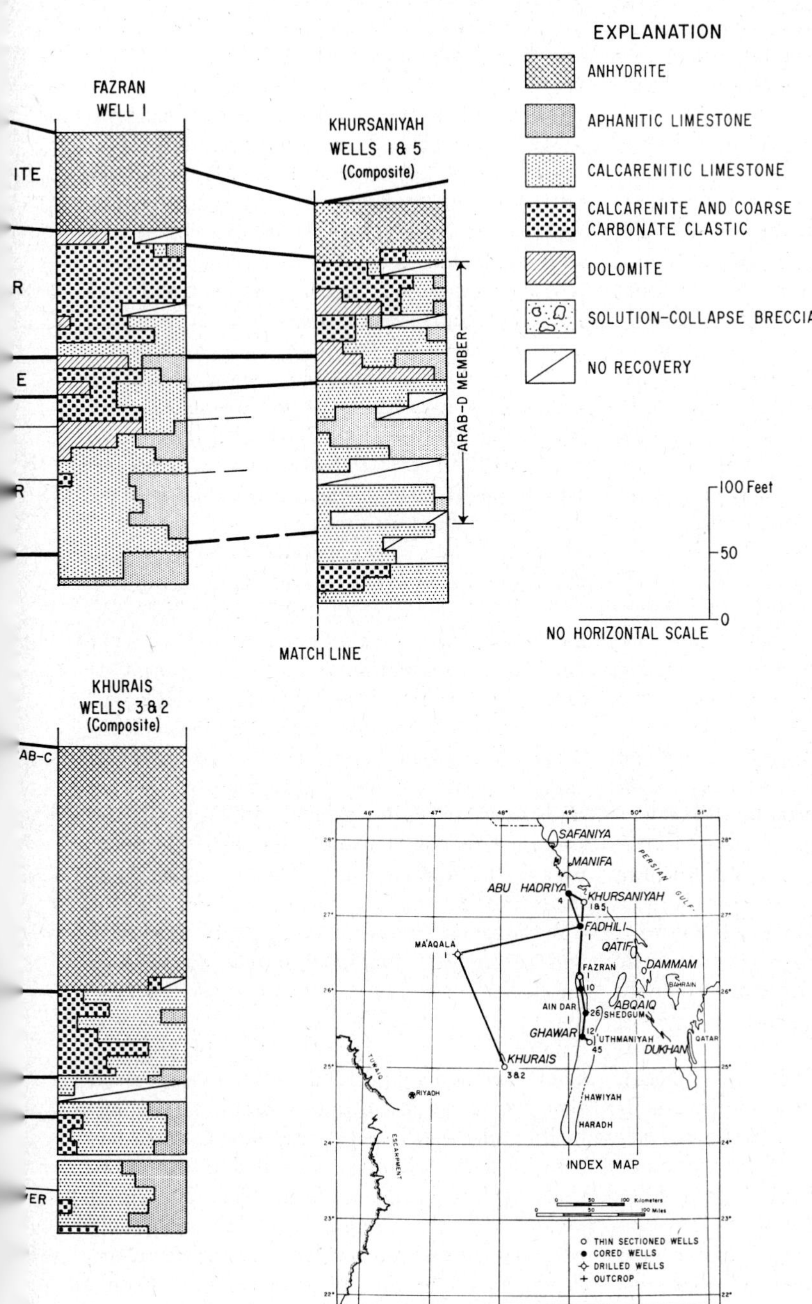

Arab-D member. Datum is top of middle Arab-D.

lets and "algal" nodules are in turn important contributors to the unit; Foraminifera rarely exceed 2 or 3 per cent and "fecal" pellets rarely occur. In all the wells examined, sand almost completely disappears in the upper 10 feet of the unit, where mud and dolomite reach a maximum.

The combined effect of mud and dolomite on the middle Arab-D has been to reduce permeability in many instances to negligible amounts.

Paleontology.—The most significant new element in the middle Arab-D is the appearance of the dasyclad alga *Clypeina jurassica* in the upper half of the unit. This distinctive form is generally rare in the middle Arab-D and increases in abundance immediately above the upper contact. Other calcareous algae identified from this unit include small *Clypeina* sp., *Polygonella incrustata*, and *Salpingoporella* sp. With the exception of *Cyclammina* sp., Foraminifera listed for the lower Arab-D are also common to the middle unit.

UPPER ARAB-D

Lithology.—Upper Arab-D rocks are characterized by a marked increase in sand, commonly skeletal and commonly in the form of massive clean-washed calcarenite beds. Regionally, the upper unit shows greater differentiation than any of the older beds. These changes, which from the data available seem to be gradual, transect and do not appear to have been controlled by the ancient counterparts of modern structure. Calcarenite development reaches a maximum in north Ain Dar and Fazran, where the upper Arab-D is almost exclusively mud-free sand. A series of belts with considerable original environmental and reservoir significance can be defined by a general estimate of the percentage of clean calcarenite as opposed to muddy, tighter rock. From northeast to southwest the belts thus defined include (1) Bahrain, Dammam, and Qatif, where most of the unit is represented by lithographic limestone or calcarenitic limestone; (2) a zone of transition, in which calcarenite makes up about 30 per cent of the unit, probably passing just east of Khursaniyah, and including the north half of north Abqaiq and possibly Dukhan oil field in Qatar; (3) a wide area of enhanced porosity and permeability in which calcarenite exceeds 50 and commonly exceeds 75 per cent, covering Ghawar north from 'Uthmaniyah No. 30 well, most of Abqaiq, Abu Hadriya, Khursaniyah, and apparently Manifa as well; and (4) a belt of generally finer grained sediment south and west of 'Uthmaniyah and probably including Fadhili. Some reversals in pattern occur in the southwest area—for example, around Hawiyah No. 1 well and at Khurais, where calcarenite makes up slightly less than half the unit. Presumably, the latter may result from an approach to a strand line. As drilled wells are now concentrated in areas of modern structural relief, it is impossible to determine whether these belts are indeed continuous or are more local than they now appear.

The upper Arab-D shows a general decrease in thickness from northeast to southwest. The unit is between 100–130 feet in north Ain Dar-Fazran and north Abqaiq, and decreases with few irregularities to about 70 feet in Haradh, Khurais, Ma'aqala, and on surface exposure (Figs. 15 and 16). Thinning is also apparent in the Khursaniyah-Fadhili-Abu Hadriya area. It is possible to arrive at an adequate explanation of Arab-D sedimentational history only by considering the upper Arab-D in conjunction with the overlying C-D anhydrite. The top of the anhydrite closely parallels the top of the middle Arab-D and lower horizons. Variations in thickness of the upper Arab-D carbonate are commonly compensated for by changes in anhydrite thickness. The conclusion seems inescapable that to the southwest the upper part of the Arab-D is progressively replaced, by facies change from the top down, by anhydrite. The transition from carbonate (mostly calcarenite and calcarenitic limestone, rarely dolomite or aphanitic limestone) to anhydrite is generally abrupt. In some instances, a thinly interbedded anhydrite-carbonate complex occurs immediately below the main anhydrite. It is interesting to note that clastic carbonate rather than dolomite normally underlies the anhydrite. This is in marked contrast to the middle Permian dolomite-gypsum-shale cycles of southwestern Oklahoma where, over a wide area, gypsum units are commonly preceded by thin beds of dolomite (Ham, 1960). Evidence, admittedly incomplete, from Fadhili and southern Ghawar, where anhydrite thickness is almost as great as in wells far to the west, suggests that maximum replacement of upper D-member carbonates takes place in these areas and persists from there to the outcrop.

Unfortunately, much of the upper Arab-D and C-D anhydrite complex is represented on outcrop for several hundred miles by a zone of hopelessly jumbled slump structures that presumably have resulted from the loss of interbedded anhydrite by solution. Outcrops of anhydrite are common only at the southern end of the solution-collapse belt near Sha'ib Haddar, where anhydrite caps a laterally persistent calcarenite bed considered to represent the top of the upper Arab-D (Fig. 15). A widespread zone of breccia, probably the result of solution of some admixed anhydrite, occurs below the calcarenite. Below this, rocks considered equivalent to the upper Arab-D are typical aphanitic and calcarenitic limestone with some calcarenite and dolomite.

As a unit, the upper Arab-D is nearly everywhere characterized by abundant carbonate sand, much of which is skeletal. Data from thin-sectioned wells indicate that the three main contributors of organic debris—calcareous algae, Foraminifera, and stromatoporoids—normally make up 25–50 per cent of each slide. Uniform change in quantity of skeletal debris, but not in types of organisms contributing, is apparent on a regional scale. The increase in sand content from southwest to northeast is accompanied by a corresponding increase in skeletal fragments; it reaches a maximum in north Ain Dar-Fazran and then decreases again somewhat in north Abqaiq and Khursaniyah wells. The fact that all the principal skeletal elements (calcareous algae, Foraminifera, and stromatoporoids) show systematic increase in abundance proportional to increase in sand, is considered presumptive evidence that these forms thrive best in areas of considerable current activity. The complementary change in amounts of mud from high in the southwest to negligible in Fazran, and occurring again in quantity in north Abqaiq, also bears this out. Nonskeletal particles are slmost exclusively aggregate pellets and "algal" nodules; "fecal" pellets were noted only rarely.

Paleontology.—The most significant and common forms recorded from the upper Arab-D are members of the dasyclad genus *Clypeina*. The most restricted species *C. jurassica* occurs only in the upper part of the middle Arab-D and through the upper Arab-D. *C.* cf. *hanabatensis* occurs through the same stratigraphic interval. As the characters which separate it from *C. jurassica* are difficult to distinguish in randomly oriented thin section and irregularly shaped fragments, the two were usually recorded simply as *C. jurassica.* Elliott (1955) points out that *C.* cf. *hanabatensis* is generally slightly larger and has 22–24 sporangial chambers as opposed to 11–20 in *C. jurassica.* Other important calcareous algae in the upper unit include small *Clypeina* sp., *Salpingoporella* sp., and *Polygonella incrustata;* sporadic occurrences of *Cylindroporella arabica* and *Solenopora?* were noted.

Foraminifera also show a marked increase in abundance in the upper Arab-D with a single form, *Pseudocyclammina* sp., confined to the unit. *Valvulinella jurassica* and *Nautiloculina oolithica* are rare to common; *Textularia* spp. and various Miliolidae are common to abundant.

AGE OF ARAB-D MEMBER

The Arab-D fauna and flora described above are of Upper Jurassic age. Ammonites collected on outcrop from the Jubaila formation which underlies the Arab formation have been dated with confidence as lower Kimeridgian by Arkell, Bramkamp, and Steineke (1952). Consequently, the age of the Arab-D can with assurance be considered at least Kimeridgian or younger. Comparison by Elliott (1955, 1957, 1959) of the same flora which occurs in beds equivalent to the Arab-D in Qatar with assemblages in Switzerland, southern France and elsewhere, suggests a Portlandian-Purbeckian age for the Arab-D.

RESERVOIR CHARACTERISTICS

The four carbonate-evaporite cycles of the Arab formation represent the transition from continuous, dominantly muddy carbonate deposition in the Jubaila formation to the precipitation of nearly pure anhydrite in the Hith formation. The Hith, which may actually be broken up by additional cycles in more basinal areas east of the presently drilled fields, is the last anhydrite phase. Information on the three upper Arab formation carbonate units—the Arab-A, Arab-B, and Arab-C members—is limited mostly to drilled samples and electric-radiation logs. Considerable data including numerous continuous cores are available from the lower member—the Arab-D.

The distribution of maximum effective reservoir porosity and oil in each of the Arab members roughly parallels increased sand, particularly calcarenite, development.

ARAB-A, ARAB-B, AND ARAB-C MEMBERS

Sparse information on these members, which are separated from each other by anhydrite, indicates that the dominant lithology in each is admixed calcarenite and aphanitic limestone. All show progressive increase in anhydrite from northeast to southwest at the expense of carbonate.

The Arab-A and -B members contain productive oil in Dammam, Khursaniyah, Abu Hadriya, and Manifa. The Arab-C member contains significant amounts of oil in Dammam, Qatif, Khursaniyah, Abu Hadriya, and Manifa, and minor accumulations in northern Ghawar and Abqaiq. Oil is absent from the C member in southern Ghawar, presumably as a result of decrease in calcarenite compensated for by an increase in anhydrite and mud in that direction.

ARAB-D MEMBER

A general summary of Arab-D member rock variations which directly affect reservoir behavior includes (1) vertical gradation from mud in the lower part of the reservoir through admixed mud and sand to dominantly sandy rocks in the upper part prior to anhydrite deposition; (2) progressive replacement of upper D-member carbonates by anhydrite from northeast to southwest; and (3) belts of finer sediment (dominantly lime mud) flanking a north-south calcarenite trend of increased porosity and permeability which covers northern Ghawar, most of Abqaiq, Abu Hadriya, Manifa, and possibly Khursaniyah.

The relation of present structure to this belt of enhanced productivity may well be fortuitous rather than causal. The largest oil accumulations in the Arab-D accompany maximum development of sand, particularly calcarenite. Consequently, it appears certain that intergranular pore space associated with the rocks at the time of deposition (original porosity) exerts a major control on the present distribution of oil. Diagenetic changes including recrystallization and cementation have all modified the original voids to some extent; however, the dominant control on reservoir rock behavior can be shown to be directly related to (1) degree of original sorting—that is, the proportion of mud to sand, and (2) the extent to which dolomite replaces original rock elements.

Effect of sorting on reservoir behavior.—Arab-D carbonate rocks, when considered in terms of the Arabian classification, can readily be used to demonstrate the effect of any particular component or group of components on reservoir behavior. All rocks with the exception of crystalline dolomite can be plotted at some point along a continuous sequence from 0 to 100 per cent mud, which translated into terms of sand, is exactly reversed, being respectively 100 and 0 per cent sand (Fig. 17). Data from more than 1,000 point-counted slides were used to compile Figures 17–23. The permeability curves, in these figures, have been dashed in the area of increased mud content where a significant number of 1 md measurements occur. These readings, instead of falling along the 1 md line, as shown, almost certainly vary between an upper limit of 1 md and the lowest values determined for limestones—that is, less than 0.001 md (Gibson, 1948; Ohle, 1951). Consequently, refined measurements would presumbly shift the permeability curve downward in these areas. In most cases, however, the rocks concerned are essentially impermeable and their reservoir characteristics are probably adequately reflected by the curves shown. In plotting Figure 17, which shows the effect of mud (or sand) on porosity and permeability, only data from rocks containing less then 5 per cent dolomite were used. This was done to eliminate the marked effect which dolomite, as will be later demonstrated, exerts on reservoir properties.

Figure 17 shows clearly that clean calcarenites (rocks with less than 10 per cent mud matrix) have both high porosity and high permeability (normally ranging between 15 and 30 per cent and 100 to 6,000 md). Equally clear is the fact that as mud content increases (and sand decreases), porosity decreases uniformly. This reduction in pore space appears to be a straight-line relation; it drops from an average of about 25 per cent in

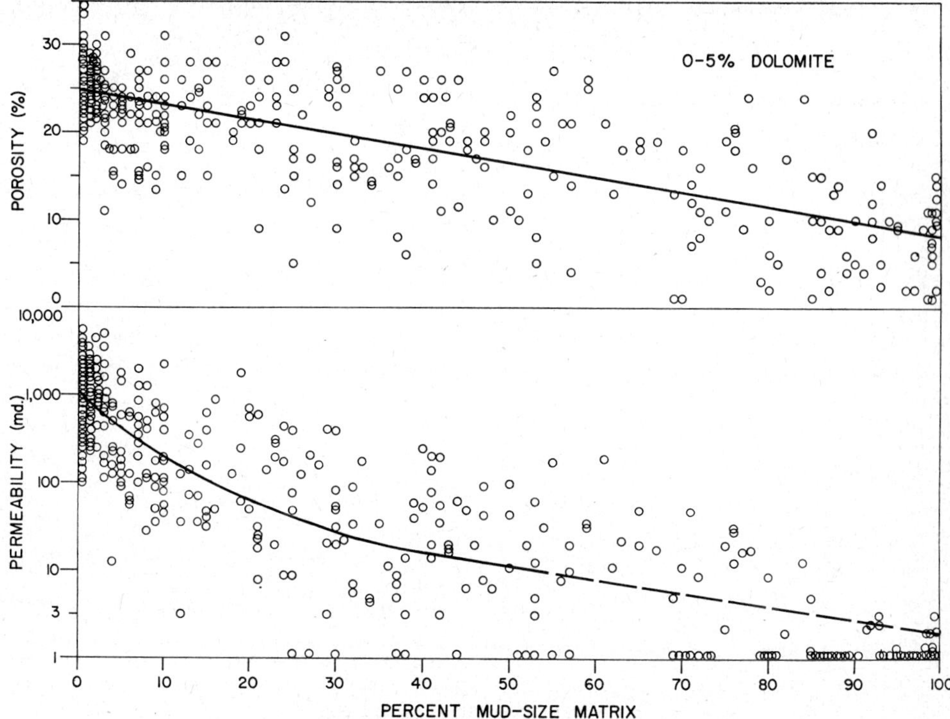

FIG. 17.—Effect of sorting on porosity and permeability.

clean calcarenite to less than 10 per cent in pure mud. The control on permeability is even more marked. Where only 10 per cent mud matrix is admixed, permeability is drastically reduced (from an average of 1,000 to about 100 md) but it remains more than sufficient for high productivity. The decrease in permeability continues as progressively more matrix is added and reaches 10 md where the rock is half mud-half sand. Rocks with more than 90 per cent mud are essentially impermeable (3 md or less).

Comparison of individual curves on Figures 8, 10, 12, and 14, shows some interesting relationships in regard to the control sorting exerts on reservoir behavior. As expected, the columns showing percentage of mud and sand-gravel are essentially mirror images of one another except where dolomite has completely replaced original elements, thus reducing both curves to zero. On the other hand, the curve showing porosity almost exactly duplicates the sand-gravel curve. The parallelism between these two curves is all the more striking when it is considered that all original rock textures and degrees of secondary alteration are represented in the slides from which these curves were constructed. The permeability curve, apparently more sensitive than porosity to changes in texture and diagenetic alteration, is a somewhat amplified but still approximate signature of the sand-gravel and porosity curves. In light of these data, the conclusion seems inescapable that much if not most of the effective porosity associated with the Arab-D reservoir results directly from original character imparted to the rock at time of deposition. Degree of sorting, which can be translated into percentage mud or sand in most carbonates, appears directly applicable to the understanding of many reservoir problems including—distribution of effective porosity, prediction of reservoir behavior during production, and delineation of belts of high porosity favorable for oil accumulation.

The implications of this relation between original sediment and reservoir behavior are ob

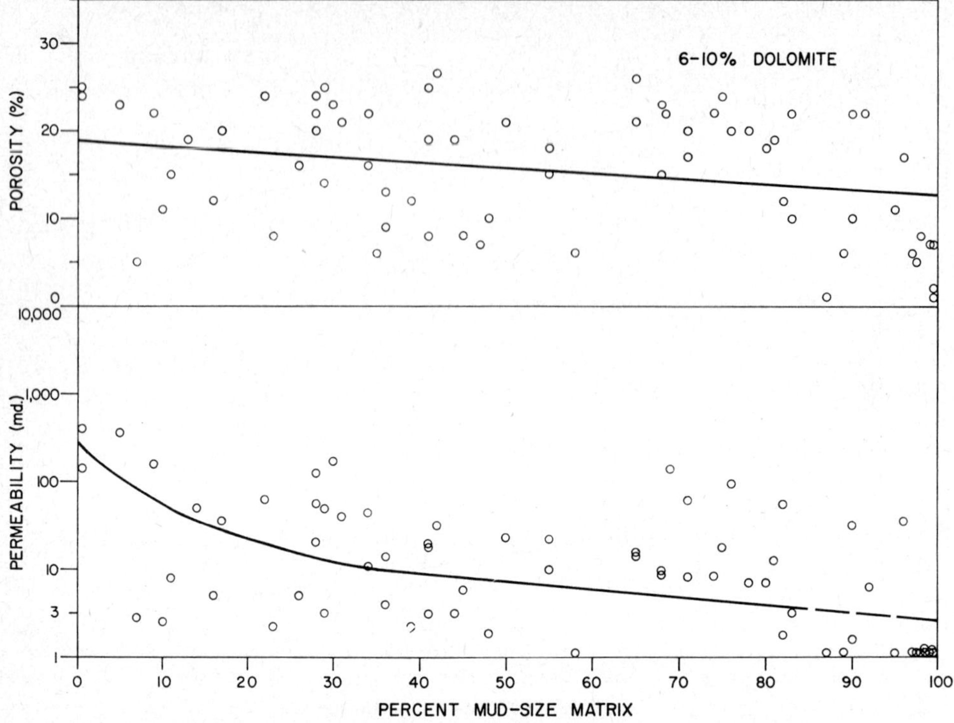

Fig. 18.—Effect of 6–10 per cent dolomite on porosity and permeability.

viously important. The thin, persistent mud unit designated in this report as the middle Arab-D almost certainly divides the reservoir, at least locally and probably regionally, into two parts with decidedly different reservoir characteristics and behavior. The vertical continuity of permeable beds in the upper Arab-D stands in sharp contrast to the irregular spacing and separation of zones of high permeability in the more muddy lower Arab-D. In addition, the middle Arab-D commonly contains zones of zero permeability which seem likely to form extensive barriers to vertical fluid migration.

Effect of dolomite on reservoir behavior.—Although original rock textures have been altered in at least 6 ways, the addition of dolomite exerts the most pronounced effect on reservoir properties. The occurrence of dolomite as well as its control on Arab-D porosity and permeability are almost completely at variance with what might be expected from a study of the literature on these subjects (Levorsen, 1954; Illing, 1959). Comparison of the curves on Figures 8, 10, 12, and 14, shows an almost perfect inverse or mirror-image relation between dolomite and sand-gravel. As the percentage of sand and coarser-than-sand grains increases, dolomite percentage invariably decreases. Where sand concentration is increased to calcarenite proportions, little or no dolomite occurs. The reason for this relationship is the apparently strong affinity between dolomite and mud-size particles for, in Arab-D rocks, dolomite is associated almost exclusively with aphanitic and calcarenitic limestone. A rough parallelism exists between the mud and dolomite curves except in intervals where dolomite replaces progressively more than 50 per cent of the original rock—thus forcing the lime mud curve to reverse itself and decrease, eventually to reach zero as dolomitization becomes complete. Evidence of dolomite preference for mud is afforded by calcarenitic limestone in which sand and mud are mixed. In rocks of this type, dolomite is generally restricted to the mud portion and leaves the sand

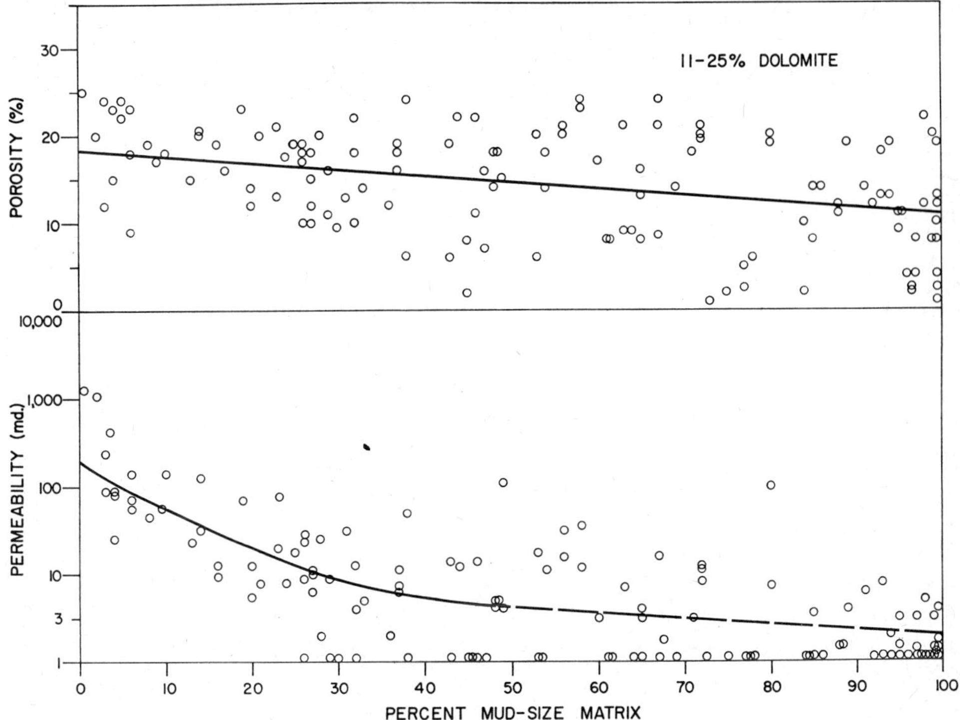

Fig. 19.—Effect of 11–25 per cent dolomite on porosity and permeability.

unaltered (Pl. 3, Fig. 5). Dolomite replacement of sand is undoubted (Pl. 7, Fig. 5); the occurrence of sand-gravel replacement in the Arab-D, however, is far less common than previously believed.

The effect of various increments of dolomite, ranging from 5 to 75 per cent, on the porosity and permeability of the main rock groups, is shown in Figures 18–21. When compared with similar, relatively unaltered rocks with less than 5 per cent dolomite (Fig. 17), the addition of 6–10 per cent dolomite decreases calcarenite porosity from about 25 to less than 20 per cent and raises aphanitic limestone porosity about 5 per cent (Fig. 18). Presence of 11–25 per cent dolomite lowers porosity values 1–2 per cent below those exhibited by rocks with 6–10 per cent dolomite (Fig. 19). Where dolomite exceeds 25 per cent (Fig. 20) it apparently becomes the dominant porosity-control factor for, regardless of original rock type, porosity averages about 11 per cent. As far as reservoir properties are concerned, it seems to make little difference whether the rocks have been partially (discrete rhombs) or strongly (interlocking crystals) dolomitized. As still more dolomite is added, porosity drops uniformly until it reaches an average of about 9 per cent for all rocks which have been replaced by 50–75 per cent dolomite (Fig. 21). Where dolomite exceeds 75 per cent, the relative percentage of mud and sand cannot generally be determined with any degree of certainty.

The influence of dolomite on permeability—the most important reservoir factor—is relatively straightforward in the range 5–75 per cent. As dolomite increases, permeability in comparative rock types decreases. With as little as 25 per cent dolomite replacement (Fig. 20) the average permeability of all but the very sandy rocks—for example, those with more than 80 per cent sand—is decreased to 3 md, an amount considered negligible. A further decrease is shown in rocks containing from 51–75 per cent dolomite (Fig. 21).

These data concerning the increment effect of

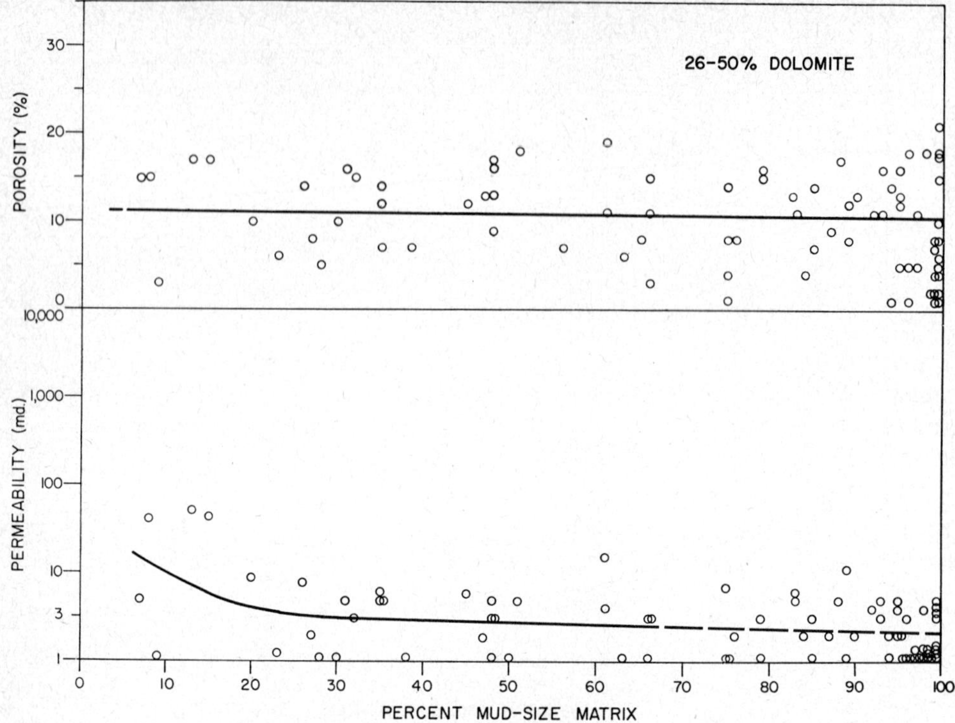

FIG. 20.—Effect of 26–50 per cent dolomite on porosity and permeability.

dolomite on porosity and permeability are summarized on Figure 22. The nearly uniform porosity achieved in all rock groups at an early stage of dolomitization (10–25 per cent) indicates that little dolomite, indeed, need be added before it becomes the dominant control on carbonate porosity. The reason for the lowered porosity in sandy rocks and the increased porosity in muds during the early stages of replacement is not understood. More significant, however, is the steady drop in permeability with progressive dolomitization.

The effect of dolomite in amounts greater than 75 per cent is shown on Figure 23. In this range, original textures are not generally decipherable, and bulk dolomite alone affords the only means of relating rock character to porosity and permeability. The low level of porosity and permeability established in rocks with 51–75 per cent dolomite (Fig. 21) continues to about 77 per cent. Near this point the dolomite network begins to open up, and effective intercrystalline porosity develops and reaches a maximum where the rock is 80 per cent dolomite. Average porosity and permeability at this level of dolomite replacement are respectively 19 per cent and 300 md. Progressive increase in dolomite above 80 per cent is accompanied by a relatively uniform decline in both porosity and permeability, although significant amounts of both are retained until dolomite reaches 90 to 95 per cent, at which point the rock becomes essentially impermeable.

The variable effects of dolomite on Arab-D reservoir rock behavior now seem adequately demonstrated; the reasons, as is so commonly the case, are not. A tentative and admittedly incomplete explanation for the relationships between observed dolomite characteristics and measured reservoir parameters appears to be—

1. During the early stages of dolomitization, discrete crystals originate at centers scattered nearly uniformly through the aphanitic part of the host rock. Enlargement of individual rhombs continues and an optimum size is reached before

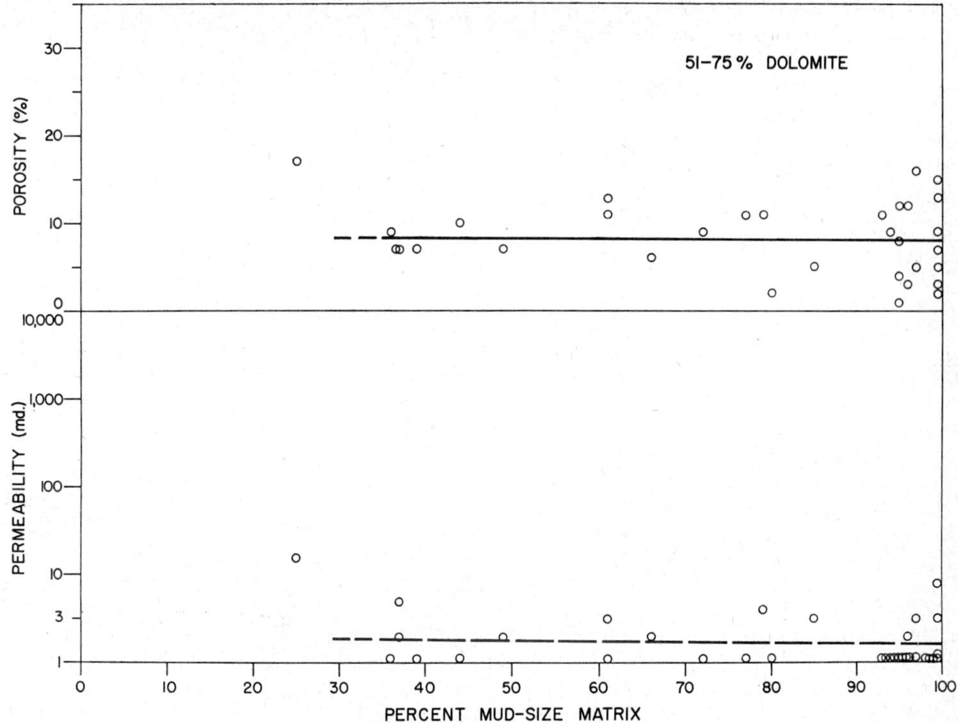

FIG. 21.—Effect of 51–75 per cent dolomite on porosity and permeability.

(or possibly while) new centers of growth are established. This is apparently true because dolomite crystals, regardless of concentration, show little size variation, generally averaging 0.1–0.2 mm (Pls. 5 and 7). As dolomitization progresses, all lime mud is replaced before sand-size particles are attacked (Pl. 7, Fig. 3). This replacement of finer particles with some intergranular openings by larger impermeable dolomite rhombs accounts for the early decrease in porosity and permeability.

2. Total replacement of original carbonate elements—most commonly lime mud—remains incomplete until somewhat more than 75 per cent dolomite is present. Up to this level of dolomitization, residual original particles fill and effectively seal all space not yet occupied by dolomite; the result is low porosity and permeability.

3. When dolomite reaches nearly 80 per cent and forms a self-supporting framework, the last traces of original sediment are commonly removed, leaving an open network of dolomite crystals joined mostly at the apices (Pl. 5, Fig. 5).

4. Following this stage, the dolomite rock may remain essentially unaltered or be changed in at least two ways. First, dissolution may continue to the point where vugs are formed and porosity is significantly increased. On the other hand, more dolomite may be added, in which case the progressive decline in porosity and permeability in rocks with more than 80 per cent dolomite is readily explained. That is, as dolomite is added, crystals progressively increase in size, impinge on one another, and ultimately give rise to a tight anhedral mosaic with little or no porosity (Pl. 5, Fig. 6).

For convenience, the sequence outlined above might be considered in terms of "early" and "late" diagenesis. Early diagenesis is in effect as long as replacement of original rock constituents continues. Late diagenesis, however, is characterized by dissolution of older elements to form intercrystalline or vuggy porosity. The still later filling of all or part of these pores by dolomite,

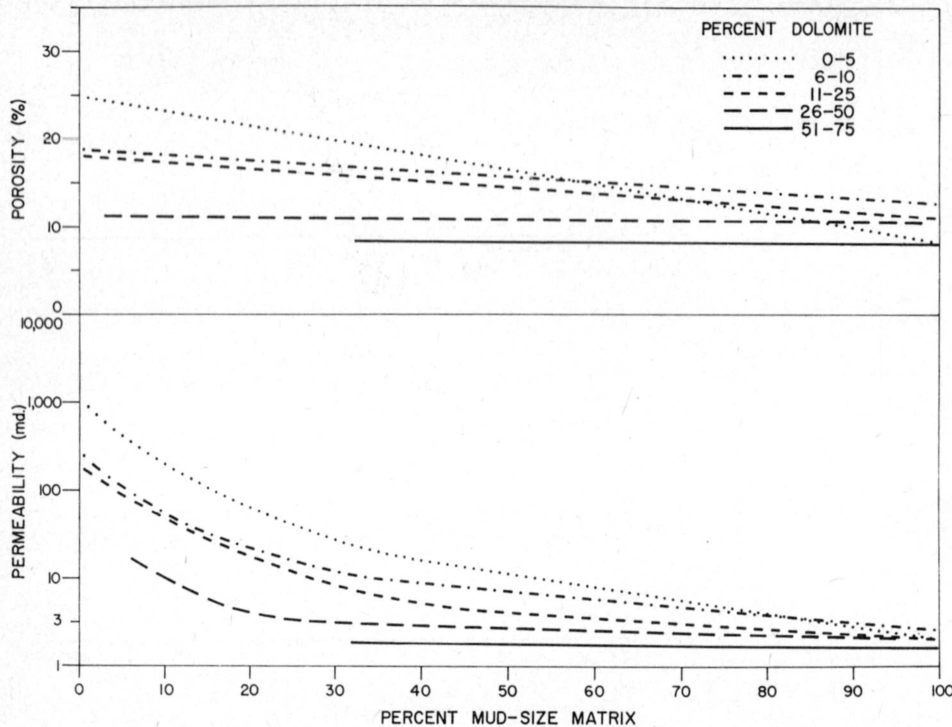

FIG. 22.—Composite effect of 0–75 per cent dolomite on porosity and permeability.

chert, or other minerals is also considered to be a phase of late diagenesis.

The origin of three types of secondary porosity discussed in this paper—that is, channel (Pl. 4, Fig. 4), secondary void (Pl. 4, Fig. 3), and late diagenetic dissolution—appears to be rather closely allied. Presumably, each involves dissolution; the principal difference is that aphanitic limestone, calcarenite, and dolomite, respectively, are affected.

A generalized summary shows that in any given textural group, porosity and permeability—(a) progressively decrease as dolomite increases from 10 to 80 per cent, (b) increase where dolomite forms 80–90 per cent of the rock, and (c) again decrease as dolomite exceeds 90 per cent.

CHERT ZONE

A thin, laterally persistent zone of cherty dolomite extends over much of Ghawar and Abqaiq fields. Stratigraphically, the zone falls just below the base of the middle Arab-D; lithologically, the chert is microcrystalline quartz, which generally fills intercrystalline dolomite pores and, in some instances, partially replaces the dolomite, or less commonly, aphanitic limestone. The thickness of the zone is rarely more than 2–3 feet, but in each case permeability has been reduced to zero. The influence which this zone exerts on the vertical migration of fluids is uncertain; it may, however, form a thin but effective barrier. Examination of cores and thin sections from this interval indicates that the silica is uniformly dispersed through the dolomite. Generally, the chert appears to have merely filled in the void space between incompletely interlocked dolomite crystals. Only rarely can actual replacement be inferred. The wide lateral continuity of the zone, its occurrence at approximately the same stratigraphic level, and the cement-like relation to dolomite suggest that the silica may form a rather extensive impermeable sheet rather than an open nodular framework as is so common in many carbonate strata. Whether the silica is in fact continuous over most of Ghawar and Abqaiq or is restricted to dolomite lenses appears to be relatively unimportant, for in either case extensive barriers to fluid migration seem likely. The possible fracturing effect of structural growth on such a zone cannot yet be evaluated.

Chert-filled dolomite occurs at several other levels, but appears in these instances to be limited in areal extent.

ORIGINAL PARTICLE SHAPE

Only in the upper part of the Arab-D has it been possible to demonstrate the effect of original particle shape on reservoir rock behavior. Some intervals in northern Ghawar wells show a decided difference in vertical and horizontal permeability which can be directly ascribed to rock fabric. In this area, where calcareous algae and, locally, brachiopods contribute great quantities of tabular fragments, well-developed particle lineation parallel to the bedding is common (Pl. 1, Fig. 1). In these rocks vertical permeability is commonly as much as 50 per cent less than horizontal permeability; in no instance, however, was it reduced sufficiently to hamper seriously rock productivity.

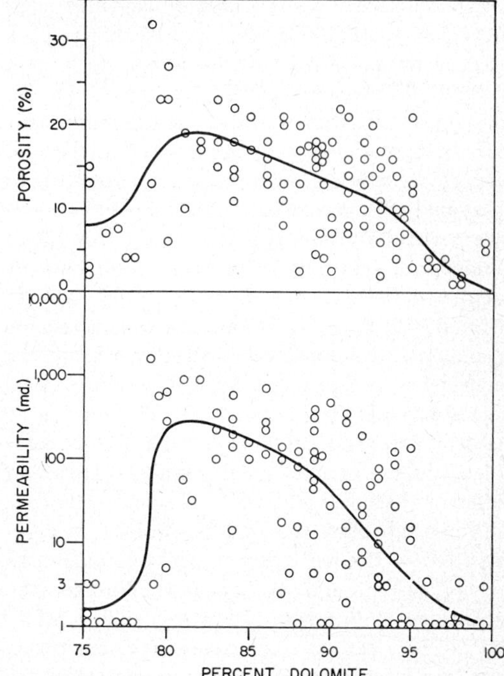

FIG. 23.—Effect of 75–100 per cent dolomite on porosity and permeability.

PALEOGEOGRAPHY AND PALEOECOLOGY

Considerable evidence is now available from which to reconstruct on a regional scale general conditions associated with Arab-D deposition. Little doubt exists that sediments of this member were deposited in a neritic environment—that is, at depths less than 600 feet, and probably for the most part, in water of considerably less depth.

LOWER ARAB-D

The high concentration of calcareous mud in the lower Arab-D, particularly in the lower half, would suggest that the particles accumulated generally below the effective wave base of the time. The paucity of skeletal grains tends to bear this out. In the upper part of the unit, sporadic occurrences of clean-washed calcarenite interbedded with aphanitic and calcarenitic limestone indicate that locally less sheltered, presumably bottom-high conditions obtained. The occurrence of considerable amounts of skeletal debris in the extreme upper part of the lower Arab-D, particularly calcareous algae and stromatoporoids, is of special significance. Algae at this level are dominantly members of the apparently mud-tolerant family Corallinaceae. "Fecal" pellets, rare in other Arab-D strata, are important contributors to the lower unit, and the presence of numerous bottom-dwelling, mud-eating organisms can be inferred.

Collectively, these data would seem to indicate that the dominantly mud-size lower Arab-D sediments accumulated on a broad, slightly irregular bottom surface generally below effective wave base. Under these conditions little vertical or horizontal differentiation took place. The increase in sand, particularly skeletal sand, toward the close of lower Arab-D time is considered to mark the beginning of less stable and more shallow-water conditions which culminated in the sedimentation of massive calcarenite and eventually anhydrite.

MIDDLE ARAB-D

The middle Arab-D records a widespread episode of muddy deposition. The thin, remarkably persistent middle unit shows little differentiation; it is dominantly mud or dolomite (which probably replaced original mud). The lowest occurrence of the environmentally significant dasyclad alga *Clypeina* was noted in the few calcarenite beds that occur in or just below the base of the middle Arab-D. The paleoecologic significance of calcareous algae stems from the fact that all require light for survival and certain groups are further restricted by temperature and latitude. Members of the family Dasycladaceae (for example *Clypeina*) are particularly limited, occurring in tropical to subtropical seas and living most commonly at depths of 9–15 feet and rarely below 90 feet (Cloud, 1952). Stromatoporoids which become common at the same level as calcareous algae, are considered by Lecompte (1956) to occupy about the same ecologic niche as corals. This may be at least a partial explanation for the almost complete absence of corals in the Arab-D. It can be inferred then, that whereas local shoal-water conditions did exist, the middle Arab-D was deposited for the most part in areas or at depths where current activity was low. Whether the spreading of this mud sheet over such a widespread area can be attributed to regional tilting and rise in effective wave base is uncertain; the widespread nature of these and other Arab-D events, however, seems to favor changes on a regional scale.

UPPER ARAB-D

The first relatively clear picture of environmental patterns during Arab-D time comes from a study of the upper Arab-D and the overlying anhydrite. The beginning of the upper Arab-D is marked over a wide area by a sharp change in particle size and type—namely, a flood of carbonate sand and gravel, much of it clean-washed, and a considerable increase in skeletal components, particularly dasyclad algae, stromatoporoids, and Foraminifera. Increased sand and skeletal content persisted until precipitation of anhydrite commenced. This change from dominantly mud sedimentation in the middle Arab-D to accumulation of muddy sand and massive calcarenite with quantities of dasyclad algae, almost certainly marks the start of widespread and persistent shoaling of the sea floor into the zone of vigorous photosynthetic activity.

Regional changes in sand to mud ratio paralleled by corresponding change in amount of shallow-water skeletal debris suggest that sedimentation took place on a broad shelf. Northeast of the shelf edge in the Dammam-Qatif-Bahrain area, the tight lithographic limestone is presumed to have been deposited as nearly pure lime mud in water of deeper but still unknown depth. It is tempting to think that this area lay slightly northeast of the mud line of the time; however, modern studies indicate that such assumptions are dangerous, as similar sediments would collect in local depressions.

Gradation through mixed mud and sand in the extreme north end of Abqaiq, and possibly Khursaniyah, to a maximum development of calcarenite and shallow-water organisms in central and southern Abqaiq, Ain Dar-Fazran, and Abu-Hadriya, indicates that the seaward edge of the shelf has been reached or lies between the two areas. A relatively unbroken sheet of calcarenite blankets the south Ain Dar-Shedgum-'Uthmaniyah area and is interpreted here as representing an offshore bar, or, more likely, a group of offshore bars. The generally finer sediment covering south 'Uthmaniyah, Haradh, Khurais, and exposed on outcrop, plus the replacement of calcarenite by anhydrite, suggests lagoonal conditions. The concentration of calcarenite in Hawiyah No. 1 well, isolated by lagoonal sediments, may result from persistent local bottom-high conditions in this area. It seems safe to assume that conditions essential to the precipitation of calcium sulphate—restricted basin where evaporation exceeds precipitation and runoff (Scruton, 1953)—obtained first over an area including the outcrop, Khurais, Ma'aqala, Fadhili, and southern Ghawar, and spread progressively north and east, eventually blanketing what is now Bahrain Island, Dammam, and Qatar.

Summary.—In summary, the most likely explanation for upper Arab-D rock and particle type distribution is considered to be a broad shelf with finer lagoonal sediments being deposited in the west, dominantly calcareous sand in the form of offshore bars accumulating just inland from the present Persian Gulf coast, and presumably deeper water mud with sparse sand being laid down in the east. The absence of reef structures cannot be assumed from the present widely scattered data; however, the wide continuity and uniform thickness of Arab-D units suggest that large structures of this type are not likely to be found.

Comparison with the modern Persian Gulf may be appropriate, for the general environment must have included muddy- and sandy-bottom areas on which isolated colonies of various types of reef builders grew. Upper Arab-D member deposition closed earlier in the west when hypersaline conditions began here. These moved progressively east and eventually terminated Arab-D sedimentation in the area studied. The distribution of sand and mud without apparent regard for modern structures suggests that structural growth along these lines of folding had not yet taken place or that their relief during this time was subdued.

CONCLUSIONS

The most significant findings from the thin-section study of Arabian Upper Jurassic carbonate reservoir rocks include—

1. The carbonate rocks and modern calcareous sediments examined can best be understood by considering them to be products of mechanical deposition subject to the same processes of sedimentation as their siliceous counterparts.

2. The carbonates can be divided according to original particle size and sorting and obliteration of original texture into five main groups—(1) aphanitic limestone, (2) calcarenitic limestone, (3) calcarenite, (4) coarse carbonate clastic, and (5) crystalline dolomite.

3. Specific particle types which contributed to the Arab-D reservoir include calcareous algae, stromatoporoids, and Foraminifera as the main skeletal elements, and aggregate pellets, "algal" nodules, and "fecal" pellets as the most important nonskeletal particles.

4. Consideration of both rock classes and specific particle types associated with the Arab-D has permitted—(a) recognition of distinctive stratigraphic units for correlation and reservoir zonation, (b) general delineation of original depositional patterns and environmental conditions associated with the Arab-D, and (c) relation of reservoir properties to these original depositional-environmental patterns and diagenetic changes.

5. Vertically, the Arab-D reservoir falls naturally into three units—a lower dominantly muddy interval, a persistent intermediate unit of aphanitic limestone, and an upper sandy sequence. Shallow-water skeletal debris, virtually absent from the lower, more muddy, unit are major contributors to the upper sands.

6. Laterally, the Arab-D reservoir (particularly the upper part) shows gradual change from mud on the northeast, through a north-south belt of muddy sand and calcarenite, to mud and sandy mud in the southwest. Increase in sand is accompanied by an increase in shallow-water skeletal debris. The most likely explanation for these sediment patterns appears to be a broad shelf with offshore bars of calcarenite flanked on the northeast by deeper water (possibly more basinal) mud and on the southwest by finer grained presumably lagoonal sediments, including saline deposits.

7. Areas of maximum oil accumulation correspond rather closely to trends of major alcarenite development which transect modern structures. Voids, now oil filled, are essentially those formed between sand grains at the time of deposition, and have since undergone little significant modification. In connection with this, degree of sorting is the most important original textural characteristic controlling reservoir rock behavior. As mud content increases relative to sand content, porosity and permeability decrease.

8. The presence of a widespread mud unit—the middle Arab-D—separating muddy rocks below from sandy carbonates above, presents the problem of two units in which reservoir behavior may be decidedly different.

9. Considerable proof exists to show that in Arab-D carbonates, dolomite has strong preference for mud-size grains; sand-size grains have been left essentially unaltered.

Replacement by dolomite strongly affects the reservoir behavior of Arab-D rocks. As dolomite increases from 10 to 80 per cent, regardless of original rock type, permeability decreases. Where the rock is 80–90 per cent dolomite, significant amounts of intercrystalline porosity and permeability occur. Where dolomite exceeds 90 per cent, porosity and permeability again decrease. Thus, only in the more intensely altered rocks does dolomite replacement contribute to the fluid conductivity of the reservoir. This secondary contribution, mostly at the expense of originally tighter aphanitic limestone, is small when compared with primary (particularly intergranular) porosity and permeability.

REFERENCES

Alderman, A. R., and Skinner, H. C. W., 1957, Dolomite sedimentation in the southeast of South Australia: Am. Jour. Sci., v. 255, no. 8, p. 561–567.

Andrieux, C., 1960, Sur l'origine du strontium dans des formations récifales du Senonien Toulonnais: Soc. Mineral. Crist. France Bull., v. 83, p. 216–220.

Arabian American Oil Company Staff, 1959, Ghawar oil field, Saudi Arabia: Am. Assoc. Petroleum Geologists Bull., v. 43, no. 2, p. 434–454.

Archie, G. E., 1952, Classification of carbonate reservoir rocks and petrophysical considerations: Am. Assoc. Petroleum Geologists Bull., v. 36, no. 2, p. 278–297.

Arkell, W. J., 1952, Jurassic ammonites from Jebel Tuwaiq, central Arabia, with stratigraphical introduction by R. A. Bramkamp and Max Steineke: Roy. Soc. London Philos. Trans., Ser. B, v. 236, p. 241–313.

——— 1956, Jurassic geology of the world: London, Oliver and Boyd, Ltd.

Baker, N. E., and Henson, F. R. S., 1952, Geological conditions of oil occurrence in Middle East fields: Am. Assoc. Petroleum Geologists Bull., v. 36, no. 10, p. 1885–1901.

Banerjee, A., 1959, Petrography and facies of some upper Viséan (Mississippian) limestones in north Wales: Jour. Sed. Petrology, v. 29, no. 3, p. 377–390.

Bathurst, R. G. C., 1958, Diagenetic fabrics in some British Dinantian limestones: Liverpool and Manchester Geol. Jour., v. 2, pt. 1, pp. 11–36.

Beales, F. W., 1956, Conditions of deposition of Palliser (Devonian) limestone of southwestern Alberta: Am. Assoc. Petroleum Geologists Bull., v. 40, no. 5, p. 848–870.

——— 1957, Bahamites and their significance in oil exploration: Alberta Soc. Petroleum Geologists Jour., v. 5, no. 10, p. 227–231.

——— 1958, Ancient sediments of Bahaman type: Am. Assoc. Petroleum Geologists Bull., v. 42, no. 8, p. 1845–1880.

Bergenback, R. E., and Terriere, R. T., 1953, Petrography of Scurry Reef, Scurry County, Texas: Am. Assoc. Petroleum Geologists Bull., v. 37, no. 5, p. 1014–1029.

Biggs, D. L., 1957, Petrography and origin of Illinois nodular cherts: Illinois Geol. Survey Circ. 245.

Bramkamp, R. A., and Powers, R. W., 1955, Two Persian Gulf lagoons (abst.): Jour. Sed. Petrology, v. 25, no. 2, p. 139–140.

——— 1958, Classification of Arabian carbonate rocks: Geol. Soc. America Bull., v. 69, no. 10, p. 1305–1318.

British Petroleum Company Geological Staff, 1956a, Geological maps and sections of southwest Persia: Internat. Geol. Cong., 20th, Mexico; London, Edward Stanford.

——— 1956b, Oil and gas in southwest Iran, *in* Symposium on the geological occurrence of oil and gas: Internat. Geol. Cong., 20th, Mexico, v. 2, p. 37–72.

Caldwell, L. T., 1940, Areal variations of calcium carbonate and heavy minerals in Barataria Bay sediments, Louisiana: Jour. Sed. Petrology, v. 10, no. 2, p. 58–64.

Carozzi, A. V., 1955, Dasycladaces du Jurassique superieur du bassin de Geneve: Ecl. Geol. Helvetiae, v. 1, p. 32–67.

——— 1957, Contribution a l'etude des proprietes geometriques des oölithes—l'example du Grand Lac Sale, Utah, U. S. A.: Inst. National Geneve Bull., v. 58, p. 1–51

——— 1960, Microscopic sedimentary petrography: New York, John Wiley & Sons, Inc.

——— and Lundwall, W. R., 1959, Microfacies study of a Middle Devonian bioherm, Columbus, Indiana: Jour. Sed. Petrology, v. 29, no. 3, p. 343–353.

Chayes, Felix, 1949, A simple point counter for thin-section analysis: Am. Mineralogist, v. 34, no. 1, p. 1–11.

——— 1954, The theory of thin-section analysis: Jour. Geology, v. 62, no. 1, p. 92–101.

——— 1955, A point counter based on the Leitz mechanical stage: Am. Mineralogist, v. 40, nos. 1–2, p. 126–127.

——— 1956, Petrographic modal analysis—an elementary statistical appraisal: New York, John Wiley and Sons, Inc.

Clapp, F. G., 1940, Geology of eastern Iran: Geol. Soc. America Bull., v. 51, no. 1, p. 1–101.

Clift, W. O., 1956, Sedimentary history of the Ogaden district, Ethiopia, *in* Symposium on the geological occurrence of oil and gas: Internat. Geol. Cong., 20th, Mexico, v. 1, p. 89–112.

Cloud, P. E., Jr., 1952, Facies relationships of organic reefs: Am. Assoc. Petroleum Geologists Bull., v. 36, no. 11, p. 2125–2149.

Correns, C. W., 1950, Zur geochemie der diagenese; I, das verhalten von $CaCO_3$ and SiO_2: Geochem. et Cosmochim. Acta, v. 1, no. 1, p. 49–54.

Cox, L. R., 1933, *in* The empty quarter, by H. St. J. B. Philby: London, Constable and Co. Ltd., p. 383–389.

Daetwyler, C. C., and Kidwell, A. L., 1959, The Gulf of Batabano, a modern carbonate basin: 5th World Petrol Cong., New York, Proc. Sec. 1, p. 1–21.

Daniel, E. J., 1954, Fractured reservoirs of Middle East: Am. Assoc. Petroleum Geologists Bull., v. 38, no. 5, p. 774–815.

Dufaure, Ph., 1958, Contribution á l'étude stratigraphique et micropaléontologique du Jurassique et du Neocomien, de l'Aquitaine á la Provence: Rev. Micropaléontologie, v. 1, no. 2, p. 87–115.

Dunbar, C. O., and Rodgers, John, 1957, Principles of stratigraphy: New York, John Wiley and Sons, Inc., 356 p.

Dunnington, H. V., 1958, Generation, migration, accumulation, and dissipation of oil in northern Iraq, *in* Habitat of Oil: Am. Assoc. Petroleum Geologists, p. 1194–1251.

Edie, R. W., 1959, Middle Devonian sedimentation and oil possibilities, central Saskatchewan, Canada: Am. Assoc. Petroleum Geologists Bull., v. 43, no. 5, p. 1026–1057.

Elliott, G. F., 1955, Fossil calcareous algae from the Middle East: Micropaleontology, v. 1, no. 2, p. 125–131.

——— 1956, Further records of fossil calcareous algae from the Middle East: Micropaleontology, v. 2, no. 4, p. 327–334.

——— 1957, New calcareous algae from the Arabian peninsula: Micropaleontology, v. 3, no. 3, p. 227–230.

——— 1958, Fossil microproblematica from the Middle East: Micropaleontology, v. 4, no. 4, p. 419–428.

——— 1959, Fossil calcareous algal floras of the Middle East with a note on a Cretaceous problematicum, *Hensonella cylindrica* gen. et sp. nov.: Geol. Soc. London Quart. Jour., v. 115, p. 217–233.

Ellis, C. W., 1960, Marine sedimentary environments

in the vicinity of the Norwalk Islands, Connecticut: unpub. doctoral dissertation, Yale Univ.

Emery, K. O., 1956, Sediments and water of Persian Gulf: Am. Assoc. Petroleum Geologists Bull., v. 40, no. 10, p. 2354–2383.

Evans, J. W., 1900, Mechanically-formed limestones from Junagahr (Kathiawar) and other localities: Geol. Soc. London Quart. Jour., v. 56, p. 559–583.

Fairbridge, R. W., 1957, The dolomite question, *in* Regional aspects of carbonate deposition: Soc. Econ. Paleontologists and Mineralogists Spec. Pub. No. 5, p. 125–178.

Falcon, N. L., 1958, Position of oil fields of southwest Iran with respect to relevant sedimentary basins, *in* Habitat of oil: Am. Assoc. Petroleum Geologists, p. 1279–1293.

Fischer, A. G., 1953, Petrology of Eocene limestones in and around the Citrus-Levy County area, Florida: Florida Geol. Survey Rept. Inv. 9, p. 41–70.

Folk, R. W., 1959, Practical petrographic classification of limestones: Am. Assoc. Petroleum Geologists Bull., v. 43, no. 1, p. 1–38.

Gianotti, A., 1958, Deux facies du Jurassique superieur en Sicile: Rev. de Micropaléontologie, v. 1, no. 1, p. 38–51.

Gibson, H. S., 1948, Oil production in southwestern Iran: World Oil, May 1948, p. 271–280.

Gilluly, J., Waters, A. C., and Woodford, A. O., 1959, Principles of geology, 2d ed.: San Francisco, W. H. Freeman and Co.

Ginsburg, R. N., 1953, Beachrock in south Florida: Jour. Sed. Petrology, v. 23, no. 2, p. 85–92.

——— 1956, Environmental relationships of grain size and constituent particles in some south Florida carbonate sediments: Am. Assoc. Petroleum Geologists Bull., v. 40, no. 10, p. 2384–2427.

——— 1957, Early diagenesis and lithification of shallow-water carbonate sediments in south Florida, *in* Regional aspects of carbonate deposition: Soc. Econ. Paleontologists and Mineralogists Spec. Pub. No. 5, p. 80–99.

Grabau, A. W., 1903, Paleozoic coral reefs: Geol. Soc. America Bull., v. 14, p. 337–352.

——— 1913, Principles of stratigraphy: New York, A. G. Seiler and Co.

Greenman, N. N., 1951a, On the bias of grain-size measurements made in thin-section: Jour. Geology, v. 59, p. 268–274.

——— 1951b, The mechanical analysis of sediments from thin-section data: Jour. Geology, v. 59, no. 5, p. 447–462.

Griffiths, J. C., 1951, Size versus sorting in some Caribbean sediments: Jour. Geology, v. 59, no. 3, p. 211–243.

——— 1952, Grain-size distribution and reservoir-rock characteristics: Am. Assoc. Petroleum Geologists Bull., v. 36, no. 2, p. 205–229.

Hadding, Assar, 1941, The pre-Quaternary sedimentary rocks of Sweden, VI, reef limestones: Lund,. Univ. Årssk., n. f., avd. 2, v. 37, no. 10.

——— 1956, The lithological character of marine shallow-water limestones; its relation to the environment of formation and to changes of the sea level: Miner.-och. Paleont. Geol. Inst., Lund, no. 33, p. 1–18.

——— 1958, The pre-Quaternary sedimentary rocks of Sweden; VII, Cambrian and Ordovician limestones: Lund, Univ. Årssk., n. f., avd. 2, v. 54.

Ham, W. E., 1960, Middle Permian evaporites in southwestern Oklahoma: Internat. Geol. Cong., 21st, Copenhagen, Proc. pt. 12, p. 138–151.

Henson, F. R. S., 1951, Observations on the geology and petroleum occurrences of the Middle East: 3rd World Petrol. Cong., The Hague, Proc. Sec. I, p. 118–140.

Hudson, R. G. S., 1956, Tethyan Jurassic hydroids of the family Milleporidiidae: Jour. Paleontology, v. 30, no. 3, p. 714–730.

——— and Chatton, M., 1959, The Musandam limestone (Jurassic and Cretaceous) of Oman, Arabia: Notes et Mem. Moyen-Orient, Mus. Natl. d'Hist. Nat., Paris, v. 8.

——— McGugan, A., and Morton, D. M., 1954, The structure of the Jebel Hagab area, Trucial Oman: Geol. Soc. London Quart. Jour., v. 110, pt. 2, p. 121–152.

Illing, L. V., 1954, Bahaman calcareous sands: Am. Assoc. Petroleum Geologists Bull., v. 38, no. 1, p. 1–95.

——— 1959, Deposition and diagenesis of some upper Paleozoic carbonate sediments in Western Canada: 5th World Petrol. Cong., New York, Proc. Sec. I, p. 23–52.

Iraq Petroleum Company Geological Staff, 1956, Geological occurrence of oil and gas in Iraq, *in* Symposium on the geological occurrence of oil and gas: Internat. Geol. Cong., 20th, Mexico, v. 2, p. 73–101.

Johnson, J. Harlan, 1951, An introduction to the study of organic limestones: Colo. School Mines Quart,. v. 46, no. 2.

——— 1954, An introduction to the study of rock-building algae and algal limestones: Colo. School Mines Quart., v. 49, no. 2.

Keller, W. D., 1941, Petrography and origin of the Rex chert: Geol. Soc. America Bull., v. 52, no. 8, p. 1279–1297.

Kent, P. E., Slinger, F. C., and Thomas, A. N., 1951, Stratigraphical exploration surveys in southwest Persia: 3rd World Petrol. Cong., The Hague, Proc. Sec. I, p. 142–161.

Krauskopf, K. B., 1959, The geochemistry of silica in sedimentary environments, *in* Silica in sediments, a symposium: Soc. Econ. Paleontologists and Mineralogists Spec. Pub. No. 7, p. 4–19.

Krumbein, W. C., 1935, Thin-section mechanical analysis of indurated sediments: Jour. Geology, v. 43, no. 5, p. 482–496.

——— and Aberdeen, E., 1937, The sediments of Barataria Bay: Jour. Sed. Petrology, v. 7, no. 1, p. 3–17.

——— and Griffith, J. S., 1938, Beach environment in Little Sister Bay, Wisconsin: Geol. Soc. America Bull., v. 49, no. 4, p. 629–652.

Lamare, P., 1936, Structure geologique de l'Arabia: Paris, Beranger,

Landes, K. K., 1946, Porosity through dolomitization: Am. Assoc. Petroleum Geologists Bull., v. 30, no. 3, p. 305–318.

Lecompte, Marius, 1956, Stromatoporidea, *in* R. C. Moore, Editor, Treatise on Invertebrate Paleontology, Part F, Coelenterata: Geol. Soc. America and Univ. Kansas Press, p. F107–F145.

Lees, G. M., 1928, The geology and tectonics of Oman and parts of southeastern Arabia: Geol. Soc. London Quart. Jour., v. 84, p. 585–670.

——— 1950, Some structural and stratigraphic aspects

of the oilfields of the Middle East: Internat. Geol. Cong., 18th, Great Britain, Repts., pt. 6, p. 26–33.

——— 1951, The oilfields of the Middle East: 3d World Petrol. Cong., The Hague, Proc., gen. v., p. 94–101.

——— and Richardson, F. D. S., 1940, Geology of the oilfield belt of southwest Iran and Iraq: Geol. Magazine, v. 77, no. 3, p. 227–252.

Levorsen, A. I., 1954, Geology of petroleum: San Francisco, W. H. Freeman and Co.

Little, O. H., 1925, The geography and geology of Makalla: Geol. Survey Egypt, Govt. Press, Cairo.

Macfayden, W. A., 1933, The geology of British Somaliland, Pt. 1: Govt. Somaliland Protectorate Pub.

Mitchell, R. C., 1958, Notes on the geology of western Iraq and northern Saudi Arabia: Geol. Rundschau, v. 46, p. 476–493.

Newell, N. D., 1955, Bahamian platforms, *in* Crust of the earth: Geol. Soc. America Spec. Paper 62, p. 303–316.

——— and Rigby, J. K., 1957, Geological studies on the Great Bahama Bank, *in* Regional aspects of carbonate deposition, a symposium: Soc. Econ. Paleontologists and Mineralogists Spec. Pub. No. 5, p. 15–72.

——— Fischer, A. G., and others, 1953, The Permian reef complex of the Guadalupe Mountains region, Texas and New Mexico: San Francisco, W. H. Freeman and Co.

——— Whiteman, A., and Bradley, J., 1951, Shoal-water geology and environments, eastern Andros Island, Bahamas: Am. Mus. Nat. History Bull., v. 97, art. 1, p. 1–29.

Newton, R. B., 1921, On a marine Jurassic fauna from central Arabia: Ann. Mag. Nat. History, v. 7, p. 389.

Ohle, E. L., Jr., 1951, The influence of permeability on ore distribution in limestone and dolomite: Econ. Geology, v. 46, no. 7, p. 667–706; 871–908.

Owen, R. M. S., and Nasr, S. N., 1958, Stratigraphy of the Kuwait-Basra area, *in* Habitat of oil: Am. Assoc. Petroleum Geologists, p. 1252–1278.

Packham, G. H., 1955, Volume-, weight-, and number-frequency analysis of sediments from thin-section data: Jour. Geology, v. 63, no. 1, p. 50–58.

Payne, T. G., 1942, Stratigraphical analysis and environmental reconstruction: Am. Assoc. Petroleum Geologists Bull., v. 26, no. 11, p. 1697–1770.

Pelto, C. R., 1952, The mechanical analysis of sediments from thin-section data; a discussion: Jour. Geology, v. 60, p. 402–406.

Pettijohn, F. J., 1957, Sedimentary rocks, 2d ed.: New York, Harper and Bros.

Philby, H. St. J. B., 1922, The heart of Arabia: London, Constable and Co., 2 v.

——— 1928, Arabia of the Wahhabis: London, Constable and Co.

——— 1933, The empty quarter: London, Constable and Co.

——— 1939, Sheba's daughters: London, Methuen and Co. Ltd.

Picard, L., 1939, On the structure of the Arabian peninsula: Internat. Geol. Cong., 17th, U.S.S.R., Rept., v. 2, p. 433–442.

Pray, L. C., 1960, Compaction in calcilutites (abst.): Geol. Soc. America Bull., v. 71, no. 12, p. 1946.

Renouard, G., 1955, Oil prospects of Lebanon: Am. Assoc. Petroleum Geologists Bull., v. 39, no. 11, p. 2125–2169.

Revelle, Roger, and Fairbridge, Rhodes, 1957, Carbonates and carbon dioxide, *in* Hedgpeth, ed., Ecology, v. 1; Treatise on marine ecology and paleontology: Geol. Soc. America Mem. 67, p. 239–296.

Rosenfeld, M. A., Jacobsen, C. L., and Ferm, J. C., 1953, A comparison of sieve and thin-section techniques for size analysis: Jour. Geology, v. 61, no. 2, p. 114–132.

Sander, N. J., 1954, Unpub. microphotographs, pre-Arab formation Foraminifera.

Scruton, P. C., 1953, Deposition of evaporites: Am. Assoc. Petroleum Geologists Bull., v. 37, no. 11, p. 2498–2512.

Shipek, C. J., 1960, Photographic study of some deep-sea floor environments in the eastern Pacific: Geol. Soc. America Bull., v. 71, no. 7, p. 1067–1074.

Sorby, H. C., 1879, On the structure and origin of limestone: Geol. Soc. London Quart. Jour. Proc., v. 35, p. 56–95.

Steineke, Max, Bramkamp, R. A., and Sander, N. J., 1958, Stratigraphic relations of Arabian Jurassic oil, *in* Habitat of oil: Am. Assoc. Petroleum Geologists, p. 1294–1329.

Stetson, H. C., 1939, Summary of sedimentary conditions on the continental shelf off the east coast of the United States, *in* Recent marine sediments: Am. Assoc. Petroleum Geologists, p. 230–244; reprinted by Soc. Econ. Paleontologists and Mineralogists as Spec. Pub. No. 4 (1955).

Sugden, W., Ms., Stratigraphic lexicon; Qatar peninsula.

Sujkowski, Zb. L., 1958, Diagenesis: Am. Assoc. Petroleum Geologists Bull., v. 42, no. 11, p. 2692–2717.

Thames, C. B., Jr., 1959, Facies relationships in Mississippian of Williston basin and their effects upon fluid migration (abs.): Am. Assoc. Petroleum Geologists Bull., v. 43, no. 5, p. 1106; also, *in* Geolog. Record, Rocky Mtn. Sec. A.A.P.G., Albuquerque, 1959, p. 83–86.

Thorp, E. M., 1939, Florida and Bahama marine calcareous deposits, *in* Recent marine sediments: Am. Assoc. Petroleum Geologists, p. 283–297: reprinted by Soc. Econ. Paleontologists and Mineralogists as Spec. Pub. No. 4 (1955).

Thralls, W. H., and Hasson, R. C., 1956, Geology and oil resources of eastern Saudi Arabia, *in* Symposium on the geological occurrence of oil and gas: Internat. Geol. Cong., 20th, Mexico, Proc. v. 2, p. 9–32.

Towse, D. F., 1957, Petrology of Beaver Lodge Madison limestone reservoir, North Dakota: Am. Assoc. Petroleum Geologists Bull., v. 41, no. 11, p. 2493–2507.

van Straaten, L. M. J. U., and Kuenen, Ph., 1958, Tidal action as a cause of clay accumulation: Jour. Sed. Petrology, v. 28, no. 4, p. 406–413.

von Wissmann, H., Rathjens, C., and Kossmat, F., 1943, Beiträge zur Tektonik Arabiens: Geol. Rundschau, v. 33, nos. 4–6, p. 221–353.

Weeks, L. G., 1952, Factors of sedimentary basin development that control oil occurrence: Am. Assoc. Petroleum Geologists Bull., v. 36, no. 11, p. 2071–2124.

Williams, H., Turner, F. J., and Gilbert, C. M., 1954, Petrography, an introduction to the study of rocks in thin sections: San Francisco, W. H. Freeman and Co.

GROUPING OF CARBONATE ROCKS INTO TEXTURAL AND POROSITY UNITS FOR MAPPING PURPOSES[1]

G. E. THOMAS[2]
Calgary, Alberta

ABSTRACT

Four case histories of textural and reservoir analyses of selected Paleozoic carbonate cycles and reef complexes of the Western Canada basin have been utilized in the formulation of a carbonate rock classification chart. This chart is presented to illustrate the relationships of grain, matrix, and cement variants of carbonate rocks, to porosity and permeability determinations, and should satisfy the requirements of an oil geologist or reservoir engineer.

Large stratigraphic accumulations of oil have been discovered at or near the Paleozoic subcrop of the Mississippian "Midale" carbonate cycle in southeastern Saskatchewan. Apart from scattered, vuggy, algal encrusted strand-line deposits, most of the carbonates of the "Midale" producing zone consist of sorted, silt-sized material and skeletal or nonskeletal limestones which have a very finely comminuted, commonly dolomitized, limestone matrix with intergranular and chalky porosity. Effective reservoir porosity is controlled by the relative distribution, grain size, and sorting of this matrix.

Major hydrocarbon (oil and gas) reserves have been found in the Mississippian "Elkton" carbonate cycle, both in the foothills belt and along the subcrop, in southwestern Alberta. Effective reservoir material of this cycle was found to consist mainly of the dolomitized equivalent of originally coarse, uncemented skeletal limestone, and skeletal limestone with a variable amount of generally porous, finely comminuted (granular) skeletal matrix. Primary porosity was very important in the control of dolomitization, which began with the replacement of this matrix by euhedral rhombohedrons, and finally affected the coarse skeletal material (now generally indicated by leached fossil-cast outlines). These porous dolomites grade laterally in a predictable way into tight, relatively nondolomitized, well sorted, coarse skeletal (locally oölitic) limestones with original high interfragmental porosity now completely infilled with clear crystalline calcite. This lithification by cementation took place early in the history of carbonate sedimentation of this area and before secondary dolomitization processes took effect.

The transgressive, reef-fringed, limestone banks or platforms of the Upper Devonian Beaverhill Lake formation in the Swan Hills region of Alberta have been found to contain major reserves of oil and gas. Successive rims of organic lattice, stromatoporoidal and algal, atoll-like "buildups," with granular matrix, separate generally medium to dark brown pelleted lime muds containing abundant amphiporids, and intercalated lighter colored lagoonal carbonates, from open marine shales and nodular, argillaceous, crinoid- and brachiopod-rich limestones. The most effective reservoir material along the reef fronts or terraces consists of vuggy organic lattice, algal encrusted amphiporids (minor developments), uncemented skeletal or nonskeletal limestone, and reworked stromatoporoidal, algal, and amphiporid material with intra-organic vugs, embedded in a porous, well sorted, micro to finely granular matrix. Matrix grain size and sorting studies are essential to exploration and secondary recovery problems, as the granular material grades laterally into chalky or micrograined limestones, which were laid down under lower energy conditions. Matrix granularity ratio outlines are considered to be superior to ecological maps (percentage of algal and stromatoporoidal material) in the prediction of shoal areas.

The highly productive Nisku, regressive, dolomitized biostromal-evaporite complex of the Edmonton and Red Deer areas of Alberta, contains numerous stratigraphic and/or structural traps. Zonation of Nisku dolomites has been accomplished by crystal size and shape studies in combination with identification of vestiges of original organic structures and skeletal or nonskeletal grain outlines. The morphological expression of the underlying Leduc reef platforms and carbonate buildups in the Duvernay formation strongly influences facies variations of the Nisku carbonate-evaporite unit. An algal, stromatoporoidal, coralline, organic lattice chain associated with generally coarse, dolomitized, clastic carbonates with a porous, granular matrix is developed on the Rimbey-Meadowbrook trend, and forms a front to a shale-limestone facies deposited under open marine conditions to the northwest. To the east of this barrier, a complex pattern of fringing organic and clastic carbonate shoals separate locally silled, lagoonal deposits of evaporites and brown carbonate muds containing abundant secondary anhydrite-replaced amphiporids. The shoal and lagoonal carbonates throughout most of this area are overlain by anhydrite or anhydritic dolomite sheets, which were precipitated in the wake of an overall regressive Nisku sea.

INTRODUCTION

The oil industry, national geological organizations, and universities have long demanded the organization of a carbonate rock classification into a single, moderately detailed system of nomenclature which will be understood and used by all

[1] Part of a symposium arranged by the Research Committee, and presented at Denver, Colorado, April 27, 1961, under joint auspices of the Association and the Society of Economic Paleontologists and Mineralogists. Manuscript received, April 26, 1961.

[2] Consulting geologist.

concerned. This thesis attempts to give an explanation for the variances in reservoir void space in limestone or dolomite sequences which will satisfy the requirements of an oil geologist or reservoir engineer.

Effective porosity isopach and allied carbonate textural maps will be essential to future exploration and exploitation programs in the Western Canada basin, because most hydrocarbons discovered to date are contained in carbonate stratigraphic traps of organic reef or clastic origin. Case histories of textural and reservoir analyses of two Mississippian carbonate cycles and two Devonian reef complexes of the Western Canada basin are presented to illustrate the relationships of grain, matrix, and cement variants of carbonate rocks to porosity and permeability determinations. These case histories, which also illustrate the position of an effective carbonate reservoir in the framework of carbonate sedimentation, have been utilized in the drafting of a chart grouping carbonate rocks into textural and porosity units for mapping purposes. This classification chart (Chart 1) has evolved not from a haphazard collection of rock specimens, but from a series of textural and reservoir analyses of carbonate sequences, which have proved to be of economic value to the oil and gas industry.

The geometry and terminology of various types of carbonate void spaces, which are known to be characteristic of many limestone and dolomite sections, are illustrated by Plates I and II.

Elaborate laboratory textural techniques have not been utilized in these carbonate studies. Rough, relatively untreated subsurface cuttings, cores, and surface section samples were examined under low-power binocular microscope. Carbonate thin-section work was fairly restricted, although used in some cases for demonstration purposes. Unfamiliar carbonate textural terms have been avoided as far as possible in the published case histories. The facies and porosity relationships in some Mississippian and Devonian carbonate cycles and reef complexes of the Western Canada basin have already been published by the author and co-authors (1960 and 1961). In order to give continuity to the philosophies expounded here, it was deemed advisable to repeat a very brief summary of the geometry of the various rock pores, which are characteristic of these limestone and dolomite sequences.

A learned European professor used to expound on the relative merits of "soft" and "hard" rock geology. He likened sedimentary to igneous petrology as "sawdust is to the living tree." In this presentation due respect is paid to the role of original living organisms in carbonate rock building, but considerable attention is paid to the "sawdust" that is found in between skeletal or nonskeletal grains. Relative distribution, grain size, and sorting studies of common carbonate matrices are fundamental to the understanding of carbonate effective reservoir distribution and dolomitization phenomena. With the use of oil-base cores, there is probably no greater field for petroleum research endeavor than the relating of carbonate textural analyses to porosity, permeability, and water saturation measurements. The chart grouping of carbonate rocks also caters to subsurface sample examination because, if anything, sample chips will indicate the type of matrix.

Glossary of Carbonate Textural Terms Utilized in Textural and Reservoir Analyses of Paleozoic Carbonate Sequences in the Western Canada Basin

Anhedral. A term applied to dolomites which are not bounded by their characteristic crystal faces (binocular-microscope resolution).

Cement. Chemically precipitated material occurring in the interstices between skeletal and nonskeletal grains of carbonate rocks. Also found as vug and fracture infilling material. Calcite cement has a crystalline appearance and clear vitreous luster which distinguishes it from common carbonate matrices.

Chalk. Porous, microtextured, and friable variety of carbonate rock. Partly of chemical origin, but also represents the "flour" formed by disintegration and abrasion of skeletal, nonskeletal grains, and algal growths. Chalky material referred to in this study is microtextured (0.01 mm approximately), has calculated porosities up to 30 per cent, high connate water content, and virtually no oil saturation because of the fine capillary pores. Generally deposited in the quiet-water environments of lagoons or intershoal areas of carbonate shelves.

Dolomitized. Refers to dolomites in which relict limestone textures are visible.

Earthy. Refers to a variety of slightly argillaceous carbonate with earthy texture, generally closely associated with chalky deposits and commonly showing similar porosity values. Microtextured (0.01 mm and slightly less).

Euhedral. Dolomite with well-developed crystal faces (binocular microscope resolution).

Suffixes—"Granular" and "Grained." This terminology will create considerable confusion unless properly understood. These suffixes, together with Wentworth size-scale prefixes, are applied to material (commonly found as a carbonate matrix) which is only resolvable under the binocular microscope by size and shape analysis.

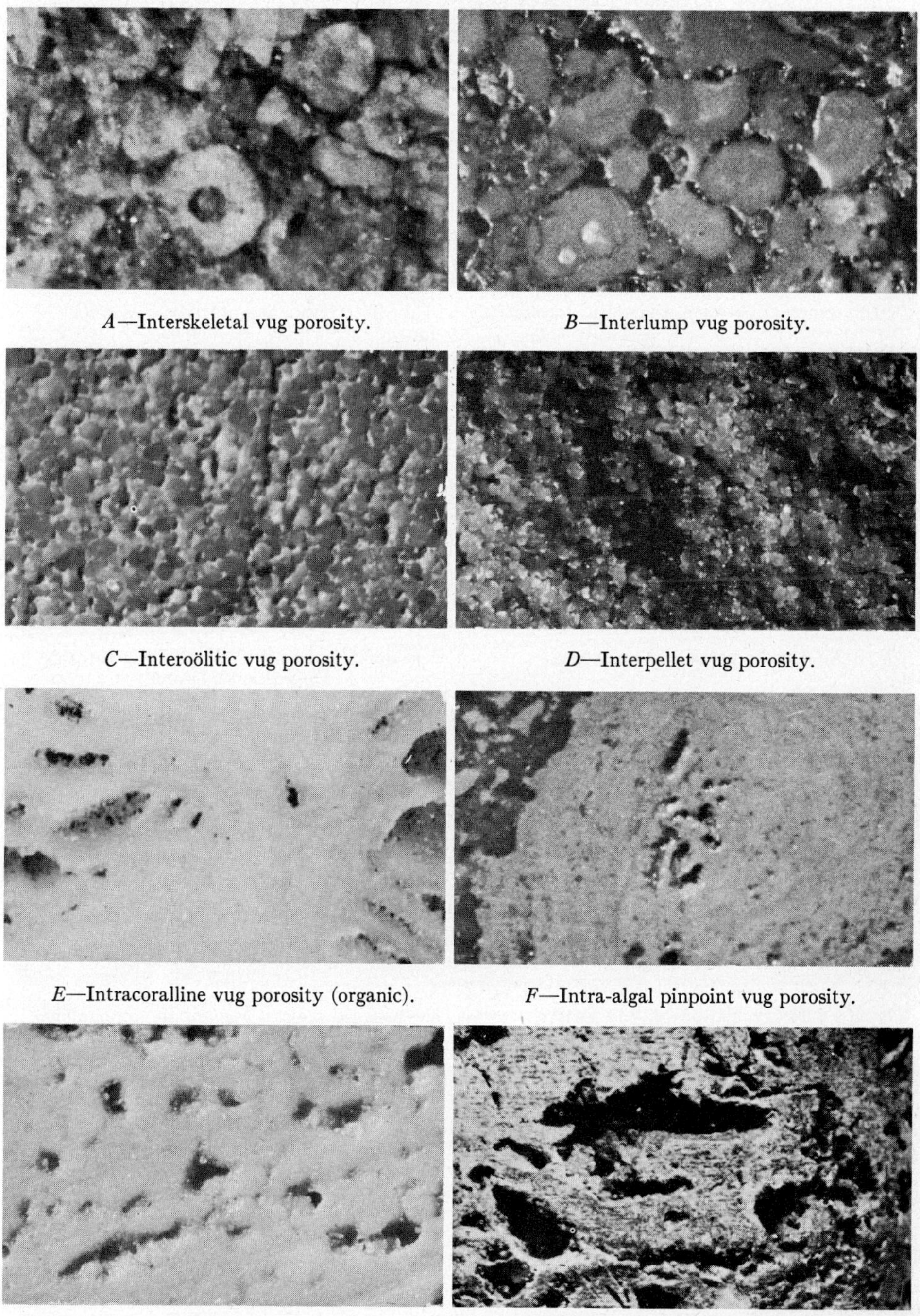

A—Interskeletal vug porosity.

B—Interlump vug porosity.

C—Interoölitic vug porosity.

D—Interpellet vug porosity.

E—Intracoralline vug porosity (organic).

F—Intra-algal pinpoint vug porosity.

G Shrinkage vug porosity.

H—Solution vug porosity. Dolomite.

PLATE I.—Examples of porosity in carbonate rocks.

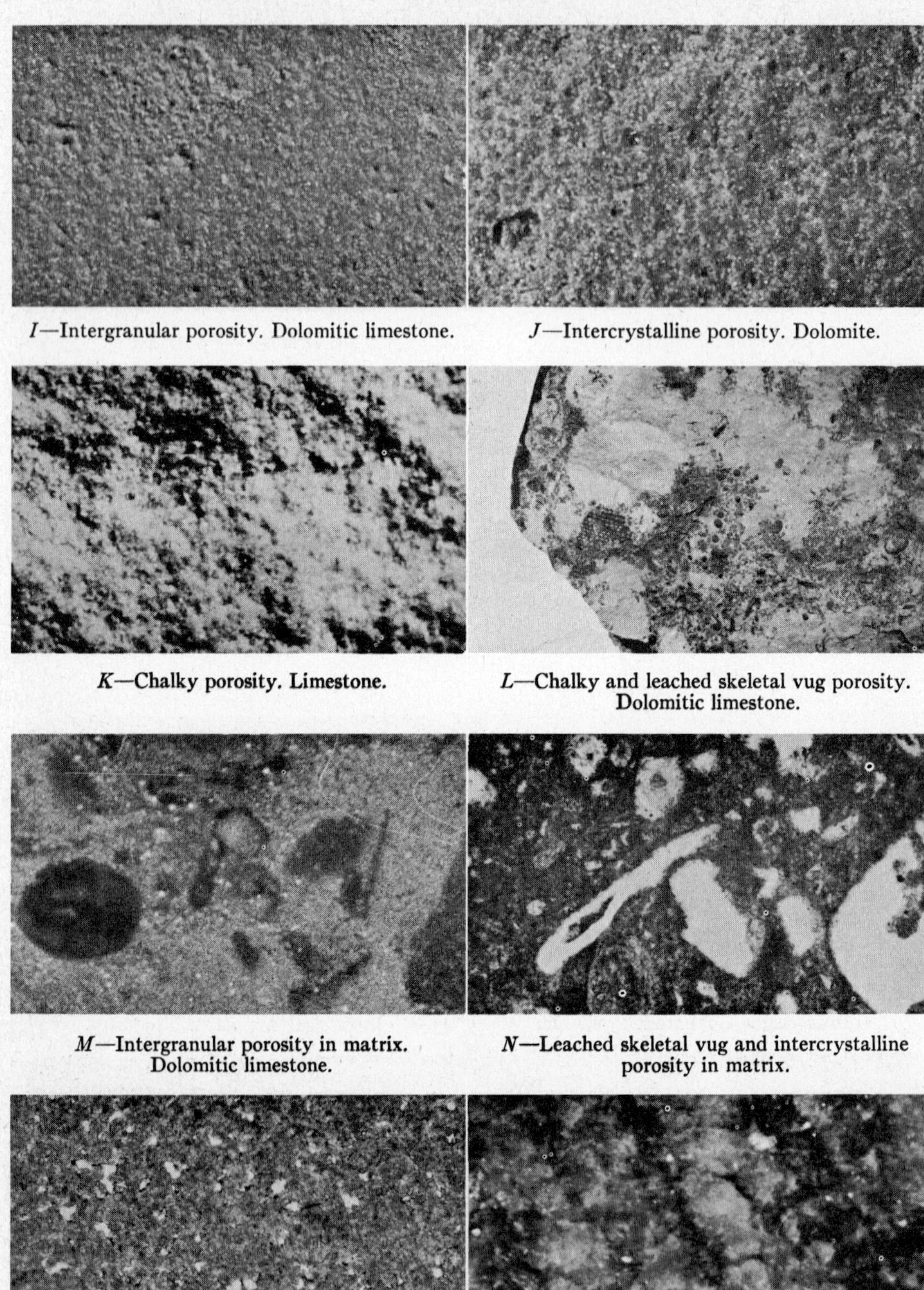

I—Intergranular porosity. Dolomitic limestone.

J—Intercrystalline porosity. Dolomite.

K—Chalky porosity. Limestone.

L—Chalky and leached skeletal vug porosity. Dolomitic limestone.

M—Intergranular porosity in matrix. Dolomitic limestone.

N—Leached skeletal vug and intercrystalline porosity in matrix.

O—Intercrystalline porosity. Coarse dolomite.

P—Dolomitized fracture porosity.

PLATE II.—Examples of porosity in carbonate rocks.

The term *"granular"* is used for approximately equal-sized granules, rounded grains produced by attrition or comminution of skeletal or nonskeletal material. Granular limestones are well sorted and show good intergranular porosity. In the Mississippian "Midale" beds of southeastern Saskatchewan they were generally represented by microgranular limestones (packed granules 0.01–0.06 mm) with effective porosities up to 37 per cent and whose permeabilities were greatly supplemented by leached ostracode vugs or casts. The packed granules in these limestones are particularly susceptible to dolomitization processes giving rise to a "crystalline-granular" texture. With growth of dolomite rhombs around the granules, a rhombic dolomite with leached fossil casts is produced. The microgranular material also forms an effective porosity matrix to skeletal and nonskeletal limestones in the "Midale" carbonate cycle.

When this granular material is poorly sorted and becomes intermixed with a clay-size fraction, then the suffix *"grained"* is applied with the retention of a prefix-size qualification for the coarsest granule. The following examples should clarify this terminology—

Microgranular	*Micrograined*
Well-sorted microgranular limestone (grain size 0.04 mm). *Effective reservoir.*	Micrograined limestone (clay- and silt-size intermixture 0.005–0.04 mm). *Ineffective.*
Well-sorted very fine granular limestone (grain size 0.09 mm). *Effective reservoir.*	Very fine grained limestone (clay- and very-fine-sand-size intermixture 0.005–0.09 mm). *Ineffective.*
Skeletal limestone with 30% dolomitized microgranular matrix (0.04 mm). *Effective reservoir.*	Skeletal limestone with micrograined matrix (<0.01 mm–0.04 mm). *Ineffective.*

The terms *"cryptograined"* and *"cryptocrystalline"* are applied to lithified lime muds or dolomitized equivalents whose grain or crystal outlines are not discernible under normal microscope magnification (less than 0.01 mm). Not only is this subtle change in sorting of common carbonate matrices invaluable for exploration mapping purposes, but also gives a better understanding of carbonate reservoir distribution and dolomitization phenomena. The size and sorting of limestone matrices controls the size and shape of the resultant dolomite unless dolomitization has continued to the "mosaic" stage—

Limestone type	*Dolomitized equivalent*
Microgranular limestone with leached fossil casts (grain size 0.04 mm). Well-sorted silt-sized material.	Micro- to very-fine-rhombic dolomite with leached fossil casts (crystal size 0.04–0.07 mm).
Micrograined limestone (grain size—<0.01 mm–0.05 mm). Poorly sorted clay- and silt-size intermixture.	Micro- to very-fine-crystalline (subhedral to interlocking) dolomite (crystal size 0.01–0.08 mm).
Cryptograined limestone (grain size <0.01 mm). Lithified lime mud.	Crypto-microcrystalline (anhedral to interlocking) dolomite (crystal size <0.01–0.02 mm).
Skeletal limestone with microgranular (0.04 mm) matrix.	Dolomitized leached skeletal limestone with micro- to very-fine-rhombic dolomite (0.04–0.07 mm) matrix.
Skeletal limestone with micrograined (<0.01 mm–0.05 mm) matrix.	Dolomitized partially leached skeletal limestone with micro- to very-fine-crystalline (subhedral to interlocking) dolomite (0.01–0.08 mm).
Skeletal limestone with chalky (0.01 mm) matrix.	Dolomitized partially leached skeletal limestone with chalky (0.01 mm) matrix.
Skeletal limestone with cryptograined (<0.01 mm) matrix.	Dolomitized skeletal limestone with crypto- to microcrystalline (anhedral to interlocking) dolomite (<0.01–0.02 mm) matrix.

Lumps. Calcareous grains such as pellets lying in contact with each other on the sea bed tend to become cemented or welded together and form a composite calcareous sand grain or "lump" (Illing, 1954). The various habits assumed by the lumps were found by Illing to be typical of certain environmental conditions, and the following specific forms he has described from the Bahamas can be recognized in the Mississippian of the Souris Valley area of Saskatchewan—grapestone, botryoidal lumps, encrusted lumps, and irregular well-cemented forms that show no outstanding feature to label them. Marine grass or algal activity played a predominant role in the cementation and binding of these composite lump bodies in the "Midale" beds.

Matrix. In a rock in which certain grains are much larger than the others the grains of the smaller size comprise the matrix (A.G.I., 1957). Sand-silt-and clay-sized material which is only resolvable by size and shape analysis is included in this study as carbonate matrix.

Mosaic. A textural term applied to dolomites. Secondary overgrowth of dolomite on rhombs produces a texture like the pieces of a mosaic. This destruction of original intercrystalline porosity by continuing growth of dolomite is analogous to the "cementation" phenomena of well-sorted skeletal or nonskeletal limestones.

Oölite. A spherical to ellipsoidal accretionary body which may or may not have a nucleus, and has concentric or radial structure, or both.

Organic lattice. Reef-building framework *"in situ."*

Pellets (pseudo-oölites). Spherical or subspherical to oval bodies with distinct boundaries, resembling oölites but possessing no comparable internal structure—for example, fecal pellets of Illing (1954). Pellet or pseudo-oölitic limestones are also of algal origin and possibly represent both accretionary algal grains and clastic material formed by fragmentation of algal colonies in areas of strong wave action. Algal "cabbages" commonly have myriads of fine pellet bodies attached to their cellular layers. Carbonate muds are commonly *pelleted*, displaying rounded or ellipsoidal aggregates of "grains of matrix" material. These muds are thought to be pelleted either by fecal activity, gas bubbling, or by algal "budding" phenomena. Devonian pelleted muds of the Western Canada basin generally contain abundant calcispheres (algal spore bodies) and are characterized by "syneresis" cracks and shrinkage vugs ("birdseye" structures), which are infilled with calcite cement.

Pisolite. Pettijohn (1949, p. 75; A.G.I., 1957, p. 221) has defined a pisolite as a spherical or subspherical, accretionary body over 2 mm in diameter. There is a great need for the differentiation of oölites and pisolites on some firm basis other than size, which is currently used. In this thesis the term pisolite is restricted to crenulated, rounded or semirounded, commonly composite carbonate bodies thought to have been formed by biochemical algal-encrustation processes, even though their size may be less than 2 mm.

Sorting. Sorting has been defined as the spread of grain-size distribution. In this carbonate study a two-component sorting system has been employed. Heterogeneous, skeletal or nonskeletal grains can be found embedded in a well sorted or poorly sorted carbonate matrix.

Subhedral. Intermediate between anhedral and euhedral (binocular-microscope resolution).

Syneresis cracks or vugs. Cracks or vugs formed by a spontaneous throwing off of water by a gel during aging.

MISSISSIPPIAN CARBONATE CYCLES OF WESTERN CANADA

TEXTURAL AND RESERVOIR PROPERTIES OF "MIDALE" CARBONATES (MISSION CANYON FORMATION) IN KINGSFORD-FLORENCE PRODUCING AREAS OF SOUTHEASTERN SASKATCHEWAN[3]

Large stratigraphic oil pools have been discovered at or near the Paleozoic subcrop of the "Midale" carbonate cycle in southeastern Saskatchewan. It was found, however, that though mechanical logs indicated fairly constant porosity up to the subcrop area, the character and distribution of carbonate lithosomes in the cycle control the quality of production in these pools. There is a wealth of core information along this trend, because reservoir evaluation of the different pools is accomplished mainly through an extensive coring program.

Figure 2, a section across the East Kingsford-Steelman oil fields, illustrates some of the facies changes of this depositional cycle toward the Paleozoic subcrop.

[3] This section summarizes the discussion published in 1960 (Thomas and Glaister, 1960, p. 571–579).

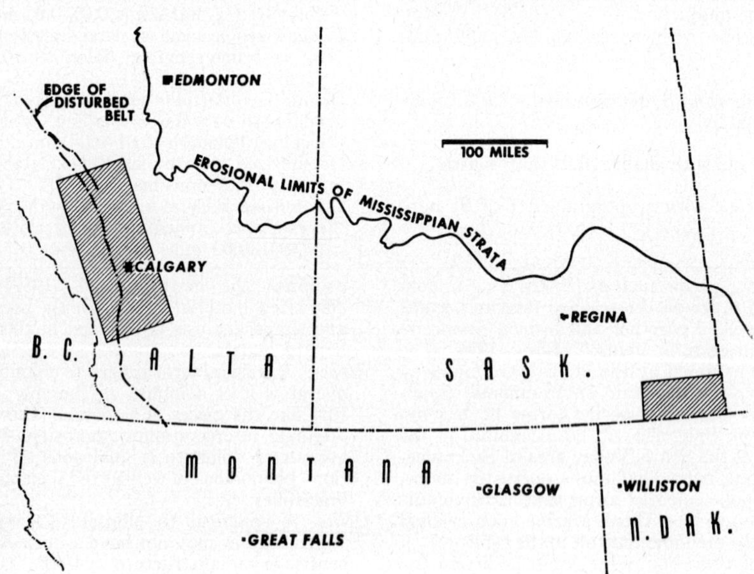

FIG. 1.—Index map of areas of study in Saskatchewan and Alberta.

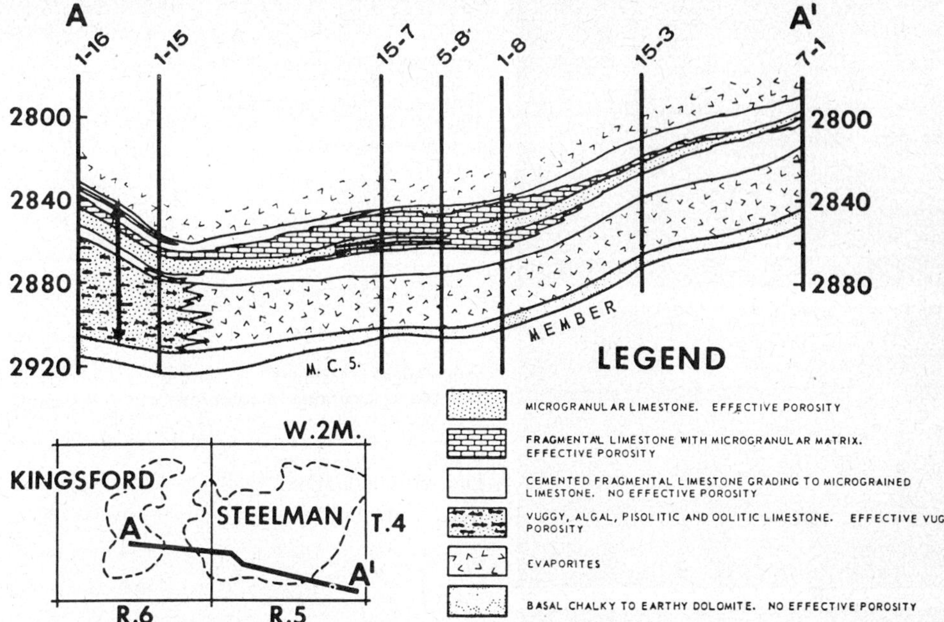

Fig. 2.—Section across East Kingsford-Steelman oil fields, illustrating some of facies changes of "Midale" carbonates toward Paleozoic subcrop.

Attempts have been made by some workers to use the marginal evaporite in the cycle as a time-stratigraphic unit, but local patch or shoal reefs of porous algal limestone were being deposited amidst submerged shoals of calcareous fossil debris and oölites, at the same time that evaporites were being precipitated in back lagoonal areas.

The "Midale" carbonates are overlain by anhydrite and underlain throughout most of the area by an anhydrite floor.

At the Paleozoic subcrop (Jurassic red-bed cover) there is considerable secondary anhydrite infilling of primary carbonate porosity, accompanied by dolomitization.

Calcareous algae played an important role in limestone building on the interior of the Souris Valley shelf area of southeastern Saskatchewan. All stages in stabilization and encrustation of submerged, drifting shoals of calcareous, skeletal, and nonskeletal debris to form vuggy, algal, reef-like bodies can be seen. Some of the strand-line deposits have the appearance of oölite and lump sand bars which have been stabilized by sediment-binding, encrusting calcareous algae. According to published reports, blue-green algae are commonly the earliest colonizers of sediment newly deposited on tidal flats. It is well known that such algae exert a strong stabilizing effect upon the sediment they colonize, largely because they bind it together with their growing filaments and ultimately cover it with a mass of felted tubes. The stabilization of drifting sand-like material is really incipient reef growth. Photochemical removal of carbon dioxide from sea water by sea plants causes a decrease in bicarbonate ions and thus promotes the precipitation of calcium carbonate. Calcium carbonate is precipitated as a colloidal gel encrusting the leaves and stems of these plants. The end result is the production of cryptograined limestone which contains "syneresis" cracks and associated primary contraction or shrinkage vugs. The algal "knolls" of the Kingsford area generally have excellent horizontal, as opposed to vertical, permeability because of thin, cryptograined layers of encrusting algal limestone which separates partly encrusted, vuggy, pisolitic, lump, and oölitic sections. From a reservoir point of view these carbonates are difficult to analyze because of anhydrite and calcite infilling of vugs and irregular, algal carbonate mud encrustation of original intergrain porosity.

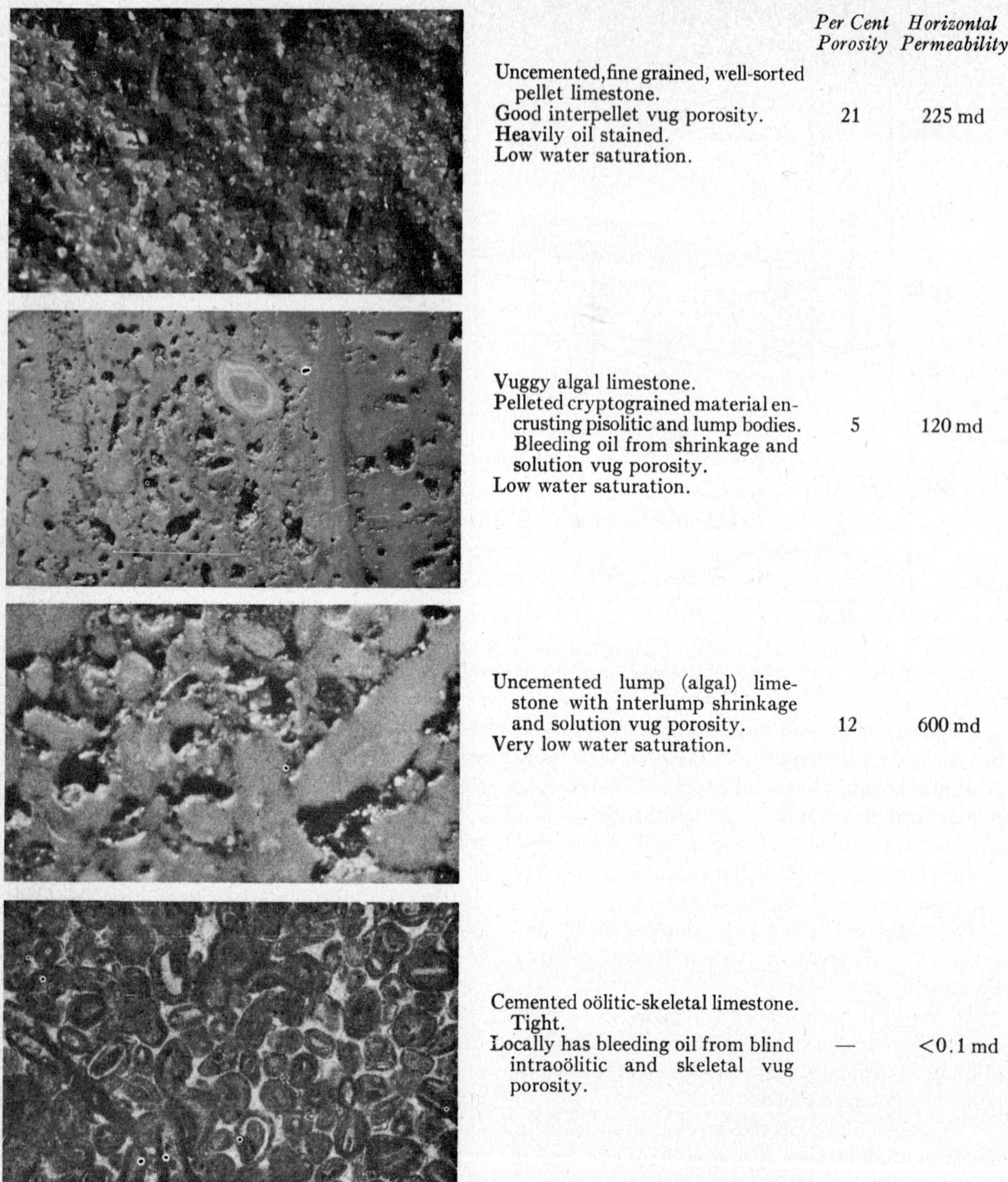

	Per Cent Porosity	*Horizontal Permeability*
Uncemented, fine grained, well-sorted pellet limestone. Good interpellet vug porosity. Heavily oil stained. Low water saturation.	21	225 md
Vuggy algal limestone. Pelleted cryptograined material encrusting pisolitic and lump bodies. Bleeding oil from shrinkage and solution vug porosity. Low water saturation.	5	120 md
Uncemented lump (algal) limestone with interlump shrinkage and solution vug porosity. Very low water saturation.	12	600 md
Cemented oölitic-skeletal limestone. Tight. Locally has bleeding oil from blind intraoölitic and skeletal vug porosity.	—	<0.1 md

Plate III.—Relation of textural variations. "Midale" carbonates with oil-saturation and porosity-permeability determinations.

One has to resort to recording the percentage of effective void space.

Screened lenses of porous, finely comminuted carbonates are found draped over the wave resistant algal "knolls" of the West and East Kingsford area (Fig. 2). Porosity, permeability, and oil-saturation properties of these carbonates can be directly related to quantitative, textural (includ-

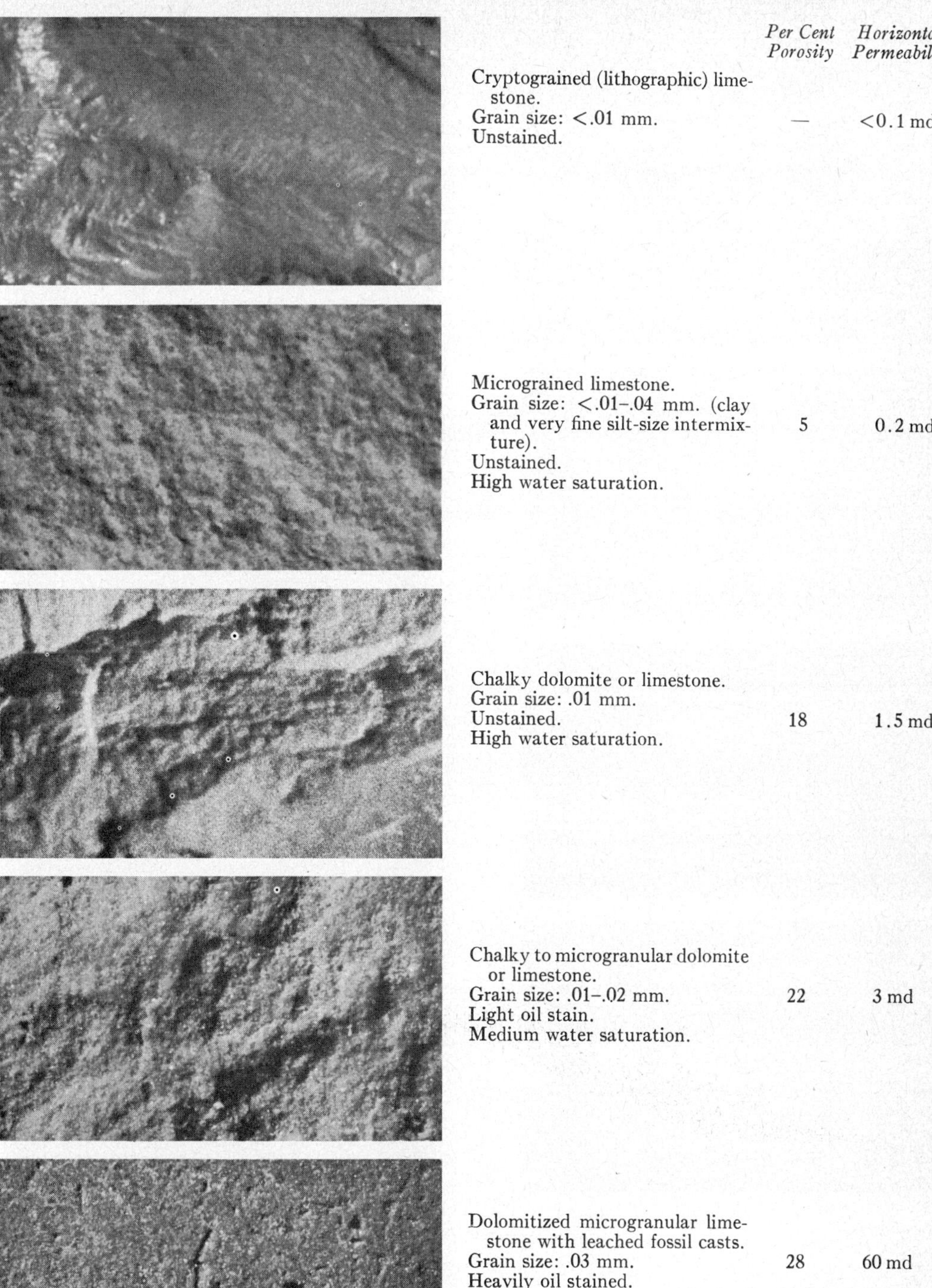

	Per Cent Porosity	Horizontal Permeability
Cryptograined (lithographic) limestone. Grain size: <.01 mm. Unstained.	—	<0.1 md
Micrograined limestone. Grain size: <.01–.04 mm. (clay and very fine silt-size intermixture). Unstained. High water saturation.	5	0.2 md
Chalky dolomite or limestone. Grain size: .01 mm. Unstained. High water saturation.	18	1.5 md
Chalky to microgranular dolomite or limestone. Grain size: .01–.02 mm. Light oil stain. Medium water saturation.	22	3 md
Dolomitized microgranular limestone with leached fossil casts. Grain size: .03 mm. Heavily oil stained. Low water saturation.	28	60 md

PLATE IV.—Relation of textural variations. "Midale" carbonates with oil-saturation and porosity-permeability determinations.

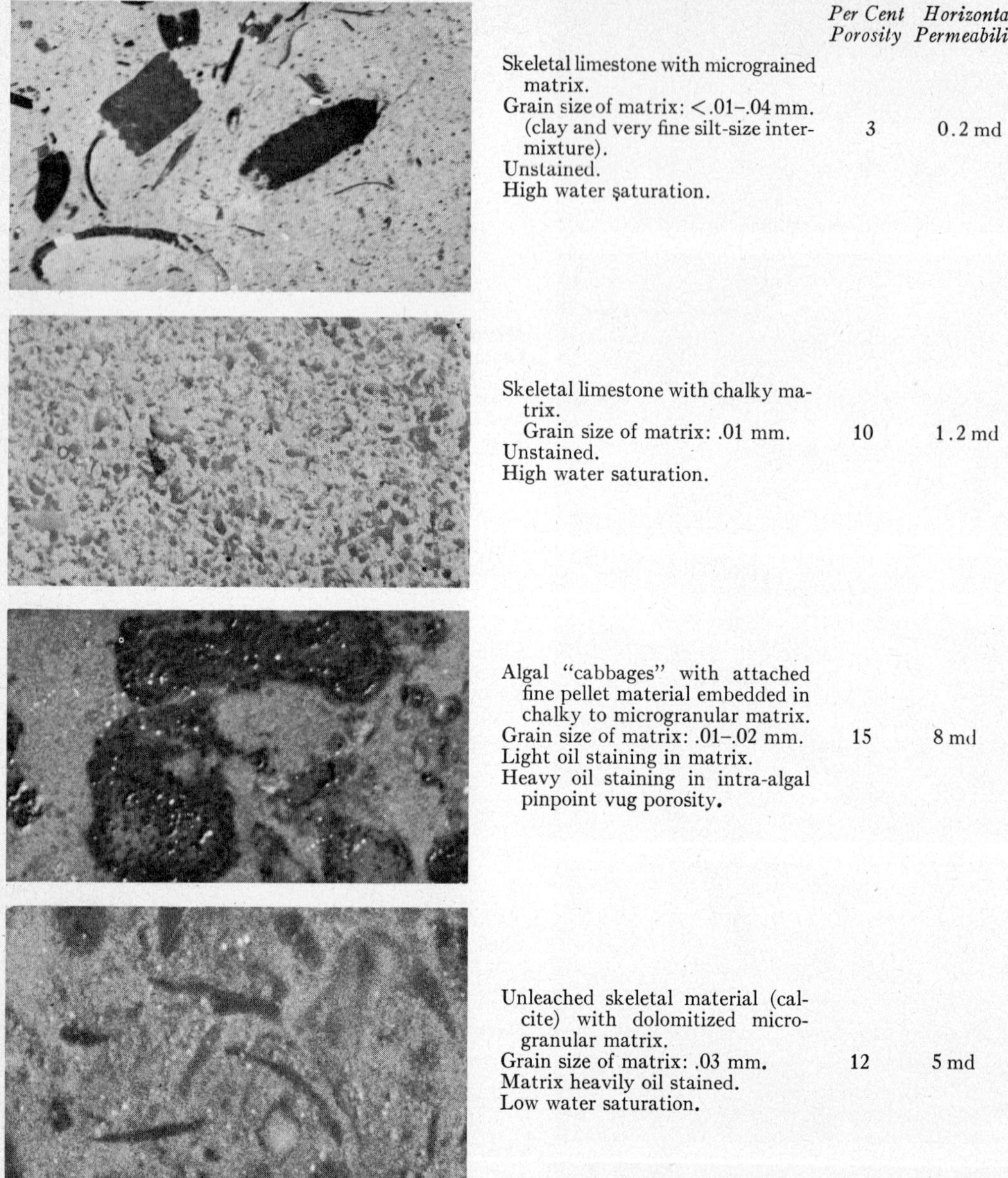

	Per Cent Porosity	Horizontal Permeability
Skeletal limestone with micrograined matrix. Grain size of matrix: <.01–.04 mm. (clay and very fine silt-size intermixture). Unstained. High water saturation.	3	0.2 md
Skeletal limestone with chalky matrix. Grain size of matrix: .01 mm. Unstained. High water saturation.	10	1.2 md
Algal "cabbages" with attached fine pellet material embedded in chalky to microgranular matrix. Grain size of matrix: .01–.02 mm. Light oil staining in matrix. Heavy oil staining in intra-algal pinpoint vug porosity.	15	8 md
Unleached skeletal material (calcite) with dolomitized microgranular matrix. Grain size of matrix: .03 mm. Matrix heavily oil stained. Low water saturation.	12	5 md

PLATE V.—Relation of textural variations. "Midale" carbonates with oil-saturation and porosity-permeability determinations.

ing grain size and sorting), carbonate measurements. Carbonate-matrix textural studies were the key to effective reservoir distribution in the upper "Midale" carbonates. Most of these carbonates consist of skeletal and oölitic limestones which have a finely comminuted, commonly dolomitized, limestone matrix with intergranular and chalky porosity. Effective reservoir porosity is controlled by the relative distribution, grain size, and sorting of this matrix. Cemented skeletal or nonskeletal limestones are commonly found interbedded with these carbonates containing effective matrix porosity.

Bar-like trends of commonly current-bedded, skeletal, or nonskeletal material of very fine-silt dimensions can be mapped in the Steelman and Oxbow areas of southeastern Saskatchewan. These deposits are generally extremely well sorted and are thought to have been developed by the attrition of crinoidal, algal, and oölitic material in current-agitated areas. Porosity in this microgranular class of carbonate is high (up to 37 per cent, with permeabilities up to 120 md). The highest permeabilities occur where fossil (generaally ostracode) casts supplement the pore space between the packed granules. This permeability is proportionately reduced when unleached skeletal material remains in the rock. The packed granules (generally in the 0.02–0.06 mm grain-size range) are particularly susceptible to dolomitization processes giving rise to a "crystalline-granular" texture. All transitions to a rhombic dolomite with leached fossil casts can be seen particularly near the subcrop, although in this area the textures are partly masked by secondary anhydrite permeation.

These microgranular carbonates grade vertically and laterally into micrograined, chalky, or cryptograined carbonates. The chalky deposits are partly of chemical origin, but probably represent the "flour" formed by disintegration and abrasion of fossil debris and algal growths developed on the Souris Valley shelf. This "flour" or fine suspension material settled in the quiet-water environments of shelf lagoons and around shoal areas during periods of relative quiescence in current activity. With decrease in grain size and increase in the amount of fine, chalky to clay-like material, the microtextured carbonates lose their oil-wetting ability and have high connate water saturation. The author includes the chalky to microgranular carbonates (grain size 0.01–0.02 mm) in the effective reservoir material because they generally have some oil saturation. The chalky carbonate sections generally contain abundant ostracode remains.

Cryptograined to micrograined carbonates and skeletal to nonskeletal carbonates with a variable, lithified, carbonate-mud matrix are well developed in the intershoal areas. All gradations from cryptograined limestone to skeletal or nonskeletal limestone with, for example, 5–10 per cent cryptograined matrix, can be seen. All this heterogeneous material appears to be genetically related and can be mapped and classed as belonging to the same group of carbonates. It appears ridiculous to place a different energy connotation on carbonates with a variable amount of mud matrix.

Thin stringers of highly permeable, uncemented, well sorted pellet and lump limestones contribute mainly to the high initial flow potential of some of the Florence-Glen Ewen wells. The pellet material is associated with, and grades to the west into, cryptograined limestones containing abundant algal "cabbages," lumps, and scattered leached ostracode casts. Owing to the erratic nature of the pinpoint vugs in the algal material and the development of leached ostracode casts, it is difficult to analyze the effectiveness of this type of limestone, which has a bleeding type of oil staining.

Typical lateral facies and porosity variations of the "Midale" carbonates are shown by Table I.

When a clasticity index approach is applied to "Midale" carbonates, the final textural results can easily be contoured into linear patterns which appear to fit oil-production behavior of the various wells.

The topographical expression of the algal banks west of the evaporite strand line must have had an important influence on current refraction patterns during later "Midale" carbonate deposition. These current patterns sifted the carbonates with effective matrix porosity into linear belts or shoals which run transverse to the Paleozoic subcrop trend of the "Midale" beds. The bar-like trends of carbonates with effective porosity are separated by quiet-water, intershoal areas in which are found higher percentages of shelf-lagoonal carbonate muds, chalky or micrograined carbonates, and fragmentals with a mud matrix, which have no effective porosity. With the use of effective porosity isopachs, isoporosity feet, and facies maps, one can be selective about development and wildcat acreage in an area formerly thought to be one huge stratigraphic pool.

TABLE I. TYPICAL LATERAL FACIES CHANGES OF "MIDALE" CARBONATES

Shoal→	*Intermediate Area*→	*Lagoon*
Uncemented, algal encrusted, lump and pisolitic limestone. Excellent interlump, solution and shrinkage vug porosity. 1% scattered selenite and calcite infilling of vugs. 15% porosity, 600 md. *Effective reservoir.*	Pelleted cryptograined (<0.01 mm) limestone with vague lump bodies. "Syneresis" cracks and shrinkage vugs partially infilled with calcite and clear selenite. 1.5% porosity, 3 md. *Poorly effective reservoir.*	Brown, cryptocrystalline (vitreous) anhydrite with minor intercalations of light brown, pelleted, cryptograined limestone with "birdseye" structures infilled with selenite. *Tight.*
Dolomitized, well-sorted, microgranular (0.04 mm) limestone, 10% leached fossil casts. 30% porosity, 60 md. *Effective reservoir.*	Dolomitized chalky to microgranular (0.01–0.02 mm) limestone with scattered (<1%) pinpoint, intra-ostracode vug porosity. 25% porosity, 2.5 md. *Poorly effective reservoir.*	Chalky to micrograined limestone (very fine silt and clay size intermixture) with 20% ostracodes. Traces very poor pinpoint intraskeletal vug porosity. 8% porosity, 1 md. *Ineffective.*
Skeletal (crinoids and brachiopods) limestone with 30% dolomitized microgranular (0.03 mm) matrix. 15% porosity, 10 md. *Effective reservoir.*	Skeletal limestone with 50% micrograined (clay and very fine silt size intermixture) matrix. Poor pinpoint vug porosity developed at contact of grains and matrix. 5% porosity, 2 md. *Poorly effective reservoir.*	Cryptograined (<0.005 mm) limestone with 30% skeletal (crinoids, brachiopods and ostracodes) material. *Tight.*
Cemented oölitic-skeletal limestone. 15% clear calcite cement. *Tight.*	Oölitic-skeletal with 25% dolomitized microgranular (0.05 mm) matrix. Good intergranular porosity in matrix. Poorly developed intraoölitic vugs partially lined with dolomite euhedra. 12% porosity, 8 md. *Effective Reservoir.*	Chalky limestone with 30% oölitic and ostracode grains. Good chalky and traces of poor intraskeletal and nonskeletal vug porosity. 22% porosity, 2 md. *Ineffective.*
Well sorted, uncemented pellet limestone (average diameter of pellets: 0.15 mm). Good interpellet vug porosity. 21% porosity, 220 md. *Effective reservoir.*	Algal "cabbages" with attached fine pellet material embedded in dolomitized chalky to microgranular matrix (40%). Intra-algal pinpoint vug and intergranular porosity. 16% porosity, 5 md. *Fairly effective reservoir.*	Cryptograined, vaguely pelleted limestone with 30% calcite infilled algal "cabbages." *Tight.*

TEXTURAL AND RESERVOIR PROPERTIES OF THE "ELKTON" CARBONATE CYCLE (TURNER VALLEY FORMATION) IN SOUTHWESTERN ALBERTA[4]

The "Elkton" carbonate cycle is one of several well defined upper Mississippian (Rundle group) shelf-carbonate cycles in southwestern Alberta. Widespread transgressive sheets of coarse, generally dolomitized, fragmental (skeletal) limestones are separated by shallow-water depositional units of silty, locally cherty, lithified carbonate muds which can be established for correlation purposes as time-stratigraphic boundaries.

[4] Summary of discussion by Thomas and Glaister (1960, p. 579–583, 588).

Major hydrocarbon (oil and gas) reserves have already been discovered in the Mississippian "Elkton" carbonate cycle, both in the foothills belt and along the subcrop in southwestern Alberta. The "Elkton" carbonate cycle generally consists of coarse skeletal (predominantly crinoidal) carbonates, ranging in thickness from 80 to 150 feet, and of variable porosity and permeability. These carbonates are overlain and underlain by tight, lithified, silty, carbonate mud deposits up to the subcrop area, where the eroded reservoir material is covered by generally impermeable Mesozoic shales and silty sandstones.

Porosity and permeability properties of the producing intervals in the major oil and gas fields, situated at or near the "Elkton" subcrop, can be directly related to quantitative carbonate textural measurements. In most of this area, as opposed to the "Midale" cycle, mechanical logs (neutron, microlog, and microlaterolog) can be used to differentiate effective and noneffective reservoir types. Effective reservoir material of this cycle was found to consist mainly of the dolomitized equivalent of an originally coarse skeletal limestone with a variable amount of porous, finely comminuted (granular) skeletal matrix. Primary porosity was very important in the control of dolomitization, which began with the replacement of this matrix by euhedral rhombohedrons and finally affected the coarse, skeletal material (now generally indicated by leached fossil-cast outlines). These porous dolomites grade laterally in a predictable way into tight, relatively nondolomitized, well sorted, coarse skeletal limestones, with original high interfragmental porosity now completely infilled with clear crystalline calcite. This lithification by cementation took place early in the history of carbonate sedimentation of this area and before secondary dolomitization processes took effect. The very nature of the clear crystalline calcite cement infilling of primary interfragmental porosity inhibited dolomitization. Dolomitization of these limestones could develop along cleavage cracks in the calcite cement or along incipient fractures. Cemented skeletal or nonskeletal limestones in Devonian or Mississippian sections of the Rockies or foothills belt generally show effects of dolomitization processes as a result of stresses induced by mountain building. Present hydrocarbon accumulation along the subcrop is controlled largely by up-dip truncation of the "Elkton" member. However, it is also strongly influenced by primary porosity pinchouts caused by lateral facies changes from dolomitized, leached, skeletal limestones with matrix, into tight, cemented, skeletal limestones. Similar facies changes exist in the Turner Valley oil field, suggesting primary hydrocarbon accumulation in the "Elkton" member before the Laramide structural movements took place.

Oölitic and associated surficially coated grains occur locally in cemented skeletal limestones of the "Elkton" member. For mapping purposes, these generally cemented, well-sorted, oölitic limestones can be grouped with cemented skeletal limestones with which they are closely associated. Oölites are rare in unsorted skeletal limestones. Of local interest are the skeletal or nonskeletal limestones containing a dolomitized chalky matrix. Poor grain sorting, pressure of delicate bryozoan fronds, and chalky to micrograined matrix, all suggest sheltered, quiet-water conditions of deposition.

The only extensively developed reservoir rock in the "Elkton" member is dolomite. Investigations so far completed suggest that secondary dolomitization of skeletal and other limestones took place on a volume-for-volume relationship, and that the porosity of the resultant dolomite (apart from leaching effects) was inherited from the original limestone. The secondary dolomites are generally coarse grained, many of them with relict limestone textures or casts of fossil debris. On the basis of relict textures in these dolomites, it is possible to carry the zonation of limestone textural types into predominantly dolomite sections.

With regard to the relation of dolomite development to textural features of original limestones, it has been observed that dolomite preferentially occurs in open pores or in matrix (chalky, granular, and carbonate mud) material that surrounds the larger skeletal or nonskeletal grains. These larger grains are generally the last to show conversion to dolomite. The final type in this sequence is a dolomite with fossil casts. This preferential development of dolomite in certain textural components of the original limestone suggests that dolomitization processes are strongly controlled by the pressure of fluids in interfragmental or intergranular porosity, or by carbonate mud material that had a high fluid content.

Highest permeabilities occur where fossil casts supplement the pore space between the packed dolomite rhombs. This permeability is proportionately reduced when relict unleached skeletal material remains in the rock.

It is possible to designate the composition of the original matrix material through studies of the grain size and shape of the resultant dolomite. An interlocking or anhedral type of crypto-microcrystalline dolomite matrix is interpreted as derived from carbonate mud. The comminuted

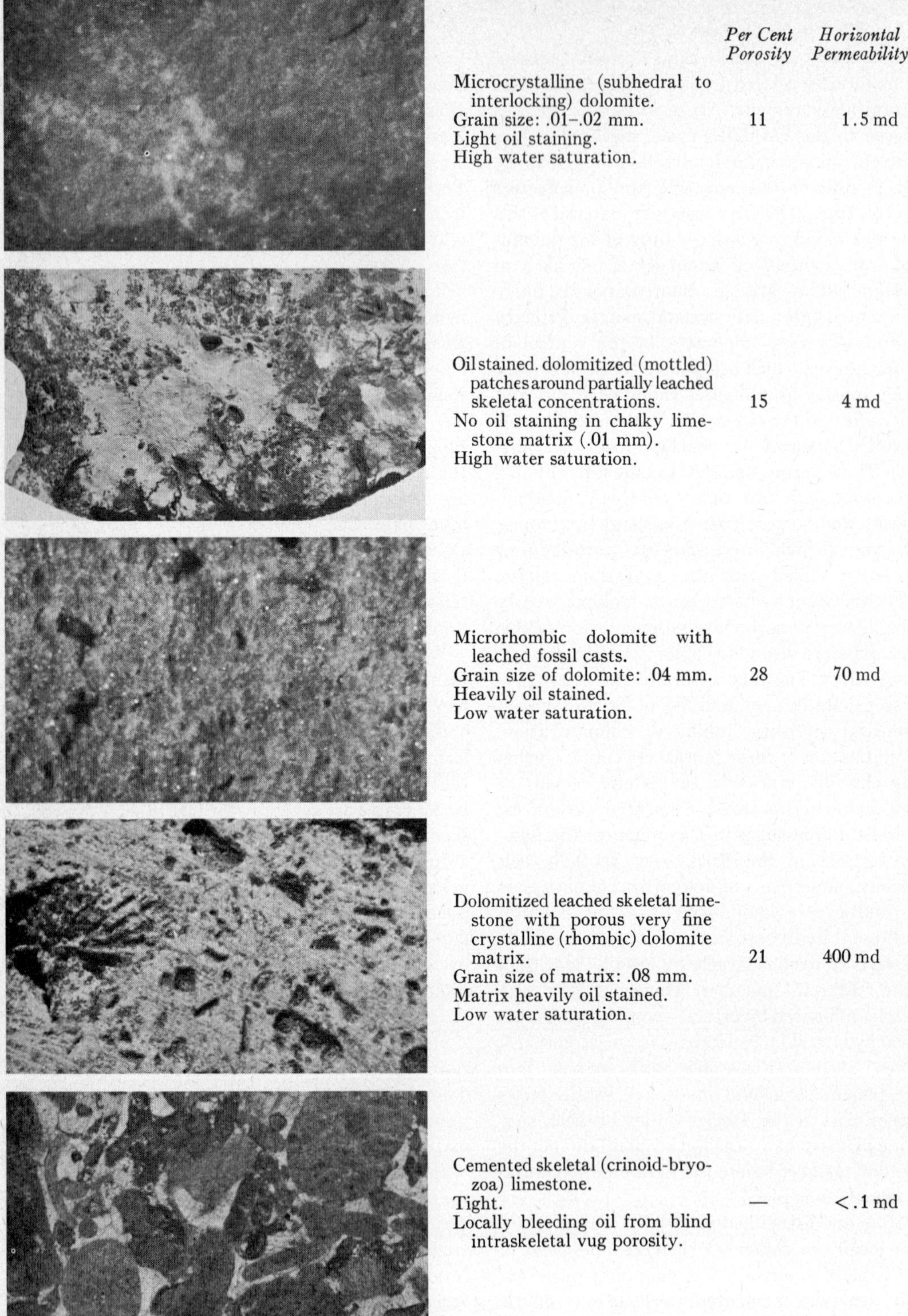

	Per Cent Porosity	Horizontal Permeability
Microcrystalline (subhedral to interlocking) dolomite. Grain size: .01–.02 mm. Light oil staining. High water saturation.	11	1.5 md
Oil stained. dolomitized (mottled) patches around partially leached skeletal concentrations. No oil staining in chalky limestone matrix (.01 mm). High water saturation.	15	4 md
Microrhombic dolomite with leached fossil casts. Grain size of dolomite: .04 mm. Heavily oil stained. Low water saturation.	28	70 md
Dolomitized leached skeletal limestone with porous very fine crystalline (rhombic) dolomite matrix. Grain size of matrix: .08 mm. Matrix heavily oil stained. Low water saturation.	21	400 md
Cemented skeletal (crinoid-bryozoa) limestone. Tight. Locally bleeding oil from blind intraskeletal vug porosity.	—	<.1 md

PLATE VI.—Relation of textural variations. "Elkton" carbonates with oil-saturation and porosity-permeability determinations.

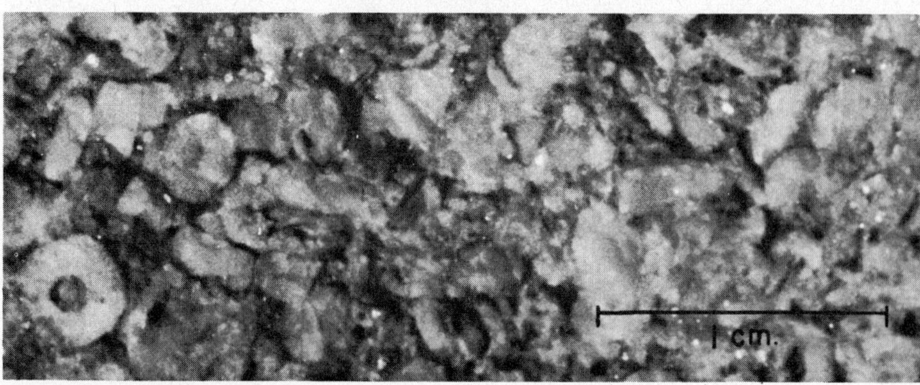

A—Dolomitized uncemented skeletal (crinoidal) limestone. Good interskeletal vug void spaces partially lined with dolomite euhedral crystals. ×4.

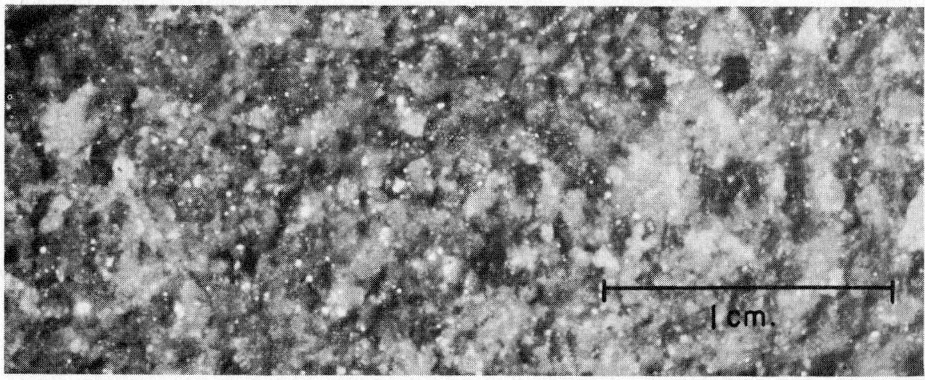

B—Dolomitized partially leached skeletal limestone with porous medium crystalline (subhedral to euhedral) dolomite matrix. Fair intercrystalline and vug porosity. Original skeletal grain outlines ill-defined. ×4.

C—Medium to coarse "rhombic" dolomite with good intercrystalline porosity. Original skeletal grain outlines completely destroyed. ×3.

PLATE VII.—"Elkton" carbonates demonstration series, illustrating progressive destruction of skeletal grain outlines during dolomitization.

or pulverized, generally porous, granular and chalky material, either of skeletal or nonskeletal origin, commonly contributes to matrix or intergranular porosity in carbonate reservoirs. On dolomitization, this porous material gives rise to subhedral or euhedral (rhombic) dolomites with intercrystalline porosity, unless the enlargement of the granules has continued too far to produce "mosaic" textural types.

There appears to be a progressive destruction of skeletal- or nonskeletal-grain outlines during the process of dolomitization of originally uncemented, skeletal or nonskeletal limestone types. The end result of such dolomitization is the production of medium- to coarse-crystalline dolomite, the generic implications of which are in doubt. This type of material is common in the stratigraphic column of the Western Canada basin (for example, the Devonian Nisku formation). Where definite skeletal-grain outlines have been destroyed and replaced by medium to coarse dolomite crystals, a crystallinity (dolomite grain size and shape) ratio map is of great value in differentiating dolomitized fragmental and dolomitized carbonate mud areas.

The micro- to fine-rhombic dolomites with leached fossil casts are considered to be the dolomitized equivalents of comminuted, skeletal or nonskeletal grains in current-agitated areas. Porosity in this class of carbonate is high, but permeability is high only where fossil casts supplement the pore space between the packed granules. Complex intermixtures of this group of carbonates with effective matrix and vug porosity and chalky to earthy carbonates with no effective porosity are generally found at the top of the "Elkton" member.

All gradations from original cryptograined limestone to relict skeletal or nonskeletal limestone (for example, with 5–10 per cent cryptograined

TABLE II. TYPICAL LATERAL FACIES CHANGES OF "ELKTON" CARBONATES

Shoal→	*Intermediate Area→*	*Lagoon*
Microrhombic dolomite with 10% leached fossil casts. 2% light gray, decomposed, nodular chert inclusions. 16% porosity, 40 md. *Effective reservoir.*	Microcrystalline (subhedral to interlocking) dolomite with traces of very poor pinpoint, intraskeletal vug porosity. Poor intercrystalline porosity. 10% gray nodular chert inclusions. 7% porosity, 1.5 md. *Poorly effective reservoir.*	Crypto-microcrystalline (anhedral-interlocking) dolomite. 15–20% dark-gray nodular chert inclusions. *Tight.*
Cemented, coarse skeletal (well sorted crinoidal and bryozoan debris) limestone. 15% clear calcite cement. *Tight.*	Dolomitized leached skeletal limestone with 30% fine rhombic dolomite matrix. Excellent relict skeletal vug and intercrystalline porosity. 21% porosity, 400 md. *Effective reservoir.*	Dolomitized partially leached mottled skeletal limestone with 50% microcrystalline, interlocking dolomite matrix. Relatively blind skeletal vug porosity mantled with coarser dolomite development. 40% porosity, 4 md. *Poorly effective reservoir.*
Coarse, subhedral to euhedral dolomite (dolomitized uncemented skeletal limestone). Excellent intercrystalline porosity. 28% porosity, 300 md. *Effective reservoir.*	Dolomitized leached skeletal limestone with 20% fine to medium rhombic dolomite matrix. Good leached skeletal vug and intercrystalline porosity. 19% porosity, 150 md. *Effective reservoir.*	Fine crystalline (subhedral to euhedral) dolomite with 10% leached skeletal vugs. 18% porosity, 70 md. *Effective reservoir.*
Cemented oölitic-skeletal limestone. 10% clear calcite cement. Traces of very poor intraoölitic vug porosity. 2% porosity, 0.2 md. *Ineffective.*	Oölitic-skeletal limestone with 15% slightly dolomitized chalky matrix. Poor intraoölitic and pinpoint vug porosity at contact of grains and matrix. 15% porosity, 2.5 md. *Poorly effective reservoir.*	Oölitic-skeletal limestone with 40% micrograined (very fine silt and clay size intermixture) matrix. Traces of poor, blind, intraoölitic blind vug porosity. 5% porosity, 0.8 md. *Ineffective.*

matrix) can be seen. Carbonate muds, probably because of an original high fluid content, alter easily to a crypto-microcrystalline, anhedral to subhedral, interlocking type of dolomite with little or no effective porosity. However, the skeletal or nonskeletal grains embedded in this original carbonate mud material are locally leached to produce generally poorly effective vug porosity. Typical lateral facies and porosity variations of "Elkton" carbonates are shown in Table II.

UPPER DEVONIAN DOLOMITE AND LIMESTONE REEF COMPLEXES, EDMONTON AND SWAN HILLS AREAS, ALBERTA[5]

Carbonate textural and reservoir evaluation techniques employed in an analysis of transgressive, reef-fringed, limestone banks or platforms of the Beaverhill Lake formation in the Swan Hills region of Alberta are compared to those utilized in the partitioning of a Nisku, regressive, dolomitized biostromal-evaporite complex in the Edmonton and Red Deer areas.

[5] Summary of discussions by Thomas and Rhodes (1960, 1961).

DEVONIAN LIMESTONE, BANK-ATOLL RESERVOIRS OF THE SWAN HILLS AREA, ALBERTA[6]

Figure 3 is an index map of the areas of study in Alberta, Canada.

Figure 4 is a chart showing the approximate correlations of Upper Devonian formations and groups from the disturbed belt to the plains area of Alberta.

Carbonate textural and reservoir evaluation techniques employed in the analysis of transgressive, reef-fringed, limestone banks or platforms of the Upper Devonian Beaverhill Lake formation in this highly prospective oil and gas area of Alberta, will now be briefly outlined. These reef-fringed carbonate banks, termed the Swan Hills member by Fong (1960), are overlain by impermeable calcareous shales and argillaceous limestones and were developed on the shelf margins of an expanding Beaverhill Lake basin.

An isopach map of the Swan Hills carbonates, showing early 1960 outlines of the various producing oil fields, is shown in Figure 5. This map, apart from illustrating the expanding to discrete out-

[6] Thomas and Rhodes (1961, p. 30–38).

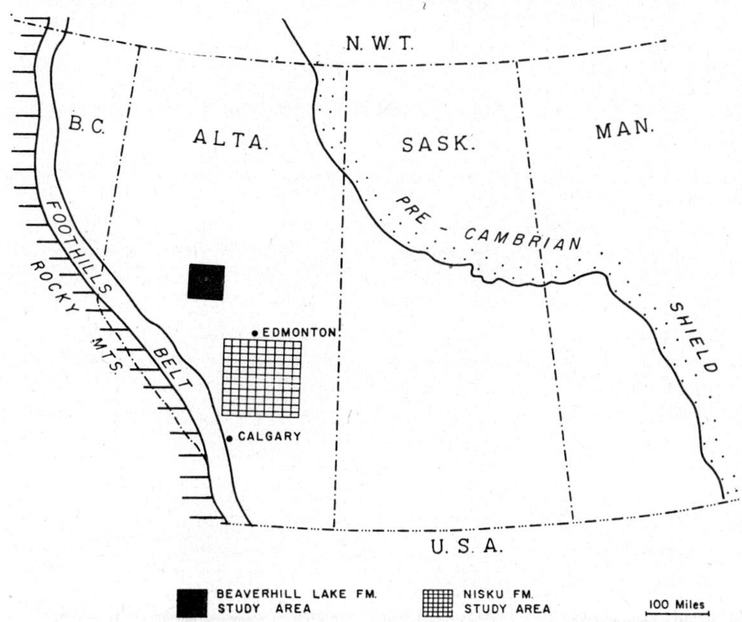

FIG. 3.—Index map of areas of study of Beaverhill Lake and Nisku reservoirs in Swan Hills and Edmonton-Red Deer areas, Alberta.

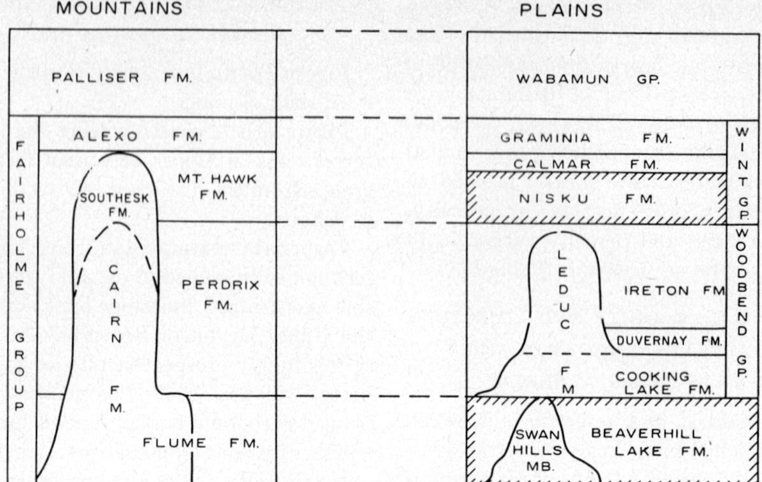

FIG. 4.—Upper Devonian correlation chart, central Alberta.

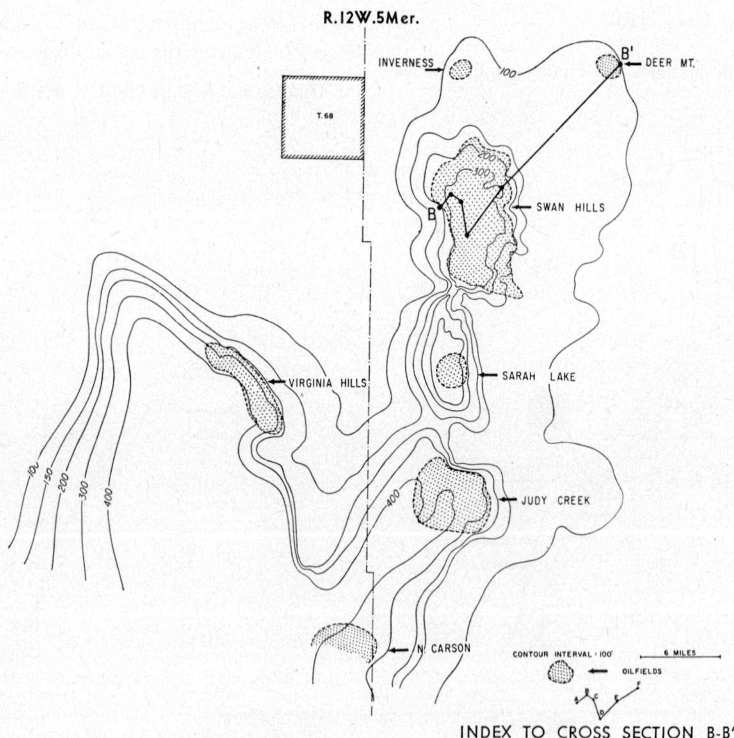

FIG. 5.—Isopach map of Swan Hills member carbonates of Beaverhill Lake formation, and producing oil fields, central Alberta. *B-B'* is trace of section shown in Fig. 6.

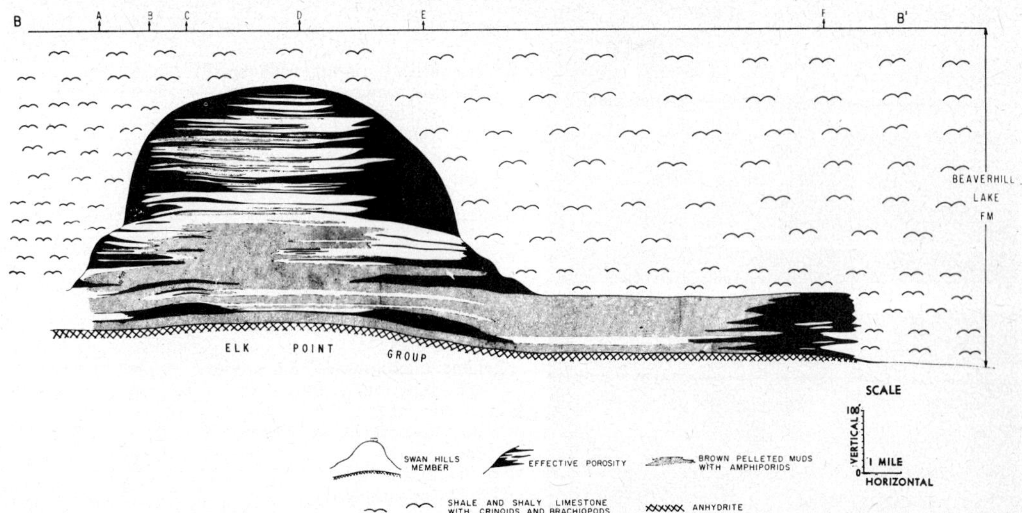

FIG. 6.—Effective reservoir and source-rock relationships, Swan Hills member of Beaverhill Lake formation, central Alberta. Trace of section shown by line *B-B'*, Fig. 5.

lines of some of the oil fields, shows the rapid increase in thickness of what one would normally assume to be potential reservoir carbonates above the 200-foot isopach. However, unlike some of the narrow Leduc reef trends of central Alberta, the thickest developments of Swan Hills carbonates, such as in the West Virginia Hills area, contain little or no effective porosity. Intermediate thicknesses such as those between 175 and 350 foot isopach values commonly contain the most effective porosity. Exploration and exploitation programs can be considerably simplified once this marginal or rim porosity is understood.

Cross section *B-B'* (Fig. 6), which crosses the Swan Hills oil field (see Fig. 5), should help to explain the distribution of effective reservoir carbonates in this area. Successive rims of organic lattice, stromatoporoidal and algal, atoll-like

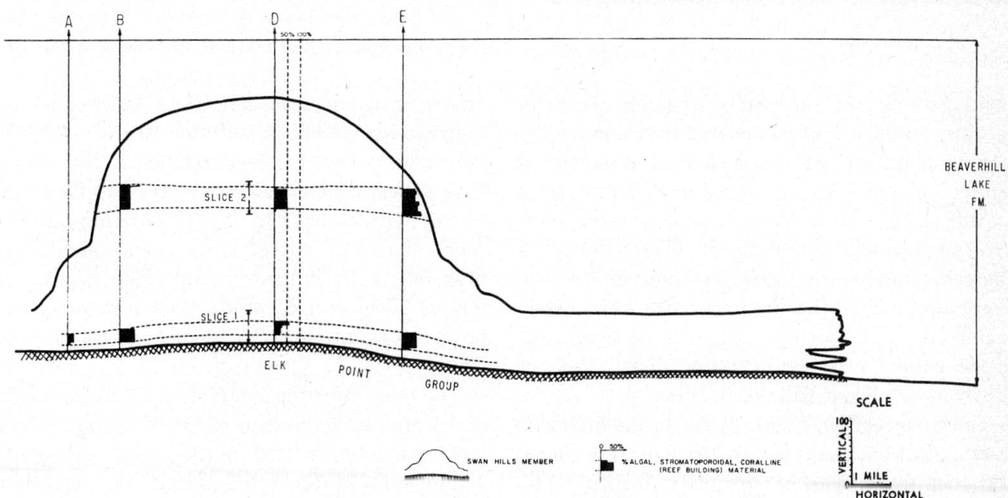

FIG. 7.—Index cross section showing 50-foot intervals of slice maps 1 and 2, Figs. 12 and 13.

		Per Cent Porosity	Horizontal Permeability
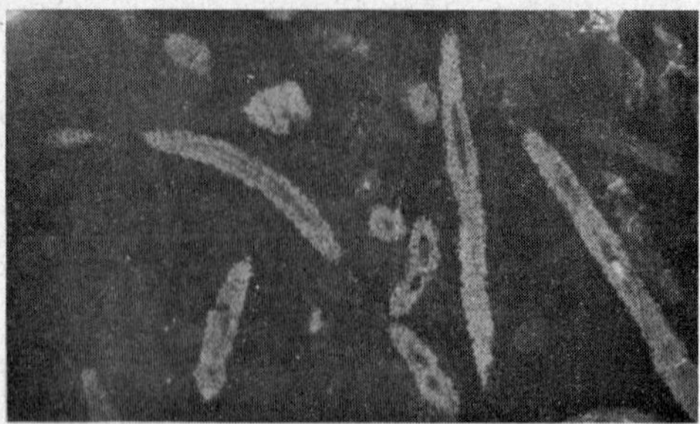	Calcite-infilled amphiporids embedded in brown, pelleted, cryptograined limestone matrix (less than .005 mm.). Calcispheres and calcite "birdseyes" in groundmass. Tight.	—	<0.1 md
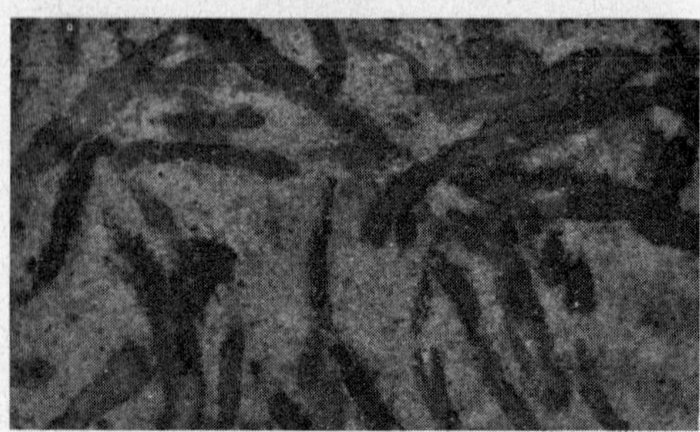	Skeletal micrograined limestone with calcite-infilled amphiporids. Grain size of matrix: <.01–.03 mm (clay and silt-size intermixture). No oil staining in matrix. High water saturation.	5	1.2 md
	Partially leached amphiporids embedded in well sorted, very fine granular matrix. Grain size of matrix: .08 mm. Matrix heavily oil stained. Low water saturation.	19	60 md

PLATE VIII.—Relation of textural variations. Swan Hills memb

buildups with granular matrix, separate, generally medium to dark brown, pelleted lime muds containing abundant amphiporids and intercalated lighter colored lagoonal carbonates from open-marine shales and nodular, argillaceous, crinoid- and brachiopod-rich limestones. The thickness of the relict, upper evaporite sequence of the Elk Point group and the accompanying minor terracing on the sea bottom, appear to be significant in the control of facies type and distribution of the overlying Swan Hills carbonates.

The cross section, Figure 7, shows the intervals used in the accompanying textural porosity charts and slice maps. The brown, pelleted lime muds with abundant amphiporids and associated organisms contain bituminous shale partings and were probably precipitated by algal activity under stagnant, nonaerated conditions in intershoal or lagoonal areas. The appellation "Brown-Reef" or "Reef Platform" has been applied to this source-rock facies, which could well have supplied some of the hydrocarbons to the surrounding reservoir rocks. This facies is of great environmental significance, as it indicates somewhere a potential porous shoal fringe, which need not necessarily have been continuous to restrict sea water circulation.

The most effective reservoir material along the reef fronts or terraces consists of vuggy organic lattice, algal-encrusted amphiporids (minor developments), uncemented skeletal or nonskeletal limestone, and reworked stromatoporoidal, algal, and amphiporid material with intraorganic vugs embedded in a porous, well sorted, micro- to

Calcite-infilled stromatoporoids embedded in brown, vaguely pelleted cryptograined limestone matrix (less than .005 mm). Tight. — < .1 md

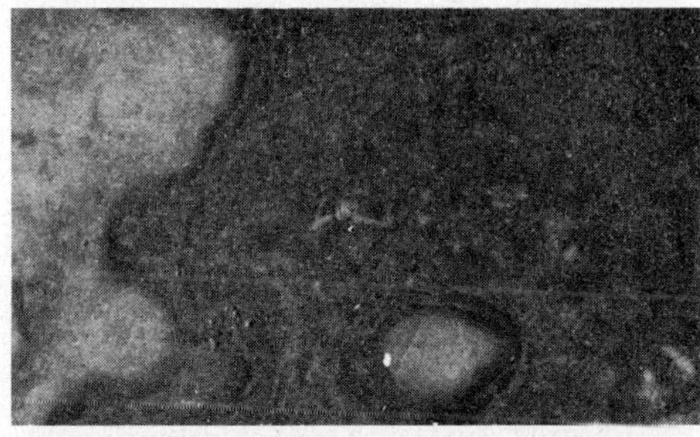

Skeletal microgranular limestone with calcite-infilled stromatoporoids. Grain size of matrix: .01–.02 mm. Light oil staining in matrix. Medium water saturation. 9 3 md

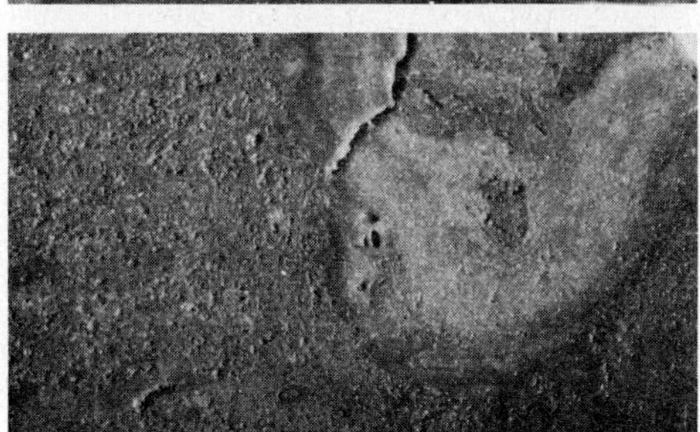

Stromatoporoids with poor intraorganic vug porosity embedded in well sorted fine granular matrix. Grain size of matrix: .15 mm. Matrix heavily oil stained. Low water saturation. 18 90 md

rbonates with oil-saturation and porosity-permeability determinations.

finely granular matrix. Matrix grain size and sorting studies are essential in exploration and secondary recovery plans, for the granular material grades laterally into chalky or micrograined ostracode-rich limestones, which were laid down under lower energy conditions. Matrix granularity ratio outlines are considered to be superior to ecological maps (percentage of algal and stromatoporoidal material) in the prediction of shoal areas. The same percentages of stromatoporoidal material can be found embedded in completely different carbonate matrices, ranging from porous microgranular limestone to tight, brown, pelleted cryptograined limestone. Periodic cessation of reef growth and destruction processes are indicated by mud intercalations and minor partings of calcareous shale.

The lithological legend of Figure 8 explains the symbols used in the textural and porosity charts. These black and white graphic symbols can be plotted directly on graph paper sepia. Porosity and permeability determinations can always be added later to this easily reproducible system of logging. Figure 9 indicates that there is good correlation between the author's type of quantitative sample logging and porosity-permeability determinations. It will be noted that although the ecological significance of particular grain types is recognized, particular emphasis is placed on size, shape, and sorting of common carbonate matrices and the presence or absence of cement. The gradations from cryptograined (clay-sized) matrix through micrograined (clay and silt) intermixture matrix, to porous microgranular (well-sorted, silt-

		Per Cent Porosity	*Horizontal Permeability*
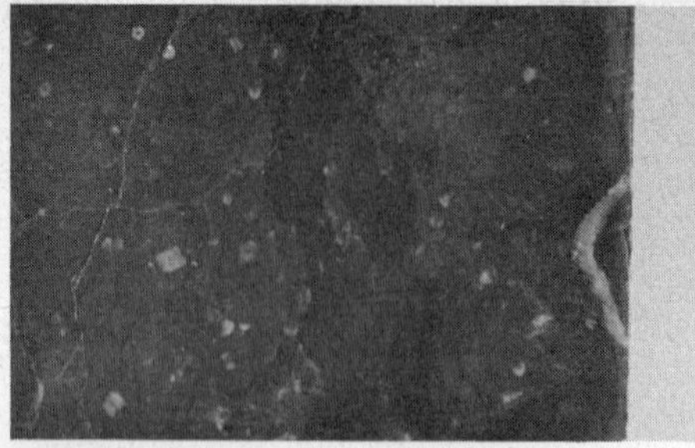	Nodular, argillaceous, cryptograined limestone with 10% crinoid ossicles and brachiopod valves, irregular laminae of greenish-gray calcareous shale. Tight. Open marine facies.	—	<0.1 md
	Vuggy organic lattice as below. Horizontal core.	3	80 md
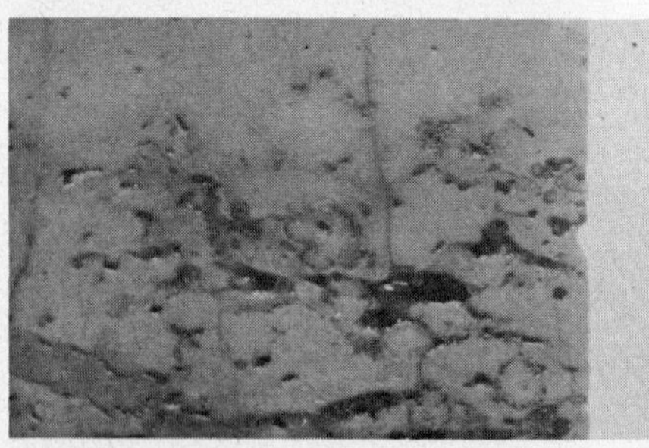	Vuggy organic lattice. Vertical core. Algal-encrusted partially leached amphiporids. Vague pellet and lump bodies in cryptograined limestone material. Shrinkage, solution and intraorganic vugs partially infilled with calcite and selenite.	3	80 md
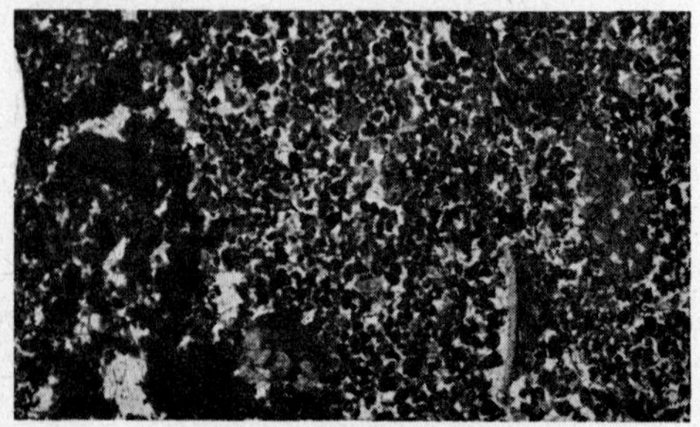	Intermixture of brown, pelleted mud containing "syneresis" cracks and sinuous "birdseye" patches infilled with clear crystalline calcite with cemented pellet limestone (5% amphiporids). Average diameter of pellets: .1 mm Tight.	—	<0.1 md
	Uncemented skeletal (gastropod)-lump (algal) limestone. Excellent interlump and leached gastropod cast vug porosity.	20	320 md

PLATE IX.—Relation of textural variations. Swan Hills member carbonates with porosity-permeability determinations. ×0.7.

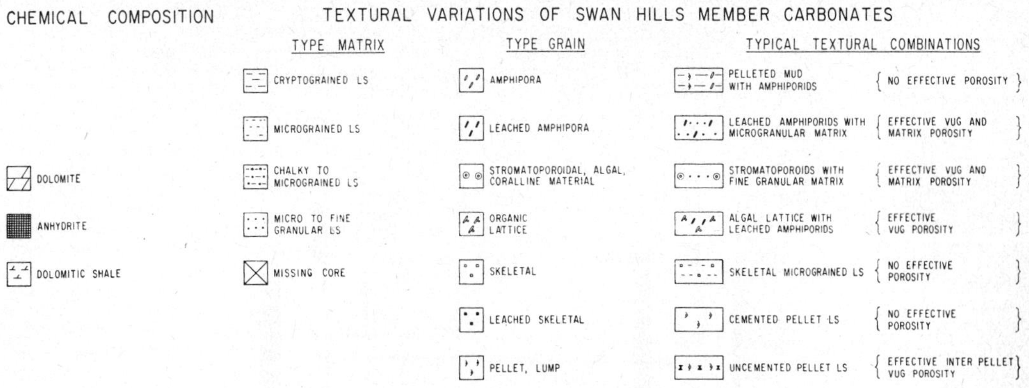

CHEMICAL COMPOSITION

DOLOMITE

ANHYDRITE

DOLOMITIC SHALE

TEXTURAL VARIATIONS OF SWAN HILLS MEMBER CARBONATES

TYPE MATRIX

CRYPTOGRAINED LS

MICROGRAINED LS

CHALKY TO MICROGRAINED LS

MICRO TO FINE GRANULAR LS

MISSING CORE

TYPE GRAIN

AMPHIPORA

LEACHED AMPHIPORA

STROMATOPOROIDAL, ALGAL, CORALLINE MATERIAL

ORGANIC LATTICE

SKELETAL

LEACHED SKELETAL

PELLET, LUMP

TYPICAL TEXTURAL COMBINATIONS

PELLETED MUD WITH AMPHIPORIDS { NO EFFECTIVE POROSITY }

LEACHED AMPHIPORIDS WITH MICROGRANULAR MATRIX { EFFECTIVE VUG AND MATRIX POROSITY }

STROMATOPOROIDS WITH FINE GRANULAR MATRIX { EFFECTIVE VUG AND MATRIX POROSITY }

ALGAL LATTICE WITH LEACHED AMPHIPORIDS { EFFECTIVE VUG POROSITY }

SKELETAL MICROGRAINED LS { NO EFFECTIVE POROSITY }

CEMENTED PELLET LS { NO EFFECTIVE POROSITY }

UNCEMENTED PELLET LS { EFFECTIVE INTER PELLET VUG POROSITY }

FIG. 8.—Lithologic legend for Figs. 9, 10, and 11.

sized) matrix not only supplies one with excellent mappable parameters for exploration purposes, but reflects the oil-saturation properties of the carbonate rock. In secondary recovery and other reservoir engineering analyses, such studies are fundamental.

Frequency curves or histograms of stromatoporoidal, algal, and coralline material (potential organic lattice) in combination with carbonate textural rhythms enable one to zone the reef complex into a series of broad cycles. The charts of Figures 10 and 11 illustrate the lateral, textural, and effective-porosity variations from a series of marginal shoals in Well *B* to an interior lagoonal sequence shown by Well *D*. The typical lateral facies changes from marginal shoal to lagoon are shown in Table III. The relatively high concentration (locally up to 80 per cent) of well-preserved amphiporids and associated organisms in the lagoonal areas can be explained by the better preservation of organic material in quiet-water conditions, and also by the fact that such fossils

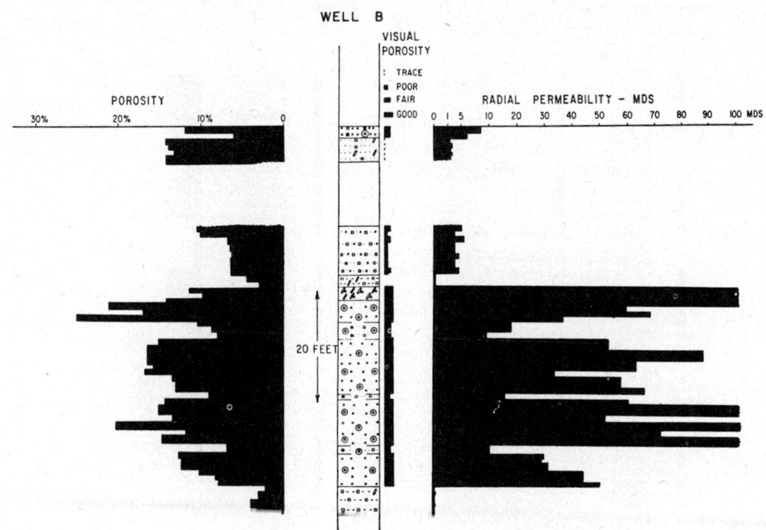

FIG. 9.—Textural, porosity, and permeability relationships in upper Swan Hills member, Swan Hills oil field.

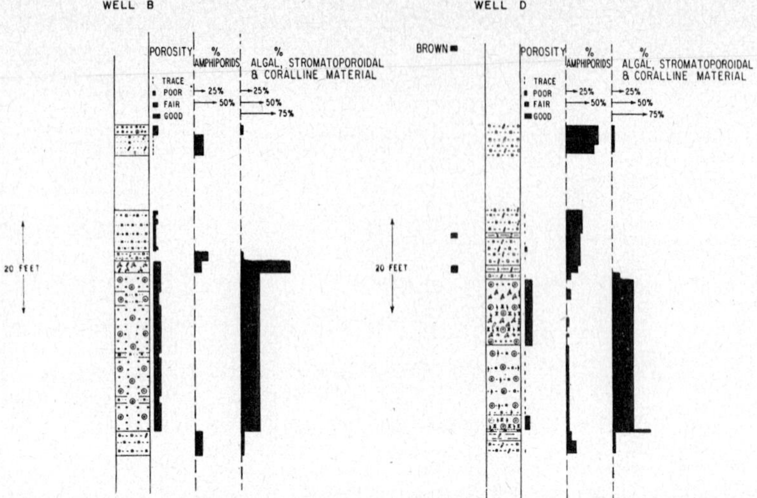

FIG. 10.—Lateral textural and porosity variations in lower Swan Hills member, Swan Hills oil field.

were easily broken up in the shoal areas to give rise to effective "granular" matrix porosity.

Textural and effective-porosity studies in combination with mechanical-log and isopach work have been applied to the construction of the slice maps, Figures 12 and 13. These slice maps are used to demonstrate transgressive shoals and progressive submergence of the bank atolls of this area.

Slice map 1 (Fig. 12) of the basal portion of the Swan Hills member indicates that even at this early stage of sedimentation, the area was dif-

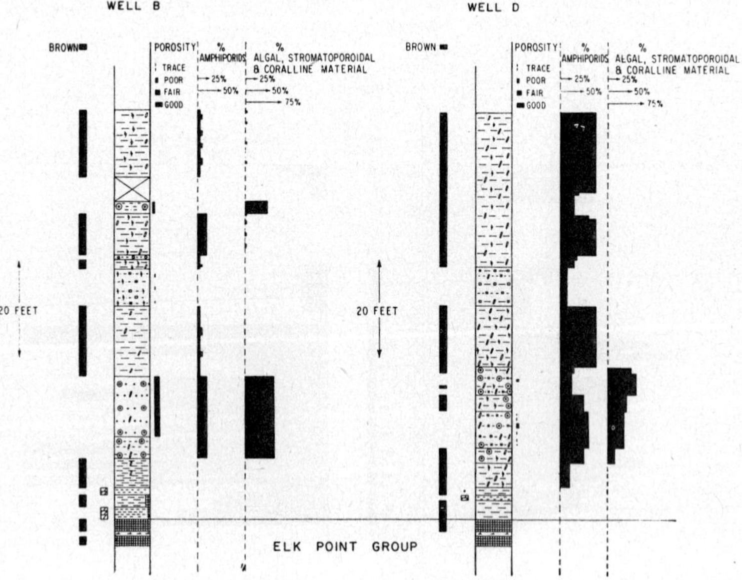

FIG. 11.—Lateral textural and porosity variations in upper Swan Hills member, Swan Hills oil field.

TABLE III. TYPICAL LATERAL FACIES CHANGES OF SWAN HILLS MEMBER CARBONATES

Marginal Shoal→	*Intermediate Area→*	*Lagoon*
Partially leached stromatoporoids with porous microgranular matrix. 18% porosity, 60 md. *Effective reservoir*	Stromatoporoids with poor intraorganic vug porosity in chalky to micrograined matrix. Poorly effective vug porosity. Ineffective matrix porosity. 8% porosity, 2.5 md. *Poorly effective reservoir.*	Stromatoporoids with brown, vaguely pelleted cryptograined matrix. *Tight.*
Partially leached amphiporids (10%) in very fine granular matrix (reworked stromatoporoidal material). 14% porosity, 40 md. *Effective reservoir.*	Amphiporids (20%) with poor intraorganic vug porosity in chalky to micrograined matrix. Ineffective matrix porosity. 6% porosity, 2 md. *Poorly effective reservoir.*	Skeletal (ostracode) micrograined limestone with 25% calcite-infilled amphiporids. *Tight.*
Algal encrusted partially leached amphiporid material (10%) with excellent shrinkage, solution, and intraorganic vug porosity. 7% porosity, 200 md. *Effective reservoir.*		Cryptograined limestone, with vague algal biscuit bodies and calcite-infilled amphiporids (20%). *Tight.*
Skeletal (ostracodes with poor intraorganic vug porosity) limestone with chalky matrix, amphiporids (15%) with traces of poor intraorganic vug porosity. 10% porosity, 1.5 md. *Doubtful to ineffective reservoir.*	Skeletal (ostracode) pellet limestone with micrograined matrix, calcite-infilled amphiporids (25%). *Tight.*	Brown pelleted, cryptograined limestone, "syneresis" cracks and "birds-eye" structures infilled with calcite cement (60%), calcite infilled amphiporids. *Tight.*
Uncemented skeletal (gastropod) lump (algal) limestone. Excellent intraskeletal and interlump vug porosity. 19% porosity, 250 md. *Effective reservoir.*	Partially cemented skeletal-lump limestone. Gastropod casts infilled with clear calcite. Fair interlump vug porosity. 8% porosity, 25 md. *Effective reservoir.*	Skeletal-lump limestone with 15% micrograined matrix. Patches of calcite and selenite cement at contact of grains and matrix. Poor blind interlump vug porosity. 4% porosity, 1.8 md. *Poorly effective reservoir.*
Well sorted, pellet limestone (0.17 mm) with 20% partially leached stromatoporoids. 21% porosity, 220 md. *Effective reservoir.*	Well sorted, fine granular limestone. 15% stromatoporoids and 10% amphiporids with intraorganic vug porosity. 18% porosity, 60 md. *Effective reservoir.*	Fine-grained (fine sand and clay-size intermixture) limestone, 10% stromatoporoids, 20% calcite-infilled amphiporids. *Tight.*

ferentiated into porous marginal shoals and interior restricted lagoons. There appears to be better porosity development in the marginal shoals on the eastern side of the banks. On the more sheltered western rims, shaly, crinoid- and brachiopod-rich limestones are found intercalated with brown pelleted muds and light-colored skeletal micrograined limestones.

Slice map 2 (Fig. 13) well illustrates the narrow, elongate reef terrace of the Sarah Lake-Swan Hills trend which is developed on a brown, pelleted mud platform, and has fairly continuous matrix and vug porosity on its rims, with inner lagoons, consisting of chalky to micrograined, locally pellet and ostracode-rich limestones. This terrace appears to be separated from Judy Creek and the much broader Virginia Hills platforms, found to the south and west, which consist largely of lime muds and skeletal or pellet micrograined limestones fringed with very narrow reef to reefoid rims. Dolomitization patterns in the banks developed in the Windfall area to the south appear to be controlled by the size and sorting of the carbonate matrices and by the presence or ab-

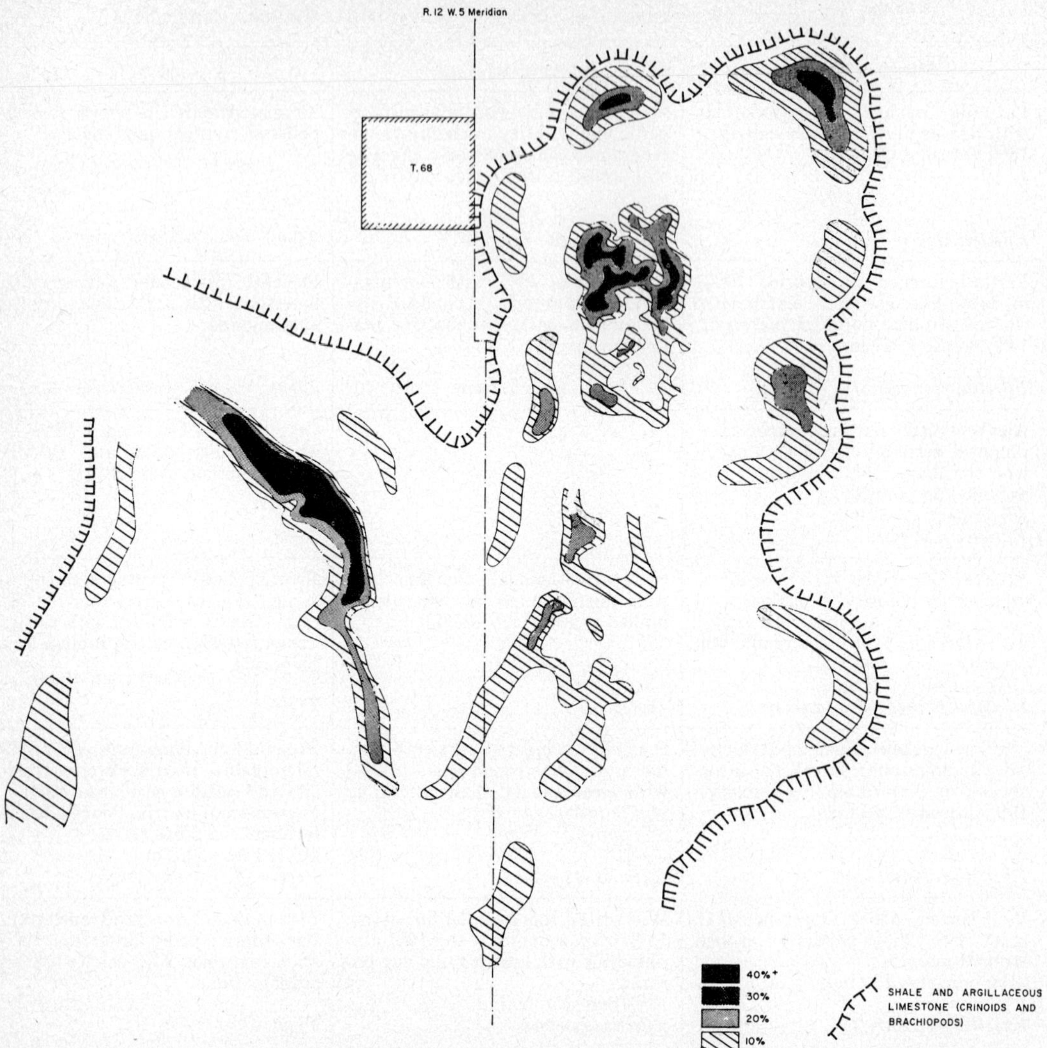

FIG. 12.—Slice map 1, 50-foot interval of Swan Hills member, showing percentage of effective matrix and intraorganic vug porosity.

sence of calcite cement in lump or pellet limestones.

TEXTURAL AND RESERVOIR PROPERTIES OF THE NISKU CARBONATE-EVAPORITE REEF COMPLEX OF THE EDMONTON AND RED DEER AREAS, ALBERTA[7]

Several major oil and gas fields have been discovered in the Upper Devonian Nisku formation, which is preserved over a large area in Central Alberta. It is lithologically complex and contains a large amount of reservoir and numerous stratigraphic and/or structural traps.

The morphological expression of the underlying Leduc reef platforms and carbonate buildups in the Duvernay formation strongly influences facies variations of the Nisku carbonate-evaporite unit. The Leduc platform index map of Figure 14 and the accompanying, very generalized, Nisku

[7] Thomas and Rhodes (1960), expanded.

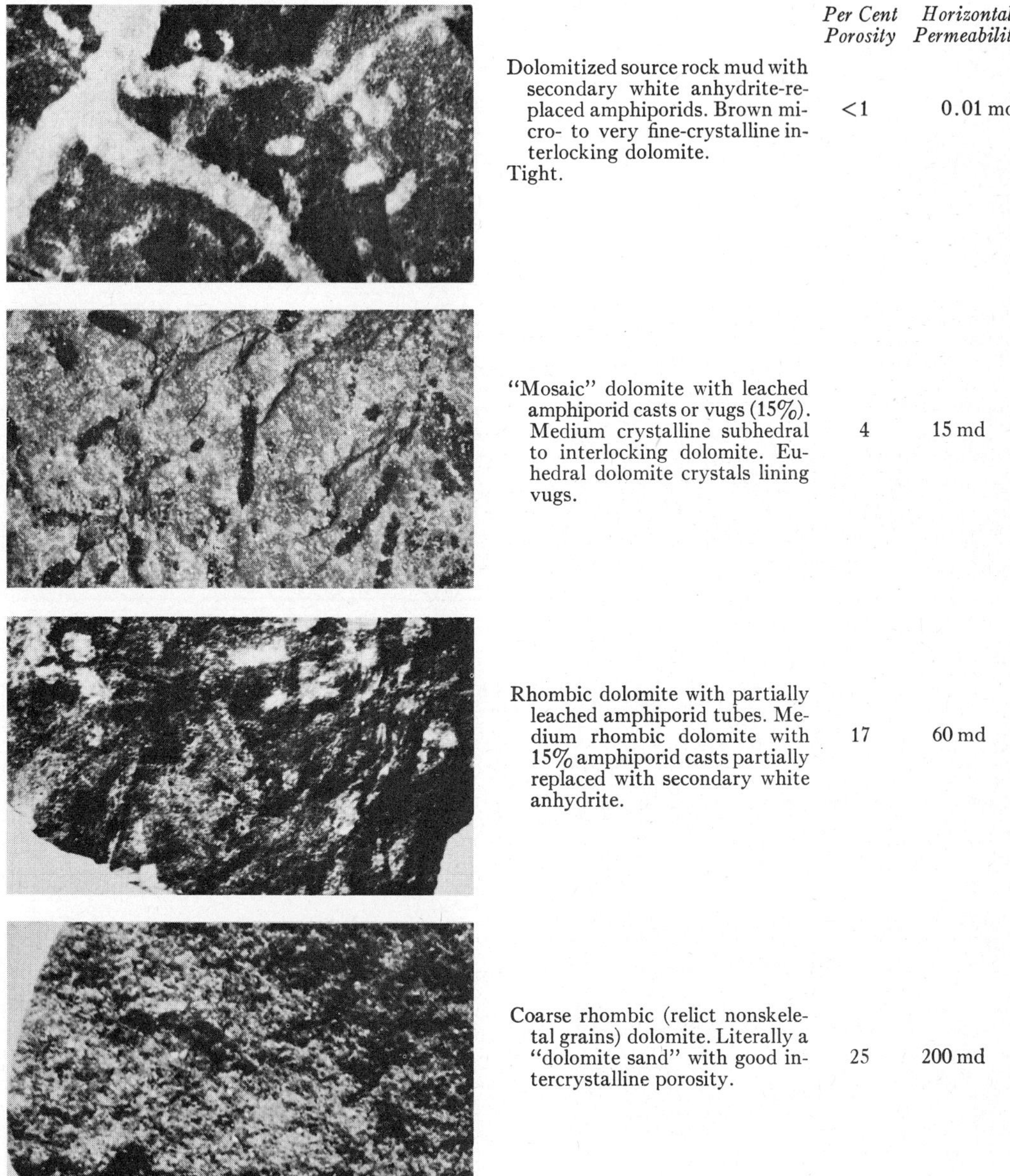

	Per Cent Porosity	*Horizontal Permeability*
Dolomitized source rock mud with secondary white anhydrite-replaced amphiporids. Brown micro- to very fine-crystalline interlocking dolomite. Tight.	<1	0.01 md
"Mosaic" dolomite with leached amphiporid casts or vugs (15%). Medium crystalline subhedral to interlocking dolomite. Euhedral dolomite crystals lining vugs.	4	15 md
Rhombic dolomite with partially leached amphiporid tubes. Medium rhombic dolomite with 15% amphiporid casts partially replaced with secondary white anhydrite.	17	60 md
Coarse rhombic (relict nonskeletal grains) dolomite. Literally a "dolomite sand" with good intercrystalline porosity.	25	200 md

PLATE X.—Relation of textural variations. Nisku carbonates with porosity-permeability determinations. ×1.0.

		Per Cent Porosity	*Horizontal Permeability*
	Nodular, argillaceous, cryptograined limestone with 5% crinoid ossicles. Irregular laminae of greenish-gray calcareous shale. Open marine facies. Tight.	—	<0.1 md
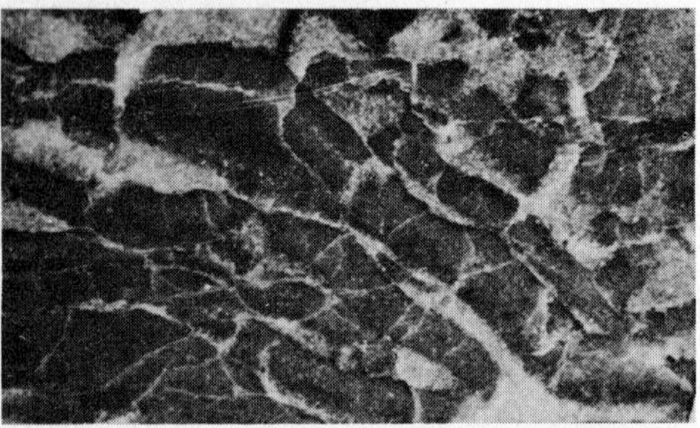	Secondary anhydrite infilled, dolomitized organic lattice. Layered, relict stromatoporoidal and algal material (now represented by very fine mosaic dolomite) has been rafted locally by anhydrite crystallization effects. Tight.	—	—
	Vuggy, dolomitized organic lattice. Relict algal material (microcrystalline interlocking dolomite) encrusting partially leached amphiporids. Vague algal filaments throughout.	5	180 md
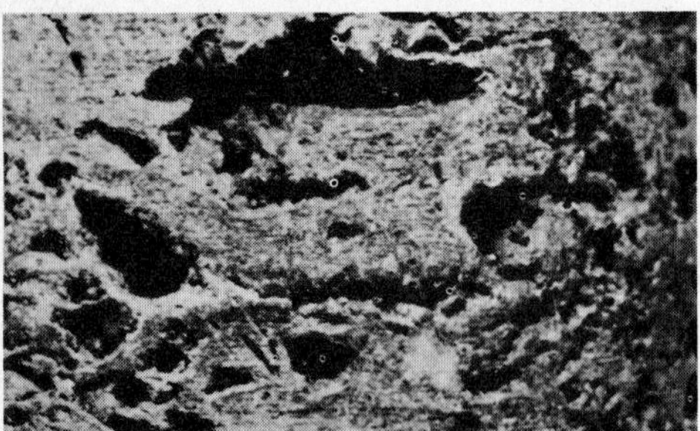	Vuggy, dolomitized organic frame work or lattice. Relict stromatoporoidal and algal material (very fine crystalline, interlocking dolomite) with excellent solution and intraorganic vug porosity.	8.4	1,100 md

PLATE XI.—Relation of textural variations. Nisku carbonates with porosity-permeability determinations. ×1.0.

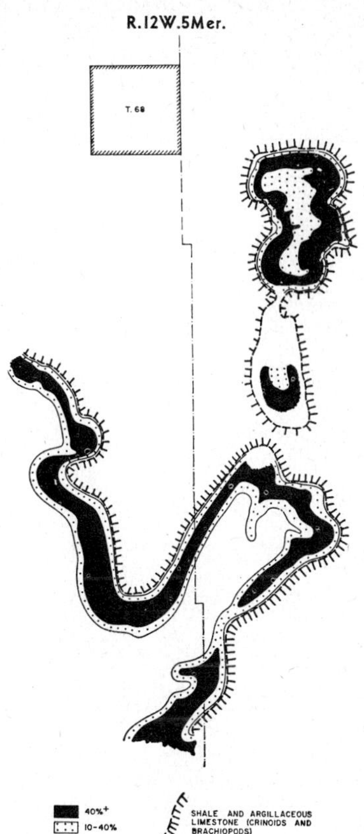

FIG. 13.—Slice map 2, 50-foot interval of Swan Hills member, showing percentage of effective matrix and intraorganic vug porosity.

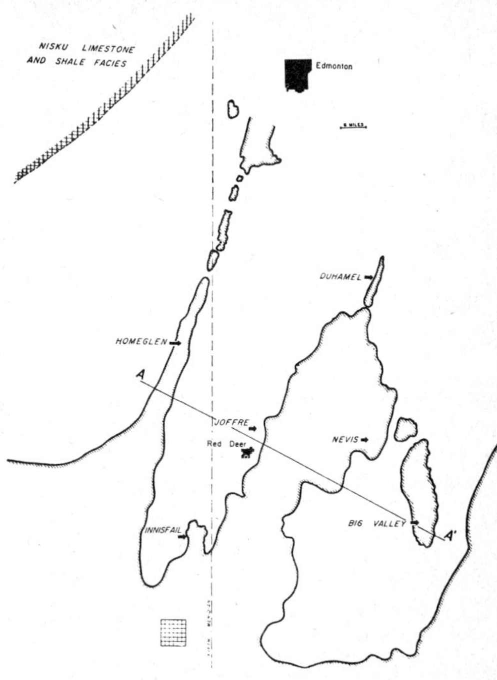

FIG. 14.—Index map of Leduc reef and platform trends of south-central Alberta. *A-A'* is trace of section in Fig. 15.

lithological cross section of Figure 15 well illustrate this relationship.

An algal, stromatoporoidal, coralline, vuggy organic lattice chain associated with generally coarse, dolomitized, clastic carbonates with a porous, granular matrix is developed on the Rimbey-Meadowbrook trend and forms a front to a shale-limestone facies deposited under open marine conditions to the northwest. To the east of this barrier a complex pattern of fringing organic and clastic carbonate shoals separate locally silled, lagoonal deposits of evaporites and brown carbonate muds containing abundant anhydrite-

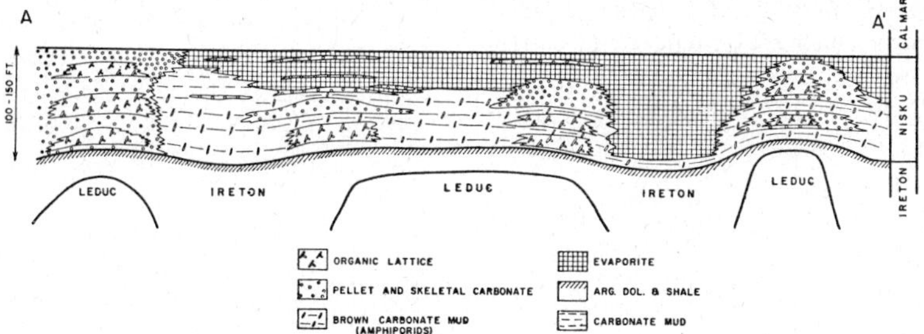

FIG. 15.—Generalized Nisku lithologic section across south-central Alberta, showing facies variations. Trace of section is line *A-A'*, Fig. 14.

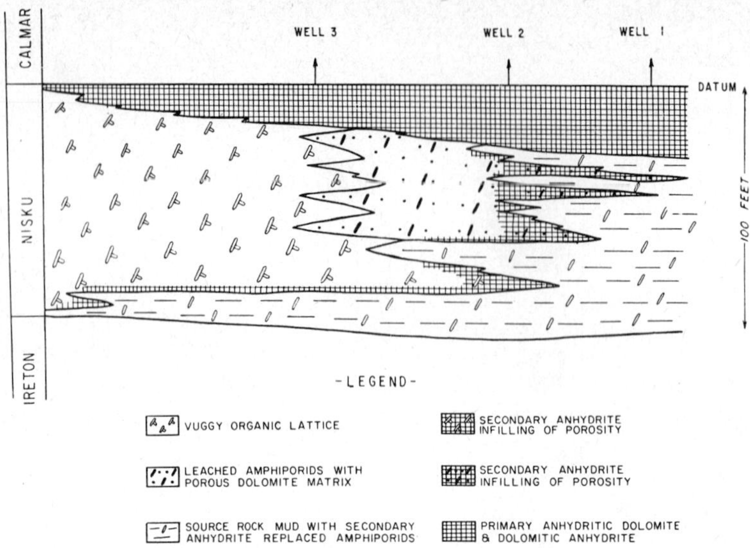

FIG. 16.—Diagrammatic section showing secondary anhydrite infilling of Nisku carbonate reservoirs.

replaced amphiporids. The shoal and lagoonal carbonates throughout most of this area are overlain by anhydrite or anhydritic dolomite sheets which were preciptiated in the wake of an overall regressive Nisku sea.

Zonation of Nisku dolomites in central Alberta into their undolomitized counterparts and porosity groups has been accomplished by crystal size and shape studies in combination with identification of vestiges of original organic structures and skeletal or nonskeletal grain outlines.

In any prediction of secondary anhydrite infilling of Nisku carbonate reservoirs, it is necessary to distinguish between infilled lattice or intercrystalline porosity and replaced discrete skeletal material. Once this distinction has been made, it is fairly easy to predict completely plugged reservoir sections which are generally found at or near rapid facies or permeability changes within the formation (Fig. 16).

The generally dark-resinous brown, dolomitized mud facies with a variable amount of secondary white anhydrite-replaced amphiporid material is of particular interest, as its equivalents have been recognized in other Upper Devonian sections in Alberta, such as the Beaverhill Lake and Cairn formations. The appellation "Brown-Reef" or "Reef Platform" has been applied to the source-rock facies which was deposited in intra-reef mud flats and lagoons. It is important to note that the secondary anhydrite replacement is restricted to the cellular amphiporid material and was probably precipitated from sulphate-rich connate water during lithification of a carbonate mud laid down in a semi-evaporitic environment. Typical lateral facies and porosity variations of the Nisku formation are shown in Table IV.

CONCLUSIONS

It is hoped that these observations on the relations of grain, matrix, and cement variants of carbonate rocks to porosity, permeability, and water and oil saturation determinations, will be helpful in the recognition and mapping of such associations in other places. Chart 1, which shows a grouping of carbonate rocks into textural and porosity units for mapping purposes, is essentially a summation of the past experience of the writer and his associates with carbonate textural and reservoir analyses of Western Canada.

REFERENCES

American Geol. Inst., 1957, Glossary of geology and related sciences: Natl. Acad. Sci. Pub. 501, p. 179.

Folk, R. L., 1959, Practical petrographic classification of limestones: Am. Assoc. Petroleum Geologists Bull., v. 43, no. 1, p. 1–38.

Fong, G., 1960, Geology of Devonian Beaverhill Lake formation, Swan Hills area, Alberta, Canada: Am

TABLE IV. TYPICAL LATERAL FACIES CHANGES OF NISKU CARBONATES

Shoal→	*Intermediate Area*→	*Lagoon*
Medium rhombic dolomite with 20% partially leached amphiporid tubes. 15% porosity, 50 md. *Effective reservoir.*	Brown, fine to medium, subhedral to interlocking dolomite with 30% amphiporids partially replaced by coarse, secondary white anhydrite. Poor intercrystalline and blind intraorganic vug porosity. 6% porosity, 3 md. *Poorly effective reservoir.*	50% secondary white anhydrite-replaced amphiporids (5% brachiopods) in resinous brown very fine crystalline, interlocking dolomite matrix. *Tight.*
Vuggy, dolomitized organic lattice partially infilled (10%) with coarse secondary white anhydrite. Shrinkage and solution vug porosity. 3% porosity, 65 md. *Effective reservoir.*	Dolomitized coarse lump limestone with original interlump vug porosity infilled with secondary anhydrite, interbedded with (50%) cryptocrystalline, interlocking, evaporitic dolomite. *Tight.*	Cryptocrystalline, interlocking dolomitic anhydrite with minor intercalations of vaguely pelleted, microcrystalline, interlocking dolomite. Shrinkage vugs or "birdseye" structure infilled with coarse secondary anhydrite. *Tight.*
Vuggy, dolomitized organic lattice. Relict algal and stromatoporoidal material (very fine mosaic dolomite) encrusting partially leached amphiporids. Solution, intraorganic and shrinkage vug porosity. Less than 2% secondary white anhydrite infilling. 8% porosity, 180 md. *Effective reservoir.*	Secondary white anhydrite-infilled organic lattice interleaved with brown, fine crystalline (subhedral to interlocking) dolomite with 15% secondary anhydrite-replaced amphiporids. Traces poor intercrystalline porosity. 5% porosity, 0.8 md. *Ineffective reservoir.*	Resinous, brown, microcrystalline, interlocking, pelleted dolomite with 30% secondary white anhydrite-replaced amphiporids. Irregular laminae of black bituminous shale. *Tight.*
Medium crystalline (mosaic) dolomite with 15% leached amphiporid casts. Fair, relatively blind, organic vug porosity. Traces of poor intercrystalline porosity. 4% porosity, 12 md. *Fairly effective reservoir.*	Fine to medium, rhombic dolomite with 25% amphiporids, partially replaced by secondary anhydrite. Good intercrystalline porosity. Poor to fair amphiporid vug porosity. 17% porosity, 60 md. *Effective reservoir.*	Brown, very fine to fine subhedral to interlocking dolomite with 35% secondary anhydrite-replaced amphiporids. Scattered poor intercrystalline porosity. 5% porosity, 1.4 md. *Poorly effective reservoir.*
Dolomitized, coarse, uncemented pellet limestone. Good relict interpellet vug porosity partially infilled with euhedral dolomite crystals. 14% porosity, 120 md. *Effective reservoir.*	Coarse, partially leached, relict pellets with 30% microrhombic dolomite matrix. Good intercrystalline and fair leached vug porosity. 16% porosity, 80 md. *Effective reservoir.*	Relict pellet material with 40% microcrystalline interlocking dolomite matrix. *Tight.*

Assoc. Petroleum Geologists Bull., v. 44, no. 2, p. 195–209.

Ham, W. E., 1954, Algal origin of the "Birdseye" limestone in the McLish formation: Oklahoma Acad. Sci. Proc., v. 33, p. 200–203, 1952.

Hemphill, C. R., 1957, History and development of the Sundre, Westward Ho, and Harmattan oil fields: Alberta Soc. Petroleum Geologists Jour., v. 5, no. 10, p. 232–247.

Illing, L. V., 1954, Bahaman calcareous sands: Am. Assoc. Petroleum Geologists Bull., v. 38, no. 1, p. 1–95.

Johnson, J. H., 1956, Studies of Mississippian algae: Colorado School of Mines Quart., v. 51, no. 4, p. 1–107.

Moore, R. C., 1957, Mississippian carbonate deposits of the Ozark region: Soc. Econ. Paleontologists and Mineralogists Spec. Pub. No. 5, p. 101–124.

Penner, D. G., 1957, The Elkton member: Alberta Soc. Petroleum Geologists Jour., v. 5, no. 5, p. 101–104.

Pettijohn, F. J., 1949, Sedimentary rocks: New York, Harper and Bros., 1st ed.

Sloss, L. L., 1953, The significance of evaporites: Jour. Sed. Petrology, v. 23, no. 3, p. 143–161.

Thomas, G. E., and Glaister, R. P., 1960, Facies and porosity relationships in some Mississippian carbonate cycles of Western Canada basin: Am. Assoc. Petroleum Geologists Bull., v. 44, no. 5, p. 569–588.

——— and Rhodes, H. S., 1960, Textural and porosity studies of some Upper Devonian dolomite and limestone reef complexes, Edmonton and Swan Hills areas, Alberta (enlarged abs.), *in* Frontiers of exploration in Canada: Am. Assoc. Petroleum Geologists and Alberta Soc. Petroleum Geologists Regional Mtg., Preprints, Banff, May 26, 1960.

——— 1961, Devonian limestone bank-atoll reservoirs of the Swan Hills area, Alberta: Alberta Soc. Petroleum Geologists Jour., v. 9, no. 2, p. 29–38.

Van Tuyl, F. M., 1916. The origin of dolomite: Iowa Geol. Survey, v. 25, p. 251–422.

SKELETAL LIMESTONE CLASSIFICATION[1]

HENRY F. NELSON,[2] CHARLES WM. BROWN,[3] AND JOHN H. BRINEMAN[4]
Tripoli, Libya; Dallas, Texas; and Guatemala City, Guatemala

ABSTRACT

The terms *reef*, *bank*, *bioherm*, and *biostrome* have been used in many different ways by geologists. This varied usage has led to misunderstanding among geologists and, very probably, to misinterpretation of the origin of many limestone deposits. The writers have reviewed past usage of these terms and, from this review, propose a threefold classification of skeletal limestone deposits based on their organic content, shape, and origin. Skeletal limestones are defined as rocks which consist of, or owe their characteristics to, the in-place accumulation of calcareous skeletal material. A skeletal limestone deposit is classified according to the organism primarily responsible for its formation, and its shape is described as biohermal or biostromal, following the definitions proposed by Cumings and Shrock. Following the concept of Lowenstam, a skeletal limestone deposit is classified as a reef or bank, depending upon the ecologic potential of the organisms to build a topographic wave-resistant structure.

This classification is proposed not as a substitute for, but rather as a supplement to, detailed descriptions of skeletal deposits. By means of this method of classification the geologist may describe an in-place accumulation of organic remains even if only part of the desired information can be acquired. Later, if all the information is obtained, the geologist may complete his description and arrive at an understanding of how the skeletal limestone deposit may have formed.

INTRODUCTION

"The time has come when the term reef, if it is to have any validity, must be given an exact definition . . . ." Rothpletz (in Ogilvie-Gordon, 1927).

Nearly three-quarters of a century has passed since Rothpletz (1894) made this statement following his study of Triassic algal dolomites in southern Tyrol. During this period many geologists attempted to clarify "reef" nomenclature. Prior to 1940, their efforts were chiefly of academic interest. However, between 1940 and 1949, large quantities of petroleum were found in ancient reefs and reef-like limestone deposits in Texas, Illinois, New Mexico, and Canada. Considerable economic interest was then focused on this group of rocks. This interest culminated in a "Reef Symposium" at the Joint Annual Meeting of The American Association of Petroleum Geologists and the Society of Economic Paleontologists and Mineralogists in St. Louis in 1949. The symposium indicated that geologists still had widely different concepts of the terms *reef*, *bank*, *bioherm*, and *biostrome*.

In an effort to clarify reef nomenclature, the writers have studied the development of *reef* terminology and concepts which has taken place during the last 67 years. Concepts and terminology commonly referred to are shown in Table I. No attempt has been made to classify all types of limestones, and to this extent the study is limited in scope. In addition, the discussion is limited to deposits formed by calcium carbonate-secreting organisms, though the terminology may also be applied to deposits formed by silica-secreting organisms. The investigation has been guided by the following principles.

1. The ultimate purpose of a classification should be to increase our understanding of the origin and properties of the things being classified. The classification should, therefore, reflect natural processes and properties. In stratigraphic studies, rock classification should lead to a better understanding of environments of deposition and al-

(*Text continued on page 234*)

[1] Part of a symposium arranged by the Research Committee, and presented at Denver, Colorado, April 27, 1961, under joint auspices of the Association and the Society of Economic Paleontologists and Mineralogists. Manuscript received, January 27, 1961. Published by permission of Mobil Oil Company, Inc., Field Research Laboratory.

[2] Mobil Oil of Canada, Ltd.

[3] Socony Mobil Oil Company, Inc., Field Research Laboratory.

[4] Argus Petroleum Company.

The writers gratefully acknowledge the assistance of following individuals—Dan E. Feray, Southern Methodist University, who first proposed the concept of defining reefs and banks in terms of their organic content, shape, and origin; Edward Heuer and Willis G. Hewatt, Texas Christian University, and William A. Jenkins, Socony Mobil Oil Field Research Laboratory, who offered many helpful suggestions; and Alexander S. Pearce and Jack T. Wall, who prepared the illustrations.

TABLE I. EVOLUTION OF SKELETAL LIMESTONE NOMENCLATURE

AUTHOR	REEF	BANK	BIOHERM	BIOSTROME
WALTHER 1891 in CUMINGS 1932	"A coral reef is an isolated calcareous mass, rising above the sea bottom, and essentially built by branching corals which collect the detritus sand and prevent it from being evenly spread over the sea bottom". – p. 332 "He repeatedly emphasizes the upstanding, isolated form of a reef and its composite character". – Cumings, p. 332			
VAUGHAN 1911	"A coral reef is a ridge or mound of limestone, the upper surface of which lies, or lay at the time of formation, near the level of the sea, and is predominantly composed of calcium carbonate secreted by organisms, of which the most important are corals. A coral reef is, therefore, primarily a limestone formed through the activity of organisms secreting carbonate of lime". – p. 238			
GRABAU 1913	Does not specifically define the term but cites these characteristics (pp. 384–466): Algae and sponges may predominate. Mound or ridge-like or tabular form. Traps sediment. Lacks stratification. Can control environment.	Structures formed by growth of shell colonies. Little or no relief above seafloor. Interstratified with surrounding sediments. Example: Teepee Buttes.		

TABLE I (Continued)

AUTHOR	REEF	BANK	BIOHERM	BIOSTROME
CUMINGS AND SHROCK 1928 b	So-called "coral reefs" may consist chiefly of other organisms; e.g., algae, bryozoa, crinoids, mollusks, etc.		Recommended the term "bioherm" to students of coral reefs. Derived from the Greek root bio-, meaning organic, and epua, meaning reef. No strict definition proposed. – p. 599	
CUMINGS 1930			".......any dome-like, mound-like, lense-like, or otherwise circumscribed mass, built exclusively or mainly by sedentary organisms such as corals, stromatoporoids, algae, brachiopods, molluscs, crinoids, etc., and enclosed in normal rock of different lithologic character. The word comes from two Greek words meaning organic, and reef or mound". – p. 207	
STOCKDALE 1931			"The term bioherm is particularly suitable for the calcareous, organically made masses which are so prominent in the upper Borden rocks,.......". – p. 711 Crinoid beds are intercalated with shales.	
CUMINGS 1932	Did not define the term reef but cited the following characteristics: Directly fabricated by organisms. Produced a topographic mound or ridge. Unstratified. Fragments of organisms constitute large percentage of reef.	"Shell banks" such as Teepee Buttes cited as bioherm, but recognized as different than normal reefs. Little or no relief above sea-floor. Interstratified with surrounding sediments.	"... a reef, bank, or mound; for reef-like, mound-like, lens-like or otherwise circumscribed structures of strictly organic origin, embedded in rocks of different lithology. – p. 333	"... purely bedded structures, such as shell beds, crinoid beds, coral beds etcetera, consisting of and built mainly by sedentary organisms, and not swelling into mound-like or lens-like forms, ..., which means a bed or layer". – p. 334

TABLE I (Continued)

AUTHOR	REEF	BANK	BIOHERM	BIOSTROME
SHROCK 1939	Synonymous with bioherm		"Organic reefs built not dominantly by corals but rather from the contributions of many animals and of certain algae". – p. 532 Refers to bioherm as "reefy mounds" and recognizes that they were built by reef-building organisms.	
LADD 1944	Suggests that "in studying organic structures the term reef be applied only to those that show clearly by geologic or biologic evidence that they were wave-resistant structures". – p. 27 Only these types of structures are considered to be true reefs and he feels that these should be distinguished from organic deposits which were formed below the zone of wave action. Term reef should be used for ".... a wave-resisting bioherm". – p. 26		Believes that the terms bioherm and biostrome are useful terms as applied to elevated "reefs".	See bioherm.
WILSON 1950	"A reef is a sedimentary rock aggregate, large or small, composed of the remains of colonial type organisms that lived near or below the surface of water bodies, mainly marine, and developed large vertical dimensions as compared with the proportions of adjacent sedimentary rocks". – p. 181			

TABLE I (Continued)

AUTHOR	REEF	BANK	BIOHERM	BIOSTROME
TWENHOFEL 1950	".... an aggregate of organic materials of significant dimensions built in part by colonial organisms, mainly, but not necessarily marine, that lived near, but below, the surface of the water (they may have some exposure at low tide) and constructed exoskeletal matter that became more or less adherent to previously formed similar matter". – p. 183		Synonymous with organic reef.	
LADD 1950	Agrees with Wilson's (1950) definition.			
HENSON 1950	Follows earlier concepts of reefs. Referred to the reef core as the reef-wall and the reef flank as the talus slope. Defined reef-complex as an aggregate of reefs sensu stricto and all genetically (?) related deposits. This included the reef core, back-reef, and fore-reef talus. Recognized that certain organisms are reef-builders.		Synonymous with reef.	
LINK 1950	Synonymous with bioherm.		"A bioherm is an accumulation of the secreted hard parts of sessile types of primitive invertebrates and plants such as corals, bryozoans, crinoids, sponges, algae, etcetera, which accumulation is greater than the surrounding contemporaneously deposited sediments, thus giving rise to mounds, ridges, or reefs. Therefore, "coral reefs" and bioherms are, in a sense, one and the same". – p. 263	"A biostrome is an accumulation of the same or similar sort of material as a "bioherm" or "reef", but the accumulations are in layers or strata which are no greater in vertical dimensions than the contemporaneously deposited surrounding sediments". – p. 263 Points out gradation between bioherms & biostromes and that even biostromes are lens if traced far enough.

TABLE I (Continued)

AUTHOR	REEF	BANK	BIOHERM	BIOSTROME
LOWENSTAM 1950	Defines reefs in terms of the biological potential of the organisms responsible for them rather than the present day shape. Thus, the emphasis is shifted from "the structure to the structure-building potential". – p. 433 "Thus a reef, in terms of ecologic principles, is the product of the actively building and sediment-binding biotic constituents, which, because of their potential wave resistance, have the ability to erect rigid, wave-resistant topographic structures". – p. 433	Banks should be distinguished from true reefs. Bank-forming organisms are incapable of raising their own substrate very high above the surrounding bottom. Thus, the organisms play a passive role in bank-building. "A critical point is that such unconsolidated banks cannot be sources of carbonate deposits, as true reefs". – p. 434 "Thus their influence on other habitats is essentially confined to their own periphery". – p. 434		
KRUMBEIN & SLOSS 1951			Larger organic structures such as reefs which "represent accumulations of organic remains and debris formed under conditions of prolific life." – p. 101	"A type of organic structure without the prominent size and steep walls of the typical bioherm....". – p. 101 "A zone of organic structures or remains spread as a blanket or in localized sheets or lenses through a formation." – p. 101 Lists some oyster reefs and coal seams as biostromes.
CLOUD 1952	Concurs with Lowenstam (1950) "Organic reefs are, or were, actually or potentially wave-resistant mounds, platforms, or linear or irregular masses that were constructed under organic influence and they rise or rose above the sea floor". – p. 2126 "Tabular or thinly lenticular organic masses composed of frame building organisms that elsewhere build recognizable reefs are perhaps best referred to as <u>incipient reefs</u>.... " – p. 2128		"The term <u>bioherm</u> .... may be reserved for reef-like organic masses of uncertain potential or doubtfully wave- resistant nature". – p. 2127	Suggests restricting term to shell beds and not beds of potential reef-builders.

TABLE I (Continued)

AUTHOR	REEF	BANK	BIOHERM	BIOSTROME
CLOUD 1952 (Cont'd.)	Recognizes the importance of distinguishing between the clastic textures of bedded limestones and the textures of reef or reef-like masses. Also believes that a distinction should be made between reef proper and reef complex. Includes in reef proper "the reef-flat and its downward irregularly interfingering or veneering extension." His reef complex includes "the reef-flat, adjacent patch-reef-studded parts of the lagoon floor, and the seaward talus slope". – p. 2144			
NEWELL, et al 1953	"Organic reefs are solid structures which tend to grow upward and outward against wave erosion." – p. 95 They speak of reefs being constructed by frame-building organisms and of reefs being consolidated masses of limestone at the time of deposition of the surrounding sediments. They also clearly differentiate reefs from bars, banks, and channels filled with shell debris.	Used in "the sense of shoal-water local mounds, ridges, and terraces of sediments rising above the surrounding sea-bottom, much more limited in extent than blanket deposits of shelf seas." – p. 94	Agree with Cloud (1952) – p. 95	
MAC NEIL 1954	Believes the term reef to have physiographic implications. "Reef–a rocky elevation rising to the surface, or within 6 fathoms of the surface of water." –p. 399 "An organic reef is a rigid structure —– composed of the calcareous skeletons of: 1) colonial and commensal animals and plants	"Bank – an isolated underwater elevation on which there is a depth of over 6 fathoms". – p. 399 "Organic bank – similar to an organic reef except that it lies below 6 fathoms of water". – p. 399	"A growth lattice of organisms whose vertical dimension exceeds the thickness of sediments deposited contemporaneously around it. A bioherm can be all or part of a bank or reef". – p. 399	

TABLE I (Continued)

AUTHOR	REEF	BANK	BIOHERM	BIOSTROME
MAC NEIL 1954 (Cont'd.)	interlocked or cemented together by growth; 2) all detrital materials derived from the breaking up of the colonial organisms.......; and 3) the remains of organisms which normally live in, on, or near the organic lattice....... which grows independently of and builds up at a rate greater than all surrounding types of sediments ...., and maintains its upper growing or depositional surface at or near the level of the sea.......". – p. 389			
STOKES & VARNES 1955	Give mining, nautical, physiographic, and organic reef definitions. Use Wilson's definition for their definition of an organic reef.		"An organic reef"	"Literally, an organic layer. A bedded or layered structure, not mound-like or lenticular, as contrasted with a bioherm, but generally of wide lateral extent, built mainly by sedentary organisms and consisting largely or exclusively of organic remains. Not limited to animal remains but including plant remains, such as coal beds."
AGI GLOSSARY 1957	Lists 5 definitions which indicate a topographic structure. Two others are as follows: 1. "A rock structure, either mound-like or layered, built by sedentary organisms such as corals, etc., and usually enclosed in a rock of differing lithology" (Petrol. Geol. Comm.) 2. "A bioherm of sufficient size to develope associated facies. Thus, all reefs are bioherms, but all bioherms are not reefs." (Johnson, J. H., Mines Mag., p. 22, Sept. 1953).	Gives 4 definitions all of which indicate a topographic rise. Uses Newell's definition of bank deposits. Uses MacNeil's definition for organic bank.	Lists 2 definitions: 1. Cumings, 1930. 2. "An organic reef or mound built by corals, stromatoporoids, gastropods, echinoderms, foraminifera, molluscs, and other organisms." (Thornberry, W. D., Prin. of Geomorphology, pp. 480–481, 1954).	Follows Cumings (1932)

TABLE I (Continued)

AUTHOR	REEF	BANK	BIOHERM	BIOSTROME
MOORE 1957			Does not feel that much value is to be gained by referring to organic reefs as bioherms.	Believes that this term has little value and suggests that it be dropped.
PETTIJOHN 1957	Does not define the term reef as such but lists the following characteristics: 1. Wave-resistant. 2. A massive fossiliferous core. 3. Surrounded by bedded sparsely fossiliferous porous granular deposits. 4. Beds commonly dip away from core.		Follows Cumings (1932). Notes that some bioherms may be true reefs whereas others are not and that they may be formed by either sediment-binding or non-sediment-binding organisms.	"... applied to deposits formed by sedentary organisms (shell bed, crinoidal limestone, algal beds and so forth) which are stratiform and not swelling into mound-like or lens-like form." – p. 398 Notes that all strata are lenses and that the distinction between bioherm and biostrome is, therefore, arbitrary.
DUNBAR & RODGERS 1957	Defines organic reef as "...... a deposit composed of the remains of organisms, mainly colonial, that have accumulated approximately in the position of growth to form non-bedded or at best poorly bedded masses of solid rock, while better bedded normally fragmental sediments were accumulating on all sides. (Pia, 1933, p. 11–12)". Though this definition does not indicate whether reefs had topographic relief, the writers evidently feel that organic reefs were topographic wave-resistant structures as indicated in their discussion. – p. 88–89. They distinguish between the reef proper (original organic framework) and the fragmental debris derived from the reef proper. Both are included in their term reef complex. – p. 88–89.			

TABLE I (Continued)

AUTHOR	REEF	BANK	BIOHERM	BIOSTROME
ANDRICHUK 1958	Uses the term <u>reef</u> (biohermal type) to refer to "a carbonate buildup having larger vertical dimensions than the surrounding sediments". It would include the part formed by active organic growth as well as related carbonate and fossil debris. – p. 12–13		Uses the term as an adjective for subsurface reefs which have relatively large vertical dimensions.	Uses the term as an adjective for subsurface reefs which have extensive lateral dimensions and small vertical dimensions.
WELLER 1958			Recommends that this term should be used as a structural term as originally intended. Feels that it is unnecessary as a substitute term for <u>organic reef.</u> Believes that it would be a useful term for <u>non-reef limestone mounds</u> that are "the record of an integrated organic community that perpetuated itself in the midst of a generally hostile environment". – p. 637	Believes this term to be superflouous.
SHROCK, 1957 in WELLER, 1958			In a letter to Weller, Shrock stated "if the remains of crinoids were spread evenly over an extensive bottom, I would not be as much inclined to call such an accumulation a bioherm or biostrome." – p. 612 He also felt that bioherms or biostromes do not necessarily have to be calcareous. In the same letter he stated "..... I would balk a little at coals being included unless it could be shown that the vegetable material accumulated in a particular area and underwent very little transportation." – p. 612	See Bioherm.

TABLE I (Concluded)

AUTHOR	REEF	BANK	BIOHERM	BIOSTROME
THIS REPORT	Follows the concept of Lowenstam (1950). Recommends that (1) the terms *reef* and *bank* be used to denote *origin*, (2) the terms *bioherm* and *biostrome* be used to denote shape, and (3) that these terms be applied only to skeletal deposits which are defined as deposits which consist of or owe their characteristics to essentially *in situ* accumulation of calcareous and possible siliceous skeletal matter. Defines *reef* as a skeletal deposit formed by *organisms* possessing the ecologic potential to erect a rigid topographic structure.	Defines *bank* as a skeletal deposit formed by organisms which do not have the ecologic potential to erect a rigid wave-resistant structure.	Follows Cumings (1932)	Follows Cumings (1932)

teration of the rocks and, ultimately, to their geologic history. Classification should not be an end point in itself.

2. Terminology and concepts should be applicable to both surface and subsurface investigations. Classifications based on criteria that cannot be recognized are of theoretical value only.

3. Use of terms already well established should be continued, providing they are based on scientifically correct observations and facts. This is preferable to the introduction of new terms. When various interpretations of a term exist, the original definition or the more scientifically correct concept should be given priority.

4. In nature, sharp divisions are the exception rather than the rule. Consequently, a given geologic feature will commonly be interpreted differently by many geologists. It is doubtful that any classification can be devised that will meet the needs of all geologists, operating under all conditions, and at all times. However, if we can classify the "end points" satisfactorily, considerable progress will have been made in bringing about better communication and understanding among geologists.

DISCUSSION

SKELETAL LIMESTONES

Early students of fossil reefs confined most of their studies to in-place accumulations of calcareous skeletal remains. Consequently, their terminology and concepts were directed toward these rocks. The writers term these in-place accumulations skeletal limestones and define them as limestones which consist of, or owe their characteristics to, virtually in-place accumulation of calcareous skeletal matter. These rocks, formed through biologic processes, are in contrast to fragmental limestones, which are formed by the physical processes of transportation, abrasion, sorting, and deposition. The writers do not feel that deposits of transported shell material should be considered as skeletal limestones any more than one would consider a sandstone an igneous rock merely because the quartz originally crystallized from a magma. One type of sediment warrants some discussion. This sediment and its lithified equivalent consist of an accumulation of the shells of planktonic organisms. Because these sediments may consist almost entirely of the whole unabraded shells of these organisms, one might consider such accumulations as skeletal deposits. The writers have not classified these sediments as such, however, because they were formed by physical means of accumulation rather than by the growth of organisms at their present site of accumulation.

The relation of skeletal limestones to other types of limestone is indicated in Figure 1. The classification is based initially on the physical properties of the rocks but, ultimately, it is based on their origin. At the present, it is a tentative classification. However, it is sufficiently complete to illustrate the writers' concept of the relation of skeletal limestones to other limestones.

Inasmuch as the terminology and classification herein proposed are restricted to skeletal limestones, recognition of a limestone deposit as an in-place accumulation is of fundamental importance. Criteria characteristic or suggestive of in-place accumulation as opposed to detrital accumulations come from several different lines.

Growth habit of organisms.—Some organisms, such as certain species of corals, construct a rigid exoskeleton in which the colony lives. A second group of organisms like the oyster *Crassostrea virginica* secrete individual shells that grow attached to the bottom and/or to other individuals. The occurrence of both types of organisms *in their growth position* is evidence of accumulation in place. The occurrence of these same organisms torn from their growth positions, and possibly fragmented but not abraded, strongly suggests the nearby presence of an in-place accumulation. A third group of organisms composed of forms such as *Mytilus*, attach themselves to the bottom by means of a *byssus* which disappears when the organism dies. Finally, many pelecypods live completely unattached or burrow into the bottom. Recognition of deposits composed of these organisms as in-place accumulations may be difficult, and other lines of supporting evidence must be sought.

Faunal zonation.—Skeletal limestones, such as reefs, locally exhibit a vertical and/or lateral zonation of fauna, indicating in-place accumulation. Faunal zonation in Silurian and Cretaceous reefs has been described by Lowenstam (1950) and by Young (1959). It has also been noted on modern reefs by Ladd and others (1950). Each of these studies, which are discussed more fully later in this paper, clearly demonstrated that the faunal zonation described was formed by biological activity, not by accumulation of hard parts by physical processes of deposition.

Distribution of shells of solitary organisms.—The valves of some pelecypods, such as *Lucina occidentalis*, which forms the Tepee Buttes, remain attached to each other after the organism dies. A large deposit of these complete shells suggests accumulation in place. More commonly, the valves disarticulate after the organism dies, and each valve, if not attached to the bottom, is then subject to mechanical processes of transportation, sorting, abrasion, and deposition. If these processes do not modify the in-place deposit, the ratio of left to right valves will be approximately 1:1, thereby suggesting accumulation in place.

When currents and waves act on a shell deposit formed by bivalved organisms, one valve may be preferentially sorted and transported from the growth site. One or two deposits of shells may then be formed, each characterized by a relatively great abundance of one valve. In this case, it may be difficult to determine which of the two deposits accumulated in place. Reefs of *Crassostrea virginica* in Atchafalaya Bay, for example, are subject to sorting action of waves and currents. The small right valves are removed from the reef by currents and deposited in the sediments on the leeward side of the reef. The larger left valve, however, remains attached to the reef framework and is not transported (D. E. Feray, personal communication).

Lithologic evidence.—A deposit of relatively whole unabraded shells surrounded by comminuted, sorted, and abraded shell material suggests accumulation in place. This is in contrast to a deposit composed wholly of comminuted, abraded, and variably sorted shell material.

Structural evidence.—Some forms of corals and algae construct a rigid sediment-trapping framework that may rise above the surrounding sediments. Fragmented skeletal material and beds of the framebuilding organisms dipping away from the main deposit indicate that the framework

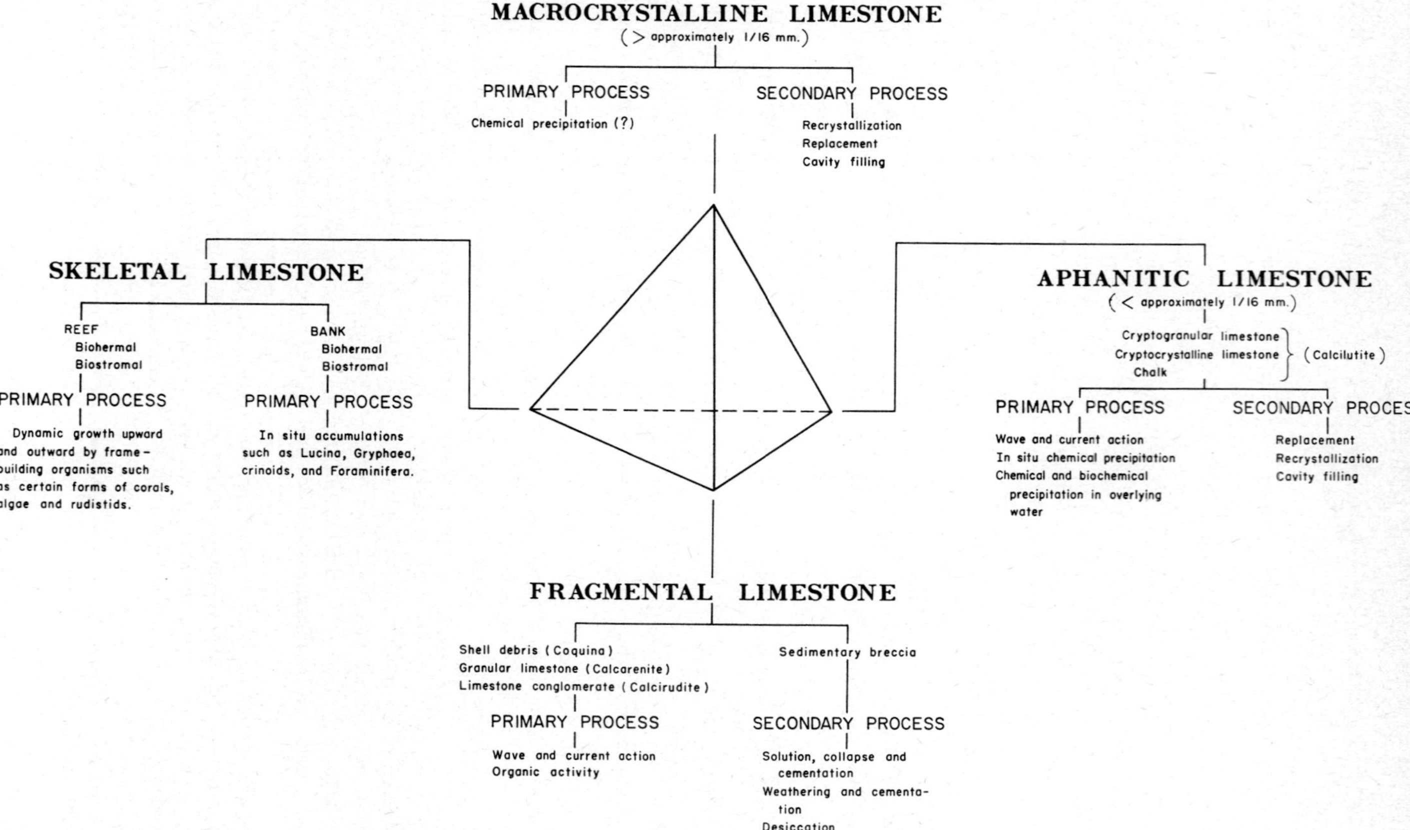

FIG. 1.—Limestones are subdivided into four principal types on the basis of their textures. Each of these four main types of limestone is shown as one corner of a tetrahedral diagram. All types grade into each other, to form numerous subtypes of limestones, which would fall within the tetrahedron, and into other types of sediments to form a multitude of impure limestones. No attempt has been made to classify these subtypes at this time.

actually stood above the surrounding sediments and, therefore, accumulated in place. Commonly, beds of framebuilding organisms extend out from these mounds like fore-set beds of a delta. They are commonly formed in place by lateral growth of the organisms and do not necessarily indicate deposition by wave and current action. In-place accumulations may have a bedded structure as a result of either temporary cessation of organic growth, or periodic wave and current planation.

PREVIOUS INVESTIGATIONS

Initial scientific investigations of modern coral reefs were begun over 100 years ago (Darwin, 1842; Jukes, 1847; and Dana, 1849). It was not long before similar investigations of ancient reefs began (Murchison, 1847; Hall, 1862; Chamberlin, 1877; Bell, 1886; Mojsisovics, 1879; and Rothpletz, 1894). Apparently these early investigations resulted in the development of many different ideas about what constituted a reef, for it was at this time that Rothpletz made the statement that is used as the introductory note of this paper. Since these early investigations, many excellent studies of living and fossil reefs have been made (see references in Pugh, 1950, and Ballard and others, 1958). Although the general concept in each study can be gleaned from their writings, few of these men clearly defined the term *reef*.

The principal contributions to the study of reefs and similar deposits are summarized chronologically in Table I. The scientists noted comprise a very small segment of those who have studied reefs—biologists as well as geologists—but their opinions are to be valued because of the influence on succeeding workers. With the exception of Walther (1891, *in* Cumings 1932), Grabau (1913), and Vaughan (1911), all have studied reefs since the terms *bioherm* and *biostrome* were introduced. During the course of their work, many of them developed concepts about reefs, or attempted to clarify the terminology regarding reefs and reef-like masses. Such an attempt on the part of Cumings and Shrock (1928a) and Cumings (1930 and 1932) led to the introduction of the new terms *bioherm* and *biostrome*. Though designed to clarify existing concepts of reefs, these terms actually resulted in more controversy. This was unfortunate because if the terms had been used as Cumings and Shrock intended, they would have served a useful purpose. It is the intent of this paper, in part, to show that they are still useful if properly applied.

Reef concepts.—The term *reef* has been used in many ways and for many purposes—in a physiographic sense, for structures built by organisms, and as a mining term (Stokes and Varnes, 1955, and A.G.I., 1957). However, all usages had one common denominator—a feature which stood topographically above, or in marked contrast to, surrounding features. Through time, geologists gradually restricted the term to carbonate rocks, the only restriction which the profession as a whole placed upon the term. This resulted in the following geologic features being incorrectly classified as either reefs or bioherms—shells piled up by current action, mounds of oölites, erosional remnants of limestone, facies changes of shale or sandstone to limestone, and porosity in limestones as interpreted on electric logs. Cumings (1932, p. 332) noted that

> . . . the word reef in geologic literature means *nothing*, unless each occurrence is accurately described, and this is seldom the case.

Despite varied use of the term, it is interesting to note that there is surprisingly close agreement among those who have studied reefs in some detail. With the exception of MacNeil (1954), there is complete agreement on one point—reefs are built by colonial organisms; they are not accumulations of transported skeletal debris. The reef builders have the ecologic potential to construct a rigid sediment-trapping framework. It is this framework which is responsible for two important features that characterize *most* reefs (1) topographic relief above surrounding contemporaneously deposited sediments, and (2) wave-resistance.

It is important to note that other *so-called* reefs may have either of the features mentioned above. An erosional remnant of limestone may be a wave-resistant structure. A dune of oölites stands above its surroundings. Porous zones in limestones, determined from electric logs, have been interpreted as reefs that stood topographically above contemporaneous sediments. However, in these examples the basic requirement for classification as true reefs is lacking—namely, construction by framebuilding organisms. Ladd (1944, p. 26) suggested that only those organic structures which had actually been wave-resistant structures should be called reefs. In 1950 he concurred with Wilson's (1950) definition, but did not indicate whether he still felt that the term should be applied only to wave-resistant structures.

Lowenstam (1950) was the first to emphasize the structure-building potential of the organisms instead of the shape of the structure. This was an important departure from previous concepts. From his study of the Niagaran reefs of the Great Lakes area, Lowenstam (1950) developed the philosophy that reefs are the product of biologic activity and should, therefore, be defined in terms of the ecologic potential of the organisms responsible for them. He defined a reef (p. 433) as

> . . . the product of the actively building and sediment-binding biotic constituents, which, because of their potential wave-resistance, have the ability to erect rigid, wave-resistant topographic structures.

He pointed out that reefs should be clearly differentiated from unconsolidated banks built by other organisms and that reef-building organisms, because they can build wave-resistant structures, have the ability directly to control or modify their environment. In applying his philosophy to the Niagaran reefs, Lowenstam showed that the framework of the Niagaran reefs was constructed by a *Clathrodictyon* type of stromatoporoid or a *Solenopora* type of algae. He demonstrated further that the reefs were wave-resistant structures which controlled their environment and contributed a large volume of sediment to the surrounding areas. In addition, Lowenstam observed that the fauna on the reefs adjusted itself to the changing environment as the reefs grew into the zone of turbulent water.

Others who have not specifically defined or discussed their concepts of reefs, but who appear to have similar views are Hadding (1950), Cloud (1952), and Rutten (1958), to mention a few.

In contrast to the men cited above, MacNeil (1954) did not agree that a reef is the product of framebuilding organisms. He defined a reef as any rocky elevation rising to within six fathoms of the surface; a rocky elevation below six fathoms was called a bank. His concept of the modified term "organic reef" agreed with the concepts of the others except for the factor of water depth. Considering our present state of knowledge of the depth of water in ancient seas, the writers fail to see how MacNeil's concept can be applied in ancient reef studies.

There is less agreement concerning the scope of the terms *reef*, *organic reef*, and *reef complex*, than there is about the manner with which they are constructed. Many writers (Grabau, 1913; Cumings and Shrock, 1928a; Shrock, 1939; Lowenstam, 1948, 1949, 1950; and Plumley and Graves, 1953) subdivided reefs into the *reef core* and *reef flank* beds. Henson (1950) referred to the reef core as the *reef wall* and the flank beds as the *talus slope*. At the same time (p. 215–216), he introduced the term *reef-complex* to include

> . . . not only the reefs *sensu stricto*, but all genetically(?) associated sediments. . . .

Henson's genetically associated sediments consisted of the talus and detrital shoal limestones derived from the reefs. However, Henson was concerned as to how far the genetic association could be carried. Cloud (1952, p. 2144) used the term *reef proper* for

> The reef-flat and its downward irregularly interfingering or veneering extension. . . .

It is not clear whether he referred only to that part within the growth lattice as the *reef proper* (the *reef core* of others and *reef wall* of Henson), or whether he included the coarse reef debris which interfingers with the growth lattice and stands above the bottom (the *reef flank* of others and the *talus slope* of Henson). Cloud used the term *reef complex* in essentially the same manner as Henson. Newell and others (1953, p. 105) and Newell (1955, p. 302), and Dunbar and Rodgers (1957, p. 88–95) felt that only the in-place accumulations of organisms constituted the reef; Dunbar and Rodgers called this the *reef proper*, and the reef flank deposits, the *reef talus*. Both followed Henson's usage of *reef-complex*. MacNeil (1954) subdivided *organic reefs* into *biohermal reef rock* (that part within the growth lattice referred to as *reef core* by Lowenstam and others, *reef-wall* by Henson, the *reef* by Newell, and the *reef proper* by Dunbar and Rodgers) and *detrital reef rock* (referred to as *reef flank* by Lowenstam and others, and *reef talus* by Newell, and Dunbar and Rodgers).

MacNeil's (1954) usage of the term *reef complex* is not clear. He termed an aggregate of all types of reef rock (*biohermal reef rock* and *detrital reef rock*) as a *reef complex* (p. 385). In effect, his terms *organic reef* and *reef complex* are synonymous. Later (p. 391), he suggested that the *reef complex* might include all rocks that form or are derived from organic reefs. This appears to coincide with Henson's (1950) original concept.

Bank concepts.—Few geologists have actually defined the term *bank*. Many have distinguished banks indirectly, however, by defining reefs as structures built by colonial framebuilding organisms. Grabau (1913) and Cumings (1932) both recognized that the Tepee Buttes are not the same type of structures as those built by colonial reef organisms. They noted that the buttes are composed of colonies of shells that apparently stood only slightly above the bottom and were interstratified with the surrounding sediments. Lowenstam (1950) considered banks to be the product of organisms which could not raise their own substrate; therefore, they could not affect the surrounding environment. Newell and others (1953, p. 36, 94) regarded banks as accumulations of bioclastic debris as well as in-place accumulations of shells. MacNeil (1954, p. 399) used the term *bank* to signify a rocky elevation at depths greater than six fathoms.

Bioherm concepts.—Cumings and Shrock (1928b, p. 599) proposed the term *bioherm* to describe structures formed by framebuilding organisms. From their discussion, it is clear that the structures were positive topographic features. However, when Cumings (1930, p. 307, and 1932, p. 333) actually defined the term, he was not so restrictive. From his definitions and supporting examples, it is clear that in 1932 Cumings considered (1) bioherms to be the result of in-place accumulations of skeletal material resulting from organic growth processes—not from current action or some other agent, (2) both framebuilding organisms and organisms which do not construct a rigid framework to be responsible for the formation of bioherms, (3) that the structures did not have to stand above the sea floor as topographic features, and (4) that bioherms are surrounded by rocks of different lithology.

Since Cumings and Shrock (1928b) introduced the term, it has been used in many ways. Pettijohn (1949 and 1957) followed Cumings' (1932) definition, but Twenhofel (1950) and Henson (1950) considered *bioherm* to be synonymous with *reef*. Link (1950) redefined the term to describe topographic structures formed by sessile organisms and considered it to be synonymous with *reef*. Ladd (1944) and MacNeil (1954) also restricted the term to topographic structures built by framebuilding organisms. Ladd (1944) further restricted its use to those structures that were actually wave resistant. Cloud (1952) and Newell and others (1953) suggested that the term be used for reef-like organic masses of doubtful origin. Weller (1958) proposed that *bioherm* be used to denote non-reef, in-place organic accumulations.

Other writers have used *bioherm* to describe organic structures formed by both framebuilding and non-framebuilding organisms, but they did not state that its use should be restricted to either group of organisms (Stockdale, 1931; Fenton and Fenton, 1933; Shrock, 1939; Laudon and Bowsher, 1941; Warthin and Cooper, 1943; Wengerd, 1951; Krumbein and Sloss, 1951; Andrichuk, 1958a). Finally, Moore (1957) suggested that the terms *bioherm* and *biostrome* do not have much value.

It is interesting to note the range in the apparent breadth:height ratios of some limestone deposits which various writers have called bioherms (Table II). The list is far from complete, but it nevertheless shows how variable are opinions concerning the dimensions of a bioherm. The ratios range from 1.3:1 to 264:1. Bioherms described by Cumings and Shrock have ratios that range from 5.5:1 to 52.8:1. Except for two bioherms in the Silurian and Mississippian of Indiana with ratios of 52.8:1 and 150:1 and the Great Barrier Reef with a ratio of 88 to 264:1, all breadth:height ratios fall below 30:1. If one were to pick a ratio that would differentiate bioherms from biostromes, an apparent breadth:height ratio of 30:1 might serve as a useful guide.

Biostrome concepts.—Most of the writers cited in Table I have not discussed the term *biostrome*. Those who have, agree that biostromes are sedimentary beds of shell material. There is considerably less agreement regarding the origin of bio-

TABLE II. APPARENT BREADTH:HEIGHT RATIOS OF LIMESTONE DEPOSITS CITED AS BIOHERMS BY VARIOUS WRITERS

Occurrence	*Source*	*Breadth*	*Height*	*B:H Ratio*
Precambrian, Belt ser. (Siyeh formation, Montana	Fenton & Fenton, 1933, *in* Twenhofel, 1950, p. 188	33′	25′	1.3:1
Precambrian, Belt ser. (Siyeh formation), Montana	Fenton & Fenton, 1933, *in* Twenhofel, 1950, p. 188	21′	15′	1.4:1
Precambrian, Kona limestone, Michigan	Twenhofel, 1950, p. 189	55′	22′	2.5:1
Precambrian, Belgian Congo	Shrock, 1947, *in* Twenhofel, 1950, p. 189	13′	6½′	2:1
Silurian, Hobergen Klint, Gotland	Twenhofel, 1950, p. 184	450′	75′	6:1
Silurian, Indiana	Cumings & Shrock, 1928b, p. 611	5,280′	100′	52.8:1
Silurian, Niagaran, Wisconsin	Twenhofel, 1950, p. 190	100′	16′	6.2:1
Silurian, Huntington formation, Indiana	Cumings & Shrock, 1928a, p. 146	400′	45′+	<8.8:1
Silurian, Huntington formation, Indiana	Cumings & Shrock, 1928a, p. 146	500′	50′+	<10:1
Silurian, Huntington formation, Indiana	Cumings & Shrock, 1928a, p. 146	300′	20′+	<15:1
Silurian, Huntington formation, Indiana	Cumings & Shrock, 1928a, p. 146	250′	45′+	<5.5:1
Silurian, Attawapiskat reef, Hudson Bay area	Savage & Van Tuyl, 1919, *in* Twenhofel, 1950, p. 192	100′ 105′	30′ 20′	3.3:1 5.2:1
Silurian, Lockport group, S. Ontario	Williams, 1915, *in* Twenhofel, 1950, p. 192	100–200′ 105–255′	15–20′ 20′	6.6 & 10:1 5.2 & 12.2:1
Devonian, Norman Wells reef, N.W.T.	Link, 1950, p. 275	11,616′	500′	23.2:1
Devonian, Alpena limestone, Thunder Bay region, Michigan	Warthin & Cooper, 1943, p. 587	150′	55′	2.7:1
Devonian, Woodbend group	Downing & Cooke, 1955, p. 199	2,500′	1,000′	2.5:1
Mississippian, Borden group, Indiana	Stockdale, 1931, p. 712	10,560′	70′	150:1
Mississippian, Lake Valley formation, New Mexico	Laudon & Bowsher, 1941, p. 2129	5,280′	200′	26.4:1
Pennsylvanian, Hermosa formation, Utah	Wengerd, 1951, p. 1046	500–1,000′ 1,000′	60′ 70′	8.3 & 16.6:1 14.3:1
Permian, Capitan formation, Guadalupe Mtns., Texas and New Mexico	Levorsen, 1954, p. 226	13,000′+	1,300′+	10.0:1
Permian, Bone Canyon patch reef, Guadalupe Mtns., Texas and New Mexico	Newell and others, 1953, p. 96	130′	45′	2.88:1
Permian, Getaway patch reefs, Guadalupe Mtns., Texas and New Mexico	Newell and others, 1953, p. 101	20′ 13′ 48′	10′ 8′ 16′	2:1 1.6:1 3:1
Recent, Great Barrier Reef, Australia	Levorsen, 1954, p. 218	30–90 mi.	1,800′	88 & 264:1

stromes. Cumings himself (1932) was not consistent in his views about their origin. Though his definition (p. 334) clearly indicated that a biostrome is built by organisms, he later stated (p. 347) that biostromes may be either in-place accumulations of shells or accumulations formed by current action. He further stated that these deposits might have a biohermal shape. Link (1950) restricted the term to layered accumulations of hard parts of sessile organisms. Cloud (1952), on the other hand, suggested that *biostrome* should be used only when referring to shell beds and not to beds of potential framebuilders. Shrock (*in* Weller, 1958) would not define accumulations of transported material as *bioherms* or *biostromes*. Weller (1958) felt that the term *biostrome* was superfluous.

PROPOSED NOMENCLATURE

In the writers' opinion, the terms *reef*, *bank*, *bioherm*, and *biostrome* should be applied only to in-place accumulations of organisms. *Bioherm* and *biostrome* were originally proposed to describe such deposits. The term *reef* was applied to these deposits by early students, though it was not specifically defined. *Bank* is recommended as a counterpart of *reef*, following Lowenstam's concept (1950, p. 433–435). Failure to restrict these terms to in-place accumulations is one reason for the confused terminology which exists today. If the terms are restricted to these deposits, the writers believe the proposed classification will create better understanding among geologists, although it will not eliminate all problems associated with skeletal limestone studies.

The proposed nomenclature is based on the composition, shape, and origin of skeletal limestone deposits. It follows the concepts of Cumings (1932) and Lowenstam (1950). Cumings' terms defined the shape of a skeletal limestone mass, whereas Lowenstam's concept emphasized its origin. Indirectly, Lowenstam's concept dealt with the fossil constituents, because some organisms are framebuilders and others are not. This system of nomenclature is designed to lead from initial petrographic and faunal description or from initial field study to broader genetic interpretation as data accumulate.

ORGANIC COMPOSITION

Skeletal limestone deposits are classified according to the faunal or floral elements responsible for their formation. Classification of reefs, for example, is based on the type of framebuilding organisms. If the faunal or floral elements cannot be positively identified at the generic or specific level, general terms such as *algal*, *coralline*, or *molluscan skeletal limestone* can be used. This is commonly the case early in an investigation.

SHAPE

On the basis of their shape, skeletal deposits are classified as bioherms or biostromes, as they were defined by Cumings (1932). His definitions are as follows.

> *Bioherm.*—" . . . a reef, bank, or mound; for reeflike, moundlike, or lenslike or otherwise circumscribed structures of strictly *organic origin*, embedded in rocks of different lithology." (p. 333)
>
> *Biostrome.*—" . . . purely bedded structures, such as shell beds, crinoid beds, coral beds, et cetera, consisting of and built mainly by sedentary organisms, and not swelling into moundlike or lenslike forms, . . . , which means a layer or bed." (p. 334)

These terms refer to the present day shape in the stratigraphic sequence, not necessarily to the relief of the unit at the time of deposition. To be classified as a bioherm, a skeletal limestone deposit need not have been a topographic feature at the time of deposition. In addition to their use as nouns, the shape terms may be used as adjectives to modify reef or bank; for example, biohermal or biostromal reef and biohermal or biostromal bank.

A geologist's concept of the shape of a skeletal limestone deposit is conditioned by the size of the area mapped compared to the size of the rock unit, and by the position of the outcrop relative to the main rock mass. To illustrate this principle, the writers have depicted a hypothetical skeletal limestone mass (Fig. 2). If field studies were restricted to area A, it would be impossible to describe the shape of the deposit. However, if the investigation covered the entire area indicated in Figure 2, the shape of the limestone mass would be apparent. Depending on the breadth:height ratio, the deposit would be described as either a bioherm or biostrome.

A skeletal limestone deposit may be described as either a bioherm or biostrome, depending upon whether the shape terms are applied to the entire deposit or merely to that part which is exposed in an outcrop. In the past, these terms have been applied to both. Figure 2 represents a skeletal mass of large horizontal extent. Though the actual shape is hypothetical, similar deposits occur in the Lower Cretaceous Edwards and Glen Rose formations of Texas, and in the Silurian rocks of the Great Lakes area. Though the breadth of the total rock unit considerably exceeds the height, if outcrops were present only along profiles *a-a′* and *b-b′* the deposit would probably be described as a group of bioherms (Figs. 3-*A* and 4-*A*). These relations are clearly demonstrated in outcrops of the Edwards formation in central Texas (Pl. 1-*A*).

Outcrops along *b-b′* and *c-c′* would expose complete sections and the extreme dimensions of the main limestone unit (Figs. 3-*B*, 3-*C*, 4-*B*, and 4-*C*). Figures 3-*C* and 4-*C* indicate that the bioherms in section *a-a′* are relatively minor features of a much larger, and possibly biostromal, skeletal

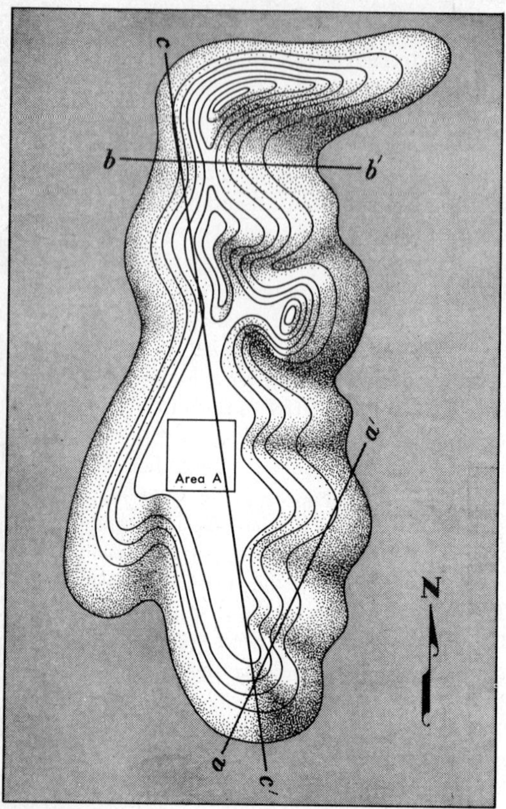

FIG. 2.—Hypothetical skeletal limestone mass.

limestone deposit. Complete gradations from biostromes with flat upper surfaces to small isolated bioherms are found in the Edwards formation (Pl. 1-*B*, *C*, and *D*), and similar gradations may be common in many other formations containing skeletal limestones. These examples indicate the necessity for stating clearly whether the shape terms refer to individual outcrops or to the entire skeletal deposit.

ORIGIN

Skeletal limestones are defined as reefs or banks in terms of the ecologic potential of the organisms responsible for forming the deposits.

Reef.—a skeletal limestone deposit formed by organisms possessing the ecologic potential to erect a rigid, wave-resistant, topographic structure.

Bank.—a skeletal limestone deposit formed by organisms which do not have the ecologic potential to erect a rigid, wave-resistant structure.

By concept and definition then, the problem of differentiating reefs from banks is reduced to determining the capabilities (ecologic potential) of the organisms to construct a rigid framework in the zone of wave action.

The zone of wave action is considered to be that portion of the sea floor over which wave energy is dissipated, and is not necessarily restricted to the surf zone. Some idea of the maximum depth of this zone is gained from data presented by Sverdrup and others (1946), and Kuenen (1950). Sverdrup described oceanic waves in detail (p. 516–604) and noted that the zone of wave action extends to a depth which is equal to approximately one-half of the wave length. Moderate wave action in deep water is rarely felt below depths of 30 meters, though wave measurements which suggest zones of wave action as deep as 65 meters are listed (p. 526, Table 68). Kuenen (1950, p. 74) noted that the oscillation of true oceanic waves is hindered by a sea floor which is less than 200 meters deep. In addition, he indicated (p. 76) that strong oceanic waves, 15 meters high, generally have a wave length of approximately 300 meters. Thus, the zone wave action would extend to a depth of 150 meters.

Earlier in this paper, criteria for the recognition of in-place skeletal deposits were presented. Criteria which indicated accumulation in place may also indicate the ecologic potential of the organisms responsible for the deposit. Growth habits and known occurrences of the madreporarian corals, for example, show that they construct a rigid framework and can do so in the zone of wave action. Several writers (Fenton and Fenton, 1933; Hadding, 1950; Lowenstam, 1950; Twenhofel, 1950; Ladd and others, 1950; Cloud, 1952; Plumley and Graves, 1953; and Newell, 1955) discussed the importance of algae in building a framework, and Newell (1955) noted that calcareous sponges were important framebuilders in the Permian Capitan reef.

A rigid framework may also be constructed by bivalved organisms as they cement themselves to each other. Some writers believe that this can

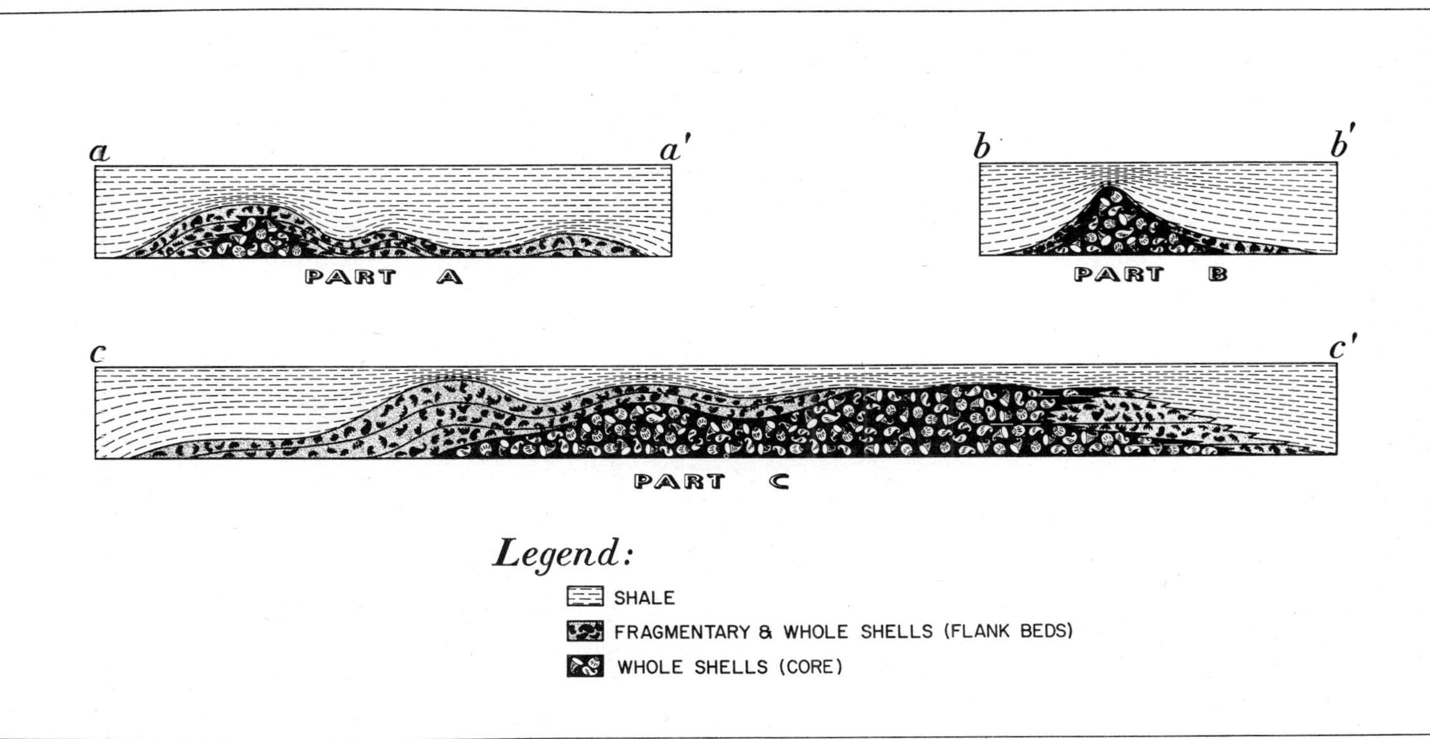

FIG. 3.—Cross sections showing the stratigraphic and structural relations which might occur if the hypothetical skeletal mass (Fig. 2) were a reef. The central part of the deposit in Part *C* stands topographically above the adjoining sediments; the right end indicates contemporaneous deposition and subsequent compaction. Examples of these stratigraphic and structural relationships may be seen in the Silurian sediments in the Great Lakes area, the Virgilian (Pennsylvanian) sediments in New Mexico, and in the Glen Rose and Edwards (Cretaceous) formations in Texas.

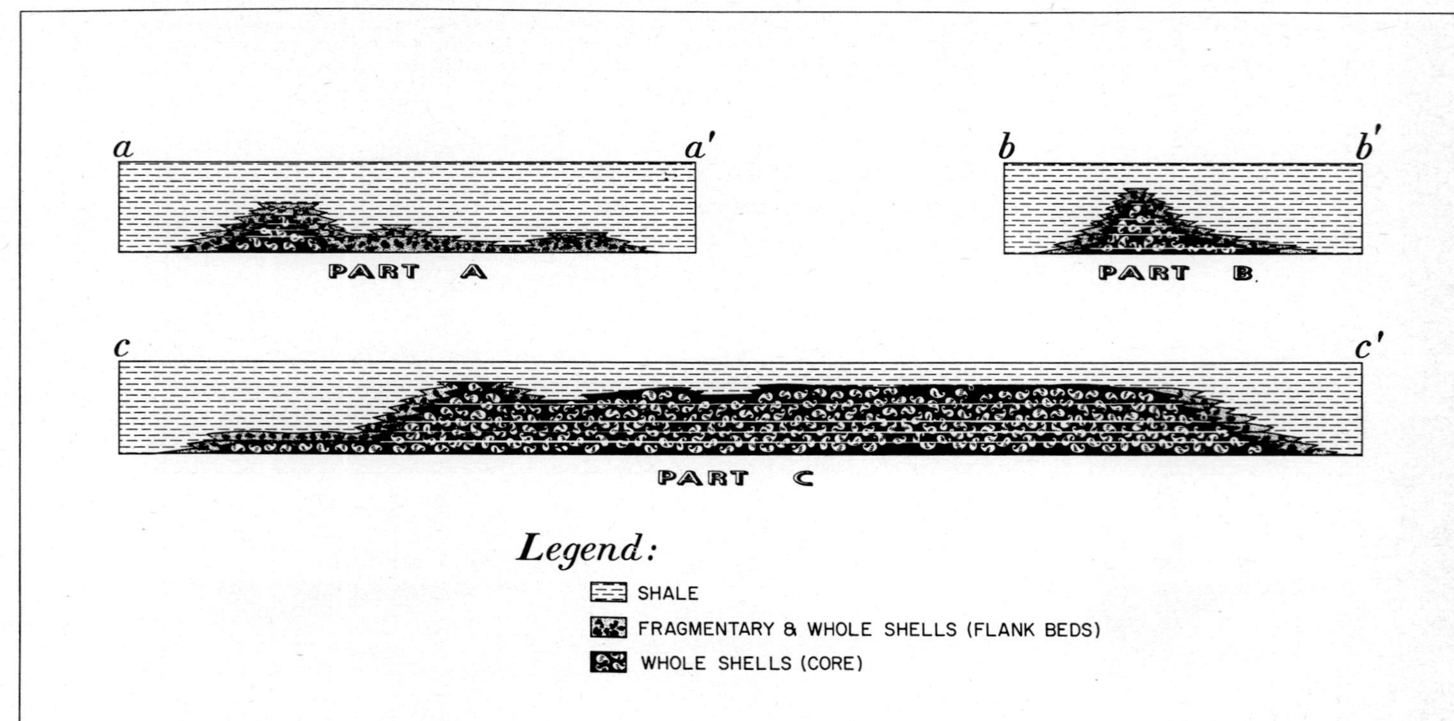

FIG. 4.—Cross sections showing the stratigraphic and structural relations which might occur if the hypothetical skeletal mass (Fig. 2) were a bank. The bank-forming organisms never formed a topographic structure. Examples of these stratigraphic and structural relationships may be seen in the Walnut (Cretaceous) formation in Texas and the Tepee Buttes in the Pierre (Cretaceous) shale in Colorado.

happen only below the zone of effective wave action, and they do not regard these organisms as true reef builders. However, Grave (1901) showed that oysters can construct reefs in the zone of wave and current action. The senior writer has observed *Crassostrea virginica* constructing large masses of shells on pilings of offshore oil well platforms in the Gulf of Mexico. These masses grow immediately beneath the surface of the water, 30 feet above the sea floor. Cretaceous rudistids and caprinids are believed to have constructed rigid frameworks in the zone of wave action by cementation of one individual to another and possibly by individual organisms becoming interlocked by their irregularly shaped valves (Nelson, 1959).

The ability of organisms to cope with wave action and build a wave-resistant structure is suggested by (1) vertical and horizontal changes in the faunal assemblage, (2) the structure and lithology of the skeletal deposit, and (3) the sediments deposited beyond the limits of the reef complex, particularly the lagoonal sediments.

Faunal changes.—Lowenstam (1950) showed that the framebuilders change from dominantly narrow based, vertical forms in the lower part of the Silurian reefs, to horizontally spreading forms in the upper part. In addition, he showed that the change in growth habit is accompanied by an upward change of the niche dwellers from quiet-water to rough-water types. Young (1959) demonstrated that four faunal zones characterize Cretaceous reefs in the Edwards formation. A *Cladophyllia* coral zone forms the base of the reefs. This zone is followed in ascending order by the *Monopleura-Toucasia*, *Caprinuloidea*, and *Eoradiolites-Chondrodonta* zones. Young noted that the three highest zones are made up of more robust and heavier walled shells than are the two lowest zones. Both writers believed the faunal changes were due to adaptation of the organisms to more rigorous environmental conditions as the reefs grew upward into the zone of wave action. Ladd and others (1950) described well developed faunal zonation on Bikini atoll and attributed zonation to adaptation of the organisms to the physical force of winds and currents.

Structure and lithology.—Structural and lithologic evidence for in-place accumulations of skeletal deposits has been presented in an earlier section of this paper. In part, this evidence also suggests growth of a rigid structure in the zone of wave action. Thus, tongues of skeletal limestone dipping away from the massive core and interbedded with abraded and sorted skeletal debris indicate that the skeletal deposit was rigid enough to stand topographically above the surrounding sediments in the zone of wave action. A mass of fossils in their growth position and embedded in a very fine-grained matrix grading laterally and successively into unabraded and unsorted coarse skeletal debris in a very fine-grained matrix, abraded and either sorted or unsorted skeletal debris in a clear-calcite matrix, and finally into well-sorted calcarenite or calcilutite, is further indication of organic growth in the zone of wave action.

Fossil debris in and around a skeletal limestone mass and dipping beds of skeletal debris, in themselves, are not evidence of organic growth in the zone of wave action, however. Studies of Recent sediments by the writers and others (Wood-Jones, 1910; Yonge, 1930; Otter, 1937) indicate that boring organisms play an important part in the comminution of skeletal material. Nearly all large communities of organisms attract predators, and, as a result, most skeletal deposits are surrounded by some fossil debris, regardless of whether or not the deposits are formed in the zone of wave action.

Dipping beds of skeletal debris may be formed by uplift and erosion of any skeletal limestone deposit followed by deposition of the debris in the surrounding area. The beds of skeletal debris might dip away from the skeletal limestone deposit and, lithologically as well as structurally, the resulting skeletal deposit and surrounding debris would superficially resemble a true reef that grew in the zone of wave action.

Topographic relief above contemporaneously deposited sediments, though generally characteristic of true reefs, is not an absolute criterion of growth of a skeletal deposit in the zone of wave action. Some organisms, totally incapable of coping with wave action, may build a topographic structure below wave base or in relatively quiet water above wave base. Newell (1955) suggested that secondary framebuilders, including some bryozoans, cemented brachiopods, pelecypods, and corals, constructed small reefs in calm water.

A
B
C
D

More recently, Teichert (1958) described "coral banks" in the deep water of the Atlantic and Indian Oceans and the Mediterranean Sea. The banks occur below effective wave base, and their rigid frameworks have been built by four species of corals and hydrozoans which include *Lophelia prolifera*, *Madrepora ramea*, *Stylaster gemmoscens*, and *Allopora norvegica*. The banks stand as much as 200 feet above the surrounding sea floor. Living *Lophelia* banks are found at a minimum depth of 185 feet, and the organisms die when raised to shallower depths. It is not clear, however, whether the inability of the organisms to build banks above wave base is due to their lack of ability to cope with wave action or to some other cause. As we have defined the term, these interesting organic structures would not be considered as true reefs. If, however, future studies should prove that the organisms which have constructed the banks are able to cope with wave action, the structures would have to be considered as true reefs.

It is apparent then, that the only clear-cut lithologic and structural evidence indicating that organisms grew and constructed a true reef in the zone of wave action are tongues of skeletal limestone that dip away from the core and are interbedded with contemporaneous detrital and/or chemically precipitated sediments.

In the preceding discussion, the writers have cited evidence which indicates growth of a rigid structure in the zone of wave action; unfortunately, such evidence is not apparent in all deposits. Link (1950), Henson (1950), and Cloud (1952) suggested that reef-building organisms living on a slowly sinking sea floor would construct a reef with great topographic relief if the vertical growth rate of the organisms kept pace with subsidence of the bottom. These writers believed, however, that the organisms would construct a reef of great lateral extent and with little topographic relief during prolonged stillstand or regression of the sea, or if their growth rate greatly exceeded subsidence of the sea floor.

Lower Cretaceous rudistid reefs in central Texas appear to support the suggestions of Link (1950), Henson (1950), and Cloud (1952). During transgression of the Fredericksburg sea, the rudistids formed an extensive reef trend on the west flank of the East Texas basin. Near Waco and Belton, the reefs stand 30 to possibly 60 feet or more above contemporaneously deposited sediments (Nelson, 1959). Tongues of the reef cores and unsorted flank deposits consisting of whole and fragmented rudistids grade laterally into and interfinger with well sorted fine shell debris and granular limestone. The flank beds dip as much as 35° away from the reef cores. These relations indicate that the organisms grew in the zone of wave action and formed topographic, wave-resistant structures. Northward, toward the ancient shoreline where the water was probably shallower or where subsidence was slower, the rudistid reef facies tends to be biostromal. The biohermal shape and the relief of individual reefs are less pronounced than they are in the Waco-Belton area.

It should not be assumed that all reefs will show evidence of wave action. Small patch reefs that grow on the lee side of larger reefs or behind a main-reef trend may not be eroded by waves and currents. Also, organic growth may begin below wave base, and no evidence of wave action is formed until the reef grows above wave base.

←««

EXPLANATION OF PLATE I

A—Undulatory flank deposits of a rudistid reef in the Lower Cretaceous Edwards formation, Coryell County, Texas.

B—Rudistid reef core and flank beds in the Edwards formation, McLennan County, Texas. The reef core is in the stream bed at the right side of the photograph. The flank deposits dip 15°–30°. Individual mounds have a relief of less than 5 feet at this locality.

C—Well-bedded inter-reef detrital limestones overlying the massive rudistid reef-flank deposits in the Edwards formation. The relief on the upper surface of the flank deposits is approximately 4 feet. This outcrop is 0.5 mile upstream from photograph *B*.

D—Well-bedded inter-reef deposits overlying massive reef flank deposits. This is a continuation and more distant view of the outcrop shown in photograph *C*. The structural features shown in these photographs, though prominent in a single outcrop, may become rather insignificant when viewed from a great distance or when compared to the size of the entire reef, which may have a horizontal dimension of several miles.

Thus, part of a reef or many individual reefs in a reef trend may provide no evidence of the capabilities of the organisms to cope with wave action. Yet the growth processes and ecologic potential of the organisms that grew below wave base might be the same as those which grew above wave base.

Sediments beyond the reef complex.—Several writers (Ladd, 1944; Lowenstam, 1950; Cloud, 1952; and Ginsburg and Lowenstam, 1958) have shown that true reef-building organisms, by virtue of their ability to grow in the zone of wave action, can indirectly control or modify their own and adjoining environments and thereby affect sedimentation in these environments. The previous discussion has noted that the reef-building organisms may shed sediments to the immediately surrounding area and create a new environment which becomes inhabited by organisms that otherwise could not live in the area. The effect of reef growth may extend for a considerable distance beyond the limits of the reef complex. Organic growth may form a barrier reef which changes the circulation pattern and the chemistry of the water mass in the basin of deposition. As a result, evaporites may form in the back-reef lagoon, and terrigenous sediments that otherwise would be transported seaward may be trapped behind the barrier reef. Examples of this type of sedimentation occur behind the Permian Capitan reef complex in West Texas and New Mexico (Newell and others, 1953) and behind the Lower Cretaceous rudistid reef complex in the Gulf Coast area.

We cannot assume, however, that reef-building organisms influence sedimentation far beyond the limits of the reef in all instances, or that their influence can be recognized. The previous discussion has suggested that true reef-building organisms may grow below wave base or in quiet water and form structures that show little or no evidence of wave action. Obviously such organisms could not affect their environment beyond the limits of the reef. However, under ideal conditions—in very shallow water, for example—the organisms may grow so prolifically that they will construct a reef of vast lateral extent, which shows little or no evidence of wave action, has no topographic relief, and occupies the area formerly characterized by mechanically or chemically deposited sediments. This is considered to be one explanation for the thick rudistid biostromes which cover large areas in north-central Texas (Nelson, 1959).

The writers have stressed Lowenstam's concept of the *ecologic potential* of organisms to construct a rigid, topographic, wave-resistant structure rather than either the *actual* construction of a topographic structure or *actual* growth in the zone of wave action. The writers have done so because we feel that this approach will lead to a better understanding of how organisms formed a skeletal deposit and what the environmental conditions were at the time of growth. The previous discussion has shown that topographic structure does not necessarily denote formation by true reef-building organisms, and, conversely that lack of topographic relief does not preclude such origin. Likewise, growth in the zone of wave action may not be evident, and, if evident, may have been the result of other processes.

Many factors other than lack of ecologic potential may obscure, eliminate, or prevent the formation of such evidence in every outcrop, well bore, or even in every reef. The writers readily admit that this concept places great reliance upon the ability of the geologist to determine the manner of organic growth and to interpret the environmental conditions under which the organisms grew. In many instances it is difficult to acquire this information or to arrive at a conclusion, but we feel that the ecologic potential of the organisms can be ascertained if an effort is made to determine the type and magnitude of the natural forces that were operative in the formation or destruction of a skeletal deposit, and to visualize the conditions under which the forces operated. Once an organism has been shown to be a true reef builder, its potential has been established. Other structures built by the organism, either below or above wave base, and in either calm or rough water, should be considered as true reefs.

SUBSIDIARY TERMS

The following subsidiary terms are useful in studies of skeletal limestone deposits.

Reef core.—that portion of the reef within the

rigid growth lattice formed by the frame-building organisms.

The reef core is referred to as the *reef wall* by Henson (1950), *biohermal reef rock* by MacNeil (1954), and *reef proper* by Dunbar and Rodgers (1957). As noted by several writers (Ladd, 1950; Fairbridge, 1950; Cloud, 1952; and MacNeil, 1954), the reef core may make up a relatively small part of the reef. Biohermal reefs generally have massive cores, but irregular growth surfaces or undulatory bedding planes may be present. The bedding planes are believed to be original growth surfaces modified by erosion, rather than depositional surfaces.

Reef flank.—that portion of the reef which surrounds, interfingers with, and locally overlies the reef core.

The reef flank is a transitional zone where biologic forces of reef expansion contend with physical and biologic forces of reef destruction. As a result, the flank sediments have properties common to both the reef core and the physically deposited inter-reef sediments. They are generally massive- to medium-bedded skeletal and fragmental limestones. Lithologically, the flank beds consist of coarse, poorly sorted, whole and broken skeletons, tongues of the reef core, and beds of variably sorted fine shell debris and carbonate sand. Lateral and vertical gradation of in-place and transported material is common. Organisms which are indigenous only to this zone are commonly present. Except for the sorted shell debris and carbonate sand, the sediments in the reef flank are considered to be virtually in-place accumulations because they show very little evidence of transportation. Many individual fossils, though fragmented, may be identified. Owing to close packing of large shell fragments or whole fossils, the flank beds commonly appear to be more fossiliferous than the reef core.

Inter-reef deposits.—the sediments deposited between reefs.

Where individual reefs are closely spaced, there may be very little distinction between the inter-reef and reef-flank deposits or, in some case, between the inter-reef, reef-flank, and reef-core deposits. They may be either limestones or terrigenous clastics. Chert is frequently present.

The terms *fore reef* and *back reef* apply only to linear reef trends, in contrast to the previously described terms *reef core* and *reef flank* which apply to all types of reefs.

Fore reef.—the seaward side of the reef trend.

The fore-reef sediments, composed primarily of reef detritus, interfinger with the reef and basin sediments.

Back reef.—the landward side of the reef trend.

The back-reef sediments are largely reef-derived fossil debris, calcarenite, and calcilutite, which may interfinger with both the reef and lagoonal facies.

Reef complex.—the aggregate of reef, fore-reef, back-reef, and inter-reef deposits which are bounded on the seaward side by the basin sediments and on the landward side by the lagoonal sediments.

This is virtually the same concept as that which has been expressed by Henson (1950). In general, the sediments in the reef complex have a skeletal or obvious clastic texture. Limestones with a clastic texture include coquinas of whole and broken shells, comminuted shells, carbonate sand, and oölites. Very fine-grained limestones (calcilutites) may be present, but they constitute a subordinate part of the reef complex. Most of the clastic limestone in the reef complex is probably derived through destruction of the reef by waves and boring organisms. Petrographic studies frequently indicate that all but the finest particles are derived from calcareous skeletal material.

Henson (1950, p. 215–216) suggested that all "genetically (?) associated sediments" should be included in the reef complex. Because reefs may indirectly control or modify the environments for a considerable distance from the reef trend, carbonate and evaporite sediments in the lagoon could be considered genetically related and be included in the reef complex. It seems clear from his discussion, however, that Henson did not mean to include these genetically associated sediments in the reef complex.

Lagoon.—the area between the reef complex and the shoreline or in the area completely circumscribed by the reef complex.

Lagoonal sediments may include terrigenous clastics, limestones, or evaporites. If limestones, they are generally more fine grained (calcilutites) and show less textural variation than the sediments in the reef complex. Patch reefs or banks in the lagoon may provide local sources for coarse sediments. Except for these local variations, the grain size of lagoonal carbonate rocks is generally too small to aid in determining the source of the particles. Lagoonal sediments are generally somewhat darker in color than the sediments of the reef complex.

SUMMARY

Many meanings have been applied to the terms *reef*, *bank*, *bioherm*, and *biostrome*. This is particularly true of the terms *reef* and *bioherm*. Varied usage has led to misunderstanding among geologists and undoubtedly to misinterpretation of the origin of many limestone deposits. A better concept of the origin of reefs and reef-like limestones can be gained by more critical use of the terms which described these deposits. It is not necessary to introduce new terms if the concepts of Cumings and Shrock (1928b), Cumings (1932), and Lowenstam (1950) are followed. The writers propose, therefore, a threefold classification of skeletal limestone deposits based on organic content, shape, and origin. Skeletal limestones are defined as rocks which consist of, or owe their characteristics to, the in-place accumulation of calcareous skeletal material. The terms noted above are restricted to these accumulations. Thus, a skeletal limestone deposit is classified according to the organism primarily responsible for its formation, and its shape is described as biohermal or biostromal according to the definitions originally proposed by Cumings and Shrock (1928b) and Cumings (1932). Finally, the skeletal limestone is classified as a *reef* or *bank*, depending upon the ecologic potential of the organisms to build a topographic, wave-resistant structure (Lowenstam, 1950). Thus, a skeletal limestone deposit may be classified as a rudistid biostromal reef or a *Lucina* biohermal bank, the generic or specific names of the organisms being used wherever possible.

The procedure outlined above makes it possible to develop the classification of an in-place accumulation of organic remains as more information becomes available. Early in an investigation, for example, it may not be possible to go beyond the point of calling the deposit a skeletal limestone. As field work proceeds, the shape of the deposit is determined. Later, after a detailed faunal study, it may finally be classified as either a reef or a bank. In a subsurface study, the shape of the deposit may actually be the last information acquired by the geologist.

This classification is proposed not as a substitute but rather as a supplement to detailed descriptions of skeletal deposits. The writers do not believe that detailed descriptions can be replaced by a few words. The writers believe that deposits other than skeletal limestones should be recognized for what they really are. It is just as important in paleogeographic studies to identify an erosional remnant of limestone properly as it is to identify a reef correctly. It is also important to differentiate secondary solution porosity, which is partially controlled by organic growth processes. Nothing is gained by calling every porosity buildup in limestone, a reef.

REFERENCES

American Geological Institute, 1957, J. V. Howell, ed., Glossary of geology and related sciences: Natl. Acad. Sci.-Natl. Research Council Pub. 501.

Andrichuk, J. M., 1958, Stratigraphy and facies analysis of Upper Devonian reefs in Leduc, Stettler, and Redwater areas, Alberta: Am. Assoc. Petroleum Geologists Bull., v. 42, no. 1, p. 1–93.

Ballard, T. W., Fairbridge, R. W., and Sachet, M. H., 1958, Selected bibliography on the geology of organic reefs: Internat. Comm. on Reef Terminology, The Pacific Sci. Board, Natl. Acad. Sci.-Natl. Research Council.

Bell, Robert, 1887, Report on an exploration of portions of the Attawapiskat and Albany Rivers, Lonely Lake to James Bay: Geol. Survey Canada Ann. Rept., 1886, v. 2, pt. g, p. 27–28.

Chamberlin, T. C., 1877, Geology of eastern Wisconsin, *in* Geology of Wisconsin, v. 2: Wisconsin Geol. Survey, p. 360–371.

Cloud, P. E., 1952, Facies relationships of organic reefs. Am. Assoc. Petroleum Geologists Bulletin, v. 36, no. 11, p. 2125–2149.

Cumings, E. R., 1930, List of species from the New Corydon, Kokoma, and Kenneth formations of Indiana, and from reefs in the Mississinewa and Liston Creek formations: Indiana Acad. Sci. Proc., v. 39, p. 204–211.

——— 1932, Reefs or bioherms?: Geol. Soc. America Bull., v. 43, no. 1, p. 331–352.

——— and Shrock, R. R., 1928a, The geology of the Silurian rocks of northern Indiana: Div. of Geology,

Indiana Dept. Conserv., Pub. 75, 226 p.
——— 1928b, Niagaran coral reefs of Indiana and adjacent states and their stratigraphic relations: Geol. Soc. America Bull., v. 39, no. 2, p. 579–620.
Dana, J. D., 1849, Geology, *in* U. S. exploring expedition, during the years 1838, 1839, 1840, 1841, 1842, under the command of Charles Wilkes, U. S. N., v. 10: Philadelphia, C. Sherman, 756 p.
Darwin, C. R., 1842, The structure and distribution of coral reefs: London, Smith, Elder, and Co., 214 p.
Downing, J. A., and Cooke, D. Y., 1955, Distribution of reefs of Woodbend group in Alberta, Canada: Am. Assoc. Petroleum Geologists Bull., v. 39, no. 2, p. 189–206.
Dunbar, C. O., and Rodgers, John, 1957, Principles of stratigraphy: New York, John Wiley and Sons, Inc., 356 p.
Fairbridge, R. W., 1950, Recent and Pleistocene coral reefs of Australia: Jour. Geology, v. 58, no. 4, p. 330–401.
Fenton, C. L., and Fenton, M. A., 1933, Algal reefs or bioherms in the Belt series of Montana: Geol. Soc. America Bull., v. 44, no. 6, p. 1135–1142.
Ginsburg, R. N., and Lowenstam, H. A., 1958, The influence of marine bottom communities on the depositional environment of sediments: Jour. Geology, v. 66, no. 3, p. 310–318.
Grabau, A. W., 1913, Principles of stratigraphy: New York, A. G. Seiler and Co.
Grave, Caswell, 1901, The oyster reefs of North Carolina; a geological and economic study: Johns Hopkins Univ. Circ. 20, p. 50–53.
Hadding, Assar, 1950, Silurian reefs of Gotland: Jour. Geology, v. 58, no. 4, p. 402–409.
Hall, James, 1862, Physical geography and general geology: Wisconsin Geol. Survey Rept., v. 1, p. 1–72.
Henson, F. R. S., 1950, Cretaceous and Tertiary reef formations and associated sediments in Middle East: Am. Assoc. Petroleum Geologists Bull., v. 34, no. 2, p. 215–238.
Jukes, J. B., 1847, Narrative of the surveying voyage of the H.M.S. Fly . . . during the years 1842–1846: London, T. and Boone, W., v. 1, 423 p.
Krumbein, W. C., and Sloss, L. L., 1951, Stratigraphy and sedimentation: San Francisco, W. H. Freeman and Co., 497 p.
Kuenen, Ph. H., 1950, Marine geology: New York, John Wiley and Sons, Inc., 568 p.
Ladd, H. S., 1944, Reefs and other bioherms: Natl. Res. Council, Div. Geol. Geog., Ann. Rept. 4, app. K, p. 26–29.
——— 1950, Recent reefs: Am. Assoc. Petroleum Geologists Bull., v. 34, no. 2, p. 203–214.
——— and others, 1950, Organic growth and sedimentation on an atoll: Jour. Geology, v. 58, no. 4, p. 410–425.
Laudon, L. R., and Bowsher, A. L., 1941, Mississippian formations of Sacramento Mountains, New Mexico: Am. Assoc. Petroleum Geologists Bull., v. 25, no. 12, p. 2107–2160.
Levorsen, A. I., 1954, Geology of petroleum: San Francisco, W. H. Freeman and Co.
Link, T. A., 1950, Theory of transgressive and regressive reef (bioherm) development and origin of oil: Am. Assoc. Petroleum Geologists Bull., v. 34, no. 2, p. 263–294.
Lowenstam, H. A., 1948a, Marine pool, Madison County, Illinois, Silurian reef producer, *in* Structure of typical American oil fields, v. 3: Am. Assoc. Petroleum Geologists, p. 153–188.
——— 1948b, Niagaran reefs in Illinois and their relation to oil accumulation: Illinois Geol. Survey Rept. Inv. 145, 36 p.
——— 1950, Niagaran reefs of the Great Lakes area: Jour. Geology, v. 58, no. 4, p. 430–487.
MacNeil, F. S., 1954, Organic reefs and banks and associated detrital sediments: Am. Jour. Sci., v. 252, no. 7, p. 385–401.
Mojsisovics von Mojsvar, E., 1879, Die Dolomitriffe von Südtirol und Venetien: Vienna, Holder, 552 p.
Moore, R. C., 1957, Modern methods of paleoecology: Am. Assoc. Petroleum Geologists Bull., v. 41, no. 8, p. 1775–1801.
Murchison, R. I., 1847, On the Silurian and associated rocks in Dalecarlia, and on the succession from lower to upper Silurian in Smoland, Oeland, and Gothland, and in Scania: Geol. Soc. London Quart. Jour., v. 3, p. 1–48.
Nelson, H. F., 1959, Deposition and alteration of the Edwards formation in central Texas, *in* Symposium on Edwards limestone in central Texas: Univ. Texas Bull. 5905, p. 21–96.
Newell, N. D., 1955, Depositional fabric in Permian reef limestones: Jour. Geology, v. 63, no. 4, p. 301–309.
——— and others, 1953, The Permian reef complex of the Guadalupe Mountains region, Texas and New Mexico: San Francisco, W. H. Freeman and Co.
Ogilvie-Gordon, M. M., 1927, Das Grödener- Fassa- und Enneberggebeit in die Südtiroler Dolomiten: Abh. der Geol. Bundesanstalt, Vienna, v. 24, p. 157–161.
Otter, G. W., 1937, Rock-destroying organisms in relation to coral reefs, Great Barrier Reef expedition, 1928–1929: British Mus. Nat. History Sci. Repts., v. 1, p. 353–391.
Pettijohn, F. J., 1949, Sedimentary rocks, 1st ed.: New York, Harper and Bros.; 2d ed., 1957.
Plumley, W. J., and Graves, R. W., Jr., 1953, Virgilian reefs of the Sacramento Mountains, New Mexico: Jour. Geology, v. 61, no. 1, p. 1–16.
Pugh, W. E., 1950, editor, Bibliography of organic reefs, bioherms, and biostromes: Tulsa, Seismograph Service Corp., 139 p.
Rothpletz, A., 1894, Ein geologischen Querschnitt durch die Ost-Alpen nebst Anhang, über de sogenannten Glarner Doppel-Falte: Stuttgart.
Rutten, M. G., 1958, Silurian reefs in Gotland (abs.): A.A.P.G.-Soc. Econ. Paleon. and Mineral. Ann. Meeting, Los Angeles, program booklet, p. 73.
Shrock, R. R., 1939, Wisconsin Silurian bioherms: Geol. Soc. America Bull., v. 50, no. 4, p. 529–562.
Stockdale, P. B., 1931, Bioherms in the Borden group of Indiana: Geol. Soc. America Bull., v. 42, no. 3, p. 707–718.
Stokes, W. L., and Varnes, D. J., 1955, Glossary of selected geologic terms with special reference to their use in engineering: Denver, Colo. Sci. Soc. Proc., v. 16, 165 p.
Sverdrup, H. U., Johnson, M. W., and Fleming, R. H., 1946, The oceans, their physics, chemistry, and general biology: New York, Prentice-Hall, Inc., 1087 p.
Teichert, Curt, 1958, Cold- and deep-water coral banks:

Am. Assoc. Petroleum Geologists Bull., v. 42, no. 5, p. 1064–1082.

Twenhofel, W. H., 1950, Coral and other organic reefs in geologic column: Am. Assoc. Petroleum Geologists Bull., v. 34, no. 2, p. 182–202.

Vaughan, T. W., 1911, Physical conditions under which the Paleozoic reefs were formed: Geol. Soc. America Bull., v. 22, p. 238–252.

Warthin, A. S., Jr., and Cooper, G. A., 1943, Traverse rocks of Thunder Bay region, Michigan: Am. Assoc. Petroleum Geologists Bull., v. 27, no. 5, p. 571–595.

Weller, J. M., 1958, Stratigraphic facies differentiation and nomenclature: Am. Assoc. Petroleum Geologists Bull., v. 42, no. 3, p. 609–693.

Wengerd, S. A., 1951, Reef limestones of Hermosa formation, San Juan County, Utah: Am. Assoc. Petroleum Geologists Bull., v. 35, no. 5, p. 1038–1051.

Wilson, W. B., 1950, Reef definition: Am. Assoc. Petroleum Geologists Bull., v. 34, no. 2, p. 181.

Wood-Jones, F., 1910, Coral and atolls: London, Lovell Reeve and Co., Ltd., 392 p.

Yonge, C. M., 1930, A year on the Great Barrier Reef: New York and London, G. P. Putnam Co., 246 p.

Young, Keith, 1959, Edwards limestone fossils as depth indicators, *in* Symposium on Edwards limestone in central Texas: Univ. Texas Bull. 5905, p. 97–104.

CLASSIFICATION OF MODERN BAHAMIAN CARBONATE SEDIMENTS[1]

JOHN IMBRIE[2] AND EDWARD G. PURDY[3]
New York, New York, and Houston, Texas

ABSTRACT

An optimum empirical classification is defined as one in which there is exactly one category for each group of samples separated from other groups by discontinuities in the ranges of their observed properties. A statistical scheme for identifying discrete sample groupings (if they exist) in a set of data is developed which gives equal weight to any number of properties, and treats nonhomogeneous properties simultaneously. Essential features of the scheme are (1) representation of each sample as a vector in an n-coordinate system, where n is the number of attributes considered, (2) use of the angle of separation between sample vectors as an inverse measure of similarity, (3) application of factor analysis to determine the minimum number of coordinates necessary to express main features of the data efficiently, and (4) inspection of the resulting vector array for discrete vector clusters.

Applied to 200 samples of modern Bahamian carbonate sediments studied by Purdy, this scheme identifies five discrete sample groups (oölite, oölitic, grapestone, coralgal, and lime mud facies) whose discrete character is not apparent if only a small number of attributes are considered simultaneously.

The same 200 samples are treated according to Folk's limestone classification, and the results compared with the optimum classification scheme. Application of Folk's criteria yields nine named categories belonging to Type I (sparry allochemical limestone) and Type II (microcrystalline allochemical limestone), although it is difficult to make the I–II distinction in many samples. In general, correspondence between the two classifications is good in Type I, and poor in Type II.

INTRODUCTION

PURPOSE

As illustrated by other papers in this symposium, limestone classifications may be formulated in various ways. The purpose of this paper is to indicate one procedure by which modern carbonate sediment data may be used to evaluate classifications designed to reflect characteristics of the depositional environment. The criterion we suggest is that of *simplicity*, and in applying it we ask—Is the classification being evaluated as simple as possible? By a simple scheme we mean a classification in which there is exactly one category for each group of samples found to be separated from other groups by discontinuities in the ranges of their observable properties.

OUTLINE OF PROCEDURE

The classification evaluation procedure followed in this paper involves four steps.

1. *Designation of study area.*—A considerable variety of carbonate sediment types are now forming over a wide area in shallow waters of the Bahama Banks (Fig. 1). A number of investigators have published studies of this region and at least the general characteristics of the sediments and the depositional environments are fairly well known (*see* Black, 1933; Illing, 1954; Newell and others, 1959; Newell, Purdy, and Imbrie, 1960; Newell and Rigby, 1957; and Smith, 1940). A paper by Purdy (Ms.) will make available for the first time detailed, quantitative, petrographic observations on 200 bottom samples taken on the Andros lobe of the Great Bahama Bank. These data form the factual basis of the present study.

2. *Development of an optimum classification of samples from study area.*—An optimum classification is here defined as a classification providing one, and only one, category for each group of samples having discrete properties—in short, a

[1] Part of a symposium arranged by the Research Committee, and presented at Denver, Colorado, April 17, 1961, under joint auspices of the Association and the Society of Economic Paleontologists and Mineralogists. Manuscript received, May 6, 1961.

Dr. Norman D. Newell introduced the authors to the study of Bahamian sediments and organism communities, and has stimulated in many ways the growth of ideas expressed here. All the computations contained in this paper were run at the Watson Scientific Computing Laboratory of Columbia University. Programs used in these calculations were written and executed by Mr. Jonathan E. Robbin, whose experience with factor analysis greatly assisted us in developing special applications of these techniques to geological problems. Dr. George R. Orme, Mr. Hugh Buchanan, and Mrs. Marjorie Darland gave valuable assistance in various phases of data processing. The statistical part of this paper was supported by grant PRF-687-A from the Petroleum Research Fund of the American Chemical Society.

[2] Columbia University.

[3] Rice University.

classification in which the designated categories correspond to natural rather than artificial units. This definition is illustrated by hypothetical data of Figure 2-*I*. For simplicity of presentation, the assumption is made that the system to be classified is completely described by three observational parameters visualized as end members of a triangular diagram. The plotted points reveal two distinct clusters representing two groups of samples with discrete properties. Each cluster represents a category in what is here defined as an optimum classification scheme for these data. Note that the boundary between the clusters is a natural one and (assuming adequate sampling) may be taken to reflect a significant discontinuity in the dynamic system responsible for the observed properties of the sediment. The facies map corresponding to the classification locates the geographic position of this discontinuity.

In the simple case being illustrated, no *a priori* decisions are required and the data, in a sense, classify themselves. In dealing with real sediments and rocks, a very large number of properties may be observed, so that the characteristics of a classification may be predetermined by the selection of a limited number of observational parameters. In order to arrive empirically at an optimum classification, therefore, it is necessary to overcome or minimize this arbitrary element. One technique for accomplishing this objective is described below.

3. *Application of the classification to be evaluated to samples from study area.*—This is possible only with limestone classifications which are based, at least in part, on properties observable in unconsolidated sediments. Figure 2-*II* illustrates the application of a classification scheme based on three 1:1 ratio lines to the same data treated in Figure 2-*I*.

4. *Comparison of results.*—The facies patterns and sample groupings resulting from application of the two classification schemes now may be di-

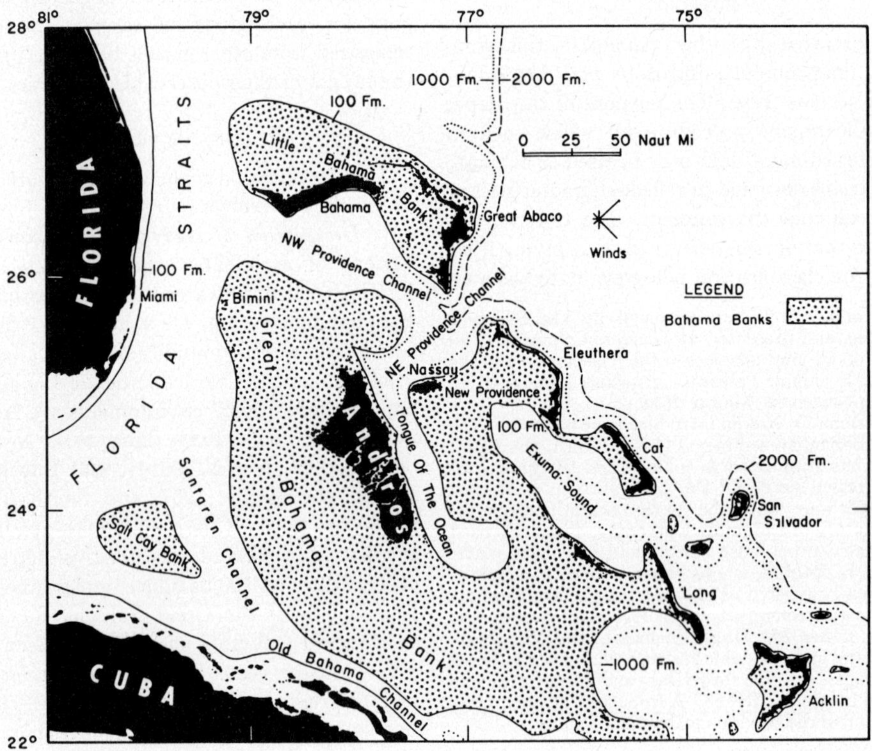

FIG. 1.—Map of the Bahama Banks.

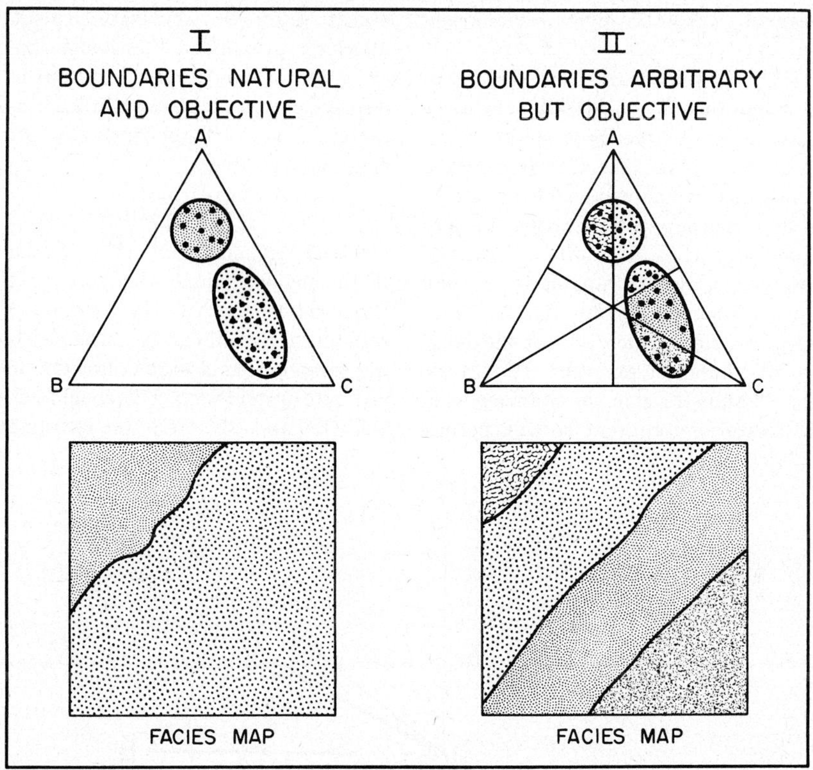

FIG. 2.—Diagram illustrating an optimum classification (I) and an objective but arbitrary classification (II).

rectly compared, and the degree of correspondence between them taken as one measure of the validity of the system being evaluated.

Figure 2 illustrates such a comparison. Although boundaries between the five categories of system II are objectively determined, the categories themselves are in a sense artificial—subdivisions are indicated where no natural discontinuity exists, and the real discontinuity is not reflected by any boundary between designated categories. None of the boundaries on facies map II corresponds with a natural discontinuity, although the mapped units do reflect a real gradient. For some purposes it might be useful to portray such a gradient by arbitrary subdivisions of natural facies; but in general it seems to us unwise to use a classification as a basis for detecting environmental or petrographic gradients. In the present example it would be more efficient to map the ratio A/C.

OPTIMUM CLASSIFICATION OF BAHAMIAN SEDIMENTS

OBJECTIVES

In the example illustrated in Figure 2, it is possible to identify discrete clusters by simple visual inspection of plotted points. As the system is here assumed to be completely described by three components, an optimum classification is automatically achieved. If we had selected only two properties, however, our results would have been satisfactory or unsatisfactory depending on which pair of properties had been selected. A–C will yield essentially the optimum classification; but A–B or B–C would give the false impression that only one cluster is present. In a real situation, with an endless number of rock properties available, the possible effect of adding information on other components must be considered. By plotting points in a tetrahedron, simultaneous consideration can of course be given to four end members.

The limitations of Euclidean space prevent us from giving simultaneous consideration to more than four coordinates, by means of standard triangle or tetrahedron plots. We therefore seek a descriptive technique which will enable us to give equal and simultaneous consideration to any number of rock properties. In addition, it will be useful to construct a system capable of treating nonhomogeneous rock properties, that is, combinations of parameters which do not meaningfully add to one hundred per cent. It may be desirable, for example, to give simultaneous consideration to data on fossil content, sorting, permeability, grain size, and trace elements, as well as allochem proportions. Although the immediate objective of the proposed system is to identify discrete clusters in an *n*-coordinate system, other useful features will appear as a by-product of this primary objective.

METHOD

Vector representation.—The position of point X in the plane triangle of Figure 3 represents the three ratios X_A/X_B, X_A/X_C, and X_B/X_C. The same information can be displayed by representing sample X as a unit vector OX in a three-coordinate system with orthogonal reference vectors OA, OB, and OC. Here, the coordinates X_A, X_B,

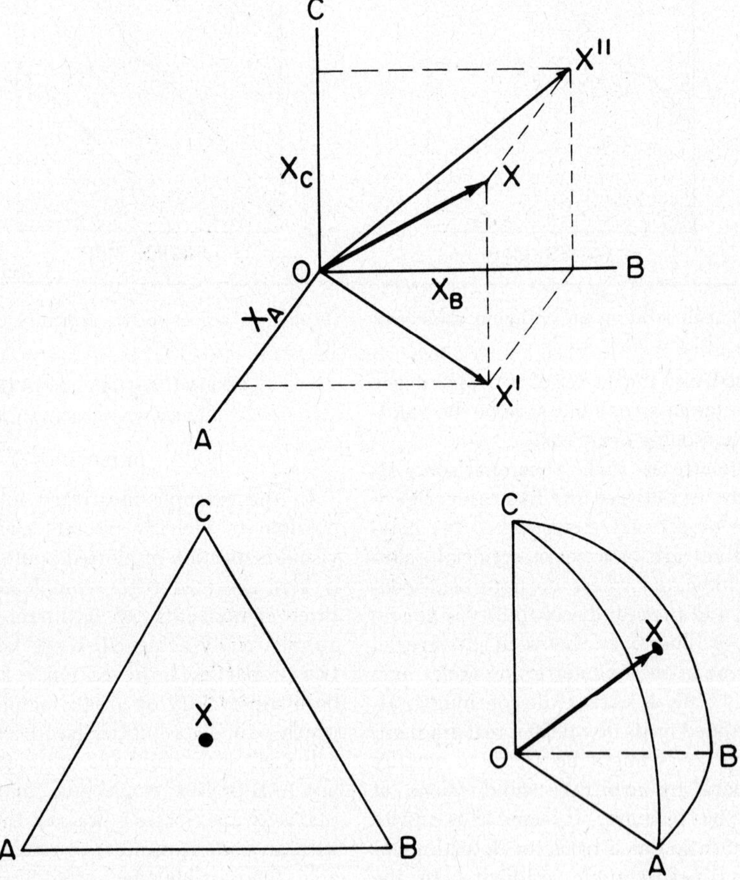

FIG. 3.—Diagram illustrating relationships between vector notation and a triangular diagram.

and X_C fix the direction of the vector OX. Note that any set of coordinates with the same proportions will determine the same vector. Ratio X_A/X_B is represented by the position of OX′, the projection of OX on plane OAB. As OX′ varies from OA to OB, this ratio will vary from infinity to zero. Thus, the 90° angle between vectors OA and OB symbolizes the maximum possible difference in the ratio X_A/X_B. Any two collinear vectors (angular separation of zero) represent two samples with identical values of the ratio. As noted by Krumbein (1957), angular transformations of ratio and percentage data have definite advantages over the untransformed measures.

As indicated in Figure 3, any sample vector OX in a three-coordinate system can be represented as a point X on the surface of a right spherical triangle with apical points A, B, and C. Here X is construed as the intersection of vector OX with the surface of a sphere of unit radius. The right spherical triangle is thus analogous to a plane triangle of conventional notation, although the plane figure distorts distance relationships to some extent.

In general, the degree of difference between any two samples X and Y (as regards the proportions of their constituent properties) is represented in vector notation by the size of the angle between their respective vectors, θ_{xy}; θ is thus the general measure of dissimilarity in the system under discussion. It may range from 0°, corresponding to identical composition, to 90°, corresponding to complete dissimilarity, and take any value between these extremes; 45° corresponds to a neutral or random relationship in which the two samples tend to be neither similar nor dissimilar.

One of the chief advantages of vector notation is that the algebraic formulation of key concepts can be easily extended into a system of any desired number of coordinates, even though our geometric intuition does not extend beyond three. Given a set of observations of n rock properties on N samples, and the generalized observation x_{ij}, of the i'th property on the j'th sample ($i=1, 2, 3, \ldots n; j=1, 2, 3, \ldots p, q, \ldots N$) the formula for computing $\angle\theta$ between any pair of samples, p and q, is

$$\cos \theta_{pq} = \frac{\sum_{i=1}^{n} x_{ip}x_{iq}}{\sqrt{\sum_{i=1}^{n} x_{ip}^2 \sum_{i=1}^{n} x_{iq}^2}}$$

The use of an angular measure of similarity strikes most geologists as bizarre, and it is convenient for some purposes to transform θ into a dimensionless parameter θ' by the following formula

$$\theta' = \frac{45° - \theta}{45°}$$

Note that θ' ranges from +1.000 through 0.000 to −1.000, with the three stated values corresponding respectively to θ values of 0°, 45°, and 90°. Negative values reflect dissimilarity, positive values similarity.

Figure 4 illustrates the use of θ' as a measure of similarity between six samples based on observations of five parameters. In each case θ' has been computed between sample a and one of the six samples.

Factor analysis of Bahamian samples.—Having defined a measure of similarity between any given pair of samples, we may now proceed to identify clusters of sample vectors in an n-coordinate system. The first step in the procedure used here is to perform an algebraic operation known as factor analysis. As the theory and practice of these techniques are fully described elsewhere (*see* especially Cattell, 1952, for a good nontechnical summary; and Harman, 1960, for

		VARIABLES					θ'_{ax}
		A	B	C	D	E	
SAMPLES	a	10	20	30	40	0	+1.00
	b	5	10	15	20	0	+1.00
	c	5	10	15	50	0	+0.49
	d	10	30	20	4	0	0.00
	e	40	30	20	10	0	−0.07
	f	0	0	0	0	80	−1.00

FIG. 4.—Hypothetical data matrix and calculated values of θ' between sample a and other samples.

detailed algebraic instructions), only an outline of objectives and procedures will be included here. A three-step procedure is involved.

1. The first step is to construct a data matrix in which every observation is recorded for each sample. Table I is a data matrix representing twelve petrographic variables observed at each of 40 Bahamian localities chosen to represent a wide range of bottom sites. A detailed description of the grain types recognized, location of samples, and genetic interpretations of grain types are to be published by Purdy (ms.). For present purposes it is necessary only to note that each bottom sample was sieved to remove the size fraction $<\frac{1}{8}$ mm; the weight per cent of that fraction was recorded; and by point-count analysis of thin sections made from plastic-impregnated samples of the coarse fraction, the volume per cent of 11 grain types was determined.

In order to give each parameter equal weight in determining the location of any sample vector, it is necessary to transform each row of the raw data matrix so that observations are recorded in per cent of the maximum value of that variable observed over the 200 Bahamian samples.

Variable	*Maximum Value in 200 Bahamian Samples (wgt. or vol. %)*
Molluscs	33.0
Peneroplids	28.6
Other foraminifera	13.2
Halimeda	39.8
Coralline algae	7.4
Corals	23.8
Pellets	76.8
Mud aggregates	30.2
Grapestone	58.6
Cryptocrystalline grains	57.0
Oölite	98.8
<1/8 mm	92.3

If this had not been done, variables constituting a large fraction of the volume would tend to exert a disproportionate influence on the position of any sample vector. Although this result might be desirable in some applications, the objective here is to give each variable equal consideration.

2. The second step is to calculate cos θ for each pair of sample vectors, and arrange the results in a square matrix. As $N=40$, the number of different calculations involved is $(N-1)\ N/2=780$. Although this would be an incredibly tedious task

TABLE I. CONSTITUENT PARTICLE COMPOSITION OF FORTY BAHAMIAN SEDIMENT SAMPLES
(Observations expressed as 0/00 of maximum range)

Sample No.	1	2	3	4	5	6	7	8	9	10	11	12	13	14	15	16	17	18	19	20
Molluscs	067	012	054	115	297	430	315	145	091	067	127	152	164	315	358	370	085	242	048	036
Peneroplidae	349	021	014	028	168	202	147	084	119	098	216	147	349	530	447	063	007	049	007	028
Other Foraminifera	666	015	106	212	227	091	136	136	091	091	151	197	409	318	545	484	273	136	045	015
Halimeda	085	015	025	040	131	281	407	005	020	005	050	075	085	136	256	643	346	316	010	025
Coralline Algae	270	000	027	000	000	000	000	000	000	000	000	000	000	000	000	000	000	459	000	000
Corals	134	000	000	017	017	000	000	000	000	000	000	000	008	000	000	000	000	319	000	000
Pellets	013	047	096	044	793	619	611	894	998	803	876	868	559	416	291	335	286	055	242	341
Mud Aggregates	126	099	060	046	225	205	099	278	278	139	291	245	649	563	556	245	305	278	119	132
Grapestone	248	218	439	751	000	007	007	000	000	000	000	000	000	003	000	000	003	082	595	180
Crypt. Grains	434	312	284	217	010	052	032	052	007	056	007	024	021	042	035	014	164	196	354	164
Oölite	004	596	392	222	026	006	030	042	028	202	042	032	016	004	012	053	331	081	162	450
< 1/8 mm.	249	076	070	027	338	433	561	635	380	343	561	688	980	942	926	963	054	024	082	060

Sample No.	21	22	23	24	25	26	27	28	29	30	31	32	33	34	35	36	37	38	39	40
Molluscs	036	048	085	273	364	158	121	042	054	315	315	206	155	048	009	000	000	000	003	321
Peneroplidae	000	000	000	021	035	098	007	077	014	056	070	251	192	028	000	000	000	000	000	021
Other Foraminifera	000	045	030	212	136	409	015	197	136	091	242	166	053	038	000	000	000	000	000	068
Halimeda	020	070	025	090	663	397	040	025	020	236	999	356	131	023	000	000	000	000	000	562
Coralline Algae	000	027	000	000	486	270	378	000	000	513	027	378	000	000	000	000	000	000	000	203
Corals	000	000	000	000	538	260	025	000	000	286	042	580	034	000	000	000	000	000	000	567
Pellets	260	151	333	057	003	023	083	042	039	029	010	000	008	006	000	000	000	001	000	027
Mud Aggregates	060	086	079	060	344	212	046	113	040	060	086	126	040	053	000	000	000	007	000	109
Grapestone	082	054	218	245	048	031	653	833	826	054	054	095	624	194	005	000	000	005	008	241
Crypt. Grains	108	658	262	798	136	616	388	560	536	301	346	476	276	208	037	024	040	051	023	205
Oölite	644	368	372	137	000	014	182	022	079	044	000	000	251	695	978	992	986	974	988	132
< 1/8 mm.	046	090	059	048	026	204	027	049	050	022	044	027	031	064	015	014	025	016	014	006

by hand, the entire calculation may be accomplished in a matter of minutes on modern digital computers. Table II displays the cos θ matrix for the 40 Bahamian sediment samples. Decimal points have been omitted and should be understood to precede each three digit sequence. This matrix displays in compact form the similarities and dissimilarities between every pair of samples considered. By scanning a column or a row, one may select the sample most similar or least similar to any given sample. Sample 26, for example, is most similar to sample 1 (cos $\theta = .827$). If samples are arranged according to position in field traverses, the values in one column will constitute a gradient of affinity between the first and each successive sample in the traverse.

3. Step three is to calculate a centroid factor matrix. This calculation is the key step for factor analytic techniques in general, for it provides an objective determination of the degree of complexity in the system being analyzed. Each dimension of complexity is spoken of as a factor.

Composite end members are a geologically meaningful way of expressing the results of a factor analysis. In the plagioclase feldspar suite, for example, it is standard practice to express the composition of any given plagioclase crystal as the sum of two end members, albite and anorthite. Mineralogically, these end members are single crystal species; chemically, they might equally well be considered composite end members with compositions $NaAlSi_3O_8$ and $CaAl_2Si_2O_8$. If a factor analysis were performed on chemical data from a varied set of plagioclase crystals, the results would indicate that the data could be expressed in terms of two factors, that is, two composite end members. If pure specimens of albite and anorthite had been included, the technique would specify exactly the composition of the end members. If such pure specimens had not been included, the results would show that all samples could be expressed as mixtures of end members having compositions of the two most distant vectors. Factor analyses of more complicated, artificially constructed test examples have shown the ability of this technique to recover simple relationships in scrambled data.

In dealing with actual examples, we can hardly expect to express perfectly all of the information with only three or four factors. Sampling error, identification error, as well as the natural perversity of geological data, all contribute to disorder. Conveniently, centroid factor analysis is an iterative procedure, so that factors (composite end members) are extracted one at a time, and their individual influence assessed. If the investigator wishes to explain every nuance exactly, then N end members will ordinarily be required (in this case forty). If he is willing to accept a more modest achievement, say explaining 90 per cent of the observed relationships with a simple hypothesis, a small number of factors may suffice. In the present example, 89 per cent of the information can be explained by four factors, a surprisingly simple and satisfactory result.

Like the computation of the cos θ matrix discussed above, and the quartimax rotation described below, centroid analysis is far too tedious for hand computation. Fortunately, digital computers of the IBM 650 class or higher perform the calculations rapidly and accurately. There is, however, an upper limit to the number of samples which can be handled; on the IBM 650, this limit is 40. On more powerful computers, the number is 200.

4. The fourth step is a rotation procedure, wherein the orthogonal reference vectors (in this case four) are placed in convenient locations with respect to the 40 sample vectors situated in a four-coordinate system. The locations used in this paper are given by the quartimax rotation procedure (Harman, 1960, p. 294–301) in which the reference axes are located so as to maximize the sums of the fourth powers of the projections of the sample vectors on the reference vectors. The final result of the factor analysis is thus a rotated quartimax factor matrix shown in Table III. Here, for each of the 40 samples, four coordinates are given for the end of the sample vector, corresponding to the projections of the end of the sample vector on the four reference vectors (Factor axes I–IV). If the position of the end of a sample vector can be located precisely in the four coordinate system, the squares of the four projections will sum to unity as indicated by the Pythagorean theorem. This sum of squares is known as the communality, symbolized as h^2, and entered in the last column of the factor matrix. This figure

TABLE II. COSINE θ MATRIX FOR FORTY BAHAMIAN SEDIMENT SAMPLES

Sample No.	1	2	3	4	5	6	7	8	9	10	11	12	13	14	15	16	17	18	19	20
1	1000																			
2	338	1000																		
3	515	893	1000																	
4	540	616	895	1000																
5	375	163	256	184	1000															
6	364	171	252	185	947	1000														
7	373	174	252	177	907	968	1000													
8	311	198	258	140	943	883	875	1000												
9	229	158	222	114	952	851	819	968	1000											
10	259	331	351	176	930	830	817	956	974	1000										
11	339	184	245	139	960	899	884	990	975	958	1000									
12	361	181	249	147	948	903	909	993	951	942	991	1000								
13	533	193	241	172	805	809	808	862	760	736	874	889	1000							
14	555	187	232	176	772	827	812	799	687	666	824	837	976	1000						
15	636	182	244	213	731	791	795	728	602	585	751	779	955	976	1000					
16	514	173	244	204	707	809	888	700	565	571	696	759	833	836	895	1000				
17	486	594	553	361	644	626	634	542	550	604	566	556	566	522	583	637	1000			
18	590	299	365	318	353	431	397	235	217	211	254	252	340	369	421	440	579	1000		
19	492	665	900	907	370	354	328	384	375	424	368	363	305	282	256	236	441	331	1000	
20	281	862	817	560	567	501	476	570	595	718	570	541	410	364	316	308	732	320	707	1000
21	135	892	730	409	377	327	327	385	397	566	381	361	246	212	182	212	657	226	488	937
22	486	813	731	441	281	305	296	307	265	390	277	285	251	245	239	251	610	402	635	713
23	366	853	869	644	570	522	493	564	577	696	550	533	381	343	304	321	704	355	806	970
24	654	608	702	603	253	313	274	203	145	215	175	197	216	248	287	284	492	456	704	483
25	454	131	193	198	298	420	412	154	138	107	180	186	277	320	391	481	531	948	175	157
26	827	368	440	363	364	438	458	291	214	237	294	326	449	469	554	579	639	798	420	297
27	538	605	835	852	160	193	170	150	129	186	134	137	116	130	126	130	305	556	870	544
28	619	525	815	918	151	164	145	142	111	137	134	140	186	193	210	161	292	322	927	443
29	557	564	844	932	117	137	126	118	084	127	100	112	127	132	146	132	266	293	938	470
30	584	268	342	288	268	368	336	153	121	140	156	169	193	251	294	342	402	936	306	238
31	431	190	260	259	300	468	526	128	104	104	159	186	230	293	400	608	645	614	237	174
32	679	278	352	320	243	331	313	133	107	119	160	161	242	305	345	339	428	880	347	221
33	533	686	896	941	185	257	235	121	096	171	142	136	176	237	247	222	392	395	884	595
34	270	977	840	564	119	130	141	132	091	280	125	124	140	144	154	162	566	258	548	828
35	026	846	599	276	035	019	043	048	031	228	046	038	023	017	022	052	471	116	234	722
36	018	839	589	267	031	014	039	045	030	226	045	036	021	013	019	049	467	109	224	717
37	028	847	597	271	035	020	045	052	034	231	050	043	029	022	026	057	472	113	232	722
38	033	853	604	279	035	019	042	050	034	230	049	040	027	019	024	052	477	119	240	727
39	020	841	594	274	032	015	040	046	030	226	045	036	022	014	019	049	467	110	230	719
40	437	321	415	423	265	391	401	122	106	124	139	152	175	227	291	430	523	849	383	309

gives (in parts per thousand) the fraction of information accounted for by four factors. For sample 38, for example, the communality is 99.5 per cent. The mean communality is 89 per cent.

If a factor analysis reduces to two or three end members, a Euclidean vector model can be constructed directly from the factor matrix, and visual inspection suffices to locate vector clusters. In the present example this cannot be done, and it is necessary to view the four dimensional vector display two dimensions at a time. Four of the possible six views of the vector model are plotted in Figure 5. Each point on the figure is a graphic plot of the coordinates contained in one row of the factor matrix, and corresponds to the end of a sample vector. If different symbols are used for each point it is clear that the 40 vectors are arranged in 5 discrete clusters. Each cluster has been named by reference to the chief constituents of samples composing the cluster. Although some clusters seem to overlap in one view (for example, the grapestone and oölitic clusters on the II–IV plot), this apparent overlap is a consequence of viewing the scheme two dimensions at a time. By examining other views it is clear that all clusters are in fact discrete groups separated by discontinuities. Two subgroups are indicated in the lime mud cluster. Although the names applied to the clusters are subjective, once the data matrix has been compiled, their definition is entirely objective.

Compositions of the four samples lying closest to the reference axes may now be taken as the compositions of four theoretical composite end members. By inspection of Table III, these samples are identified as 38, 12, 29, and 25. Within a tolerance limit indicated by the communalities, each of the 40 samples can be represented as a simple mixture of the 4 end members.

The procedure of factor analysis outlined above is known as a Q-type factor analysis, in which samples are compared with each other and factored. Alternatively, using different techniques, variables may be compared and clustered by a technique known as R-type factor analysis. The reader is cautioned that in the published literature

TABLE II (*continued*)

Sample No.	21	22	23	24	25	26	27	28	29	30	31	32	33	34	35	36	37	38	39	40
1																				
2																				
3																				
4																				
5																				
6																				
7																				
8																				
9																				
10																				
11																				
12																				
13																				
14																				
15																				
16																				
17																				
18																				
19																				
20																				
21	1000																			
22	649	1000																		
23	868	801	1000																	
24	344	875	650	1000																
25	085	235	183	320	1000															
26	171	663	403	762	738	1000														
27	387	570	651	666	375	494	1000													
28	223	558	580	756	188	501	858	1000												
29	271	571	609	750	160	457	879	992	1000											
30	168	452	326	545	859	786	603	327	318	1000										
31	102	380	247	500	728	726	268	290	269	562	1000									
32	116	490	305	588	852	865	516	418	385	892	613	1000								
33	460	542	675	665	293	433	854	890	902	386	383	451	1000							
34	917	703	789	484	113	272	516	401	448	226	161	208	631	1000						
35	910	501	620	186	008	043	228	047	104	075	015	021	340	929	1000					
36	908	489	612	170	003	032	217	035	092	066	008	012	329	923	1000	1000				
37	910	504	619	185	006	045	224	044	102	073	013	020	335	928	1000	1000	1000			
38	913	514	626	196	009	052	234	055	112	078	017	027	344	932	1000	1000	1000	1000		
39	909	489	615	172	004	032	223	041	099	067	009	013	336	925	1000	1000	1000	1000	1000	
40	240	363	365	455	913	708	499	378	379	795	737	863	527	301	150	143	147	151	146	1000

most of the work to date has been done with R-type analyses, and that the present paper is the first application of cos θ to Q-type problems.

Representation of hierarchical relationships.—As four dimensions are required to display relationships among the five clusters, it is impossible to view the entire system simultaneously. By a slight modification of a system of hierarchical representation proposed by Sokal and Michener (1958) it is possible, however, to extract the main features of the inter-cluster relationships and display them in a two dimensional figure, as follows.

1. Represent each cluster by a single vector of unit length passing through the centroid of the cluster. This is equivalent to representing the cluster by a unit vector extended in the direction of a vector sum of all members of the cluster. In a sense, this unit centroid vector represents the average qualities of the cluster.

2. Compute the angle between all pairs of unit centroid cluster vectors. This can be done conveniently by using a formula derived from an expression given by Spearman (1913)

$$\cos \theta qQ = \frac{\Box qQ}{\sqrt{q + 2\Delta q}\sqrt{Q + 2\Delta Q}}$$

where $\Box qQ$ is the sum of all cos θ's between members of one group and the other group, Δq is the sum of cos θ's between all possible pairs formed from members of the first group, ΔQ is a similar sum between members of the second group, q is the number of vectors in group one, and Q the number of vectors in group two. The necessary values of cos θ are contained in the original cos θ matrix.

3. The results of these calculations are then displayed in a 5×5 matrix, representing cosines of angles between the unit centroids (*see* Table IV). The location of the highest number in the matrix (in this case 0.810) identifies the pair of clusters which is most closely related (oölite and oölitic clusters). The value of cos θ is then converted into θ' ($\theta' = 0.20$), and on a hierarchy diagram (Fig. 6) a horizontal line drawn at the appropriate level linking the two facies. A measure of the homogeneity within each cluster can be achieved by taking Δq and dividing by the number of sum-

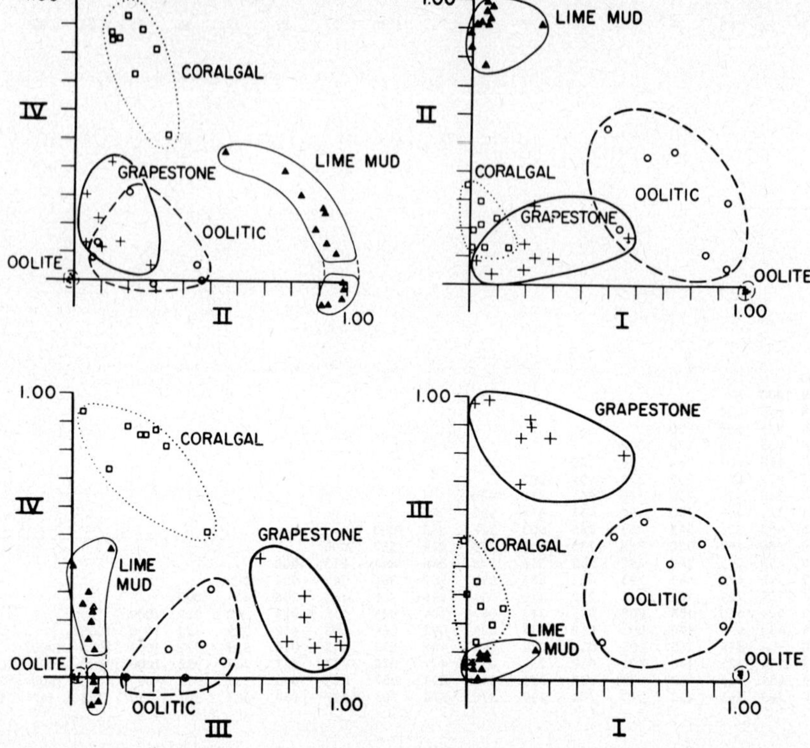

FIG. 5.—Two-dimensional plots of the ends of 40 Bahamian sample vectors as located by the rotated quartimax factor matrix in Table III. Descriptive terms refer to facies names.

mated pairs (q) $(q-1)/2$. The resulting $\cos\theta$ is then converted to θ' and the lower line of the plotted rectangle drawn to symbolize the value. For the oölite facies, this value is 1.00; for the oölitic facies, 0.27.

4. The highest number in the matrix must represent a pair of samples having mutually strongest resemblance. Other such pairs may exist and can be discovered by scanning each row and each column for the highest value outside the principal diagonal. Any location that is the highest value in its row and column will constitute a pair having highest mutual resemblance and should be grouped together on the hierarchy diagram.

5. Combined facies (in this example only the oölite facies plus the oölitic facies) are now each considered as a unit and represented in the next matrix by an appropriate number of collinear unit vectors (one for each vector in the new combined cluster) extended along the direction of the combined centroid. The reduced (4×4) matrix of cosines is conveniently computed from the previous matrix, using the formula

$$\cos\theta_{AB} = \frac{Na(Nb\theta ab + Nb'\theta ab') + Na'(Nb\theta a'b + Nb'\theta a'b')}{\sqrt{Na^2 + Na'^2 + 2NaNa'\theta aa'}\sqrt{Nb^2 + Nb'^2 + 2NbNb'\theta bb'}}$$

where A and B stand for two groups of vectors each composed of one or two subgroups, a and a' and b and b' respectively; and N_a, $N_{a'}$, N_b, and $N_{b'}$, stand respectively for the number of vectors in each subgroup.

6. Steps three and five are repeated until a

TABLE III. ROTATED QUARTIMAX FACTOR MATRIX OF FORTY BAHAMIAN SAMPLES
(Values expressed in 0/00)

Problem Code	Field Sample Code	Facies	Projections on Factor Axes I	II	III	IV	h^2
38	413	Oolite	997	-008	030	012	995
37	414		995	-005	020	008	991
35	418		995	-009	023	009	991
39	438		994	-009	019	002	988
36	417		994	-010	012	003	988
21	334	Oolitic	927	293	197	-005	984
34	411		924	059	359	101	996
02	31		851	103	482	120	982
20	330		738	474	413	007	940
23	312		638	452	559	062	928
22	310		529	197	505	311	670
17	374		491	549	138	449	763
12	369	Pellet Mud	052	989	071	-007	986
11	368		060	986	072	-028	982
08	360		068	973	088	-048	961
10	367		248	905	104	-087	899
09	366		062	930	074	-086	882
06	174	Skeletal Mud	035	918	075	238	906
13	370		017	915	058	127	857
07	380		059	909	037	257	897
05	171		047	956	082	097	932
14	371		-001	876	067	191	808
15	372		-001	826	057	296	773
16	373		042	774	006	394	756
29	317	Grapestone	079	039	982	122	987
28	514		022	081	974	149	978
19	328		227	280	916	047	971
04	59		231	095	889	105	864
33	409		299	093	854	219	875
27	512		195	051	850	293	849
03	43		569	166	789	126	990
24	502		195	141	688	415	703
25	504	Coralgal	001	192	043	927	898
18	207		095	236	196	882	881
32	7-47		000	127	304	870	865
30	537		054	130	256	847	803
40	250		138	127	250	846	813
26	279		040	294	344	814	869
31	37		038	213	132	733	602
01	1		-012	344	487	509	615

2×2 matrix is left. The results of the above procedure are displayed in Figure 6.

Sequential grouping system.—From the factor analysis of 40 Bahamian sediments, 5 distinct groups (and 2 subgroups) have been identified. One hundred and sixty Bahamian samples remain to be examined and classified. In principle, this objective can be accomplished by factoring the entire 200×200 matrix. Such an approach strains the storage capacity of computers now available,

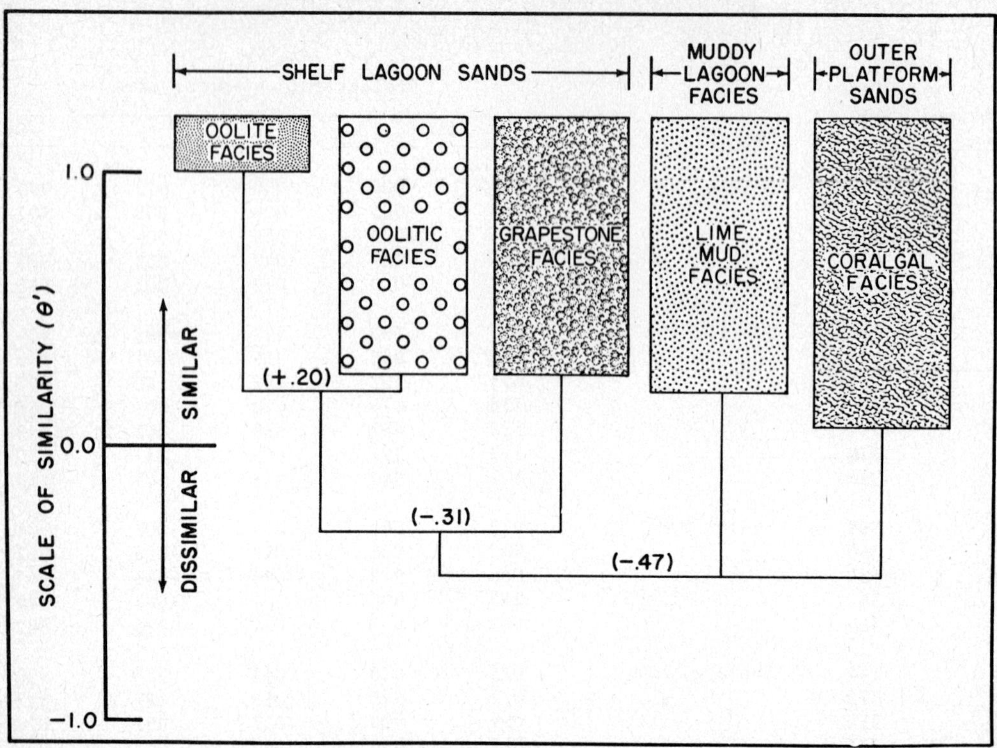

FIG. 6.—Hierarchy diagram depicting similarities among five major Bahamian facies. For explanation, see text.

however; and supplementary grouping procedures must therefore be sought. One such procedure (described below) views the clusters provided by factor analysis as the skeletons of denser clusters to be filled in by subsequent comparisons.

1. Compute a cos θ matrix for all samples. In this case, a 200×200 matrix was computed on an IBM 7090 in approximately 12 minutes. For obvious reasons, it is not reproduced in this paper.

2. Identify the 40 elements of the skeletal clusters with suitable colored notations on the large matrix.

3. Choose one facies, and examine, in turn, each member. Designate a sample under scrutiny as a "host sample." For each host determine the unclassified sample most similar to it. Designate this sample a "trial" sample. If the trial sample is related to any member of another facies more closely than it is to the host sample, do not include the trial sample in the host sample facies. If the trial sample is not related to any member of another facies more closely than it is to the host sample, admit the trial sample as a new member of the host facies.

TABLE IV. VALUES OF COSINE θ AMONG UNIT CENTROID FACIES VECTORS

	Oölite	*Oölitic*	*Lime Mud*	*Grapestone*	*Coralgal*
Oölite	1.000	.810	.091	.268	.062
Oölitic	.810	1.000	.411	.674	.338
Lime Mud	.091	.411	1.000	.256	.399
Grapestone	.268	.674	.256	1.000	.492
Coralgal	.062	.338	.399	.492	1.000

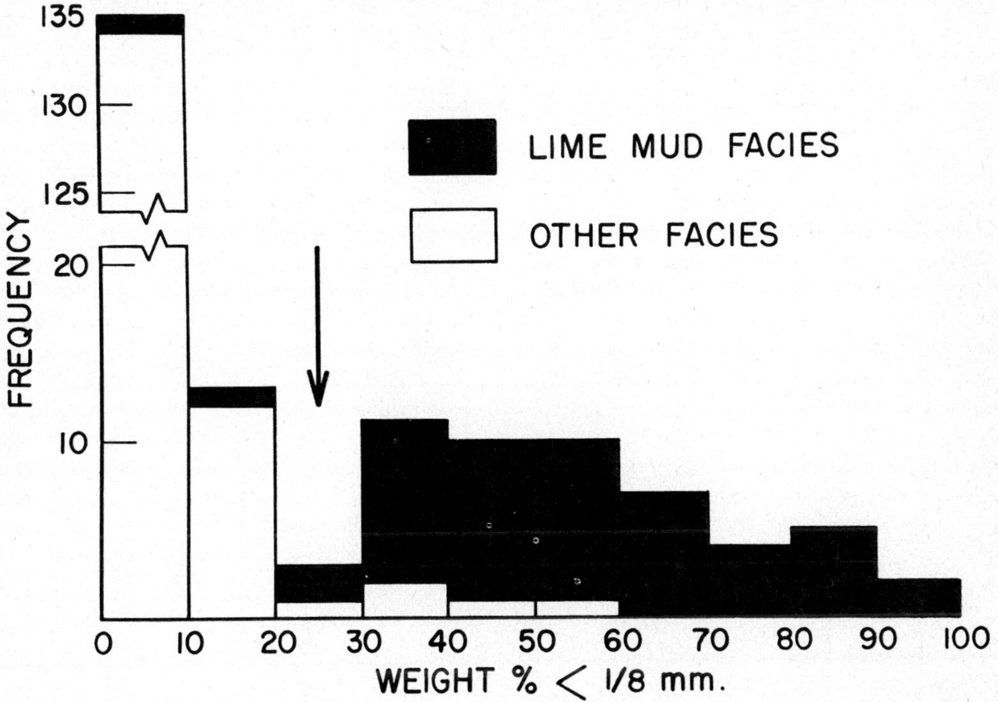

FIG. 7.—Frequency distribution of weight per cent less than $\frac{1}{8}$ mm in 200 samples of Bahamian sediments. Arrow indicates optimum dividing line between lime mud and other facies.

4. When each member of the first facies has been examined in this way, proceed to the next facies and repeat step 3.

In effect, this procedure allows each skeleton cluster to grow or be filled in independently of other such clusters, and natural discontinuities in the vector configuration are discovered, if they exist. In the present case, each of the initially unclassified samples was shown to belong clearly with one of the skeletal clusters. Definite discontinuities exist among the six clusters.

RESULTS

The principal results of applying the methods outlined above to the 200 samples of Bahamian bottom sediments can be summarized as follows

1. Based on an equal and simultaneous consideration of the 12 sediment properties examined by Purdy (Ms.), the samples group themselves into five discrete groups, with definite discontinuities among them. These boundaries are considered to reflect significant discontinuities in the dynamic system responsible for the observed properties. Note that they are not reflected in the distributions shown on Figures 7, 8, 9, and 11.

2. Eighty-nine per cent of the observational data gathered by Purdy can be accounted for by considering each sample as a mixture of four complex end members (samples 38, 12, 29, and 25). Considering that sampling and identification errors are inherent in the data, and that twelve parameters were measured, the simplicity of this result is notable. Its meaning is clear—the many processes responsible for the distribution and abundance of grain types are highly interdependent, integral parts of a tightly organized marine ecosystem. "*Natura simplex est.*"

3. Each of the recognized facies is characterized by distinctive properties. Purdy (Ms.) has described and interpreted these in detail. For present purposes it is necessary only to review the salient characteristics of each facies.

Oölite facies.—Nearly pure oölite sand.

Oölitic facies.—Cleanly washed sand with a high portion of oölite grains and considerable quantities of other grain types.

Grapestone facies.—Cleanly washed sand characterized chiefly by grapestone lumps and recrystallized grains, but containing significant proportions of oölite and skeletal grains.

Lime mud facies.—Poorly sorted sediments with a sufficient quantity of grains smaller than $\frac{1}{8}$ mm to keep the modal class of sand grains from being in contact. Two subfacies are recognized, skeletal mud and pellet mud, the former with relatively more fine material and skeletal grains, the latter with relatively more pellets and less fine material.

Coralgal facies.—Cleanly washed sands characterized by relatively abundant corals and algae, including *Halimeda* and coralline algae.

4. As indicated in the hierarchy diagram (Fig. 6) three facies families are recognizable—shelf lagoon sands, muddy lagoon facies, and outer platform sands. The families are equally distinct from each other ($\theta' = 0.47$) and represent sharply contrasting bottom types. The grapestone facies, although distinct from the combined oölite facies, has its closest relationship with that facies. Note that the petrographic relationships symbolized in the hierarchy diagram are borne out by the distribution of the corresponding map patterns (Fig. 10). The field distribution of the three facies families corresponds with three distinct hydrographic environments.

5. Figures 7, 8, and 9 illustrate the most efficient means of classifying the 200 samples into the 5 major facies by observing four characteristics—per cent of fines (wgt. per cent less than $\frac{1}{8}$ mm); and volume per cent of oölite, grapestone, and corals plus algae.

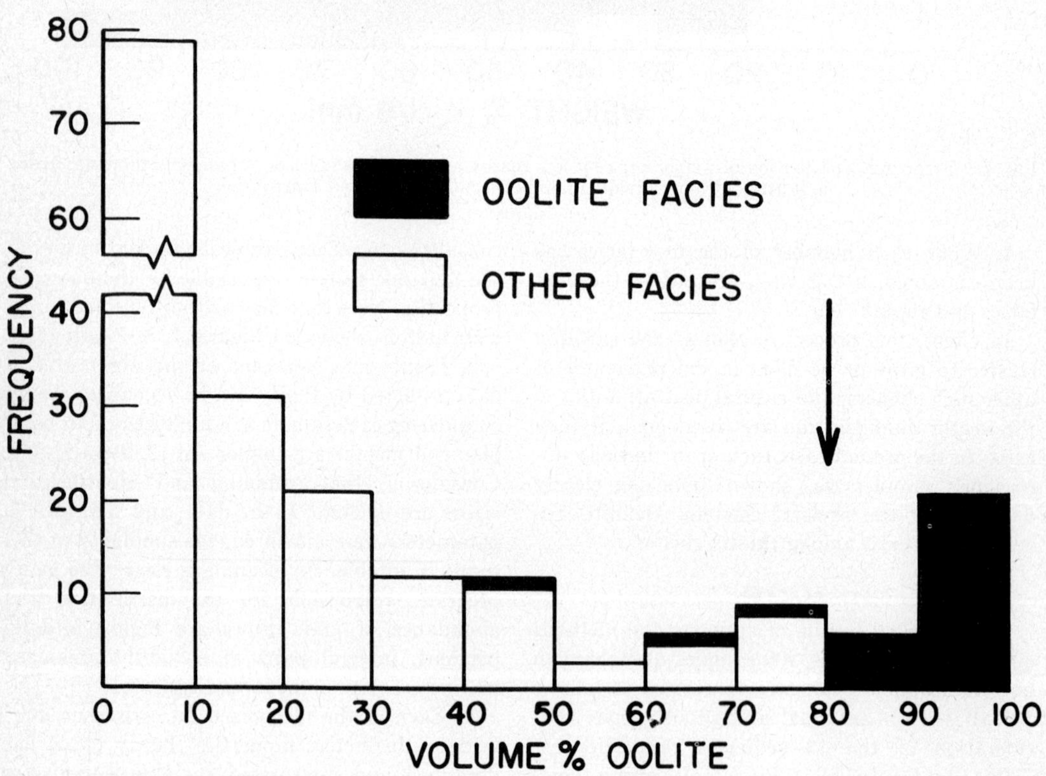

FIG. 8.—Frequency distribution of volume per cent oölite in the coarse fraction of 200 samples of Bahamian sediments. Arrow indicates optimum dividing line between oölite and other facies.

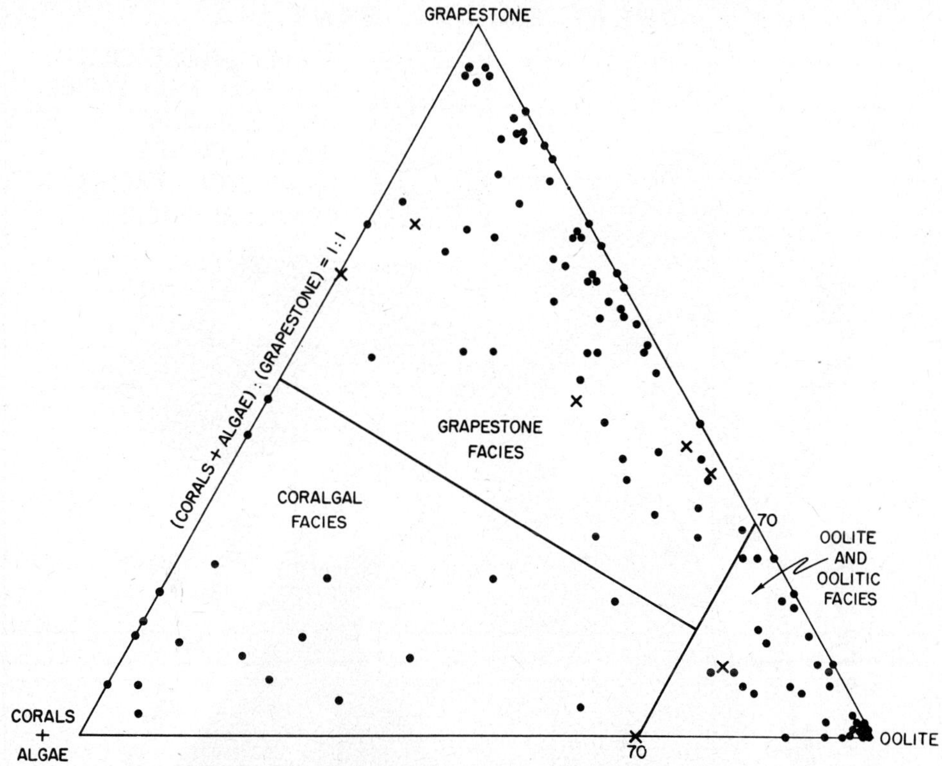

FIG. 9.—Triangular plot of Bahamian samples classified by an optimum procedure as coralgal, grapestone, oölite, and oölitic facies. Using the suggested ratio boundaries, samples plotted as points are correctly classified. Samples plotted as crosses are incorrectly classified.

(1) Classify all samples having more than 25 per cent fines as lime mud. A total of six identification errors are committed.

(2) Classify samples having more than 80 per cent oölite as oölite facies. Three errors are committed.

(3) Classify the remaining samples according to the ratio boundaries in Figure 9. Nine identification errors are committed.

With this scheme, identification errors total eighteen, or just under 10 per cent.

6. Figure 10 represents the facies map corresponding to the sample groupings identified by the optimum classification procedure described in this paper. Mapped facies boundaries have been drawn between control points to conform with hydrographic and other information available to the writers. As discussed by Purdy (Ms.), the facies patterns bear systematic relationships to hydrographic parameters.

APPLICATION OF FOLK'S CLASSIFICATION TO BAHAMIAN SEDIMENTS

CRITERIA

Many of the limestone varieties recognized in the classification proposed by Folk (1959) are undoubtedly represented in unconsolidated sediments forming today on the Bahama Banks. Several of these are not considered in detail here, as they are forming in areas not covered by the 200 sample localities. Algal biolithite or dismicrite is clearly accumulating in intertidal mud flats, for example, and coral-algal biolithite is being formed in some areas of reef growth and on rocky shoals. In this paper, attention is directed principally to

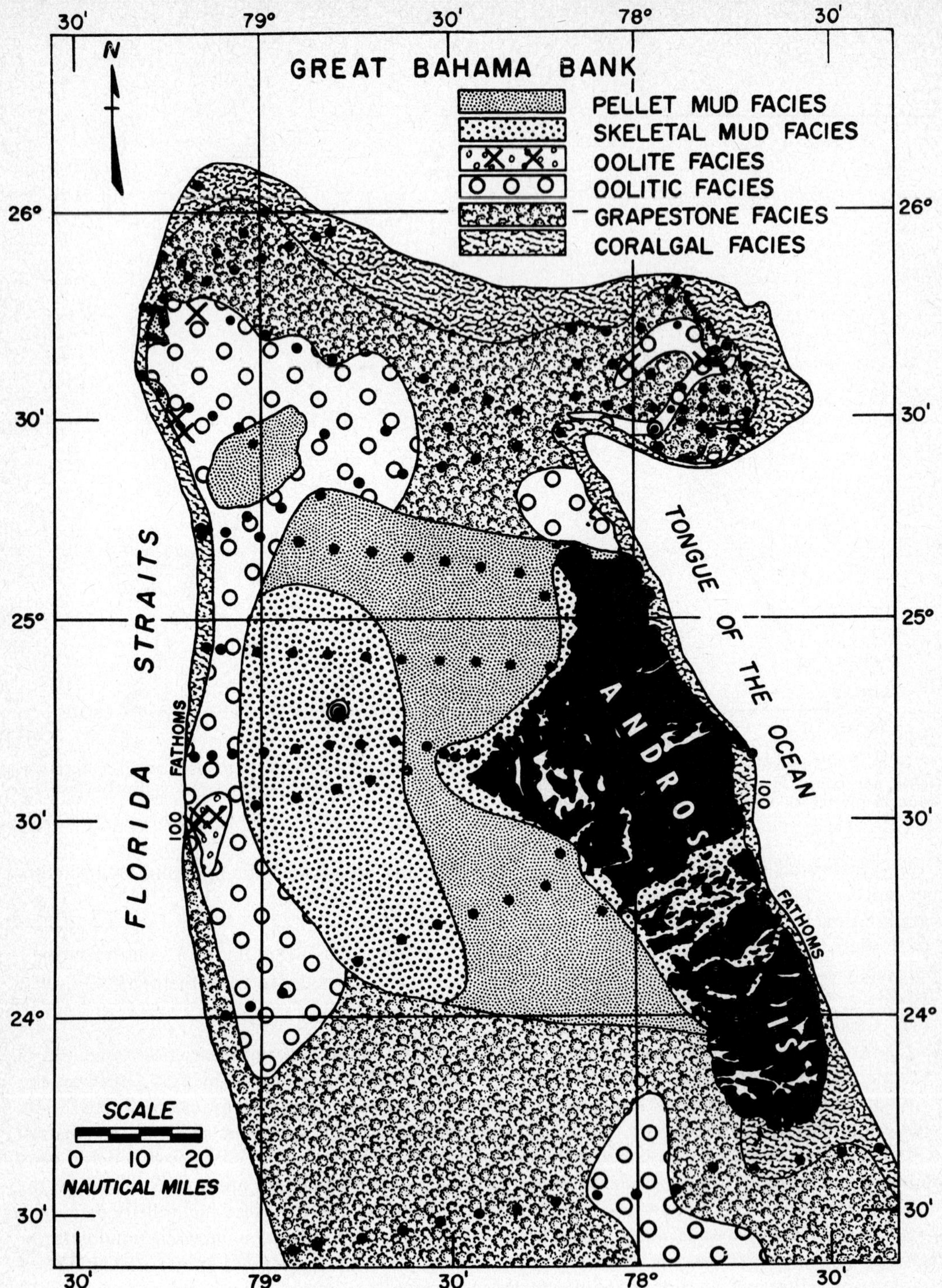

FIG. 10.—Facies map of the Andros lobe of the Great Bahama Bank based on optimum classification procedure. Heavy dots show location of 200 sample stations.

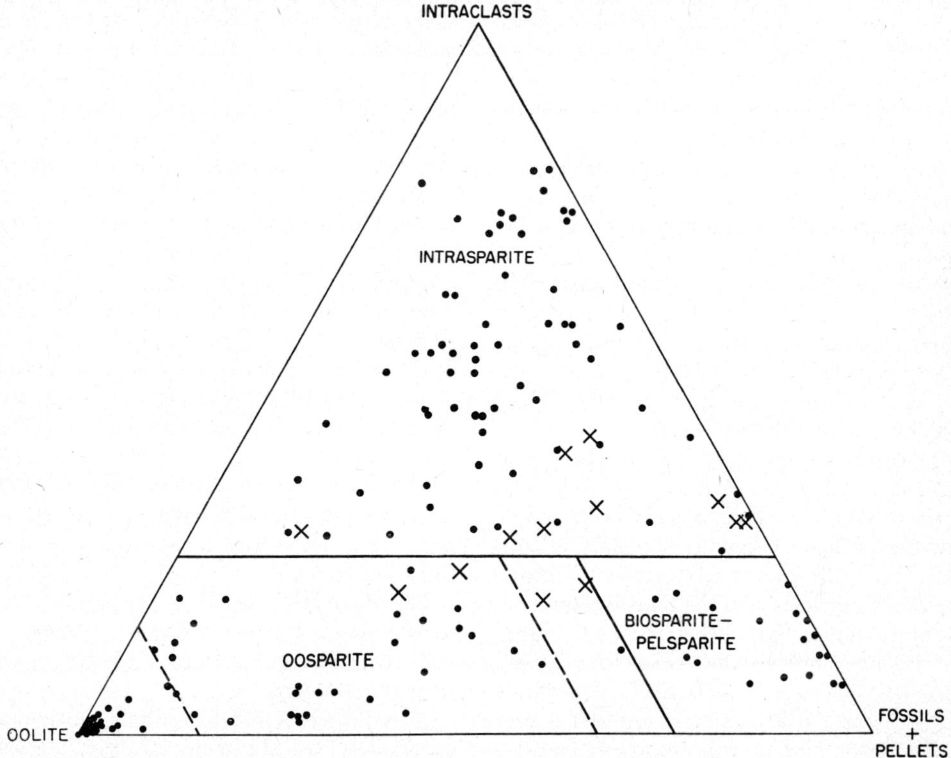

FIG. 11.—Triangular plot of Bahamian samples according to the classification proposed by Folk. Only samples judged to represent Type I limestones are considered. Heavy lines are Folk's boundaries; dashed lines are revised boundaries suggested in this paper. Samples plotted as points are correctly classified according to the optimum classification procedures used in present paper. Samples plotted as crosses are incorrectly classified. Compare with Fig. 12.

infratidal areas covered by the 200 localities indicated on Figure 10. These clearly fall into Folk's limestones of Type I (sparry allochemical limestone) or Type II (microcrystalline allochemical limestone). Possibly a few of the samples should be classified as Type III (micrite), indicating that the lithified and compacted equivalent would contain less than 10 per cent allochems.

In judging whether these modern samples should be classified as Type I or Type II, decision must be based on a judgment as to the relative volumes of sparry calcite cement and microcrystalline calcite matrix in their unknown lithified and compacted equivalents. For samples consisting of cleanly washed sand this decision can be made without difficulty, and the samples classified as Type I. For samples containing significant quantities of fine material, however, this decision is unfortunately very difficult to make, at least from data and samples available to the authors. For this reason, we have somewhat arbitrarily chosen to classify every sample of the lime-mud facies as Type II, and the remaining samples as Type I. Two exceptions were made for samples designated by the optimum classification system as belonging to the lime-mud facies, but which contained so little fine material relative to intergranular voids that the resulting rock can be expected to be a Type I limestone.

By making this arbitrary division between Type I and Type II, we have maximized the degree of correspondence between Folk's classification and the optimum system. From an inspection of wet and dried samples of the lime-mud facies, however, and from an inspection of three thin sections prepared from unsieved, undisturbed, plastic-impregnated samples, we are reasonably certain that a considerable number of samples from this facies would be classified by Folk's scheme as Type I, and thus be considered as cleanly washed limestones. If this suspicion is borne out by future work, it would suggest a flaw in the basis for distinguishing Types I and II, for it would class together some samples coming from environments distinct in terms of circulation and bottom agitation. Illustrations of this are particularly prevalent in the pellet-mud facies, where many samples are relatively cleanly washed below a grain size within the silt grade.

After distinguishing Type I from Type II samples, each group was subdivided according to the criteria proposed by Folk. Figure 11 shows the properties of Type I samples. In plotting these points, mud aggregates and grapestone were lumped as intraclasts, and the total skeletal grain content was lumped with pellets. Using the definition of oölite employed by Newell, Purdy, and Imbrie (1960), any grain is classified as an oölite if a recognizable oölitic coating of any size is present. Solid ratio lines on this figure correspond to those recommended by Folk. The nine samples plotted as crosses (6 per cent of 151 samples) correspond to Type I samples misclassified according to the category equivalence indicated in Figure 12. Disregarding the lack of subdivision of the two oölitic facies in Folk's scheme, and disregarding the subdivision of the coralgal facies into biosparite and biopelsparite, this figure for identification error can be compared with a corresponding identification error of seven achieved by application of the four-parameter optimum classification scheme described above. This result is a striking confirmation of the correctness of the boundary locations proposed by Folk for subdividing Type I limestones. A slight improvement can be achieved by moving the oösparite-biosparite boundary to 35 per cent oölite as suggested by the dashed line in Figure 11. Also, if an oölite per cent boundary of 85 per cent is used to partition off a high-oölite subdivision of oösparite, the distinction in Bahamanian sediments between oölite and oölitic facies can be recognized with only three errors.

The distinction between biosparite and pelsparite does not correspond with a natural dividing line among Bahamian sediment samples treated in this paper.

As indicated in Figure 12, Folk's classification subdivides Type II samples into five categories—oömicrite, intramicrite, biomicrite, biopelmicrite, and pelmicrite. These do not correspond to the skeletal mud and pellet mud subfacies, and sug-

PRESENT PAPER			FOLK (1959)	
SHELF LAGOON SANDS	OOLITE FACIES		OOSPARITE	TYPE I
	OOLITIC FACIES			
	GRAPESTONE FACIES		INTRASPARITE	
OUTER PLATFORM SANDS	CORALGAL FACIES		BIOSPARITE	
			BIOPELSPARITE	
MUDDY SANDS OF THE SHELF LAGOON	SKELETAL MUD SUBFACIES	LIME MUD FACIES	OOMICRITE	TYPE II
			INTRAMICRITE	
			BIOMICRITE	
	PELLET MUD SUBFACIES		BIOPELMICRITE	
			PELMICRITE	

FIG. 12.—Comparison between categories of the optimum classification scheme of the present paper and those of Folk's classification.

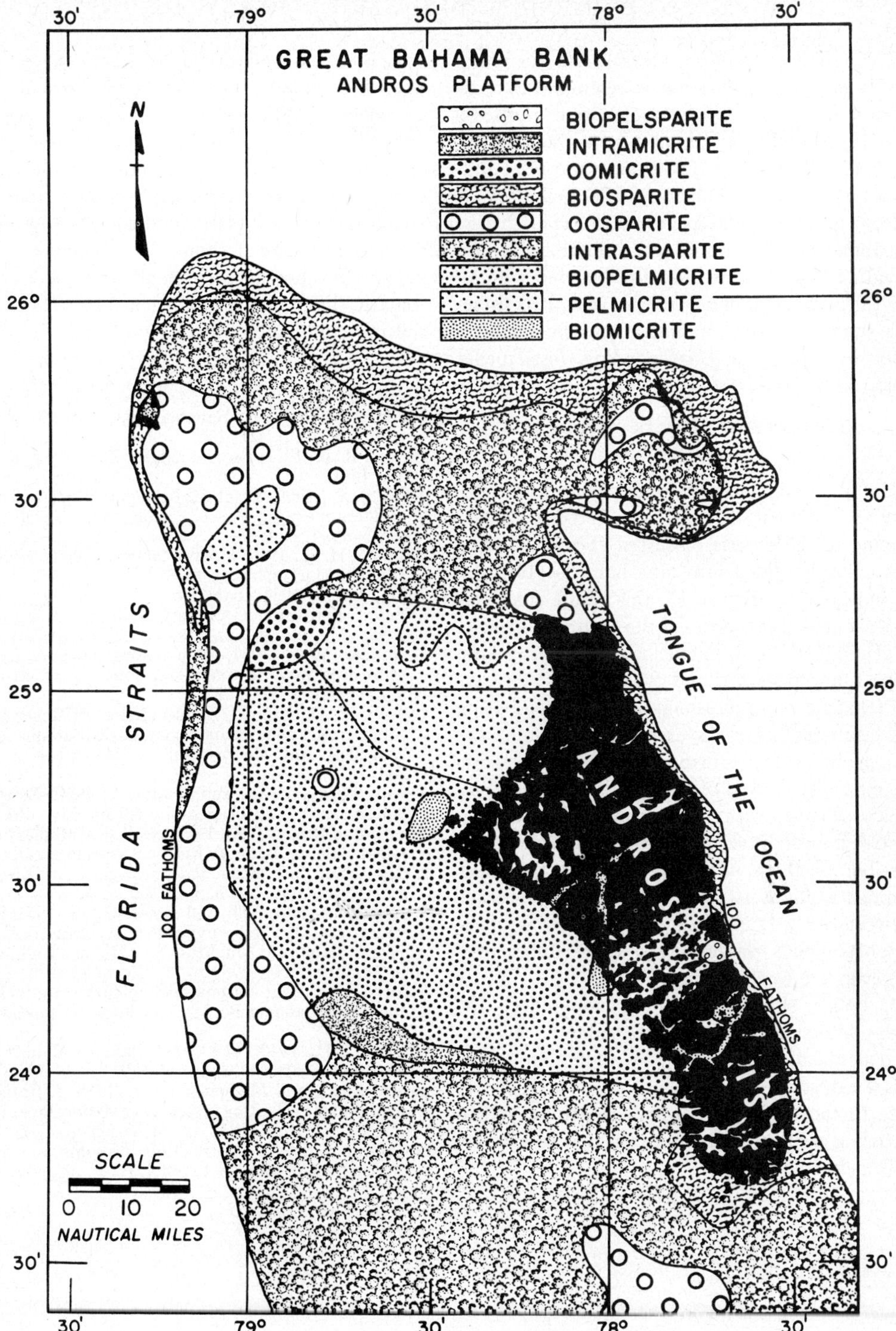

FIG. 13.—Facies map of the Andros lobe of the Great Bahama Bank based on Folk's classification. For discussion of criteria, see text.

gest (for Bahamian data at least) that this group is oversplit. The situation here resembles that indicated in Figure 2, where objective gradients have been subdivided along *a priori* boundaries. If, instead of the two fossil-pellet ratio boundaries proposed by Folk, a single boundary is placed at a skeletal:pellet ratio of 1:2, the Bahamian samples can be split into groups corresponding to skeletal mud and pellet mud with an identification error of only 10 per cent. It is therefore suggested that empirical tests be made in limestones using a corresponding fossil:pellet ratio.

COMPARISON OF RESULTS OF THE TWO CLASSIFICATIONS

If Folk's classification is applied to the Bahamian sediment samples considered here, according to the criteria discussed above, the samples are subdivided into nine named categories. As indicated on Figure 12, this result compares with six named categories of the optimum scheme. In general, the correspondence is excellent within Type I, and poor within Type II.

Perhaps a more meaningful way of comparing the results of the two systems is to examine the corresponding facies maps. Figure 13 represents the map distribution of the categories yielded by Folk's scheme, with facies boundaries between control points drawn to correspond as closely as possible to those of Figure 10. For the areas mapped as Type I (sparites) the correspondence between the two systems is excellent, and strongly supports Folk's classification. Three differences, however, are worth noting.

1. Folk's classification does not reflect the high-oölite shoals. As suggested above, this discrepancy could be removed by adding an appropriate category.

2. In the Berry Islands area (north of Andros Island) a portion of an oölite shoal is ignored by Folk's classification.

3. Some sediment samples along the western edge of the Banks on the outer platform are misclassified by Folk's scheme.

For areas mapped as Type II (micrites), a considerable discrepancy exists between the results of the two classifications. The facies boundary between skeletal and pellet mud is missed by Folk's scheme, although it should be remembered that his subdivisions do correspond to objective, systematic differences in allochem proportions and reflect actual compositional gradients.

REFERENCES

Black, Maurice, 1933, The precipitation of calcium carbonate on the Great Bahama Bank: Geol. Magazine, v. 70, no. 10, p. 455–466.

Cattell, R. B., 1952, Factor analysis: New York, Harper and Bros.

Folk, R. L., 1959, Practical petrographic classification of limestones: Am. Assoc. Petroleum Geologists Bull., v. 43, no. 1, p. 1–38.

Harman, H. H., 1960, Modern factor analysis: Chicago, Ill., The Univ. Chicago Press.

Illing, Leslie, 1954, Bahaman calcareous sands: Am. Assoc. Petroleum Geologists Bull., v. 38, no. 1, p. 1–95.

Krumbein, W. C., 1957, Comparisons of percentage and ratio data in facies mapping: Jour. Sed. Petrology, v. 27, no. 3, p. 293–297.

Newell, N. D., Imbrie, J., and others, 1959, Organism communities and bottom facies, Great Bahama Bank: Am. Mus. Nat. History Bull., v. 117, art. 4, p. 181–288.

——— Purdy, E. G., and Imbrie, J., 1960, Bahaman oölitic sand: Jour. Geology, v. 68, no. 5, p. 481–497.

——— and Rigby, J. K., 1957, Geological studies on the Great Bahama Bank, *in* Regional aspects of carbonate deposition: Soc. Econ. Paleontologists and Mineralogists Spec. Pub. No. 5, p. 15–72.

——— Whiteman, A. J., and Bradley, J. S., 1951, Shoal water geology and environments, eastern Andros Island, Bahamas: Am. Mus. Nat. History Bull., v. 97, p. 1–29.

Purdy, E. G., Ms., Recent calcium carbonate facies of the Great Bahama Bank. (Scheduled for publication in 1963.)

Smith, C. L., 1940, The Great Bahama Bank: Jour. Marine Research, v. 3, p. 147–189.

Sokal, R. R., and Michener, C. D., 1958, A statistical method for evaluating systematic relationships: Univ. Kansas Sci. Bull., v. 38, pt. 11, no. 22, p. 1409–1438.

Spearman, C., 1913, Correlations of sums and differences: British Jour. of Psychology, v. 5, p. 417–426.

INDEX[1]

[1] Titles of papers are shown in capital and small capital letters.

G

H

I

J

K

L